Mathematics

SCOTT FORESMAN • ADDISON WESLEY

Authors

Randall I. Charles

Warren Crown

Francis (Skip) Fennell

Janet H. Caldwell
Mary Cavanagh
Dinah Chancellor
Alma B. Ramirez

Jeanne F. Ramos
Kay Sammons
Jane F. Schielack

William Tate
Mary Thompson
John A. Van de Walle

Consulting Mathematicians

Edward J. Barbeau
Professor of Mathematics
University of Toronto
Toronto, Ontario, Canada

David M. Bressoud
DeWitt Wallace Professor
of Mathematics
Macalester College
Saint Paul, Minnesota

Gary Lippman
Professor of Mathematics
and Computer Science
California State University Hayward
Hayward, California

Editorial Offices: Glenview, Illinois • Parsippany, New Jersey • New York, New York

Sales Offices: Needham, Massachusetts • Duluth, Georgia • Glenview, Illinois
Coppell, Texas • Ontario, California • Mesa, Arizona

Teacher's Edition
Available online and on CD-ROM

Grade 1 • Volume 4 (Chapters 10-12)

Reading Consultants

Peter Afflerbach
Professor and Director of
The Reading Center
University of Maryland
College Park, Maryland

Donald J. Leu
John and Maria Neag
Endowed Chair in Literacy
and Technology
University of Connecticut
Storrs, Connecticut

ESL Consultant

Jim Cummins
Professor of Curriculum
Ontario Institute for Studies in Education
University of Toronto
Toronto, Ontario, Canada

Professional Development Consultant

David C. Geary
Chair and Middlebush Professor
Department of Psychological Sciences
University of Missouri
Columbia, Missouri

ISBN: 0-328-11718-8

5 6 7 8 9 10 V064 12 11 10 09 08 07 06

The
SCOTT FORESMAN
Difference

SCOTT FORESMAN • ADDISON WESLEY

Mathematics

You can count on us.

The difference that counts . . .

Our all-new scientifically research-based program has been designed to make math simpler to teach, easier to learn, and more accessible to every student. With the Scott Foresman Difference, students, teachers, and parents can all say: "I get it!"

Pre-Kindergarten

Count on our unique, **scientifically research-based** Pre-K math program to help early math learners bloom. **Field tested for eight years** in diverse classrooms, it has been proven to build essential math background.

Pre-K
Kindergarten
Grade 1

Kindergarten

We follow up in Kindergarten with a flexible, **research-based,** full-day curriculum that successfully **develops and extends mathematical thinking.** Stories, games, and center activities teach your students basic math understandings.

Grade 2
Grade 3
Grade 4

Grades 1 and 2

To help your students comprehend and successfully apply basic facts, our **research-based program** begins with an **understanding of number** and what the number sentence means. This leads to **algebra success.**

Grades 3 through 6

In the upper grades, the Scott Foresman Difference is evident from cover-to-cover. From **instruction right on the student page** to daily assessment and **customized intervention,** our **research-based program** ensures that your students **achieve progress and test success.**

Grade 5
Grade 6

and the research that proves it.

Completely planned, written, and reviewed by the authors, our program is backed by more than 100 years of research into what really works in the classroom. Four phases of research were integrated into the program's development by the authors, who are all recognized experts in the acquisition of mathematical learning.

1 Ongoing Research

The proven effectiveness of Scott Foresman, Addison Wesley, and Silver Burdett Ginn previous math programs provides a longitudinal research base that spans more than 100 years. Pretest and posttest results show that these programs improve students' math proficiency.

2 Scientific Research Base

An experienced authorship team provided expertise in synthesizing and contributing to a rich body of scientific evidence. Research-based techniques were embedded into the program's instructional materials, assessments, and professional development.

3 Formative Research

Classroom field studies, school administrators, mathematics teachers, and reviewers contributed valuable recommendations as the program was designed and written. Pretest and posttest scores were part of the information gathered during program development.

4 Summative Research

Scientific evidence, including longitudinal studies in the classroom, further validate the efficacy of our program. Control group research designs and test score data ensure that the program is of the highest quality and predictive of success.

Authors

Randall I. Charles
Professor Emeritus,
Department of Mathematics
and Computer Science
San Jose State University
San Jose, California

Warren Crown
Professor of Mathematics
Education
Rutgers University
New Brunswick, New Jersey

Francis (Skip) Fennell
Professor of Education
McDaniel College
Westminster, Maryland

Janet H. Caldwell
Professor of Mathematics
Rowan University
Glassboro, New Jersey

Mary Cavanagh
Project Coordinator, Math,
Science and Beyond
Solano Beach School District
San Diego County, California

Dinah Chancellor
Coordinator of Math, Science,
Gifted/Talented, Title IV
Carroll ISD
Southlake, Texas

Alma B. Ramírez
Senior Research Associate,
Mathematics
Case Methods Project
WestEd
Oakland, California

Jeanne F. Ramos
Administrative Coordinator,
K–12 Mathematics
Los Angeles Unified School
District
Los Angeles, California

Kay Sammons
Supervisor of Mathematics
Howard County Public Schools
Ellicott City, Maryland

Jane F. Schielack
Associate Professor of Mathematics
Texas A&M University
College Station, Texas

William Tate
Professor and Chair of the
Department of Education
College of Arts and Sciences
Washington University
St. Louis, Missouri

Mary Thompson
Mathematics Instructional Specialist
New Orleans Public Schools Louisiana
New Orleans, Louisiana

John Van de Walle
Professor Emeritus of Mathematics
Education/Consultant
Virginia Commonwealth University
Richmond, Virginia

Consulting Mathematicians

Edward J. Barbeau
Professor of Mathematics
University of Toronto
Toronto, Ontario, Canada

David M. Bressoud
DeWitt Wallace Professor of Mathematics
Macalester College
Saint Paul, Minnesota

Gary Lippman
Professor of Mathematics and Computer Science
California State University Hayward
Hayward, California

Reading Consultants

Peter Afflerbach
Professor and Director of the Reading Center
University of Maryland
College Park, Maryland

Donald J. Leu
John and Maria Neag Endowed Chair
in Literacy and Technology
University of Connecticut
Storrs, Connecticut

ESL Consultant

Jim Cummins
Professor of Curriculum
Ontario Institute for Studies in Education
University of Toronto
Toronto, Ontario, Canada

Professional Development Consultant

David C. Geary
Chair and Middlebush Professor
Department of Psychological Sciences
University of Missouri
Columbia, Missouri

Reviewers

Mary Bacon
Mathematics Specialist
East Baton Rouge Parish School System
Baton Rouge, Louisiana

Cheryl Baker
Mathematics Teacher
Norton Middle School
Norton, Ohio

Marcelline A. Barron
Curriculum Leader Math and Science, Grades K–5
Fairfield Public Schools
Fairfield, Connecticut

Mary Connery-Simmons
Mathematics Specialist
Springfield Massachusetts Public Schools
Springfield, Massachusetts

Anthony C. Dentino
Supervisor of Curriculum
Brick Township Schools
Brick, New Jersey

Donna McCollum Derby
Teacher
Kernersville Elementary School
Kernersville, North Carolina

Dawn Evans
Mathematics Teacher
Bret Harte Elementary School
Chicago, Illinois

Terri Geaudreau
Title I Math Facilitator
Bemiss Elementary
Spokane, Washington

Sister Helen Lucille Habig, RSM
Assistant Superintendent of Catholic Schools
Archdiocese of Cincinnati
Cincinnati, Ohio

Sam Hanson
Teacher
Totem Falls Elementary
Snohomish, Washington

Allison Harris
Professional Development School Coach
Seattle Public Schools
Seattle, Washington

Kim Hill
Teacher
Hayes Grade Center
Ada, Oklahoma

Pamela Renee Hill
Teacher
Durham Public Schools
Durham, North Carolina

Martha Knight
Teacher
Oak Mountain Elementary
Birmingham, Alabama

Catherine Kuhns
Teacher
Country Hills Elementary
Coral Springs, Florida

Madeleine A. Madsen
District Curriculum Resource
District Community Consolidated School District 59
Arlington Heights, Illinois

Susan Mayberger
Supervisor of English as a Second Language/Director of Migrant Education
Omaha Public Schools
Omaha, Nebraska

Judy Peede
Elementary Lead Math Teacher
Wake County Schools
Raleigh, North Carolina

Lynda M. Penry
Teacher
Wright Elementary
Fort Walton Beach, Florida

Jolyn D. Raleigh
District Math Curriculum Specialist, Grades K–2
Granite School District
Salt Lake City, Utah

Deanna P. Rigdon
District Math Curriculum Specialist, Grades 3–4
Granite School District
Salt Lake City, Utah

Thomas Romero
Principal
Adams Elementary
Wapato, Washington

Wendy Siegel
Mathematics Coordinator, Grades K–12
Orchard Park Middle School
Orchard Park, New York

Sandra Smith
Teacher
Cheat Lake Elementary
Morgantown, West Virginia

Vickie H. Smith
Assistant Principal
Phoenix Academic Magnet Elementary School
Alexandria, Louisiana

Rochelle A. Solomon
Mathematics Resource Teacher
Cleveland Municipal School District
Cleveland, Ohio

Frank L. Sparks
Curriculum Design and Support Specialist, Secondary Mathematics
New Orleans Public Schools
New Orleans, Louisiana

Beth L. Spivey
Lead Teacher, Elementary Mathematics
Wake County Public School System
Raleigh, North Carolina

Paula Spomer
Teacher
Chisholm Elementary
Edmond, Oklahoma

Robert Trammel
Math Consultant
Fort Wayne Community Schools
Fort Wayne, Indiana

Annemarie Tuffner
Mathematics Lead Teacher, Grades K–12
Neshaminy School District
Langhorne, Pennsylvania

Ann Watts
Mathematics Specialist
East Baton Rouge Parish School System
Baton Rouge, Louisiana

Judy L. Wright
Curriculum and Staff Development Specialist
Columbus Public Schools
Columbus, Ohio

Theresa Zieles
Teacher
Indianapolis Public School #88
Indianapolis, Indiana

National Math Advisory Board

F. William Amorosi
Saugus Public Schools
Saugus, Massachusetts

Linda Bailey
Oklahoma City, Oklahoma

Mary Bording
Huntsville Public Schools
Huntsville, Alabama

Patti Bridwell
Austin, Texas

Merry Brown
Lake Jackson, Texas

Gayle D. Coleman
St. Louis Public Schools
St. Louis, Missouri

Steven T. Cottrell
Davis School District
Farmington, Utah

Brenda DeBorde
Grand Prairie ISD
Grand Prairie, Texas

Toni Lynn De Vore
Wood County Schools
Parkersburg, West Virginia

Sandra Eliason
Orland School District 135
Orland Park, Illinois

Larue Evans
Cherry Hill Elementary Schools
Cherry Hill, New Jersey

Ann R. Flanagan
Sachem Central School District
Holbrook, New York

Nancy C. French
Davenport Community School District
Davenport, Iowa

Marguerite Hart
Indianapolis, Indiana

Cathy Hutchins
Laird Elementary School
Tempe, Arizona

Nancy B. Knight
Mount Laurel Township Schools
Mount Laurel, New Jersey

Suzzanne Legg
Kansas City Public Schools
Kansas City, Kansas

Gale Levow
Community School District 8
Bronx, New York

Lynda M. Penry
Wright Elementary
Fort Walton Beach, Florida

Patricia Paluch Pockl
Ohio County Schools
Wheeling, West Virginia

Sylvia O. Reeder-Tucker
Prince George's County Public Schools
Capitol Heights, Maryland

Beverly Kendrick Ross
Kyrene School District
Tempe, Arizona

Kathy Ross
New Orleans, Louisiana

Edward J. Sahagian
North Bergen School District
North Bergen, New Jersey

Kathleen Savage
Mesa Public Schools
Mesa, Arizona

Beth Ann Schefelker
Henry David Thoreau Elementary
Milwaukee Public Schools
Milwaukee, Wisconsin

Dana Smith Simmons
Flint Community Schools
Flint, Michigan

Toni Vela
Laredo, ISD
Laredo, Texas

Julie Victory
Pocono Mountain School District
Swiftwater, Pennsylvania

Jesse Warren
South Bend Community School Corporation
South Bend, Indiana

Nancy Zirkelbach
Cloverdale Elementary
Bonneville School District #93
Idaho Falls, Idaho

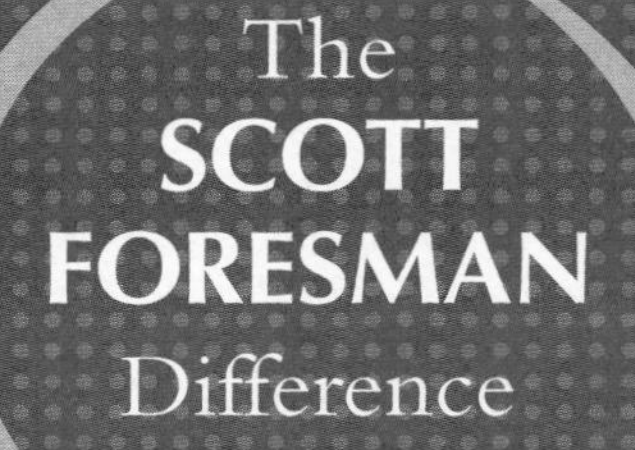

We truly teach for understanding.

Research shows that teaching for understanding is the best test prep you can provide. That's why every program claims to teach for understanding. But our program is different.

Includes instruction right on the student page

Everything your students need to "get it" is always accessible. Students are able to engage in deeper, independent learning while parents can help at home.

Instructional Stories

At the primary level, Read-Together Math Stories in the Student Edition and in Big Book format actually teach math concepts. Your students build math background while improving their reading fluency.

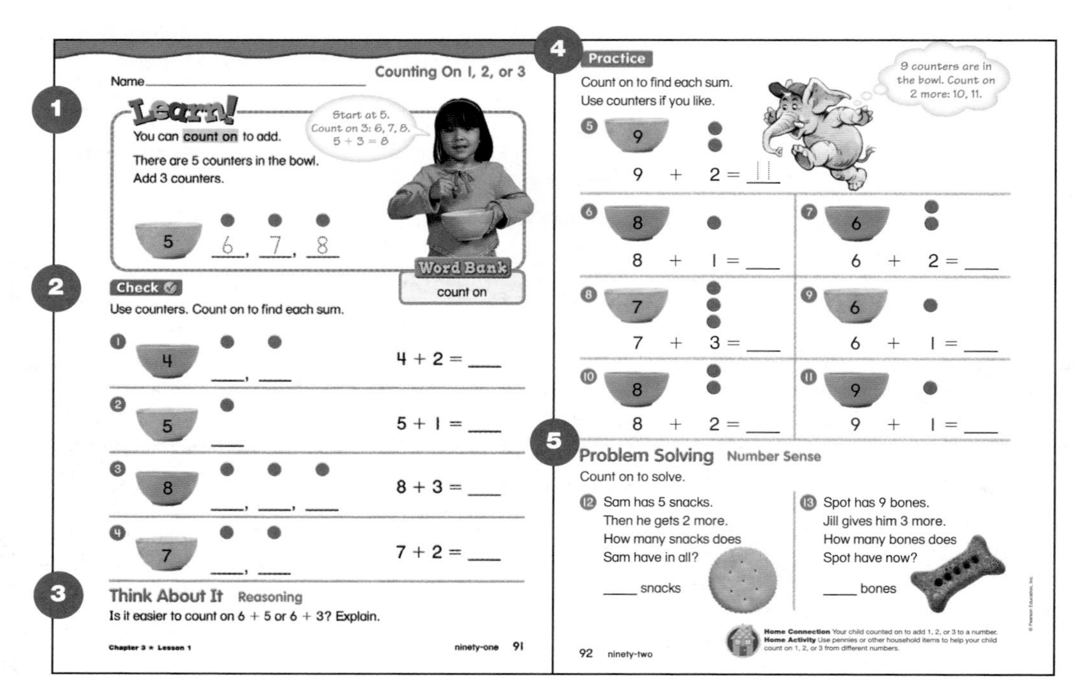
Name______ Counting On 1, 2, or 3

1 Learn!
You can count on to add.
There are 5 counters in the bowl.
Add 3 counters.
Start at 5. Count on 3: 6, 7, 8. 5 + 3 = 8
5 6, 7, 8
Word Bank
count on

2 Check
Use counters. Count on to find each sum.
1. 4 + 2 = ___
2. 5 + 1 = ___
3. 8 + 3 = ___
4. 7 + 2 = ___

3 Think About It Reasoning
Is it easier to count on 6 + 5 or 6 + 3? Explain.

Chapter 3 • Lesson 1 ninety-one 91

4 Practice
Count on to find each sum.
Use counters if you like.
9 counters are in the bowl. Count on 2 more: 10, 11.
5. 9 + 2 = 11
6. 8 + 1 = ___
7. 6 + 2 = ___
8. 7 + 3 = ___
9. 6 + 1 = ___
10. 8 + 2 = ___
11. 9 + 1 = ___

5 Problem Solving Number Sense
Count on to solve.
12. Sam has 5 snacks. Then he gets 2 more. How many snacks does Sam have in all? ___ snacks
13. Spot has 9 bones. Jill gives him 3 more. How many bones does Spot have now? ___ bones

92 ninety-two

1. **Learn**
   Introduces concepts and vocabulary clearly

2. **Check**
   Quickly assesses your students' grasp of the new concept before practice

3. **Think About It**
   Gives your students a chance to verbalize and clarify understanding before practice begins

4. **Practice**
   Provides instruction with more examples your students can explore with manipulatives

5. **Problem Solving**
   Engages your students with daily problem-solving activities

6. **Magnetic Manipulatives**
   Fun, no-mess manipulatives your students can hold up to display their work and help you check for understanding

Identifies explicitly what your students need to achieve

Lessons in the Student Edition clearly explain the mathematics your students need to understand and the skills they need to master. Step-by-step instruction guides their thinking when they need it most.

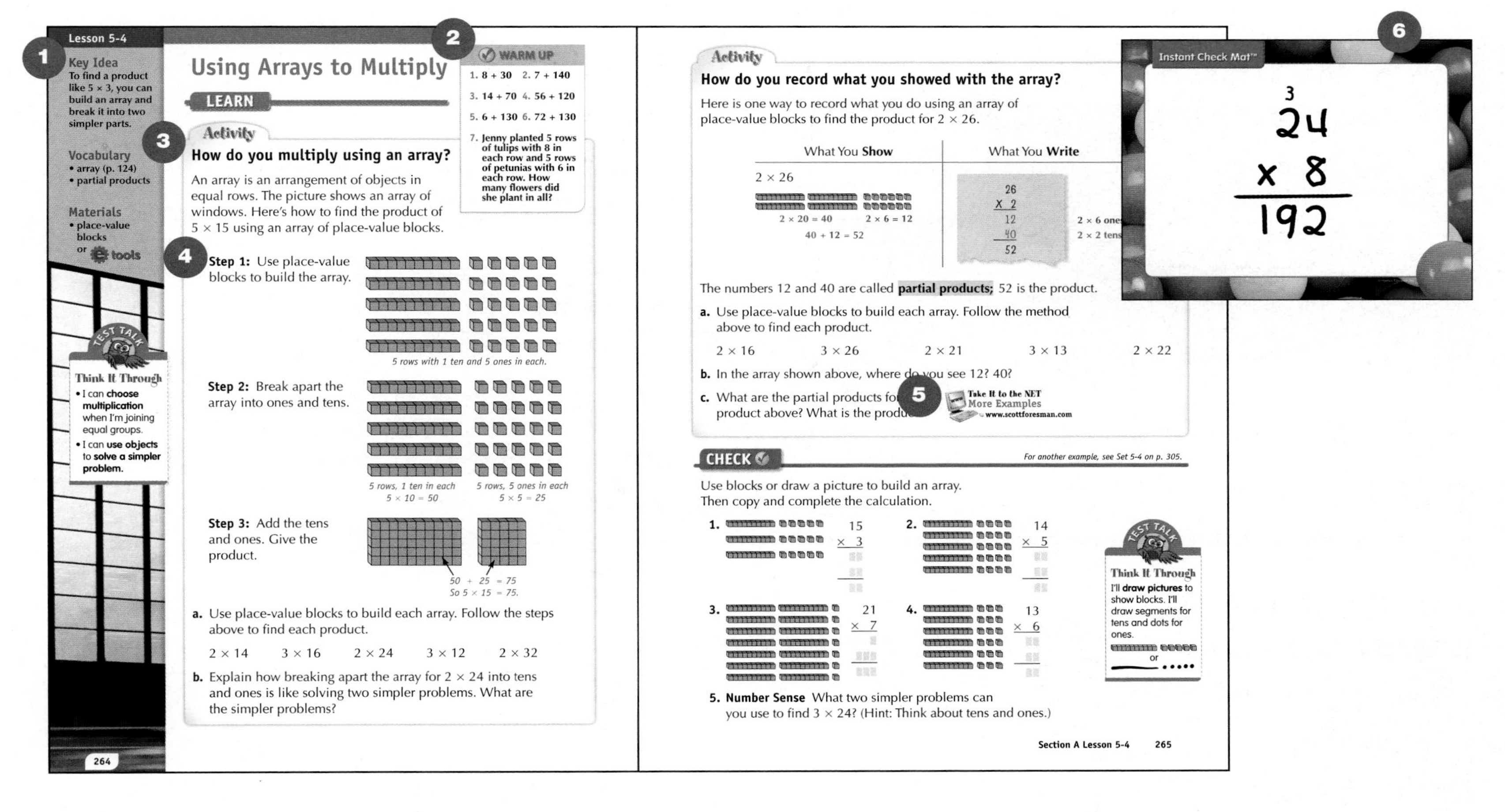

Lesson 5-4

Key Idea To find a product like 5 × 3, you can build an array and break it into two simpler parts.

Vocabulary
- array (p. 124)
- partial products

Materials
- place-value blocks or tools

Using Arrays to Multiply

LEARN

WARM UP

1. 8 + 30
2. 7 + 140
3. 14 + 70
4. 56 + 120
5. 6 + 130
6. 72 + 130
7. Jenny planted 5 rows of tulips with 8 in each row and 5 rows of petunias with 6 in each row. How many flowers did she plant in all?

Activity

How do you multiply using an array?

An array is an arrangement of objects in equal rows. The picture shows an array of windows. Here's how to find the product of 5 × 15 using an array of place-value blocks.

Step 1: Use place-value blocks to build the array.

5 rows with 1 ten and 5 ones in each.

Step 2: Break apart the array into ones and tens.

5 rows, 1 ten in each 5 × 10 = 50

5 rows, 5 ones in each 5 × 5 = 25

Step 3: Add the tens and ones. Give the product.

50 + 25 = 75
So 5 × 15 = 75.

TEST TALK — Think It Through
- I can **choose multiplication** when I'm joining equal groups.
- I can **use objects** to **solve a simpler problem.**

a. Use place-value blocks to build each array. Follow the steps above to find each product.

2 × 14 3 × 16 2 × 24 3 × 12 2 × 32

b. Explain how breaking apart the array for 2 × 24 into tens and ones is like solving two simpler problems. What are the simpler problems?

264

Activity

How do you record what you showed with the array?

Here is one way to record what you do using an array of place-value blocks to find the product for 2 × 26.

What You Show	What You Write
2 × 26 2 × 20 = 40 2 × 6 = 12 40 + 12 = 52	26 × 2 12 2 × 6 ones 40 2 × 2 tens 52

The numbers 12 and 40 are called **partial products**; 52 is the product.

a. Use place-value blocks to build each array. Follow the method above to find each product.

2 × 16 3 × 26 2 × 21 3 × 13 2 × 22

b. In the array shown above, where do you see 12? 40?

c. What are the partial products for each product above? What is the product?

Take It to the NET More Examples www.scottforesman.com

CHECK

For another example, see Set 5-4 on p. 305.

Use blocks or draw a picture to build an array. Then copy and complete the calculation.

1. 15 × 3
2. 14 × 5
3. 21 × 7
4. 13 × 6

TEST TALK — Think It Through I'll **draw pictures** to show blocks. I'll draw segments for tens and dots for ones.

5. **Number Sense** What two simpler problems can you use to find 3 × 24? (Hint: Think about tens and ones.)

Section A Lesson 5-4 265

Instant Check Mat™

3
24
× 8
192

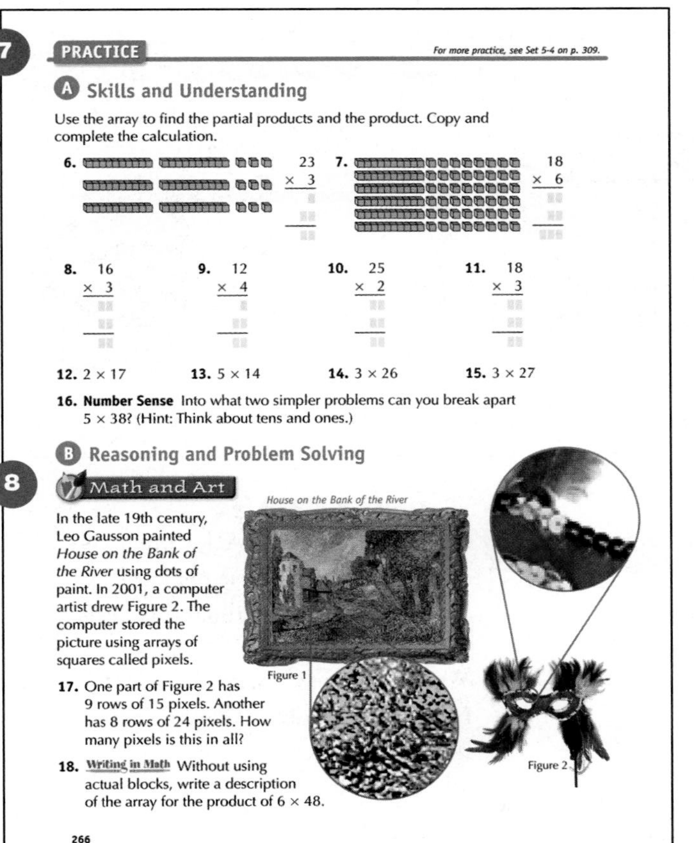

PRACTICE

For more practice, see Set 5-4 on p. 309.

A Skills and Understanding

Use the array to find the partial products and the product. Copy and complete the calculation.

6. 23 × 3
7. 18 × 6
8. 16 × 3
9. 12 × 4
10. 25 × 2
11. 18 × 3
12. 2 × 17
13. 5 × 14
14. 3 × 26
15. 3 × 27
16. **Number Sense** Into what two simpler problems can you break apart 5 × 38? (Hint: Think about tens and ones.)

B Reasoning and Problem Solving

Math and Art

In the late 19th century, Leo Gausson painted *House on the Bank of the River* using dots of paint. In 2001, a computer artist drew Figure 2. The computer stored the picture using arrays of squares called pixels.

House on the Bank of the River

Figure 1

Figure 2

17. One part of Figure 2 has 9 rows of 15 pixels. Another has 8 rows of 24 pixels. How many pixels is this in all?
18. **Writing in Math** Without using actual blocks, write a description of the array for the product of 6 × 48.

266

1. Key Idea
Identifies important mathematics concepts clearly right at the start

2. Warm Up
Activates prior knowledge of skills your students will need in the upcoming lesson

3. Focus Questions
Sets up instruction for your students' understanding

4. Guided Instruction
Makes concepts easier for your students to grasp with step-by-step instruction and clear models right on the student page

5. Take It to the Net
Provides online access to test prep, more practice, and more examples

6. Instant Check Mat™
See all your students' work at a glance and assess their understanding instantly

7. Built-in Leveled Practice
Allows you to customize instruction to match your students' abilities

8. Curriculum Connections
Encourages your students to transfer the concepts they acquire to other subject areas

Monitors understanding every step of the way

With embedded assessment opportunities right on the student page, it's easy to gauge your students' progress on an ongoing basis. This frees you to focus your time and energy on helping each student acquire the skills and understanding needed for test success.

Before the Lesson

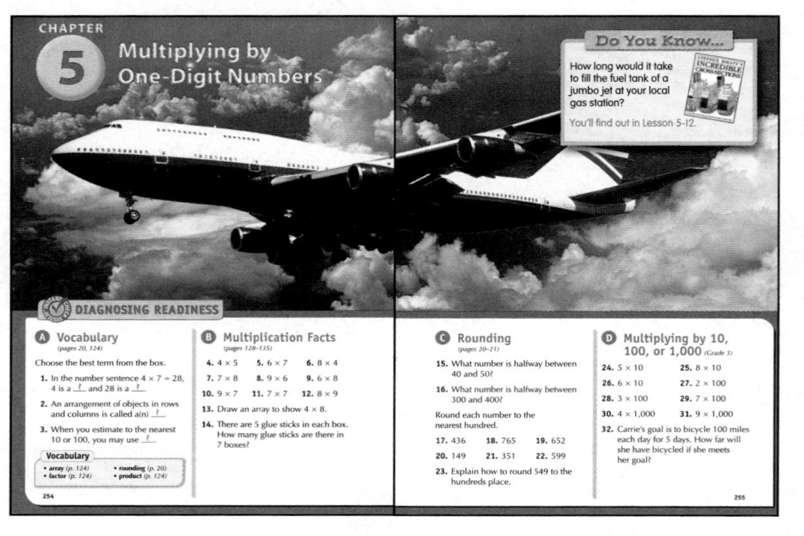

Diagnosing Readiness

Helps you assess your students' knowledge of vocabulary, skills, and concepts, and then prescribe individualized intervention prior to chapter lessons

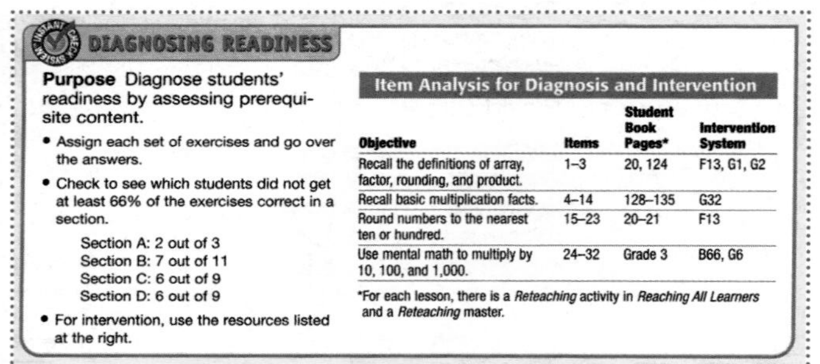

DIAGNOSING READINESS

Purpose Diagnose students' readiness by assessing prerequisite content.

- Assign each set of exercises and go over the answers.
- Check to see which students did not get at least 66% of the exercises correct in a section.
  - Section A: 2 out of 3
  - Section B: 7 out of 11
  - Section C: 6 out of 9
  - Section D: 6 out of 9
- For intervention, use the resources listed at the right.

Item Analysis for Diagnosis and Intervention

Objective	Items	Student Book Pages*	Intervention System
Recall the definitions of array, factor, rounding, and product.	1–3	20, 124	F13, G1, G2
Recall basic multiplication facts.	4–14	128–135	G32
Round numbers to the nearest ten or hundred.	15–23	20–21	F13
Use mental math to multiply by 10, 100, and 1,000.	24–32	Grade 3	B66, G6

*For each lesson, there is a *Reteaching* activity in *Reaching All Learners* and a *Reteaching* master.

Every assessment aligns with customized intervention in the Teacher's Edition

During the Lesson

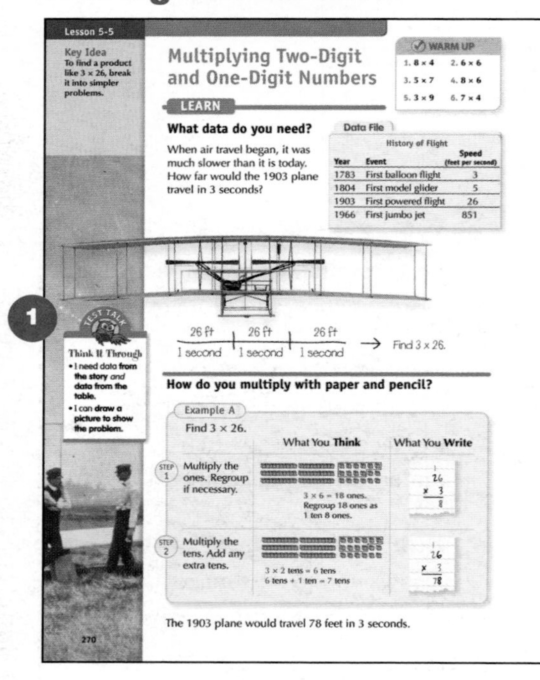

1. **Test Talk—Think It Through**
   Gives your students practice in the type of thinking and problem-solving strategies they'll use on tests

2. **Talk About It**
   Supplies your students with an informal assessment opportunity that lets them verbalize their understanding

3. **If . . . Then**
   Provides instant intervention before your students get too far off track

4. **Check**
   Sees if your students "get it" before beginning independent practice

5. **Writing in Math**
   Prepares your students for open-ended and short- or extended-response questions on state and national tests

6. **Mixed Review and Test Prep**
   Helps your students keep their test-taking skills sharp

Aligns all assessments with immediate and systematic remediation

Our unique Item Analysis for Diagnosis and Intervention in the Teacher's Edition lets you quickly assess your students' understanding of math concepts and prescribe individualized intervention.

After the Lesson *at the End of Each Section . . .*

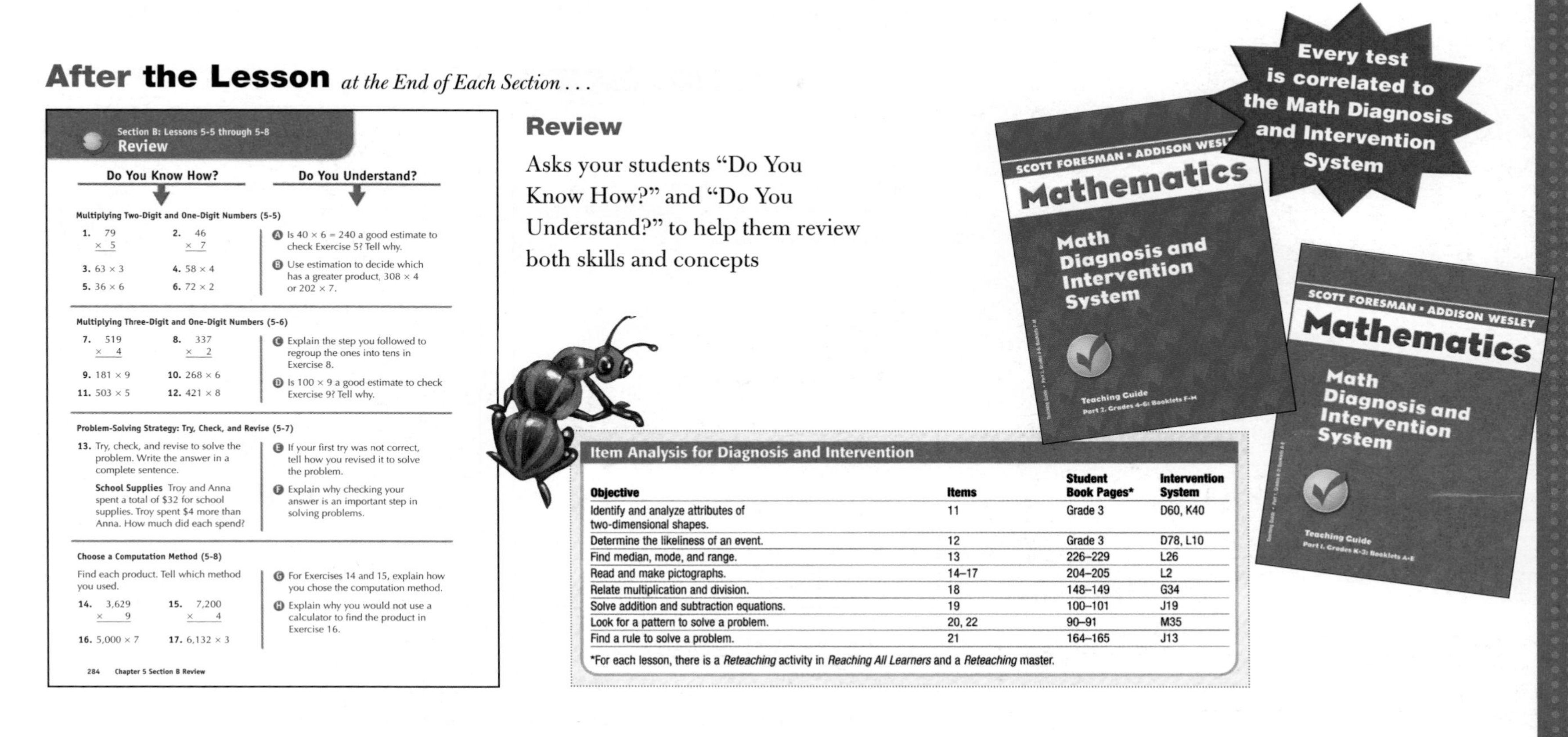

Section B: Lessons 5-5 through 5-8
Review

Do You Know How? | Do You Understand?

Multiplying Two-Digit and One-Digit Numbers (5-5)

1. 79 × 5
2. 46 × 7
3. 63 × 3
4. 58 × 4
5. 36 × 6
6. 72 × 2

A. Is 40 × 6 = 240 a good estimate to check Exercise 5? Tell why.
B. Use estimation to decide which has a greater product, 308 × 4 or 202 × 7.

Multiplying Three-Digit and One-Digit Numbers (5-6)

7. 519 × 4
8. 337 × 2
9. 181 × 9
10. 268 × 6
11. 503 × 5
12. 421 × 8

C. Explain the step you followed to regroup the ones into tens in Exercise 8.
D. Is 100 × 9 a good estimate to check Exercise 9? Tell why.

Problem-Solving Strategy: Try, Check, and Revise (5-7)

13. Try, check, and revise to solve the problem. Write the answer in a complete sentence.
School Supplies Troy and Anna spent a total of $32 for school supplies. Troy spent $4 more than Anna. How much did each spend?

E. If your first try was not correct, tell how you revised it to solve the problem.
F. Explain why checking your answer is an important step in solving problems.

Choose a Computation Method (5-8)

Find each product. Tell which method you used.

14. 3,629 × 9
15. 7,200 × 4
16. 5,000 × 7
17. 6,132 × 3

G. For Exercises 14 and 15, explain how you chose the computation method.
H. Explain why you would not use a calculator to find the product in Exercise 16.

284 Chapter 5 Section B Review

Review

Asks your students "Do You Know How?" and "Do You Understand?" to help them review both skills and concepts

Item Analysis for Diagnosis and Intervention

Objective	Items	Student Book Pages*	Intervention System
Identify and analyze attributes of two-dimensional shapes.	11	Grade 3	D60, K40
Determine the likeliness of an event.	12	Grade 3	D78, L10
Find median, mode, and range.	13	226–229	L26
Read and make pictographs.	14–17	204–205	L2
Relate multiplication and division.	18	148–149	G34
Solve addition and subtraction equations.	19	100–101	J19
Look for a pattern to solve a problem.	20, 22	90–91	M35
Find a rule to solve a problem.	21	164–165	J13

*For each lesson, there is a *Reteaching* activity in *Reaching All Learners* and a *Reteaching* master.

After the Lesson *at the End of Each Chapter . . .*

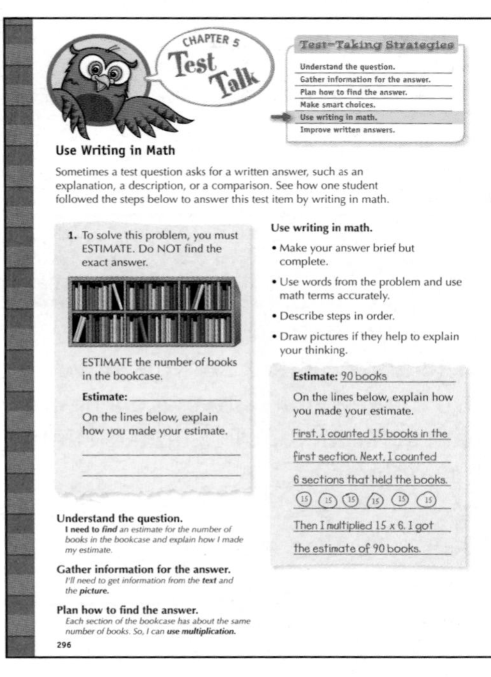

Use Writing in Math

Sometimes a test question asks for a written answer, such as an explanation, a description, or a comparison. See how one student followed the steps below to answer this test item by writing in math.

1. To solve this problem, you must ESTIMATE. Do NOT find the exact answer.

ESTIMATE the number of books in the bookcase.

Estimate: ______

On the lines below, explain how you made your estimate.

Understand the question.
I need to find an estimate for the number of books in the bookcase and explain how I made my estimate.

Gather information for the answer.
I'll need to get information from the text and the picture.

Plan how to find the answer.
Each section of the bookcase has about the same number of books. So, I can use multiplication.

Use writing in math.
- Make your answer brief but complete.
- Use words from the problem and use math terms accurately.
- Describe steps in order.
- Draw pictures if they help to explain your thinking.

Estimate: 90 books

On the lines below, explain how you made your estimate.

First, I counted 15 books in the first section. Next, I counted 6 sections that held the books. Then I multiplied 15 x 6. I got the estimate of 90 books.

296

Test Talk

Gives your students in-depth instruction and practice on the test-taking strategies introduced at the beginning of the Student Edition

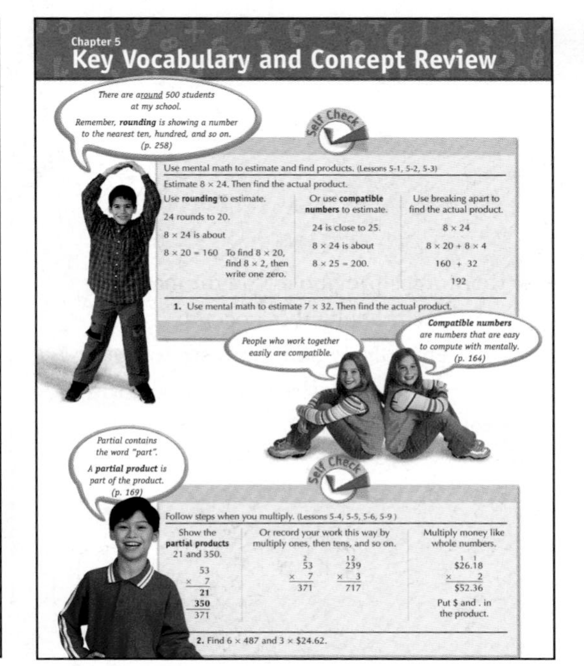

Key Vocabulary and Concept Review

Checks your students' understanding of math concepts and provides them with real-world vocabulary connections

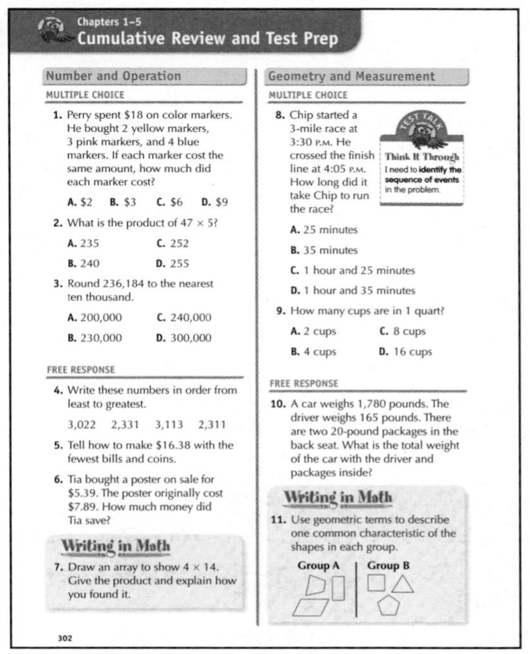

Number and Operation

MULTIPLE CHOICE

1. Perry spent $18 on color markers. He bought 2 yellow markers, 3 pink markers, and 4 blue markers. If each marker cost the same amount, how much did each marker cost?
A. $2 B. $3 C. $6 D. $9
2. What is the product of 47 × 5?
A. 235 B. 240 C. 252 D. 255
3. Round 236,184 to the nearest ten thousand.
A. 200,000 B. 230,000 C. 240,000 D. 300,000

FREE RESPONSE

4. Write these numbers in order from least to greatest.
3,022 2,331 3,113 2,311
5. Tell how to make $16.38 with the fewest bills and coins.
6. Tia bought a poster on sale for $5.39. The poster originally cost $7.89. How much money did Tia save?

Writing in Math

7. Draw an array to show 4 × 14. Give the product and explain how you found it.

Geometry and Measurement

MULTIPLE CHOICE

8. Chip started a 3-mile race at 3:30 P.M. He crossed the finish line at 4:05 P.M. How long did it take Chip to run the race?
Think It Through: I need to identify the sequence of events in the problem.
A. 25 minutes
B. 35 minutes
C. 1 hour and 25 minutes
D. 1 hour and 35 minutes
9. How many cups are in 1 quart?
A. 2 cups B. 4 cups C. 8 cups D. 16 cups

FREE RESPONSE

10. A car weighs 1,780 pounds. The driver weighs 165 pounds. There are two 20-pound packages in the back seat. What is the total weight of the car with the driver and packages inside?

Writing in Math

11. Use geometric terms to describe one common characteristic of the shapes in each group.
Group A | Group B

302

Cumulative Review and Test Prep

Provides ongoing assessment and practice of previously taught content

The SCOTT FORESMAN Difference

We create better problem solvers.

Problem solving is incredibly important to math proficiency and test success. That's why every program has a problem-solving component. But our program is different.

Connects reading and writing to problem solving

Research shows math performance is often connected to literacy. We apply familiar reading and writing strategies to math and explain to your students how these strategies can help them become more successful problem solvers.

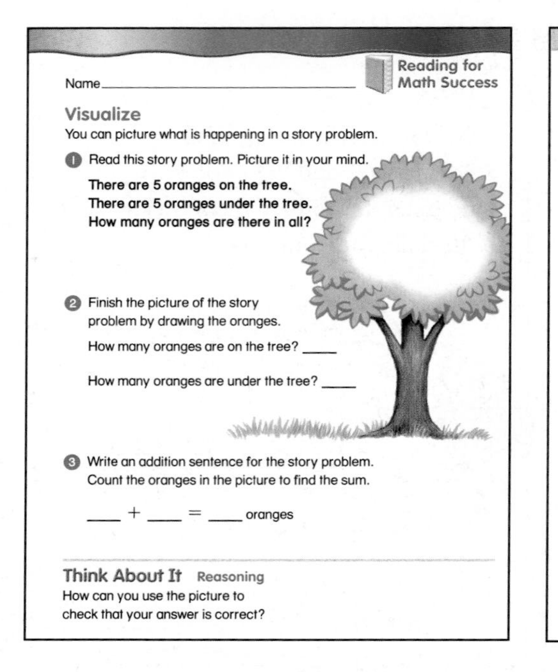

Name ______ Reading for Math Success

Visualize

You can picture what is happening in a story problem.

1. Read this story problem. Picture it in your mind.

There are 5 oranges on the tree.
There are 5 oranges under the tree.
How many oranges are there in all?

2. Finish the picture of the story problem by drawing the oranges.

How many oranges are on the tree? ____

How many oranges are under the tree? ____

3. Write an addition sentence for the story problem. Count the oranges in the picture to find the sum.

___ + ___ = ___ oranges

Think About It Reasoning
How can you use the picture to check that your answer is correct?

Reading for Math Success

Identifies a reading strategy your students already know and shows them how to apply the strategy to math word problems

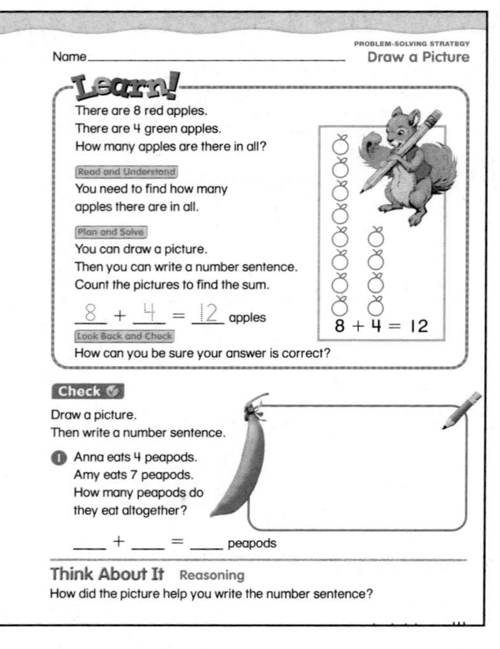

Name ______ PROBLEM-SOLVING STRATEGY Draw a Picture

Learn!

There are 8 red apples.
There are 4 green apples.
How many apples are there in all?

Read and Understand
You need to find how many apples there are in all.

Plan and Solve
You can draw a picture.
Then you can write a number sentence.
Count the pictures to find the sum.

8 + 4 = 12 apples

8 + 4 = 12

Look Back and Check
How can you be sure your answer is correct?

Check

Draw a picture.
Then write a number sentence.

1. Anna eats 4 peapods.
Amy eats 7 peapods.
How many peapods do they eat altogether?

___ + ___ = ___ peapods

Think About It Reasoning
How did the picture help you write the number sentence?

Problem-Solving Strategy

Teaches your students how and when to use the reading strategy to solve problems, and then provides an opportunity for them to demonstrate what they have learned

Problem of the Day Transparencies Flip Chart

Reinforces previously taught math content and enhances specific problem-solving skills and strategies each day for whole-class or small group problem-solving

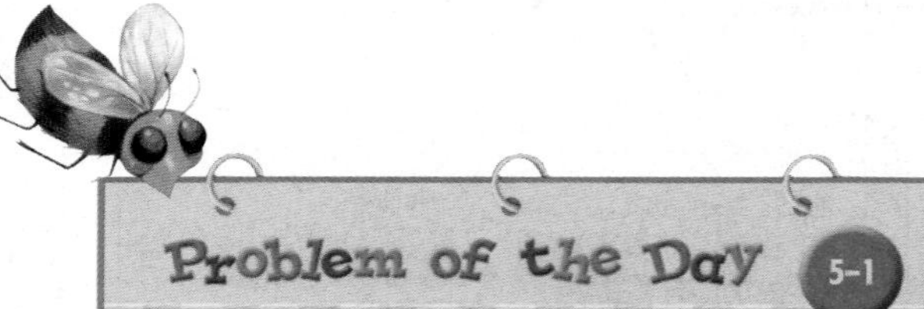

Problem of the Day 5-1

The figure below has a perimeter of 18 units. Where can you move two of the squares to make a figure with a perimeter of 12 units? (Hint: Use objects.)

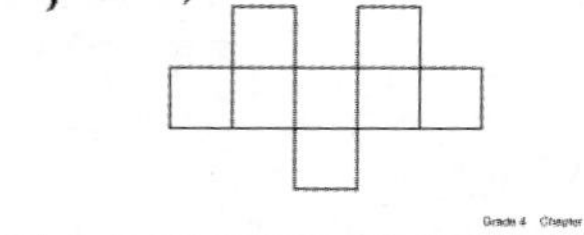

Links techniques to understanding and solving word problems

By linking reading and writing to math, students become more adept at understanding word problems and identifying what they need to do. Your students will improve their abilities to recognize and organize the important details and learn how to describe their solutions by writing clear, concise, and accurate answers.

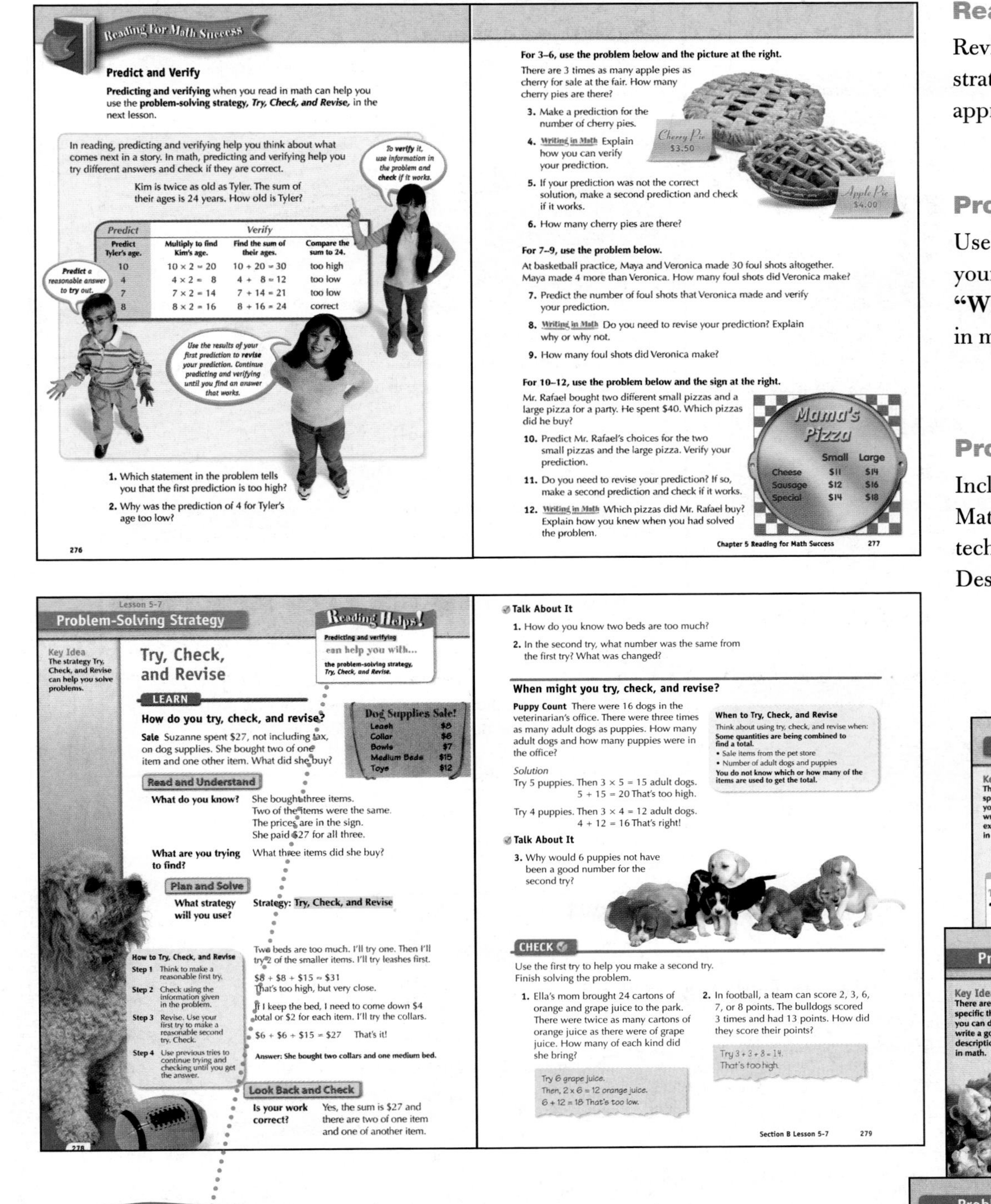

Reading For Math Success

Predict and Verify

Predicting and verifying when you read in math can help you use the **problem-solving strategy, *Try, Check, and Revise,*** in the next lesson.

In reading, predicting and verifying help you think about what comes next in a story. In math, predicting and verifying help you try different answers and check if they are correct.

Kim is twice as old as Tyler. The sum of their ages is 24 years. How old is Tyler?

Predict	Verify		
Predict Tyler's age.	Multiply to find Kim's age.	Find the sum of their ages.	Compare the sum to 24.
10	10 × 2 = 20	10 + 20 = 30	too high
4	4 × 2 = 8	4 + 8 = 12	too low
7	7 × 2 = 14	7 + 14 = 21	too low
8	8 × 2 = 16	8 + 16 = 24	correct

1. Which statement in the problem tells you that the first prediction is too high?
2. Why was the prediction of 4 for Tyler's age too low?

276

For 3–6, use the problem below and the picture at the right.

There are 3 times as many apple pies as cherry for sale at the fair. How many cherry pies are there?

3. Make a prediction for the number of cherry pies.
4. Writing in Math Explain how you can verify your prediction.
5. If your prediction was not the correct solution, make a second prediction and check if it works.
6. How many cherry pies are there?

For 7–9, use the problem below.

At basketball practice, Maya and Veronica made 30 foul shots altogether. Maya made 4 more than Veronica. How many foul shots did Veronica make?

7. Predict the number of foul shots that Veronica made and verify your prediction.
8. Writing in Math Do you need to revise your prediction? Explain why or why not.
9. How many foul shots did Veronica make?

For 10–12, use the problem below and the sign at the right.

Mr. Rafael bought two different small pizzas and a large pizza for a party. He spent $40. Which pizzas did he buy?

10. Predict Mr. Rafael's choices for the two small pizzas and the large pizza. Verify your prediction.
11. Do you need to revise your prediction? If so, make a second prediction and check if it works.
12. Writing in Math Which pizzas did Mr. Rafael buy? Explain how you knew when you had solved the problem.

Mama's Pizza

	Small	Large
Cheese	$11	$14
Sausage	$12	$16
Special	$14	$18

Chapter 5 Reading for Math Success 277

Lesson 5-7

Problem-Solving Strategy

Key Idea
The strategy Try, Check, and Revise can help you solve problems.

Try, Check, and Revise

Reading Helps! Predicting and verifying can help you with... the problem-solving strategy, *Try, Check, and Revise.*

LEARN

How do you try, check, and revise?

Sale Suzanne spent $27, not including tax, on dog supplies. She bought two of one item and one other item. What did she buy?

Dog Supplies Sale!

Leash	$8
Collar	$6
Bowls	$7
Medium Beds	$15
Toys	$12

Read and Understand

What do you know? She bought three items. Two of the items were the same. The prices are in the sign. She paid $27 for all three.

What are you trying to find? What three items did she buy?

Plan and Solve

What strategy will you use? Strategy: Try, Check, and Revise

How to Try, Check, and Revise
Step 1 Think to make a reasonable first try.
Step 2 Check using the information given in the problem.
Step 3 Revise. Use your first try to make a reasonable second try. Check.
Step 4 Use previous tries to continue trying and checking until you get the answer.

Two beds are too much. I'll try one. Then I'll try 2 of the smaller items. I'll try leashes first.

$8 + $8 + $15 = $31
That's too high, but very close.

If I keep the bed, I need to come down $4 total or $2 for each item. I'll try the collars.

$6 + $6 + $15 = $27 That's it!

Answer: She bought two collars and one medium bed.

Look Back and Check

Is your work correct? Yes, the sum is $27 and there are two of one item and one of another item.

278

Talk About It

1. How do you know two beds are too much?
2. In the second try, what number was the same from the first try? What was changed?

When might you try, check, and revise?

Puppy Count There were 16 dogs in the veterinarian's office. There were three times as many adult dogs as puppies. How many adult dogs and how many puppies were in the office?

Solution
Try 5 puppies. Then 3 × 5 = 15 adult dogs.
5 + 15 = 20 That's too high.

Try 4 puppies. Then 3 × 4 = 12 adult dogs.
4 + 12 = 16 That's right!

When to Try, Check, and Revise
Think about using try, check, and revise when:
Some quantities are being combined to find a total.
- Sale items from the pet store
- Number of adult dogs and puppies

You do not know which or how many of the items are used to get the total.

Talk About It

3. Why would 6 puppies not have been a good number for the second try?

CHECK

Use the first try to help you make a second try. Finish solving the problem.

1. Ella's mom brought 24 cartons of orange and grape juice to the park. There were twice as many cartons of orange juice as there were of grape juice. How many of each kind did she bring?

   Try 6 grape juice.
   Then, 2 × 6 = 12 orange juice.
   6 + 12 = 18 That's too low.

2. In football, a team can score 2, 3, 6, 7, or 8 points. The bulldogs scored 3 times and had 13 points. How did they score their points?

   Try 3 + 3 + 8 = 14.
   That's too high.

Section B Lesson 5-7 279

Reading for Math Success

Reviews reading comprehension skills and strategies and provides a clear connection to appropriate math strategies

Problem-Solving Strategy

Uses explicit and systematic instruction to focus your students' thinking on exactly **"How"** and **"When"** to use specific problem solving strategies in math

Problem-Solving Skill

Includes lessons that reinforce the Writing in Math exercises by teaching your students specific techniques for Writing to Explain, Writing to Describe, and Writing to Compare

Reading Helps!

Predicting and Verifying

can help you with...

the problem-solving strategy, *Try, Check, and Revise.*

Reading Helps

Provides quick, memorable reminders that teach your students to recognize how reading skills and strategies connect with problem solving

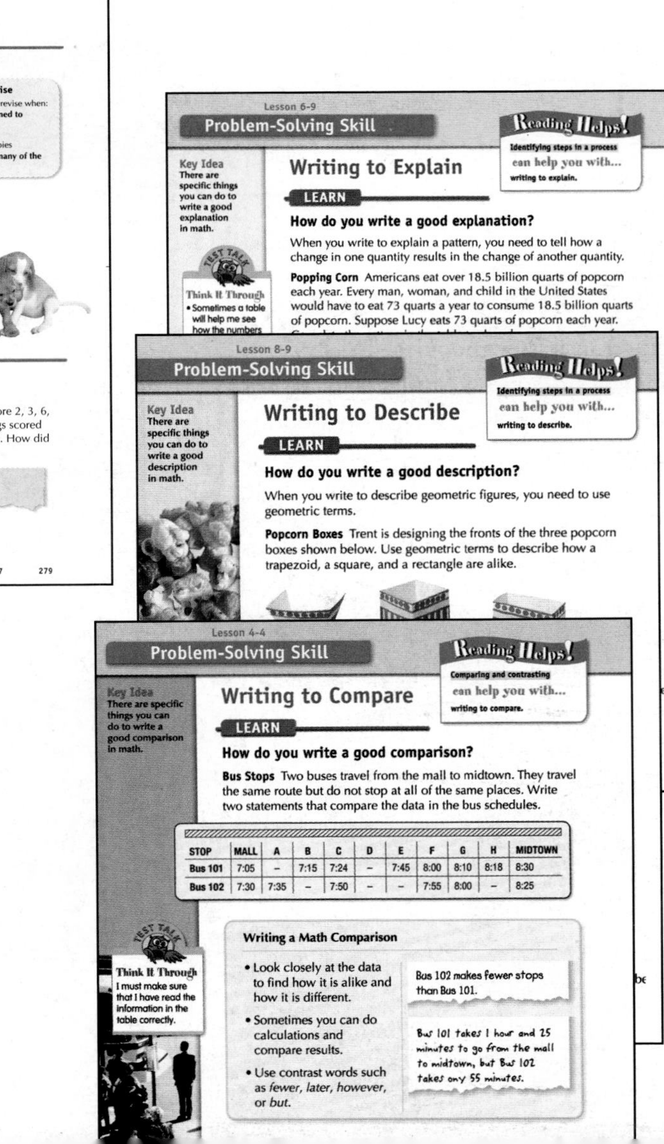

Lesson 6-9

Problem-Solving Skill

Key Idea
There are specific things you can do to write a good explanation in math.

Writing to Explain

Reading Helps! Identifying steps in a process can help you with... writing to explain.

LEARN

How do you write a good explanation?

When you write to explain a pattern, you need to tell how a change in one quantity results in the change of another quantity.

Popping Corn Americans eat over 18.5 billion quarts of popcorn each year. Every man, woman, and child in the United States would have to eat 73 quarts a year to consume 18.5 billion quarts of popcorn. Suppose Lucy eats 73 quarts of popcorn each year.

Think It Through
• Sometimes a table will help me see how the numbers

Lesson 8-9

Problem-Solving Skill

Key Idea
There are specific things you can do to write a good description in math.

Writing to Describe

Reading Helps! Identifying steps in a process can help you with... writing to describe.

LEARN

How do you write a good description?

When you write to describe geometric figures, you need to use geometric terms.

Popcorn Boxes Trent is designing the fronts of the three popcorn boxes shown below. Use geometric terms to describe how a trapezoid, a square, and a rectangle are alike.

Lesson 4-4

Problem-Solving Skill

Key Idea
There are specific things you can do to write a good comparison in math.

Writing to Compare

Reading Helps! Comparing and contrasting can help you with... writing to compare.

LEARN

How do you write a good comparison?

Bus Stops Two buses travel from the mall to midtown. They travel the same route but do not stop at all of the same places. Write two statements that compare the data in the bus schedules.

STOP	MALL	A	B	C	D	E	F	G	H	MIDTOWN
Bus 101	7:05	–	7:15	7:24	–	7:45	8:00	8:10	8:18	8:30
Bus 102	7:30	7:35	–	7:50	–	–	7:55	8:00	–	8:25

Think It Through
I must make sure that I have read the information in the table correctly.

Writing a Math Comparison

- Look closely at the data to find how it is alike and how it is different.
- Sometimes you can do calculations and compare results.
- Use contrast words such as *fewer, later, however,* or *but.*

Bus 102 makes fewer stops than Bus 101.

Bus 101 takes 1 hour and 25 minutes to go from the mall to midtown, but Bus 102 takes ony 55 minutes.

Provides real-world applications

Our unique partnerships with Discovery Channel School™ and Dorling Kindersley provide your students with rich real-world applications that answer the common question: "When am I ever going to use this?"

Name__________

PROBLEM-SOLVING APPLICATIONS

Hop to It!

Dorling Kindersley

Do You Know... that rabbits like to eat lettuce and clover?

1. 4 rabbits is ____ more than 3 rabbits.
2. 2 rabbits are brown. I rabbit is white. How many rabbits are there in all?
   ____ rabbits
3. There are 10 rabbits. 5 of them are brown. The rest are white. How many rabbits are white?
   ____ + 5 = 10 rabbits
4. 5 big rabbits are eating. 2 ants are eating. 3 little rabbits are eating. How many rabbits are eating?
   ____ + ____ = ____ rabbits

Fun Fact! Tiny baby rabbits are called kittens.

Chapter 3 ★ Lesson 10 — one hundred thirteen 113

5. 4 rabbits hop in the grass. 5 more rabbits join them. How many rabbits are there in all?
   There are ____ rabbits in all.

Very long rabbit ears pick up at sounds of danger!

6. 3 rabbits are resting. 3 more rabbits sit with them. How many rabbits are there in all?
   There are ____ rabbits in all.
7. 10 rabbits are in the garden. The rabbits are in two groups. One group has 7 rabbits. How many rabbits are in the other group?
   There are ____ rabbits in the other group.
8. **Writing in Math**
   Draw a picture to show 10 rabbits in two groups. Write an addition sentence for your picture.

114 one hundred fourteen

Home Connection Your child learned to solve problems by applying his or her math skills. **Home Activity** Talk to your child about how he or she solved the problems on these two pages.

© Pearson Education, Inc.

Problem-Solving Applications

Dorling Kindersley provides visually stunning ways for your students to see how math concepts apply to the world around them.

Math Leveled Literature Library also available!

EYEWITNESS VISUAL DICTIONARIES THE VISUAL DICTIONARY of BUILDINGS

POCKETS SPACE FACTS

DK Literature Library

Engaging nonfiction books from Dorling Kindersley, the world-famous publisher of the DK Eyewitness Books, provide real-world, high-interest data for problem solving.

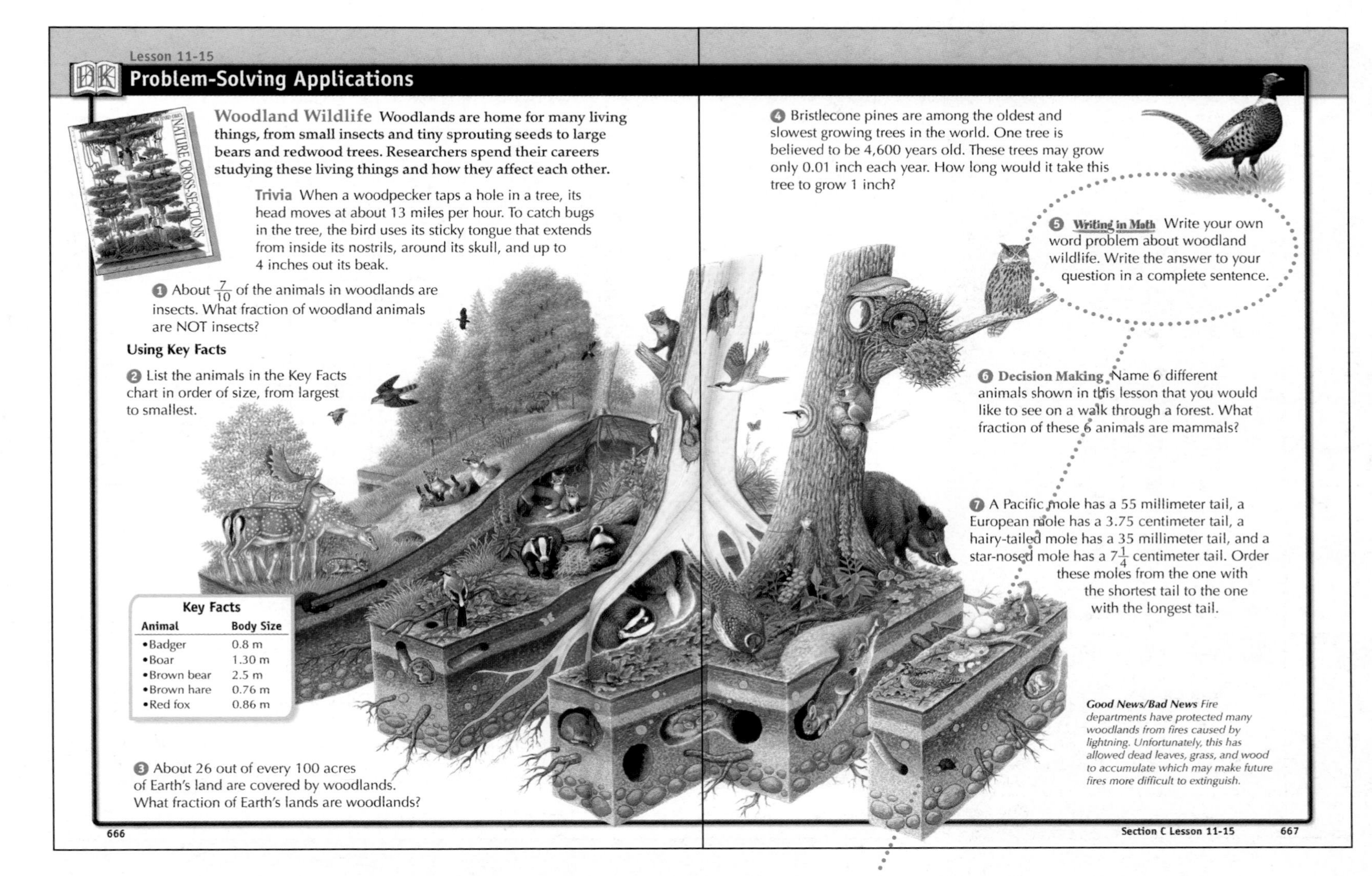

Lesson 11-15

Problem-Solving Applications

Woodland Wildlife Woodlands are home for many living things, from small insects and tiny sprouting seeds to large bears and redwood trees. Researchers spend their careers studying these living things and how they affect each other.

Trivia When a woodpecker taps a hole in a tree, its head moves at about 13 miles per hour. To catch bugs in the tree, the bird uses its sticky tongue that extends from inside its nostrils, around its skull, and up to 4 inches out its beak.

1. About $\frac{7}{10}$ of the animals in woodlands are insects. What fraction of woodland animals are NOT insects?

Using Key Facts

2. List the animals in the Key Facts chart in order of size, from largest to smallest.

Key Facts

Animal	Body Size
• Badger	0.8 m
• Boar	1.30 m
• Brown bear	2.5 m
• Brown hare	0.76 m
• Red fox	0.86 m

3. About 26 out of every 100 acres of Earth's land are covered by woodlands. What fraction of Earth's lands are woodlands?

4. Bristlecone pines are among the oldest and slowest growing trees in the world. One tree is believed to be 4,600 years old. These trees may grow only 0.01 inch each year. How long would it take this tree to grow 1 inch?

5. **Writing in Math** Write your own word problem about woodland wildlife. Write the answer to your question in a complete sentence.

6. **Decision Making** Name 6 different animals shown in this lesson that you would like to see on a walk through a forest. What fraction of these 6 animals are mammals?

7. A Pacific mole has a 55 millimeter tail, a European mole has a 3.75 centimeter tail, a hairy-tailed mole has a 35 millimeter tail, and a star-nosed mole has a $7\frac{1}{4}$ centimeter tail. Order these moles from the one with the shortest tail to the one with the longest tail.

Good News/Bad News Fire departments have protected many woodlands from fires caused by lightning. Unfortunately, this has allowed dead leaves, grass, and wood to accumulate which may make future fires more difficult to extinguish.

666 | Section C Lesson 11-15 | 667

Writing in Math

Gives your students a chance to explain their thinking and improve their writing skills and helps them become better problem solvers

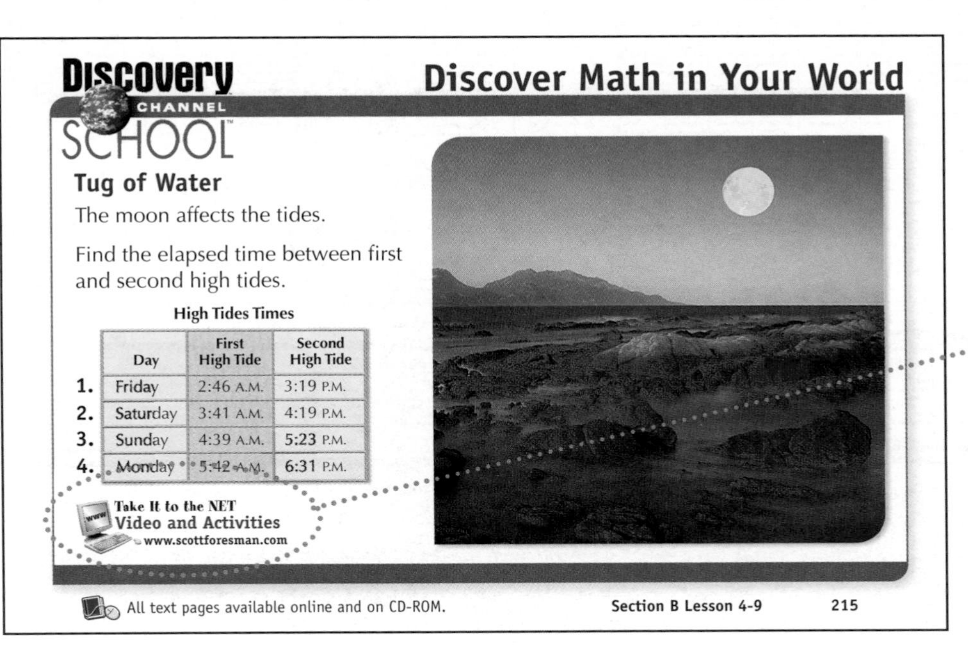

Discovery Channel School

Discover Math in Your World

Tug of Water

The moon affects the tides.

Find the elapsed time between first and second high tides.

High Tides Times

	Day	First High Tide	Second High Tide
1.	Friday	2:46 A.M.	3:19 P.M.
2.	Saturday	3:41 A.M.	4:19 P.M.
3.	Sunday	4:39 A.M.	5:23 P.M.
4.	Monday	5:42 A.M.	6:31 P.M.

Take It to the NET
Video and Activities
www.scottforesman.com

All text pages available online and on CD-ROM. | Section B Lesson 4-9 | 215

Discovery Channel School™

Helps your students discover math in their world with engaging real-world applications in every chapter

Take It to the NET

Shows your students how math connects to the world outside the classroom with online real-world video links from Discovery Channel School

The
SCOTT
FORESMAN
Difference

We meet the needs of all teachers.

Teachers need help simplifying the planning and instruction process and saving time. Every program offers teacher resources and classroom support for their materials. But our program is different.

Teaches important content before the test

Exclusive daily warm-up activities in Pacing for Test Success cover all the important content in later chapters and prepare your students for test success.

Pacing for Test Success

Pacing for Test Success (continued)

Simplifies the planning process

Everything you need to create effective lessons is organized into an easy-to-read Lesson Planner. From ongoing assessment opportunities to Student Edition resources, you'll always be completely prepared for every lesson.

CHAPTER 2 Lesson Planner

Adding and Subtracting Whole Numbers and Money

Reaches all learners with differentiated instruction options

Customize your instruction to meet the individual needs of all your students. Research-based suggestions for approaching lessons allow you to reach every child effectively and individually.

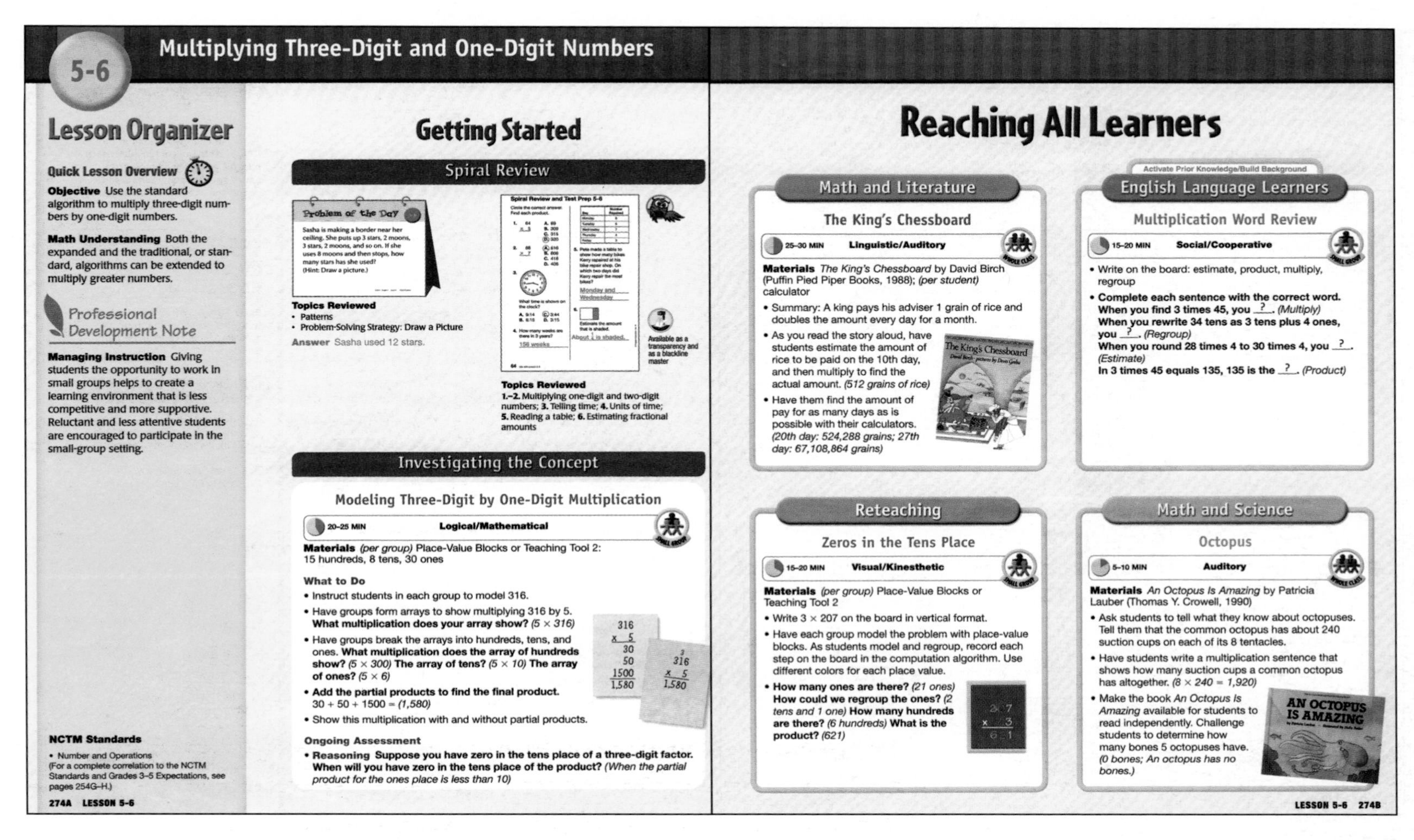

Lesson Organizer

Quick lesson overviews include math objectives and understanding while Professional Development Notes improve your teaching methods

Getting Started

Includes daily suggestions for spiral review and investigating the concept

Reaching All Learners

Meet the diverse needs in your classroom with fun and stimulating activities that are easy to incorporate directly into your lesson plan

- Math Vocabulary
- Reading in Math
- Writing in Math
- Oral Language in Math
- Math and Literature
- English Language Learners
- Reteaching
- Math and Technology
- Advanced Learners
- Students with Special Needs
- Cross-Curriculum Connections

Every Student Learns

Lesson-specific suggestions help your students overcome language barriers to access math content

Simplifies the instruction process

Our lessons include all the resources you need right at the point of use to help you keep all your lessons on track.

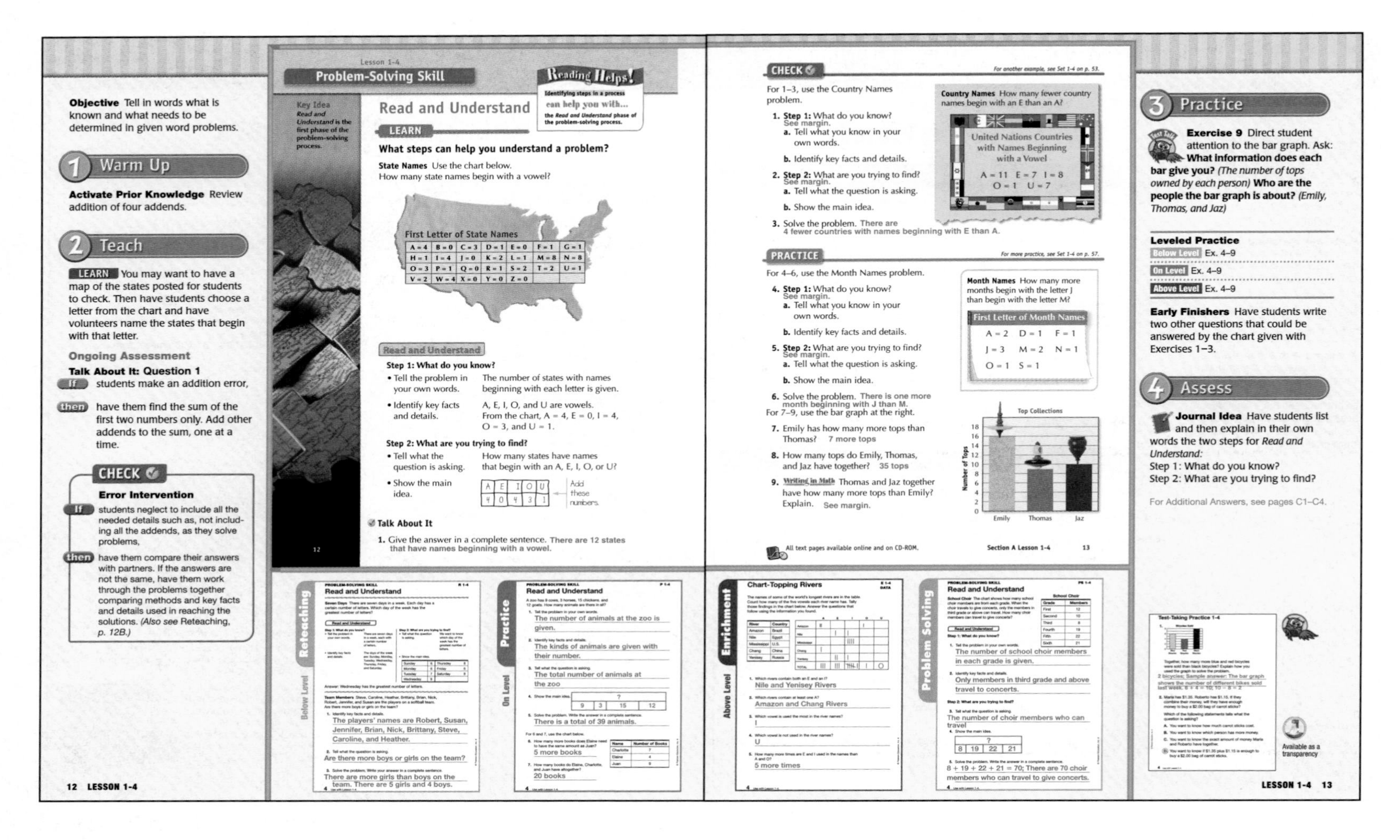

Objective Tell in words what is known and what needs to be determined in given word problems.

1 Warm Up

Activate Prior Knowledge Review addition of four addends.

2 Teach

LEARN You may want to have a map of the states posted for students to check. Then have students choose a letter from the chart and have volunteers name the states that begin with that letter.

Ongoing Assessment

Talk About It: Question 1

If students make an addition error,

then have them find the sum of the first two numbers only. Add other addends to the sum, one at a time.

CHECK

Error Intervention

If students neglect to include all the needed details such as, not including all the addends, as they solve problems,

then have them compare their answers with partners. If the answers are not the same, have them work through the problems together comparing methods and key facts and details used in reaching the solutions. *(Also see Reteaching, p. 12B.)*

Lesson 1-4

Problem-Solving Skill

Key Idea *Read and Understand is the first phase of the problem-solving process.*

Read and Understand

Reading Helps! Identifying steps in a process can help you with... the Read and Understand phase of the problem-solving process.

LEARN

What steps can help you understand a problem?

State Names Use the chart below. How many state names begin with a vowel?

First Letter of State Names

A = 4	B = 0	C = 3	D = 1	E = 0	F = 1	G = 1
H = 1	I = 4	J = 0	K = 2	L = 1	M = 8	N = 8
O = 3	P = 1	Q = 0	R = 1	S = 2	T = 2	U = 1
V = 2	W = 4	X = 0	Y = 0	Z = 0		

Read and Understand

Step 1: What do you know?

- Tell the problem in your own words. — The number of states with names beginning with each letter is given.
- Identify key facts and details. — A, E, I, O, and U are vowels. From the chart, A = 4, E = 0, I = 4, O = 3, and U = 1.

Step 2: What are you trying to find?

- Tell what the question is asking. — How many states have names that begin with an A, E, I, O, or U?
- Show the main idea.

A	E	I	O	U
4	0	4	3	1

Add these numbers.

Talk About It

1. Give the answer in a complete sentence. There are 12 states that have names beginning with a vowel.

12

CHECK — For another example, see Set 1-4 on p. 53.

For 1–3, use the Country Names problem.

1. **Step 1:** What do you know? See margin.
   a. Tell what you know in your own words.
   b. Identify key facts and details.
2. **Step 2:** What are you trying to find? See margin.
   a. Tell what the question is asking.
   b. Show the main idea.
3. Solve the problem. There are 4 fewer countries with names beginning with E than A.

Country Names How many fewer country names begin with an E than an A?

United Nations Countries with Names Beginning with a Vowel

A = 11 E = 7 I = 8
O = 1 U = 7

PRACTICE — For more practice, see Set 1-4 on p. 57.

For 4–6, use the Month Names problem.

4. **Step 1:** What do you know? See margin.
   a. Tell what you know in your own words.
   b. Identify key facts and details.
5. **Step 2:** What are you trying to find? See margin.
   a. Tell what the question is asking.
   b. Show the main idea.
6. Solve the problem. There is one more month beginning with J than M.

Month Names How many more months begin with the letter J than begin with the letter M?

First Letter of Month Names

A = 2 D = 1 F = 1
J = 3 M = 2 N = 1
O = 1 S = 1

For 7–9, use the bar graph at the right.

7. Emily has how many more tops than Thomas? 7 more tops
8. How many tops do Emily, Thomas, and Jaz have together? 35 tops
9. Writing in Math Thomas and Jaz together have how many more tops than Emily? Explain. See margin.

Top Collections (Number of Tops: Emily, Thomas, Jaz)

All text pages available online and on CD-ROM.

Section A Lesson 1-4 13

3 Practice

Exercise 9 Direct student attention to the bar graph. Ask: **What information does each bar give you?** *(The number of tops owned by each person)* **Who are the people the bar graph is about?** *(Emily, Thomas, and Jaz)*

Leveled Practice

Below Level Ex. 4–9

On Level Ex. 4–9

Above Level Ex. 4–9

Early Finishers Have students write two other questions that could be answered by the chart given with Exercises 1–3.

4 Assess

Journal Idea Have students list and then explain in their own words the two steps for *Read and Understand:*

Step 1: What do you know?

Step 2: What are you trying to find?

For Additional Answers, see pages C1–C4.

Reteaching — Below Level — Read and Understand

Practice — On Level — Read and Understand

Enrichment — Above Level — Chart-Topping Rivers

Problem Solving — Read and Understand

Test-Taking Practice 1-4 — Available as a transparency

12 LESSON 1-4 — LESSON 1-4 13

Four manageable and familiar steps

1 Warm Up

Helps you activate prior knowledge

2 Teach

Suggests how to introduce the math concept, assess your students, and intervene if necessary

3 Practice

Uses leveled exercises to help you reach every student in your classroom

4 Assess

Provides specific strategies for checking your students' understanding before moving on

Ongoing Assessment

Provides multiple checkpoints in each lesson with immediate intervention for your students who may be struggling with the concept

Blackline Masters

Leveled Practice and Problem-Solving blackline masters are shown right at the point of use along with the Test-Taking Practice Transparencies.

Supports professional development every day

We include the professional development resources you need to be more effective and successful in the classroom, no matter what your experience level may be.

Successful Beginnings

Professional Development Needs Assessment

Shows your school how to interpret student achievement test scores, assess staff development needs, and implement a professional development program that incorporates research-based best practices

On-Site Inservice

Occurs at the beginning of the school year to introduce the program philosophy and explain the Teacher's Edition and program components

Chapter Facilitator Guides

Provides workshop or discussion-group leaders the support they need on content and instruction for every chapter

In the Teacher's Edition

Professional Development

Appears at the beginning of each chapter and includes a Skills Trace as well as Math Background and Teaching Tips for each section in the chapter

Professional Development Note

Provides insights for every lesson, every day, on Math Background, How Children Learn Math, Effective Questioning Techniques, Managing Instruction, or Research Base

CHAPTER 5 Professional Development

Skills Trace - Multiplying by One-Digit Numbers

Math Background and Teaching Ti

5-6 Multiplying Three-Digit and One-Digit Numbers

Lesson Organizer

Getting Started

Spiral Review

Investigating the Concept

Professional Development Note

Managing Instruction Giving students the opportunity to work in small groups helps to create a learning environment that is less competitive and more supportive. Reluctant and less attentive students are encouraged to participate in the small-group setting.

Ongoing Professional Development

Professional Development Series

Contains a set of three modules with videos of real classroom lessons and all the resources necessary for presenting a two- to three-hour workshop on specific math content or for doing independent study

Math Across the Grades

Gives you more in-depth math background for every strand

★ Look for **LessonLab BreakThrough™ Professional Development** on page T20.

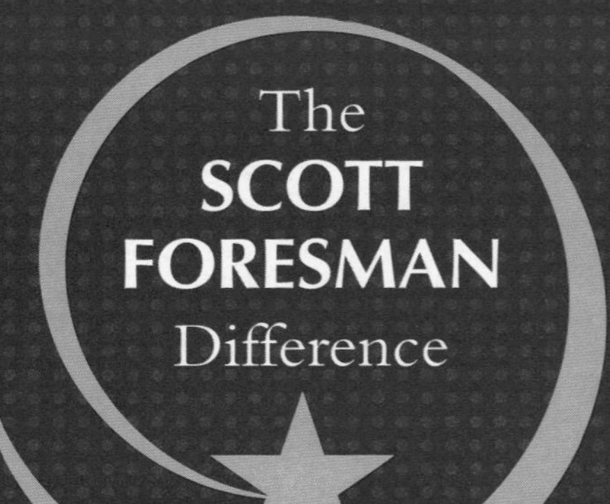

We offer integrated technology solutions.

Technology is not only changing the nature of mathematics, it also is changing students' needs for success in the 21st century. Most math programs feature technology. But our program is different.

Integrates technology with curriculum

We bring technology and curriculum together, providing technology solutions for all students, teachers, and parents that directly improve student learning and increase test success.

SF SuccessNet

Offers a personalized online community where teachers can optimize planning and teaching time. Students can practice skills and do homework while their parents can see what they're learning in school!

Professional Development

Professional Development Series

Enables you to grow as an educator and help all your students succeed with videos that show flexible ways to implement research-based best practices for instruction

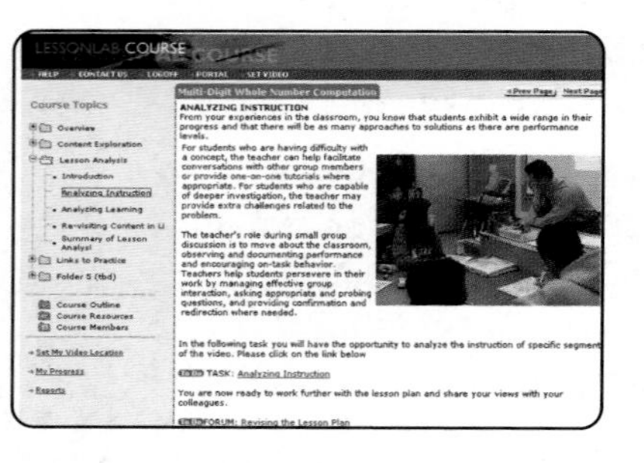

LessonLab BreakThrough™ Professional Development

Utilizes cutting-edge, interactive, online technology to provide facilitated professional development designed exclusively for our program

Teach and assess efficiently with versatile resources

Our technology options make it easy for you to monitor your students' progress and provide each of them with individualized intervention.

Ask about Accelerated Math

Teacher Resources

Student Resources

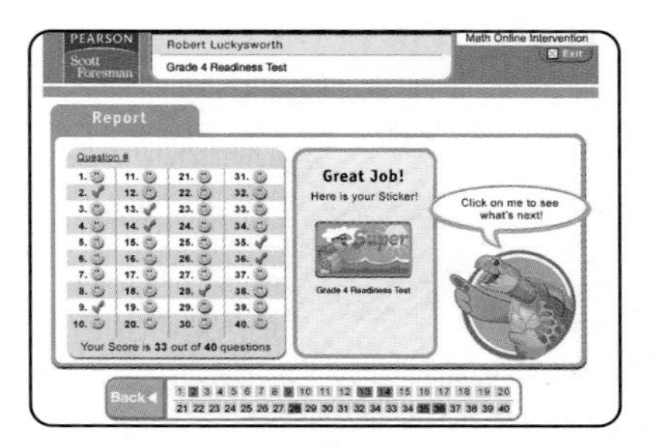

Math Online Intervention

Helps diagnose your entire class with online diagnostic tests that assess every student and prescribe individualized intervention with reports to monitor adequate yearly progress

Scott Foresman's Web Site "Take It to the NET"

Provides your students with access to more examples, more practice, test prep, videos, and Math eTools tied directly to their lessons

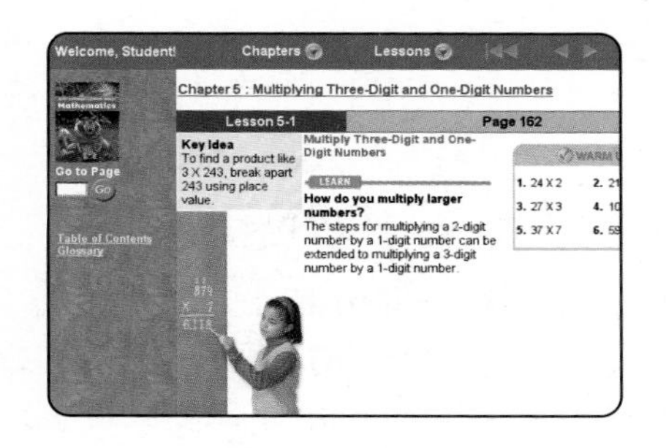

Online Student Edition

Gives your students easy access to their textbooks online or on CD-ROM from any home computer—a great solution to heavy backpacks!

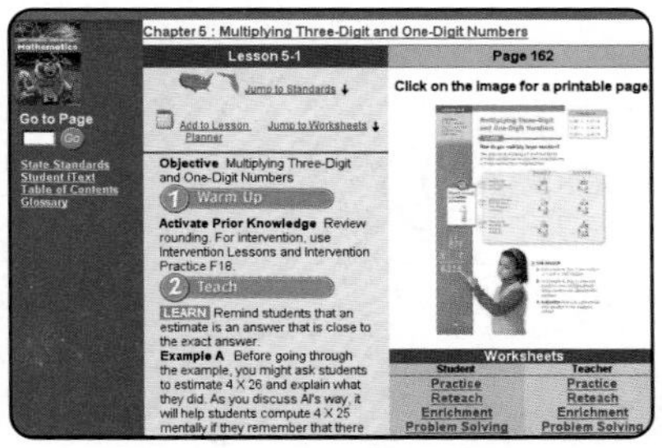

Online Teacher's Edition

Provides complete access to your entire Teacher's Edition, an online lesson planner, and selected ancillary pdf files online or on CD-ROM

Math eTools

Helps your students grasp difficult math concepts with electronic manipulatives and software tools online or on CD-ROM

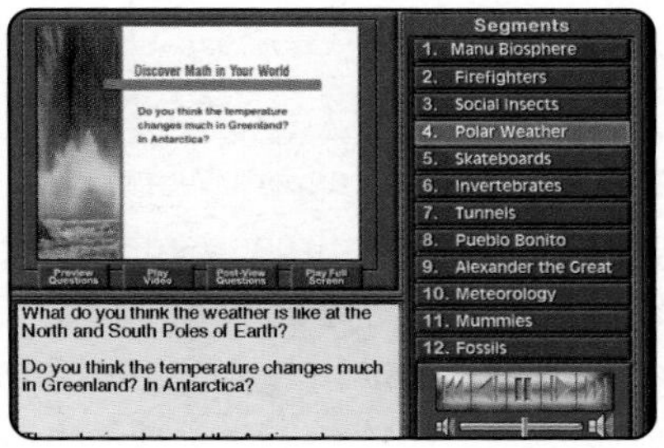

Discovery Channel School™ Video Library

Engages your students with online, CD-ROM, or videocassette segments for every chapter in the Student Edition, helping them discover math in their world

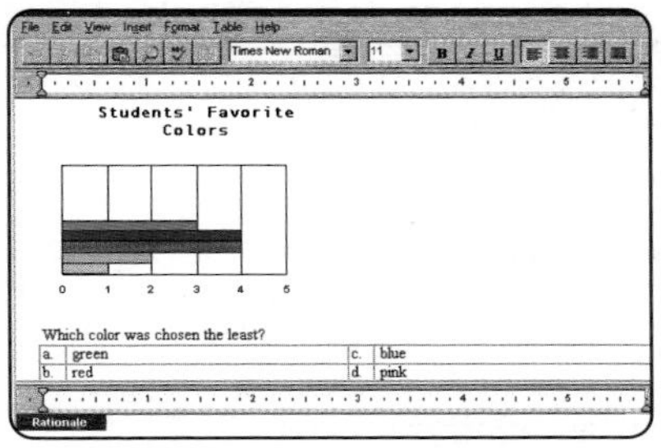

ExamView® Test Generator

Allows you to create and print customized tests quickly and easily with varied questions and test formats that assess your students' math understanding of key concepts and skills

MindPoint™ Quiz Show CD-ROM

Uses multiple-choice questions in a fun format to give your students additional math practice

Digital Learning CD-ROM powered by KnowledgeBox®

Supplies an interactive, completely customizable, educational multimedia center where your students can play games, watch videos, take tutorials, or participate in sing-alongs

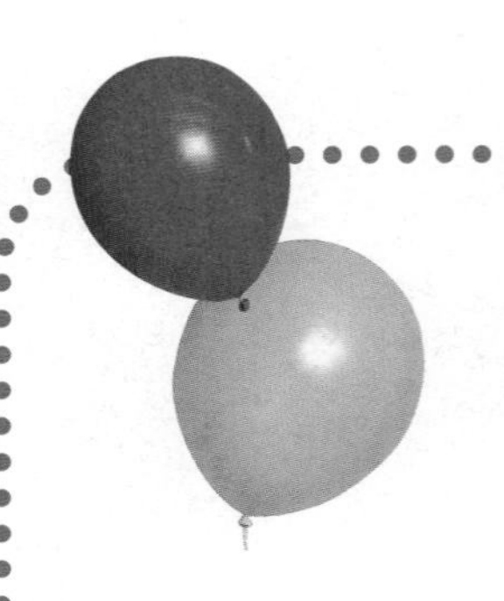

SCOTT FORESMAN • ADDISON WESLEY

Mathematics

Components

Teaching for Understanding

Pre-K Program (Pre-K)
Student Big Book (K)
Student Edition Chapter Booklets (K)
Student Edition (K–6)
Practice Masters/Workbook (K–6)
Reteaching Masters/Workbook (1–6)
Enrichment Masters/Workbook (K–6)
Homework Workbook (1–6)
Instant Check Mat (K–6)
Workmats (K–2)
Assessment Sourcebook (K–6)
Test-Taking Practice Transparencies (1–6)
Spiral Review and Test Prep Masters/Workbook (1–6)
Spiral Review and Test Prep Transparencies (1–6)
Math Diagnosis and Intervention System (K–6)
SAT 9/10 Practice and Test Prep (1–6)
TerraNova Practice and Test Prep (1–6)
ITBS Practice and Test Prep (3–6)
Benchmark Tests (3–6)
Review from Last Year Masters (1–6)

Problem-Solving Connections

Problem-Solving Masters/Workbook (1–6)
Problem of the Day Transparencies/Flip Chart (K–6)
Math Vocabulary Kit (K–6)
Discovery Channel School™ Masters/Videos (1–6)
Read-Together Math Stories Big Books (K–2)
DK Literature Library (Pre-K–6)
Math Leveled Literature Library (K–6)

Teaching Support

Teacher's Edition (Pre-K–6)
Teaching Tool Masters (K–6)
Every Student Learns (K–6)
Home-School Connection (K–6)
Chapter File Folders (K–6)
Classroom Manipulatives Kit (Pre-K–6)
Overhead Manipulatives Kit (K–6)
Solution Manual (3–6)
Student Magnetic Manipulatives Kit (K–6)
Teacher Magnetic Manipulatives Kit (K–2)
Math Games (K–6)
Calendar Time Kit (K–5)
Professional Development Series (K–6)
Chapter Facilitator Guide (K–6)
Math Across the Grades (K–Algebra)

Technology

SuccessNet Portal (K–6)
Math eTools (Pre-K–6)
Digital Learning CD-ROM
powered by KnowledgeBox® (1–6)
Online Student Edition (1–6)
MindPoint™ Quiz Show (1–6)
Discovery Channel School™ Video Library (1–6)
www.scottforesman.com (K–6)
Online Teacher's Edition (K–6)
LessonLab's BreakThrough™ Mathematics (K–6)
Professional Development Series (K–6)
Math Online Intervention (1–6)
ExamView® Test Generator (1–6)

Table of Contents

Volume 1: Chapters 1-3

Volume 2: Chapters 4-6

Volume 3: Chapters 7-9

Volume 4: Chapters 10-12

** Shown in Volumes 1-4 of the Teacher's Edition*
*** Shown in Volume 1 of the Teacher's Edition*

Pacing Guide

The pacing suggested below assumes one day for most lessons plus time for assessment for a total of 180 days.
You may need to adjust pacing to meet the needs of your students and your district curriculum.

Chapter 1 ... 16 days
Chapter 2 ... 16 days
Chapter 3 ... 11 days
Chapter 4 ... 10 days
Chapter 5 ... 19 days
Chapter 6 ... 12 days
Chapter 7 ... 14 days
Chapter 8 ... 20 days
Chapter 9 ... 12 days
Chapter 10 ... 22 days
Chapter 11 ... 15 days
Chapter 12 ... 13 days

CHAPTER 1

Table of Contents

Patterns and Readiness for Addition and Subtraction

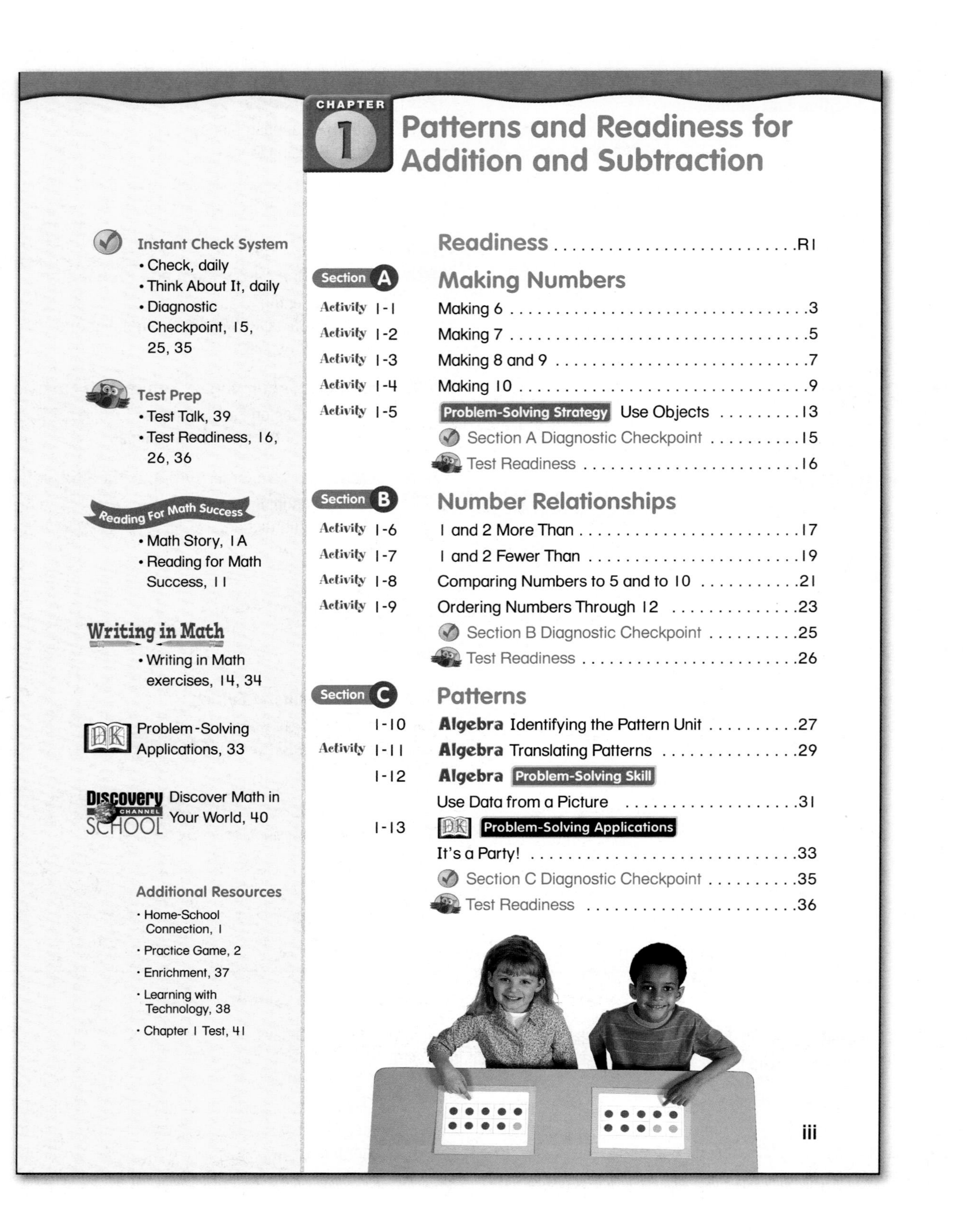

CHAPTER 1

Patterns and Readiness for Addition and Subtraction

Instant Check System
- Check, daily
- Think About It, daily
- Diagnostic Checkpoint, 15, 25, 35

Test Prep
- Test Talk, 39
- Test Readiness, 16, 26, 36

Reading For Math Success
- Math Story, 1A
- Reading for Math Success, 11

Writing in Math
- Writing in Math exercises, 14, 34

DK Problem-Solving Applications, 33

Discovery Channel School Discover Math in Your World, 40

Additional Resources
- Home-School Connection, 1
- Practice Game, 2
- Enrichment, 37
- Learning with Technology, 38
- Chapter 1 Test, 41

EC NTL 12 11 10 9 8 7 6 5

CHAPTER 2

Table of Contents

Understanding Addition and Subtraction

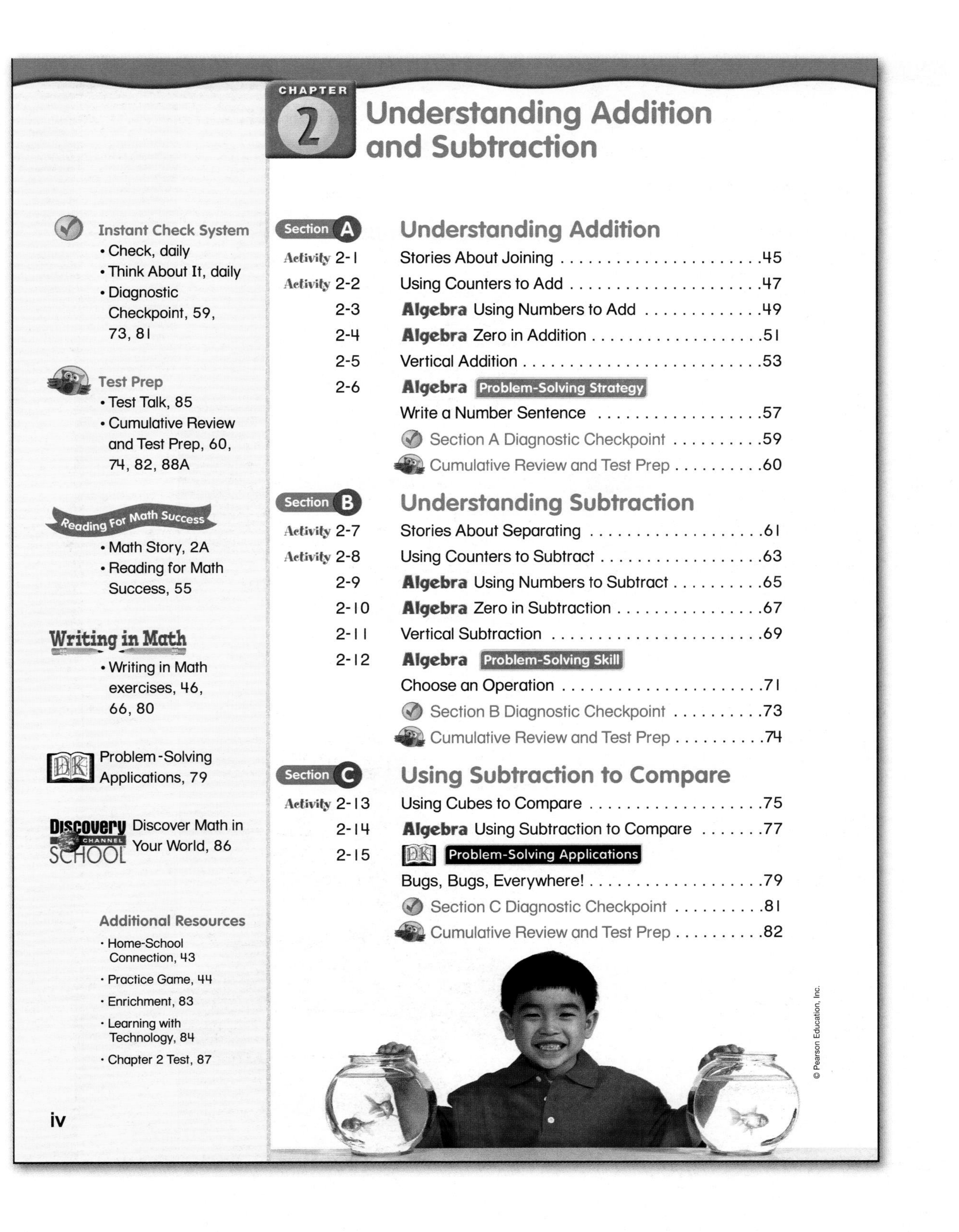

CHAPTER 2

Understanding Addition and Subtraction

Instant Check System
- Check, daily
- Think About It, daily
- Diagnostic Checkpoint, 59, 73, 81

Test Prep
- Test Talk, 85
- Cumulative Review and Test Prep, 60, 74, 82, 88A

Reading For Math Success
- Math Story, 2A
- Reading for Math Success, 55

Writing in Math
- Writing in Math exercises, 46, 66, 80

DK Problem-Solving Applications, 79

Discovery Channel School Discover Math in Your World, 86

Additional Resources
- Home-School Connection, 43
- Practice Game, 44
- Enrichment, 83
- Learning with Technology, 84
- Chapter 2 Test, 87

iv

Table of Contents

Strategies for Addition Facts to 12

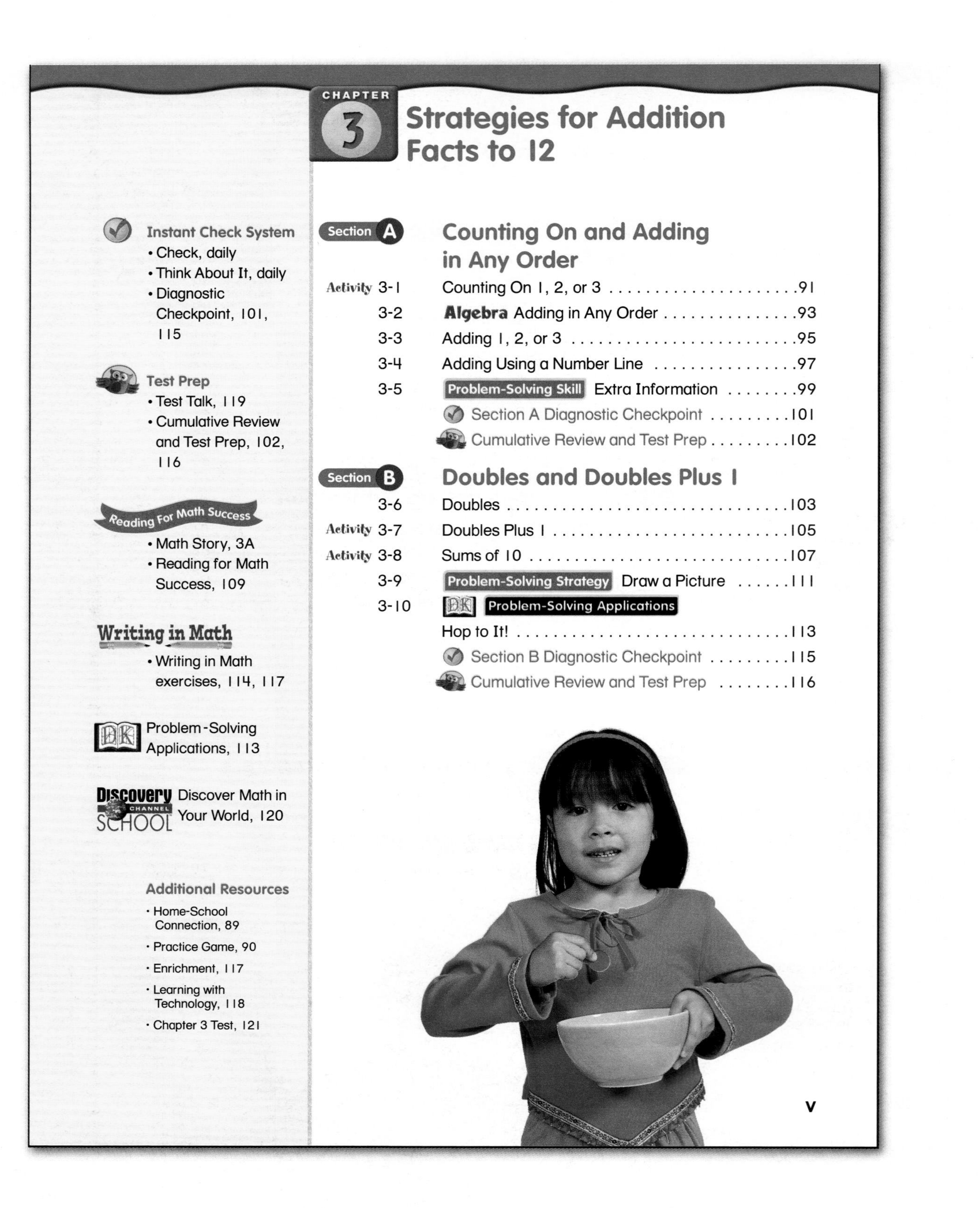

CHAPTER 3

Strategies for Addition Facts to 12

Instant Check System
- Check, daily
- Think About It, daily
- Diagnostic Checkpoint, 101, 115

Test Prep
- Test Talk, 119
- Cumulative Review and Test Prep, 102, 116

Reading For Math Success
- Math Story, 3A
- Reading for Math Success, 109

Writing in Math
- Writing in Math exercises, 114, 117

Problem-Solving Applications, 113

Discovery Channel School Discover Math in Your World, 120

Additional Resources
- Home-School Connection, 89
- Practice Game, 90
- Enrichment, 117
- Learning with Technology, 118
- Chapter 3 Test, 121

v

Table of Contents

Strategies for Subtraction Facts to 12

CHAPTER 4

Strategies for Subtraction Facts to 12

CHAPTER 5

Table of Contents

Geometry and Fractions

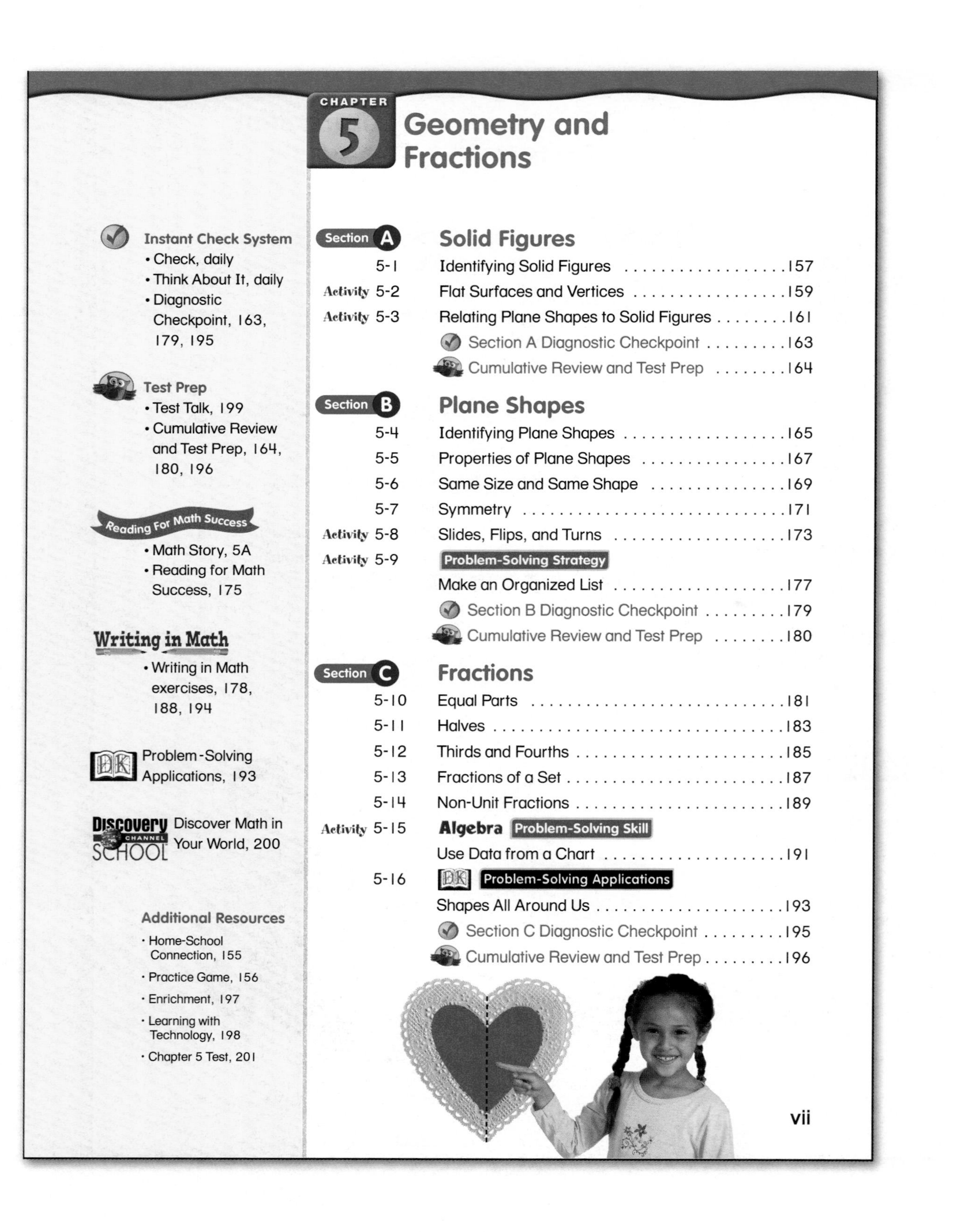

CHAPTER 5

Geometry and Fractions

vii

CHAPTER 6

Table of Contents

Time

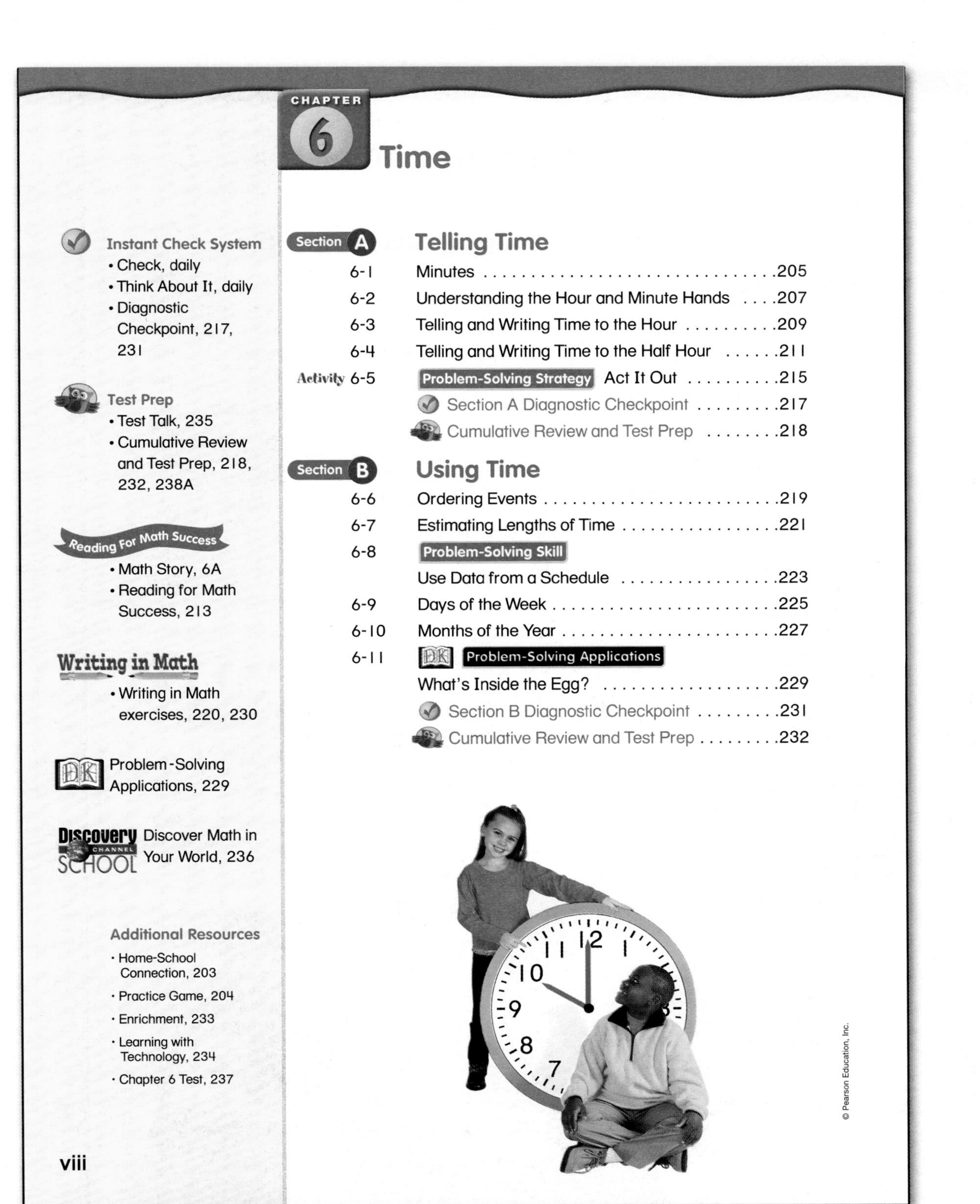

CHAPTER 6

Time

CHAPTER 7

Table of Contents

Counting to 100

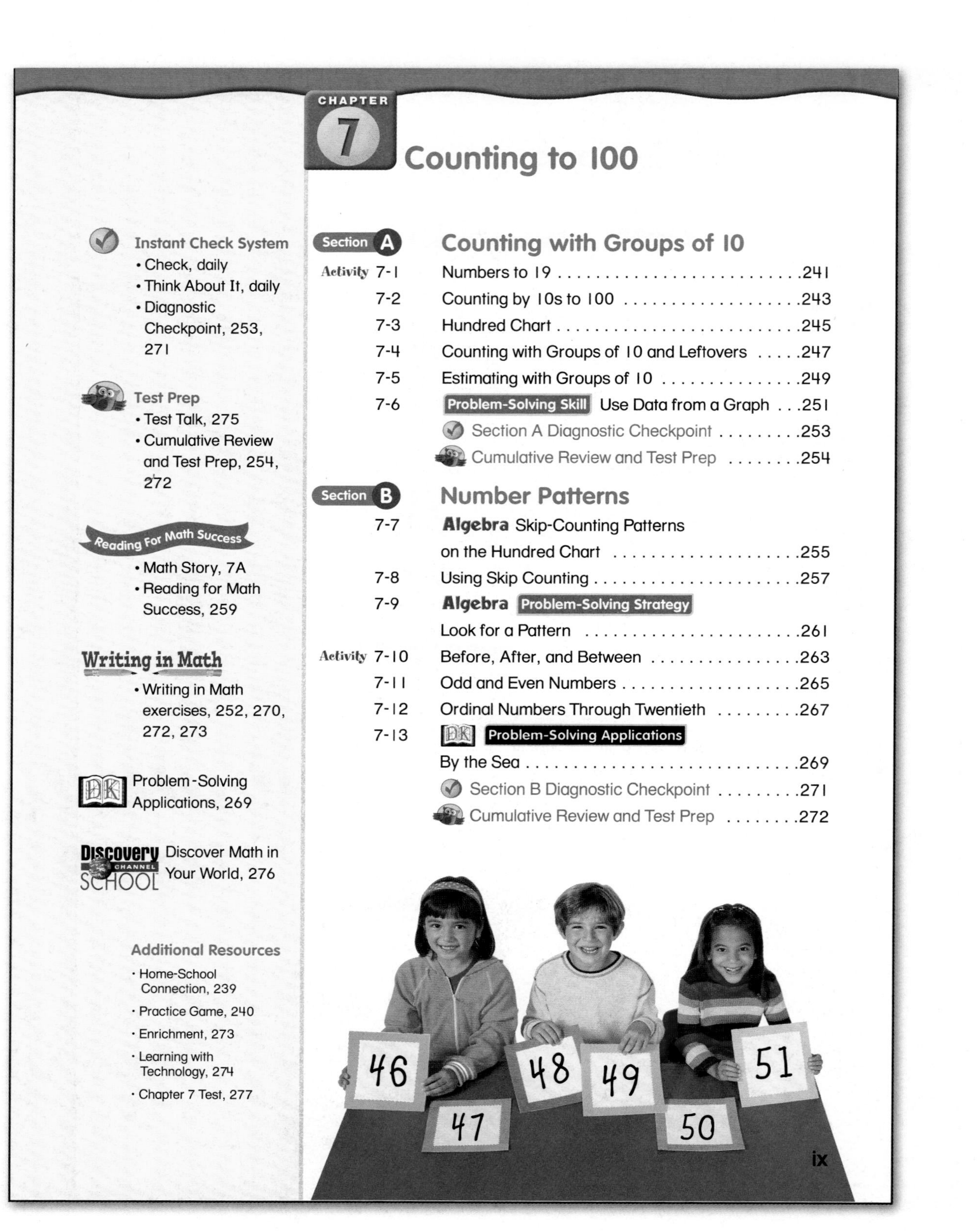

Instant Check System
- Check, daily
- Think About It, daily
- Diagnostic Checkpoint, 253, 271

Test Prep
- Test Talk, 275
- Cumulative Review and Test Prep, 254, 272

Reading For Math Success
- Math Story, 7A
- Reading for Math Success, 259

Writing in Math
- Writing in Math exercises, 252, 270, 272, 273

DK Problem-Solving Applications, 269

Discovery Channel School Discover Math in Your World, 276

Additional Resources
- Home-School Connection, 239
- Practice Game, 240
- Enrichment, 273
- Learning with Technology, 274
- Chapter 7 Test, 277

CHAPTER 7 Counting to 100

ix

Place Value, Data, and Graphs

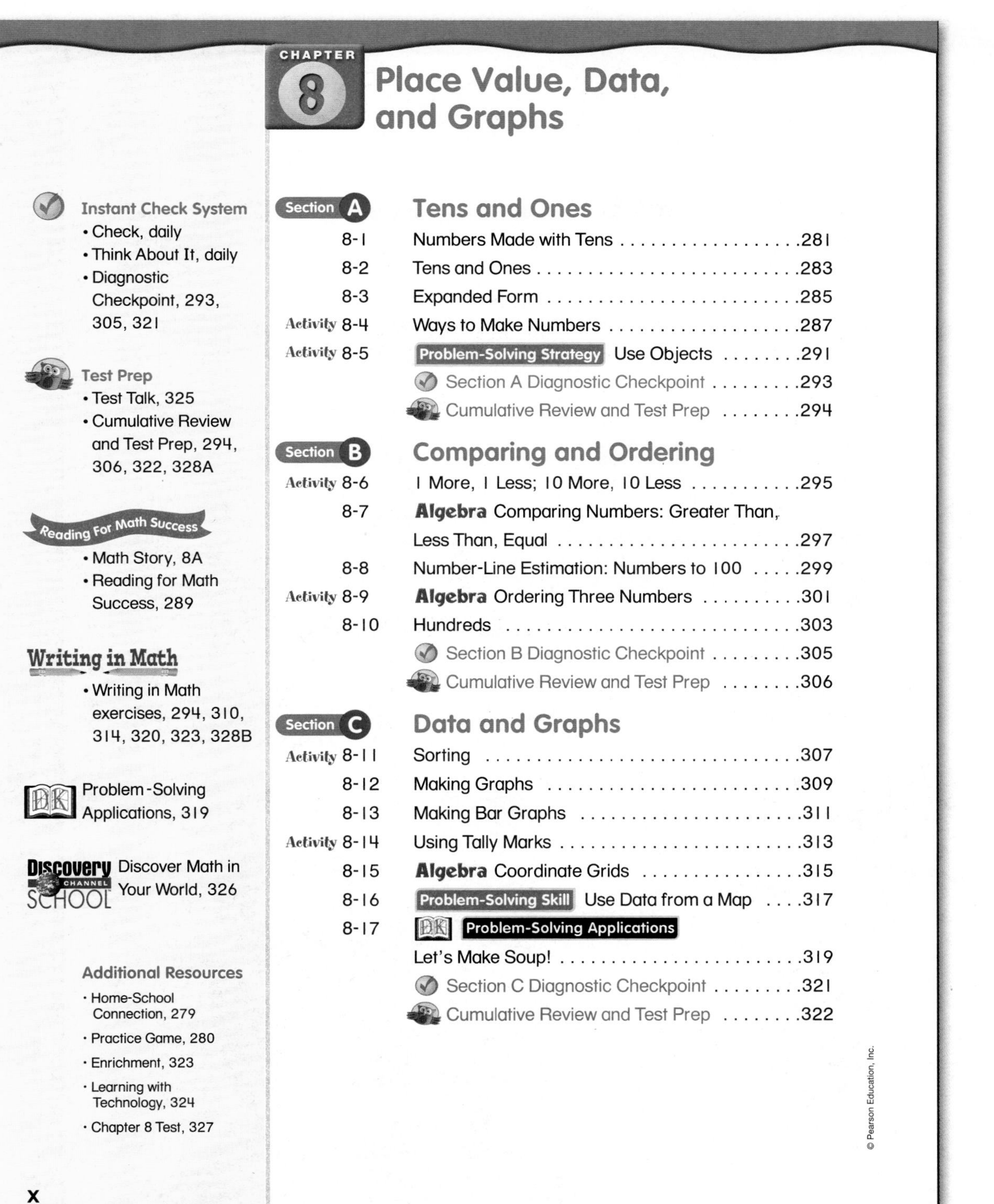

CHAPTER 8

Place Value, Data, and Graphs

Instant Check System
- Check, daily
- Think About It, daily
- Diagnostic Checkpoint, 293, 305, 321

Test Prep
- Test Talk, 325
- Cumulative Review and Test Prep, 294, 306, 322, 328A

Reading For Math Success
- Math Story, 8A
- Reading for Math Success, 289

Writing in Math
- Writing in Math exercises, 294, 310, 314, 320, 323, 328B

DK Problem-Solving Applications, 319

Discovery Channel School Discover Math in Your World, 326

Additional Resources
- Home-School Connection, 279
- Practice Game, 280
- Enrichment, 323
- Learning with Technology, 324
- Chapter 8 Test, 327

CHAPTER 9

Table of Contents

Money

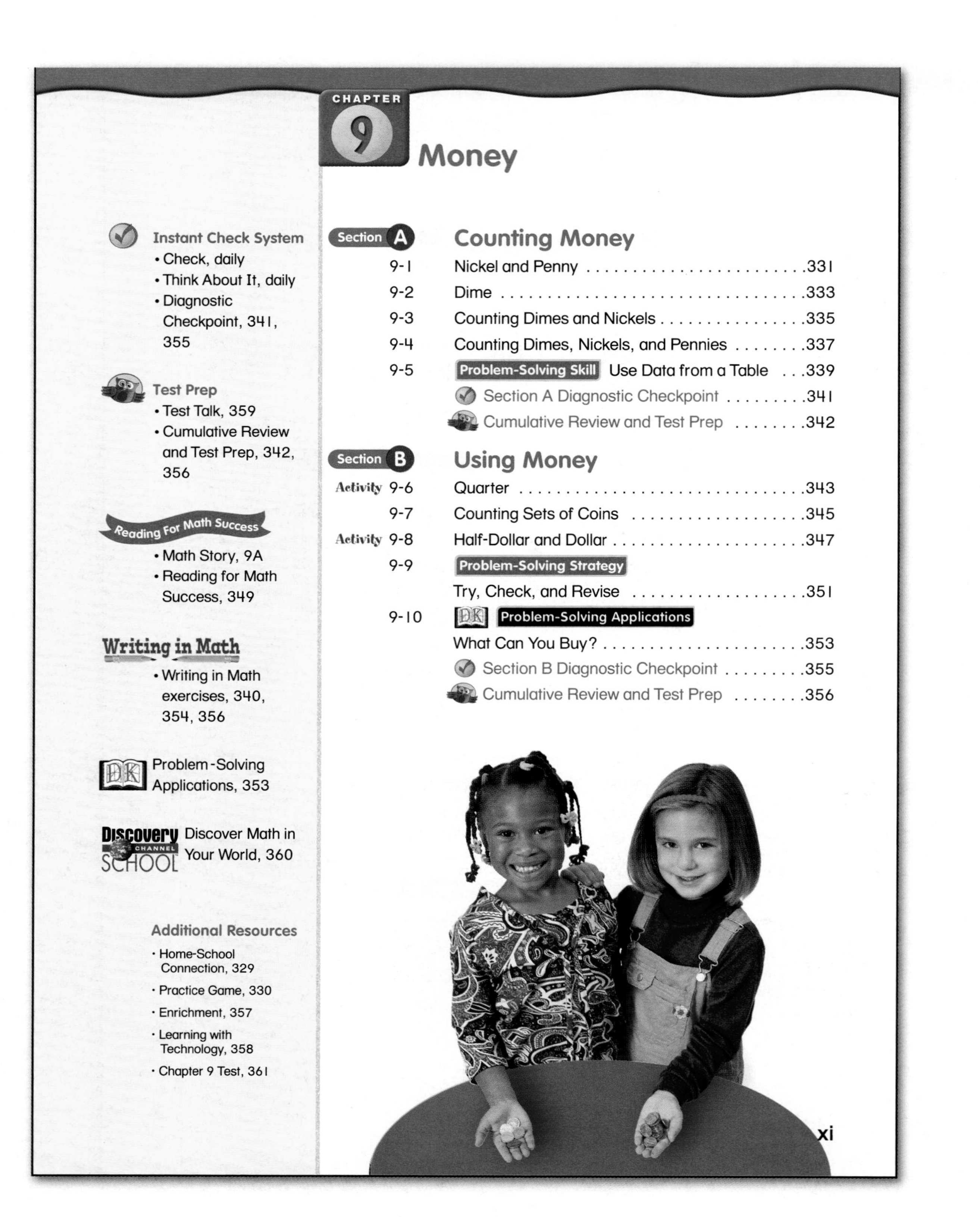

CHAPTER 9

Money

Instant Check System
- Check, daily
- Think About It, daily
- Diagnostic Checkpoint, 341, 355

Test Prep
- Test Talk, 359
- Cumulative Review and Test Prep, 342, 356

Reading For Math Success
- Math Story, 9A
- Reading for Math Success, 349

Writing in Math
- Writing in Math exercises, 340, 354, 356

Problem-Solving Applications, 353

Discovery Channel School Discover Math in Your World, 360

Additional Resources
- Home-School Connection, 329
- Practice Game, 330
- Enrichment, 357
- Learning with Technology, 358
- Chapter 9 Test, 361

xi

CHAPTER 10

Table of Contents

Measurement and Probability

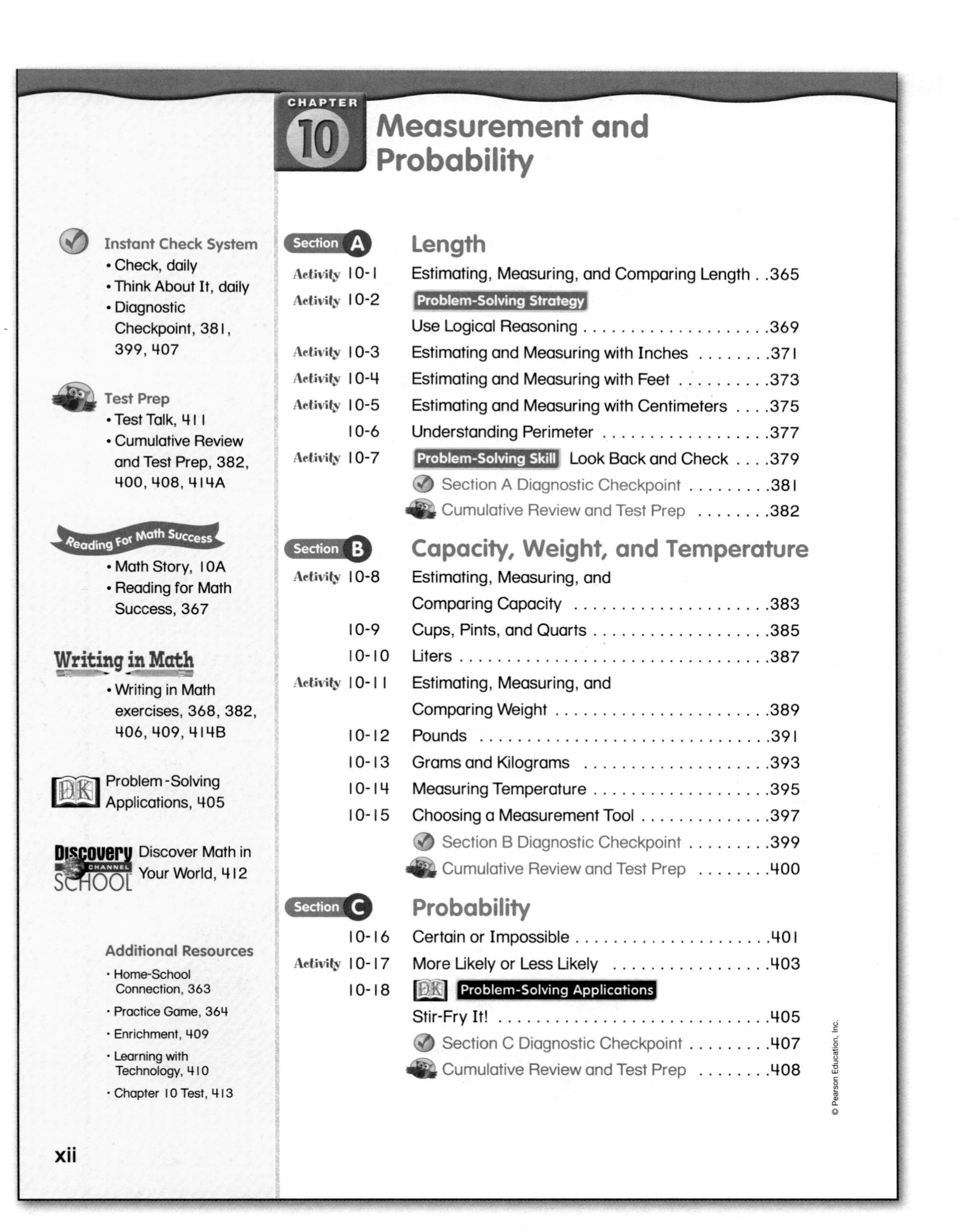

CHAPTER 10

Measurement and Probability

Instant Check System
- Check, daily
- Think About It, daily
- Diagnostic Checkpoint, 381, 399, 407

Test Prep
- Test Talk, 411
- Cumulative Review and Test Prep, 382, 400, 408, 414A

Reading For Math Success
- Math Story, 10A
- Reading for Math Success, 367

Writing in Math
- Writing in Math exercises, 368, 382, 406, 409, 414B

DK Problem-Solving Applications, 405

Discovery Channel School Discover Math in Your World, 412

Additional Resources
- Home-School Connection, 363
- Practice Game, 364
- Enrichment, 409
- Learning with Technology, 410
- Chapter 10 Test, 413

xii

CHAPTER 11

Table of Contents

Addition and Subtraction Facts to 18

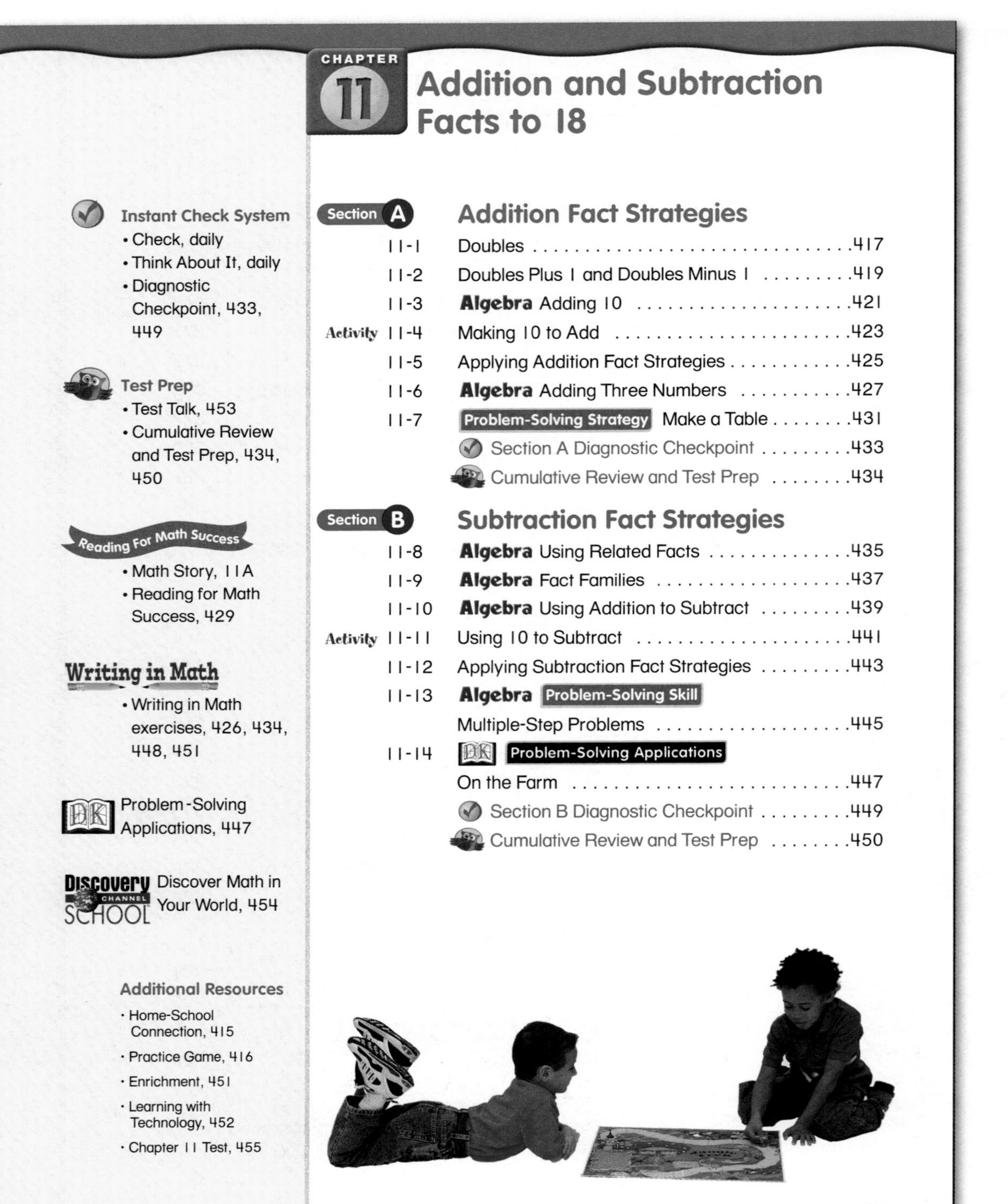

CHAPTER 11

Addition and Subtraction Facts to 18

xiii

Two-Digit Addition and Subtraction

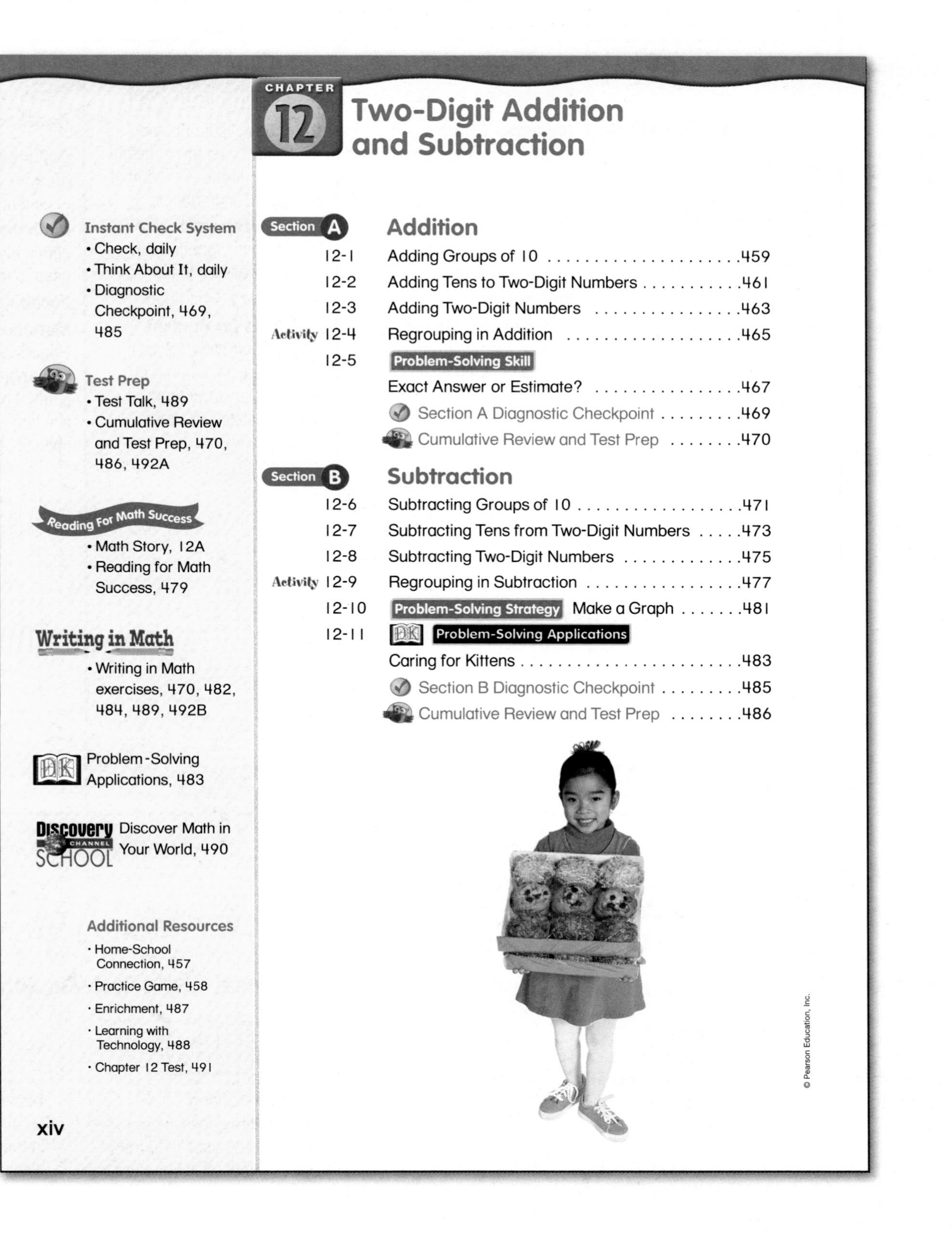

CHAPTER 12

Two-Digit Addition and Subtraction

Instant Check System
- Check, daily
- Think About It, daily
- Diagnostic Checkpoint, 469, 485

Test Prep
- Test Talk, 489
- Cumulative Review and Test Prep, 470, 486, 492A

Reading For Math Success
- Math Story, 12A
- Reading for Math Success, 479

Writing in Math
- Writing in Math exercises, 470, 482, 484, 489, 492B

DK Problem-Solving Applications, 483

Discovery Channel School Discover Math in Your World, 490

Additional Resources
- Home-School Connection, 457
- Practice Game, 458
- Enrichment, 487
- Learning with Technology, 488
- Chapter 12 Test, 491

Lesson Planner

Measurement and Probability

Suggested Pacing: 19 to 22 days

Section A Length

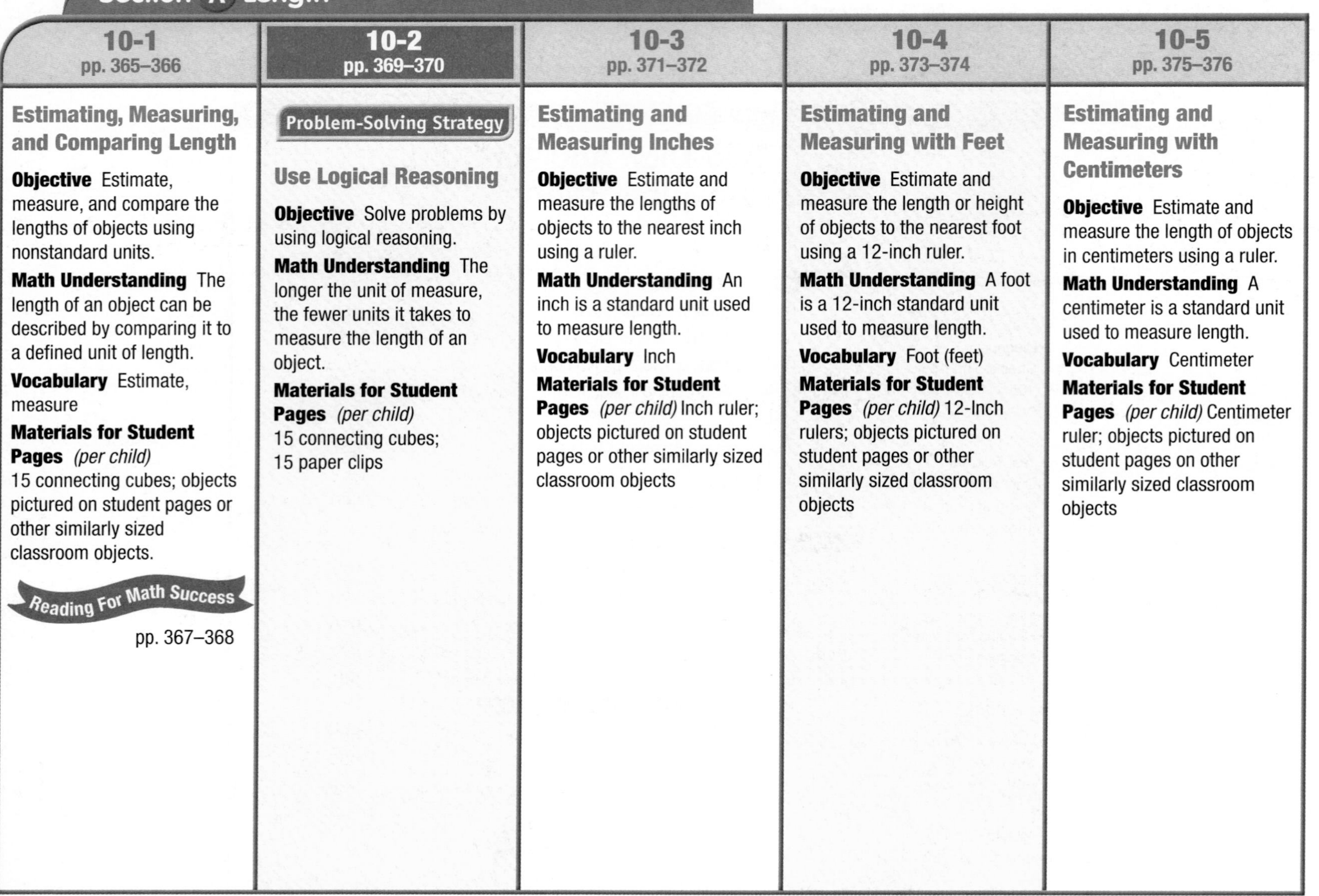

10-1 pp. 365–366	10-2 pp. 369–370	10-3 pp. 371–372	10-4 pp. 373–374	10-5 pp. 375–376
Estimating, Measuring, and Comparing Length **Objective** Estimate, measure, and compare the lengths of objects using nonstandard units. **Math Understanding** The length of an object can be described by comparing it to a defined unit of length. **Vocabulary** Estimate, measure **Materials for Student Pages** *(per child)* 15 connecting cubes; objects pictured on student pages or other similarly sized classroom objects. Reading For Math Success pp. 367–368	Problem-Solving Strategy **Use Logical Reasoning** **Objective** Solve problems by using logical reasoning. **Math Understanding** The longer the unit of measure, the fewer units it takes to measure the length of an object. **Materials for Student Pages** *(per child)* 15 connecting cubes; 15 paper clips	**Estimating and Measuring Inches** **Objective** Estimate and measure the lengths of objects to the nearest inch using a ruler. **Math Understanding** An inch is a standard unit used to measure length. **Vocabulary** Inch **Materials for Student Pages** *(per child)* Inch ruler; objects pictured on student pages or other similarly sized classroom objects	**Estimating and Measuring with Feet** **Objective** Estimate and measure the length or height of objects to the nearest foot using a 12-inch ruler. **Math Understanding** A foot is a 12-inch standard unit used to measure length. **Vocabulary** Foot (feet) **Materials for Student Pages** *(per child)* 12-Inch rulers; objects pictured on student pages or other similarly sized classroom objects	**Estimating and Measuring with Centimeters** **Objective** Estimate and measure the length of objects in centimeters using a ruler. **Math Understanding** A centimeter is a standard unit used to measure length. **Vocabulary** Centimeter **Materials for Student Pages** *(per child)* Centimeter ruler; objects pictured on student pages on other similarly sized classroom objects

Math Story: ***One Very Smart Chicken*, pp. 10A–10F** **Home-School Connection, p. 363**

Practice Game: ***More Likely or Less Likely?*, p. 364**

Resources in the Student Book

Ongoing Assessment and Test Prep *Also see* pp. 363G–363H.

Instant Check System™
- **Check** before Practice
- **Think About It** after examples
- **Diagnostic Checkpoint** end of sections

Test Prep
- **Test Talk** end of chapter
- **Cumulative Review and Test Prep** end of sections

Daily Real-World Problem Solving plus ...

Problem-Solving Applications lesson on pp. 405–406 uses data from Dorling Kindersley literature.

Discover Math in Your World on p. 412 uses data from a topic in the Discovery Channel School Video Library, Segment 10.

Section B Capacity, Weight, and Temperature

10-6 pp. 377–378	10-7 pp. 379–380	10-8 pp. 383–384	10-9 pp. 385–386	10-10 pp. 387–388
Understanding Perimeter **Objective** Find the distance around a shape using inches. **Math Understanding** The distance around a shape (perimeter) can be measured by combining the measurements of each of the sides of the shape.	Problem-Solving Skill **Look Back and Check** **Objective** Look back and check is a strategy that can help confirm the solution to a problem. **Math Understanding** The area inside a shape can be measured by placing the square units on the shape and counting how many will fit. **Materials for Student Pages** *(per child)* 9 connecting cubes **Section A Diagnostic Checkpoint, p. 381** **Cumulative Review and Test Prep, p. 382**	**Estimating, Measuring, and Comparing Capacity** **Objective** Estimate, measure, and compare the capacities of containers. **Math Understanding** The capacity of a container can be described by comparing it to that of a defined unit of capacity. **Materials for Student Pages** *(per pair)* Measuring cup; rice; containers pictured on student pages or other similarly sized containers	**Cups, Pints, and Quarts** **Objective** Compare the capacities of cups, pints, and quarts. **Math Understanding** Cups, pints, and quarts are standard units used to measure capacity. **Vocabulary** Cup, pint, quart	**Liters** **Objective** Compare the capacity of containers to one liter. **Math Understanding** A liter is a standard unit used to measure capacity. **Vocabulary** Liter

Reading and Writing in Math *Throughout*

This feature shows how reading skills and strategies can help with problem-solving skills and strategies in math.
Also, **Reading Assists** are in the Teacher's Edition.

Writing in Math

Some lessons include **Writing in Math** exercises. Also, daily **Journal Ideas** are in the Teacher's Edition.

Technology Resources for Students *Also see* p. T20.

More activities, Discovery Channel School Video Library, and Math eTools

Math eTools: electronic manipulatives online, on CD-ROM, and in the Online Student's Edition

All text pages are available online and on CD-ROM. The Online Student's Edition includes Math eTools plus glossary links for vocabulary.

Measurement and Probability

(continued)

Section B Capacity, Weight, and Temperature

10-11 pp. 389–390	10-12 pp. 391–392	10-13 pp. 393–394	10-14 pp. 395–396	10-15 pp. 397–398
Estimating, Measuring, and Comparing Weight **Objective** Estimate, measure, and compare the weights of different objects. **Math Understanding** You can tell how heavy or light an object is by using a balance scale to measure its weight. **Materials for Student Pages** *(per child)* Balance; 25 connecting cubes; objects pictured on student pages or other similarly sized classroom objects	**Pounds** **Objective** Compare the weights of objects to one pound. **Math Understanding** A pound is a standard unit used to measure weight. **Vocabulary** Pound	**Grams and Kilograms** **Objective** Select the appropriate unit for measuring, given the choice of grams or kilograms. **Math Understanding** A gram and a kilogram are standard units used to measure weight; 1 kilogram is the same as 1000 grams. **Vocabulary** Gram, kilogram	**Measuring Temperature** **Objective** Compare temperatures on a thermometer and match them to activities or objects. **Math Understanding** Temperature is a measure of how hot or cold something is. **Vocabulary** Thermometer, temperature	**Choosing a Measurement Tool** **Objective** Identify appropriate tools for measuring length, weight, capacity, and temperature. **Math Understanding** There are many ways to measure an object, and each way uses a different tool. **Section B Diagnostic Checkpoint, p. 399** **Cumulative Review and Test Prep, p. 400**

Additional Resources for ...

Reaching All Learners

- **Practice** Masters/Workbook, every lesson
- **Reteaching** Masters/Workbook, every lesson
- **Enrichment** Masters/Workbook, every lesson
- **Every Student Learns** A teacher resource with daily suggestions for helping students overcome language barriers to learning math
- **Spiral Review and Test Prep** Transparencies and Masters/Workbook, every lesson
- **Math Games** Use *Inchworm* anytime after Lesson 10-1. Use *Strawberry Patch Stories* anytime after Lesson 10-13.
- **Investigation** See pp. 363I–363J.

Problem Solving

- **Problem Solving** Masters/Workbook, every lesson
- **Problem of the Day** Flipchart/Transparencies, every lesson
- **Discovery Channel School** Masters, follow-up to Segment 10 in the Discovery Channel School Video Library

Section C Probablility

10-16 pp. 401–402	10-17 pp. 403–404	10-18 pp. 405–406
Certain or Impossible **Objective** Describe the likelihood of an event as certain or impossible. **Math Understanding** An event that is certain to happen will always happen; an event that is impossible will never happen. **Vocabulary** Certain, impossible	**More Likely or Less Likely** **Objective** Describe the likelihood of an event as more likely or less likely. **Math Understanding** An event that is more likely will occur more often than an event that is less likely. **Vocabulary** More likely, less likely **Materials for Student Pages** *(per pair)* Pencil; paper clip	DK Problem-Solving Applications **Stir-Fry It!** **Objective** Review and apply concepts, skills, and strategies learned in this and previous chapters. **Math Understanding** Some real-world problems can be solved using known concepts, skills, and strategies. **Section C Diagnostic Checkpoint, p. 407** **Cumulative Review and Test Prep, p. 408**

Wrap Up

pp. 409–414

Enrichment: Standard and Nonstandard Units, p. 409

Learning with Technology: Make Predictions Using a Computer, p. 410

Test Talk: Plan How to Find the Answer, p. 411

Discovery Channel School

Discover Math in Your World: Light as a Feather?, p. 412

Chapter 10 Test, pp. 413–414

Cumulative Review and Test Prep Chapters 1–10, pp. 414A–414B

Reading in Math

- **Vocabulary Kit** Word Cards plus transparencies and activities for instructional word walls and for small groups
- **Dorling Kindersley Literature Library** Books with interesting data

Assessment, Intervention, and Test Prep

- **Assessment Sourcebook** See pp. 363G–363H.
- **Math Diagnosis and Intervention System** See pp. 363G–363H.
- **Test-Taking Practice** Transparencies, every lesson
- **SAT 9, SAT 10, TerraNova Practice and Test Prep** Includes practice tests, correlations, and more

Teacher Support

- **Teaching Tools** Masters: paper manipulatives and more
- **Home-School Connection** Masters, use Chapter 10 Family Letter at the start of the chapter. Use Study Buddies 19 and 20 after Lessons 10-6 and 10-12.
- **Professional Development Resources** See p. T18.
- **Technology Resources** See p. T20.

CHAPTER 10

Professional Development

Skills Trace - Measurement and Probability

BEFORE Chapter 10	DURING Chapter 10	AFTER Chapter 10
Grade K introduced measuring and comparing length, capacity, and weight using nonstandard units. The concept of temperature was also introduced.	**Chapter 10** reviews measuring with nonstandard units, and introduces estimating and measuring length, capacity, weight/mass, and temperature in the customary and metric systems. The chapter also develops identifying events that are certain or impossible, and more likely or less likely.	**Grade 2** focuses on choosing appropriate customary or metric measures for length, capacity, weight/mass, and temperature and develops the meaning of probability.

Math Background and Teaching Tips

Section A

Length

pp. 363–382

Measurement provides a real-world context for revisiting mathematics from other strands in the elementary curriculum. The process of measurement is the same for every attribute that is measurable.

- The attribute being measured is identified (i.e., length).
- An appropriate unit is selected and used to measure (i.e., a unit of length).
- The number of units is reported. (The desk is about 24 inches.)

Choosing an appropriate unit gives children an opportunity to discover an important idea about the relationship between the size of the unit and the number of units required to measure an object. If a larger unit of length is chosen (such as a foot) to measure the length of a desk, it will take fewer of them but may not be quite as accurate as choosing a smaller unit (such as an inch). Students need opportunities to choose appropriate units for measuring.

TIP! Encourage Flexibility *Frequently ask children whether they think a distance could be measured using more or fewer of a variety of units (inches or feet, a long length of rope or a pencil) so that they use the notion of selecting units flexibly, while also engaging their spatial sense.*

All measures are approximate. Measurement results are generally reported as "about 6 inches" or "about 4 feet." Using a smaller unit gives a more accurate measure.

The units of length in the customary system are inch, foot, yard, and mile. The units of length in the metric system are millimeter, centimeter, decimeter, meter, and kilometer. Relationships among the metric units are based on the Hindu-Arabic base-ten system.

10 millimeters = 1 centimeter
10 centimeters = 1 decimeter
10 decimeters = 1 meter

(Other units that continue this relationship are decameter, hectometer, and kilometer.)

Math Understandings

- The length of an object can be described by comparing it to a defined unit of length.
- The longer the unit of measure, the fewer units it takes to measure the length of an object.
- An inch and a foot are standard units used to measure length.
- A centimeter is a standard unit used to measure length.
- The distance around a shape (perimeter) can be measured by combining the measurements of each of the sides of the shape.
- The area inside a shape can be measured by placing square units on the shape and counting how many will fit.

Section B

Capacity, Weight, and Temperature

pp. 383–400

The ideas about measurement presented with length are repeated with capacity, weight, and temperature. At this level, the focus with respect to weight and capacity is on developing a sense of benchmark units and thinking about whether given objects weigh or hold more than, less than, or about the same as known objects.

about 1 pound

Capacity is the volume of an object expressed in units of liquid measure. In the customary system, these units are ounce, cup, pint, quart, and gallon. In the metric system, the most commonly used unit is the liter.

TIP! Reinforce Big Ideas *Use language such as "The pitcher holds about 7 cups" to emphasize that all measurements are approximate.*

Ounces and pounds are customary units used to measure and record weight. Equivalent units of weight require children to use number sense—1 pound is equal to 16 ounces. Developing this kind of mathematical thinking supports children's later work in algebra.

Grams and kilograms are metric units used to measure and record the mass of objects. 1 kilogram is approximately equal to 2.2 pounds.

Math Understandings

- The capacity of a container can be described by comparing it to that of a defined unit of capacity.
- Cups, pints, quarts, and liters are standard units used to measure capacity.
- You can tell how heavy or light an object is by using a balance scale to measure its weight.
- A pound, gram, and kilogram are standard units used to measure weight.
- Temperature is a measure of how hot or cold something is.
- There are many ways to measure an object, and each way uses a different tool.

It is also important for children to use estimation to predict how heavy an object is in cubes, discuss the strategies used to make the estimate, use a tool to find the weight in cubes, and determine if the weight is more or less than estimated.

TIP! Reinforce Big Ideas *Ask children to make predictions about which objects are heavy or light or weigh more or less than a pound or a kilogram as you go through your daily activities.*

Children use both Fahrenheit and Celsius scales to describe temperatures. On the Fahrenheit scale, water freezes at 32°F and boils at 212°F. Room temperature is about 70°F. On the Celsius scale, water freezes at 0°C and boils at 100°C. Room temperature is about 20°C.

Section C

Probability

pp. 401–408

Probability involves the relative likelihood of events. An event is something that may happen or may not happen. The likelihood of an outcome in an event can be predicted using probability.

In the classroom, probability activities offer opportunities for children to pose questions, determine the data needed, and decide on ways to collect and organize that data. Probability experiments have a special appeal to children because they involve real-world simulations.

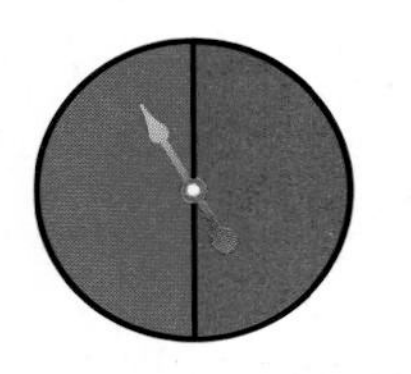

It is equally likely to spin red or blue using this spinner. There is a 50 percent ($\frac{50}{100}$) chance to spin either color on each turn.

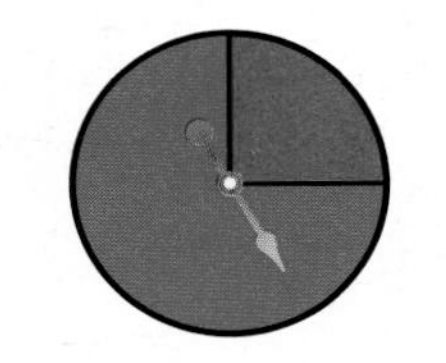

It is more likely to spin blue than red with this spinner. There is a 25 percent ($\frac{25}{100}$) chance of spinning red and a 75 percent ($\frac{75}{100}$) chance of spinning blue.

Math Understandings

- An event that is certain to happen will always happen; an event that is impossible will never happen.
- An event that is more likely will occur more often than an event that is less likely.

The probability of an event can be expressed using numbers between 0 and 1, inclusive. An event with a probability of 0 cannot happen, and an event with a probability of 1 is certain to happen. In tossing a fair number cube, the possible outcomes are 1, 2, 3, 4, 5 and 6. Three of these outcomes are even numbers: 2, 4, and 6. So the probability of getting an even number on one toss of the cube is $\frac{3}{6}$, or $\frac{1}{2}$. The chance of tossing a 7 has a probability of 0.

It is important for children to develop an intuitive feel for likelihood and to use language such as *always, never, more likely,* and *less likely* to describe probability. Understanding the likelihood of an event helps in making predictions and decisions.

TIP! Make Connections *Emphasize language such as* likely, less likely, *and* equally likely *when talking about events coming up in school. For instance, "It is likely that the school fair will be held indoors because of rain."*

CHAPTER 10

Assessment, Intervention, Test Prep

Assessment Resources

DIAGNOSING READINESS

Start of Year Diagnosing Readiness for Grade 1, Assessment Sourcebook pp. 43–46 and in Online Intervention

✓ **Start of Chapter** Diagnosing Readiness for Chapter 10, Assessment Sourcebook p. 185 and in Online Intervention

✓ **Start of Lesson** Warm Up, Teacher's Edition pp. 365, 369, 371, 373, 375, 377, 379, 383, 385, 387, 389, 391, 393, 395, 397, 401, 403, 405

✓ Instant Check System™

ONGOING ASSESSMENT

✓ **Before Independent Practice** Check and Think About It, Student Book, every lesson

✓ **After a Section** Diagnostic Checkpoint, pp. 381, 399, 407 and in Online Intervention

Basic-Facts Timed Test 10 Assessment Sourcebook, p. 36

FORMAL EVALUATION

Chapter Tests Chapter 10 Test, Student Book pp. 413–414; Assessment Sourcebook Forms A and B Free Response pp. 187–190, Forms C and D Multiple Choice pp. 191–198, Performance Assessment p. 19; Multiple-Choice Chapter Test in Online Intervention

Cumulative Tests Chapters 1–3, 1–6, 1–9, 1–12, Assessment Sourcebook, pp. 89–92, 135–138, 181–184, 227–230; Online Intervention

Test Generator Computer-generated tests; can be customized

Correlation to Assessments, Intervention, and Standardized Tests

	Assessments		Intervention	Standardized Tests				
Lessons	Diagnostic Checkpoint	Chapter Test	Math Diagnosis and Intervention System	SAT 9/10	ITBS	CTBS	CAT	MAT
10-1 Estimating, Measuring, and Comparing Length	p. 381: Ex. 1		Booklet D: D21	•/•	•	•	•	•
10-2 Problem-Solving Strategy: Use Logical Reasoning			Booklet E: E38	•/•	•	•	•	•
10-3 Estimating and Measuring with Inches	p. 381: Ex. 2	Ex. 1	Booklet D: D22	•/•	•	•	•	•
10-4 Estimating and Measuring with Feet		Ex. 3	Booklet D: D22	•/•	•	•	•	•
10-5 Estimating and Measuring with Centimeters	p. 381: Ex. 3	Ex. 2	Booklet D: D23	•/•	•	•	•	•
10-6 Understanding Perimeter	p. 381: Ex. 4	Ex. 4	Booklet D: D23	•/		•	•	•
10-7 Problem-Solving Skill: Look Back and Check	p. 381: Ex. 5	Ex. 5	Booklet E: E14			•	•	
10-8 Estimating, Measuring, and Comparing Capacity			Booklet D: D24		•	•	•	
10-9 Cups, Pints, and Quarts	p. 399: Ex. 1, 2	Ex. 6	Booklet D: D25	/•	•	•	•	
10-10 Liters	p. 399: Ex. 3	Ex. 7	Booklet D: D26	/•	•	•	•	
10-11 Estimating, Measuring, and Comparing Weight	p. 399: Ex. 5		Booklet D: D27	/•	•	•	•	
10-12 Pounds		Ex. 8	Booklet D: D28	/•	•	•	•	
10-13 Grams and Kilograms	p. 399: Ex. 4	Ex. 9	Booklet D: D29	/•	•	•	•	
10-14 Measuring Temperature	p. 399: Ex. 6	Ex. 10	Booklet D: D9	/•			•	
10-15 Choosing a Measurement Tool			Booklet D: D10	•/•		•	•	
10-16 Certain or Impossible	p. 407: Ex. 1, 2		Booklet D: D69	•/•		•	•	•
10-17 More Likely or Less Likely	p. 407: Ex. 3, 4		Booklet D: D69	•/•		•	•	•

KEY:
SAT 9 Stanford Achievement Test
SAT 10 Stanford Achievement Test
ITBS Iowa Test of Basic Skills
CAT California Achievement Test
CTBS Comprehensive Test of Basic Skills (TerraNova)
MAT Metropolitan Achievement Test

Intervention and Test Prep Resources

INTERVENTION

During Instruction Helpful "If ... then ..." suggestions in the Teacher's Edition in Ongoing Assessment and Error Intervention

Math Diagnosis and Intervention System Diagnostic tests, individual and class record forms, two-page Intervention Lessons (example, practice, test prep), and one-page Intervention Practice (multiple choice), all in cross-grade strand booklets (Booklets A–E for Grades K–3, Booklets F–M for Grades 4–6)

Online Intervention Diagnostic tests; individual, class, school, and district reports; remediation including tutorials, video, games, practice exercises

TEST PREP

Test Talk before the Chapter Test, p. 411

Cumulative Review and Test Prep end of sections, pp. 382, 400, 408 and end of Chapter 10, pp. 414A–414B

Test-Taking Practice Transparencies for every lesson

Spiral Review and Test Prep for every lesson

SAT 9, SAT 10, TerraNova Practice and Test Prep section quizzes, practice tests

Correlation to NCTM Standards and Grades Pre-K through 2 Expectations

Number and Operations

Understand numbers, ways of representing numbers, relationships among numbers, and number systems.

Grades Pre-K through 2 Expectations

- Count with understanding and recognize "how many" in sets of objects. *Lessons 10-1, 10-2, 10-7, 10-8, 10-11*
- Develop understanding of the relative position and magnitude of whole numbers and of ordinal and cardinal numbers and their connections. *Lessons 10-1, 10-2, 10-3, 10-4, 10-5, 10-7, 10-8, 10-11, 10-14*
- Develop a sense of whole numbers and represent and use them in flexible ways, including relating, composing, and decomposing numbers. *Lessons 10-1, 10-2, 10-3, 10-4, 10-5, 10-7, 10-8, 10-11, 10-14*
- Connect number words and numerals to the quantities they represent, using various physical models and representations. *Lessons 10-1, 10-2, 10-3, 10-4, 10-5, 10-6, 10-7, 10-8, 10-11, 10-14*

Measurement

Understand measurable attributes of objects and the units, systems, and processes of measurement.

Grades Pre-K through 2 Expectations

- Recognize the attributes of length, volume, weight, area, and time. *Lessons 10-1, 10-2, 10-3, 10-4, 10-5, 10-6, 10-7, 10-8, 10-9, 10-10, 10-11, 10-12, 10-13, 10-15*
- Compare and order objects according to these attributes. *Lessons 10-2, 10-9, 10-10, 10-12, 10-13*
- Understand how to measure using nonstandard and standard units. *Lessons 10-1, 10-2, 10-3, 10-4, 10-5, 10-6, 10-7, 10-8, 10-11, 10-14*
- Select an appropriate unit and tool for the attribute being measured. *Lessons 10-3, 10-4, 10-5, 10-6, 10-15*

Apply appropriate techniques, tools, and formulas to determine measurements.

Grades Pre-K through 2 Expectations

- Measure with multiple copies of units of the same size, such as paper clips laid end to end. *Lessons 10-1, 10-2, 10-11*
- Use tools to measure. *Lessons 10-3, 10-4, 10-5, 10-6*
- Develop common referents for measures to make comparisons and estimates. *Lessons 10-1, 10-2, 10-3, 10-4, 10-5, 10-8, 10-9, 10-10, 10-11, 10-12, 10-13, 10-14*

Data Analysis and Probability

Develop and evaluate inferences and predictions that are based on data.

Grades Pre-K through 2 Expectations

- Discuss events related to students' experiences as likely or unlikely. *Lesson 10-17*

Understand and apply basic concepts of probability. *Lessons 10-16, 10-17*

The NCTM 2000 Pre-K through Grade 12 Content Standards are Number and Operations, Algebra, Geometry, Measurement, and Data Analysis and Probability. The Process Standards (Problem Solving, Reasoning and Proof, Communication, Connections, and Representation) are incorporated throughout lessons.

CHAPTER 10

Investigation

Measurement and Probability

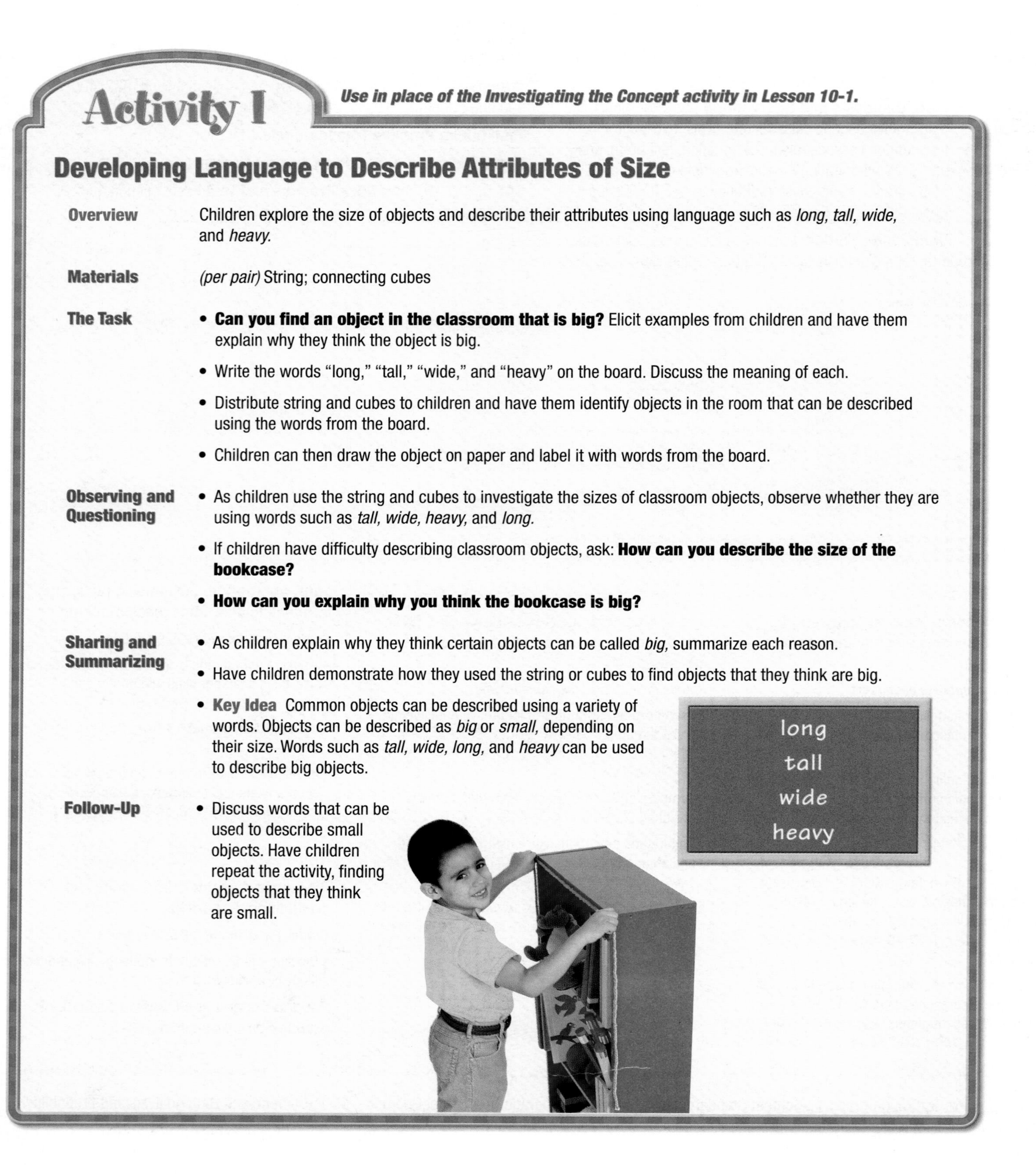

Activity 1

Use in place of the Investigating the Concept activity in Lesson 10-1.

Developing Language to Describe Attributes of Size

Overview Children explore the size of objects and describe their attributes using language such as *long, tall, wide,* and *heavy.*

Materials *(per pair)* String; connecting cubes

The Task

- **Can you find an object in the classroom that is big?** Elicit examples from children and have them explain why they think the object is big.
- Write the words "long," "tall," "wide," and "heavy" on the board. Discuss the meaning of each.
- Distribute string and cubes to children and have them identify objects in the room that can be described using the words from the board.
- Children can then draw the object on paper and label it with words from the board.

Observing and Questioning

- As children use the string and cubes to investigate the sizes of classroom objects, observe whether they are using words such as *tall, wide, heavy,* and *long.*
- If children have difficulty describing classroom objects, ask: **How can you describe the size of the bookcase?**
- **How can you explain why you think the bookcase is big?**

Sharing and Summarizing

- As children explain why they think certain objects can be called *big,* summarize each reason.
- Have children demonstrate how they used the string or cubes to find objects that they think are big.
- **Key Idea** Common objects can be described using a variety of words. Objects can be described as *big* or *small,* depending on their size. Words such as *tall, wide, long,* and *heavy* can be used to describe big objects.

Follow-Up

- Discuss words that can be used to describe small objects. Have children repeat the activity, finding objects that they think are small.

Link to ***Investigations in Number, Data, and Space®*** See the **Joint-Usage Plan** available from Pearson Scott Foresman.

Activity 2

Use in place of the Investigating the Concept activity in Lesson 10-16.

Certain and Impossible Spinners

Overview Children use spinners to investigate events that are more likely, less likely, certain, and impossible to occur.

Materials *(per pair)* 3 copies of Spinner Pattern (Teaching Tool 34); Tally Chart (Teaching Tool 38); paper clip; red crayon; blue crayon

The Task

- Discuss the concepts *more likely, less likely, certain,* and *impossible* and have children give examples of each.
- Have pairs create one spinner with equal parts red and blue. Have children then spin twenty times and record the results on the tally chart.
- Then have children create a spinner in which one color is more likely to be spun and another spinner where one color is certain to be spun.
- Share spinners as a class.

Observing and Questioning

- As you circulate around the room, observe whether children create one spinner in which one section is larger than the other, so that it is more likely to spin one color than the other, and one spinner that has only one color, so that it is impossible to spin the other color.
- Ask the following questions if children have difficulty creating spinners:
- **How is a spinner where one color is more likely different from the first one you made?** *(One section is larger.)*
- **How can you create a spinner so that it will never land on blue?** *(Do not color any of the spinner blue.)*
- **How do you know that one color is more likely to be spun than the other color is?** *(The color with the larger section is more likely to be spun.)* **How do you know that one color is impossible?** *(It is not on the spinner at all.)*

Sharing and Summarizing

- As children share spinners, sketch each design on the board. Organize each under the headings "Certain Red," "Certain Blue," "Impossible Red," and "Impossible Blue." You may wish to also create headings for "More Likely" and "Less Likely."
- **Key Idea** Children can tell whether an event is certain or impossible to occur by comparing the parts of the spinner. Events are equally likely if the parts are of equal size. An event is more likely if one part is larger than the other.

Follow-Up

- Show a spinner that is mostly red with a small blue section. **Do you think the spinner will land on red or blue? Why?** Show a spinner that is entirely red. **Do you think the spinner will land on red or blue? Why?**

CHAPTER 10

Math Story

One Very Smart Chicken **(Genre: Animal fantasy)**

In this adaptation of *The Little Red Hen,* a modern chicken entices a pig, a horse, and a duck to grind the flour, mix the batter, and bake the bread. But who will do the dishes?

Introducing the Story

Ask children if they've ever heard the story *The Little Red Hen.* Then show them the cover of *One Very Smart Chicken.* Tell them that this story is a modern retelling of *The Little Red Hen.*

Reading the Story

Have children read the story through once without stopping so that they can enjoy the story and the art.

Read the story again, this time inviting children to draw conclusions as they read. Explain that readers use both what they read and what they know about real life to draw conclusions. Explain that drawing conclusions will help them better understand what they read. (For more on *Draw Conclusions,* see Reading for Math Success, pp. 367–368.)

Page 10A

Page 10B **Page 10C**

So the duck helped grind the wheat.
It was hard work,
but when she was done
there were 5 cups of flour.

The pig helped make the dough.
That was hard work too.
He added about 2 cups of water
to the flour.
Then he put in some
sugar and some yeast.

Page 10D

And the horse put the bread
into the oven.
That was hard work too.
Each loaf weighed about 1 pound,
and this horse had not been
getting much exercise.
(Too much TV.)

Page 10E

Everybody ate the bread.
Everybody enjoyed the bread.

"Now, who will help me do the dishes?"
asked the little red hen.

What do YOU think will happen next?

Are the duck, the pig, and the horse
likely or unlikely to jump up and
help the little red hen with the dishes?

Page 10F

Follow-up Activities

- **Use Picture Clues** Have children examine the art and read the text to answer these questions: **How many cups of flour did the duck grind?** *(5 cups)* **Which tool do you think the duck used to measure the flour?** *(A measuring cup)* **How much did each loaf of bread weigh?** *(1 pound)*
- **Make Predictions** Ask children to tell whether they thought the duck, the pig, and the horse would work for some bread. *(Accept reasonable answers.)* **Who do you think will do the dishes? How do you know?** *(Sample responses: The hen; because everyone else is too tired, because it's her turn, or because the other animals will only work if they get something in return.)*
- **Extend the Story** Ask leading questions: **What do you think will happen the next time the hen wants to make bread?** *(Sample responses: She will get the animals to help her; she will make them do the dishes before they get any bread.)*

Home-School Connection

Purpose Provide families with a quick overview of the material that will be covered in Chapter 10. Included on this page: a family letter, a math activity, references to literature related to the chapter, and new math vocabulary words.

Using Student Page 363

You may wish to read and discuss the family letter with children prior to having them sign it and sending the page home.

Literature: Dorling Kindersley

Available in the Scott Foresman Dorling Kindersley Literature Library.

Twisters!
by Kate Hayden
(Dorling Kindersley Ltd., 2000)

Information about twisters is presented through real-life events and photographs. Readers learn how scientists use computers to predict when and where a twister will strike.

The Home-School Connection booklet includes:

- Chapter 10 Family Letter in English and Spanish
- Study Buddies 19
- Study Buddies 20

Study Buddies pages provide reinforcement activities, one for the child and one for the person guiding the child's learning.

Vocabulary

estimate, measure *(pp. 365–366)*
inch *(pp. 371–372)*
foot (feet) *(pp. 373–374)*
centimeter *(pp. 375–376)*
cup *(pp. 383–386)*
pint, quart *(pp. 385–386)*
liter *(pp. 387–388)*
pound *(pp. 391–392)*
gram, kilogram *(pp. 393–394)*
thermometer, temperature *(pp. 395–396)*
certain, impossible *(pp. 401–402)*
more likely, less likely *(pp. 403–404)*

Home-School Connection

Dear Family,

Today my class started Chapter 10, **Measurement and Probability.** I will learn to estimate and measure length, capacity, weight, and temperature. I will also learn to predict how likely or unlikely it is for an event to happen. Here are some of the math words I will be learning and some things we can do to help me with my math.

Love,

____

Math Activity to Do at Home

Have some fun measuring with pieces of cereal! Try measuring the length of a spoon by laying the cereal pieces end to end beside the spoon. Then fill a cup with cereal and count the cereal pieces to see how many pieces it took to fill the cup.

Books to Read Together

Reading math stories reinforces concepts. Look for these titles in your local library:

Me and the Measure of Things
By Joan Sweeney
(Crown, 2001)

Measuring Penny
By Loreen Leedy
(Holt, 2000)

My New Math Words

We measure length in inches, feet, and centimeters.

inch

There are 12 inches in 1 **foot**.

centimeter

We measure capacity in cups, pints, quarts, and liters.

cup **pint** **quart** **liter**

We measure weight in **pounds**, **grams**, and **kilograms**.

thermometer A thermometer measures **temperature**.

three hundred sixty-three 363

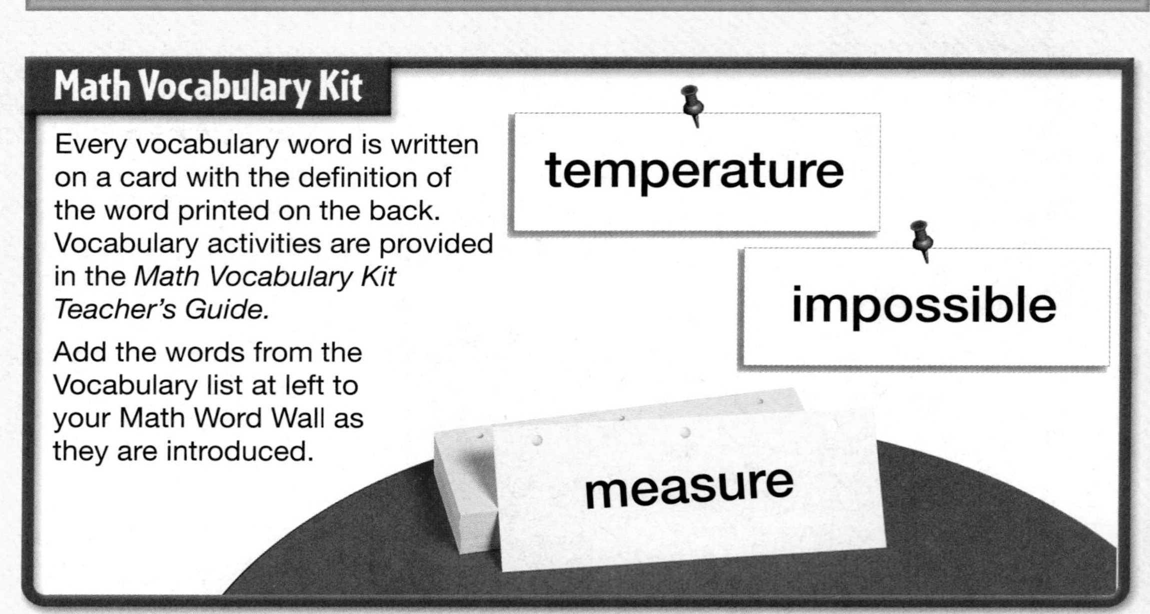

Math Vocabulary Kit

Every vocabulary word is written on a card with the definition of the word printed on the back. Vocabulary activities are provided in the *Math Vocabulary Kit Teacher's Guide.*

Add the words from the Vocabulary list at left to your Math Word Wall as they are introduced.

EC NTL 12 11 10 9 8 7 6 5

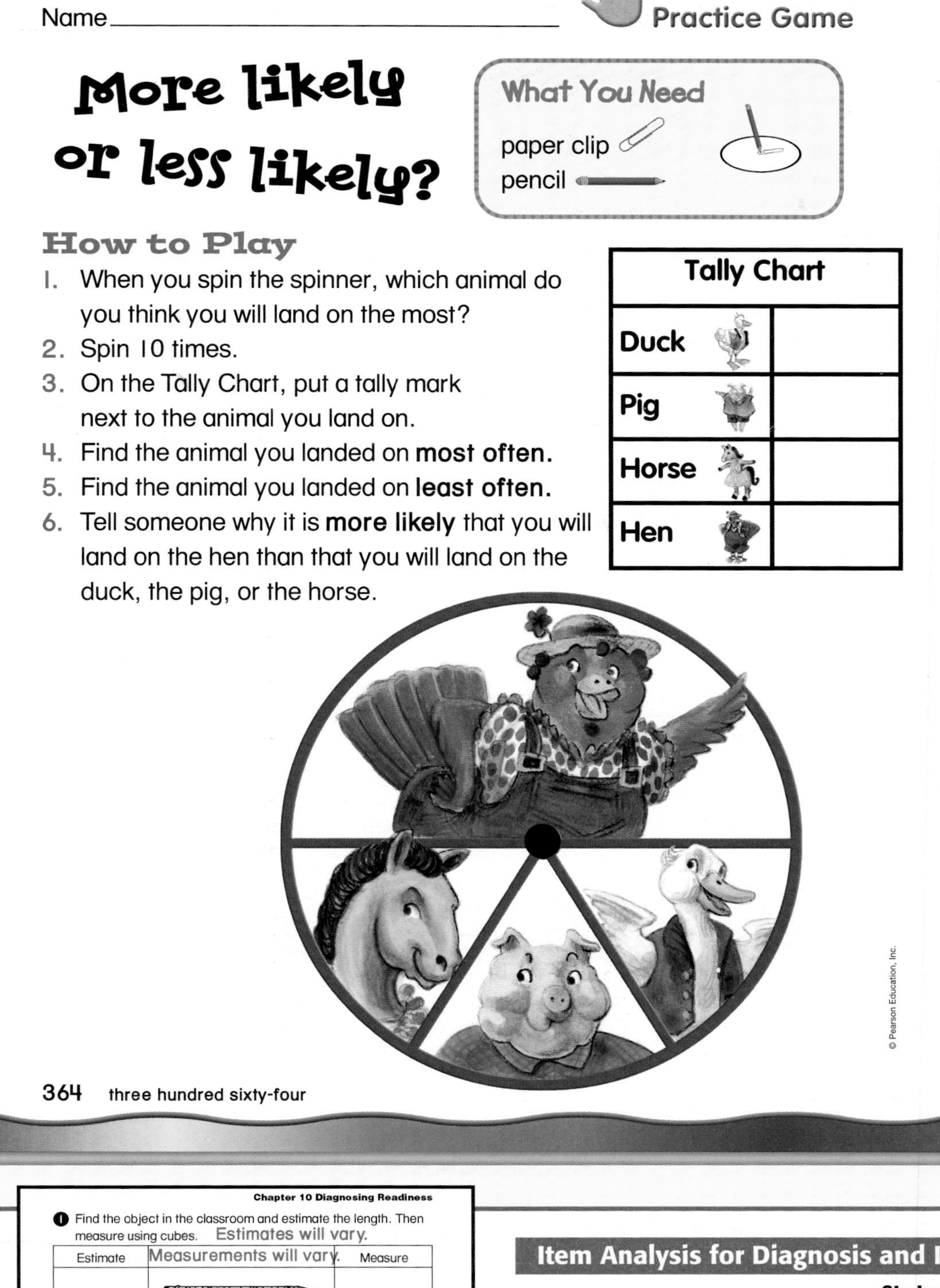

Name ____________________ Practice Game

More likely or less likely?

What You Need

paper clip

pencil

How to Play

1. When you spin the spinner, which animal do you think you will land on the most?
2. Spin 10 times.
3. On the Tally Chart, put a tally mark next to the animal you land on.
4. Find the animal you landed on **most often.**
5. Find the animal you landed on **least often.**
6. Tell someone why it is **more likely** that you will land on the hen than that you will land on the duck, the pig, or the horse.

Tally Chart	
Duck	
Pig	
Horse	
Hen	

Practice Game
for School or Home

Purpose Provide children with an opportunity to practice skills they have previously learned.

Using Student Page 364

You may wish to discuss these questions with your children before they play "More Likely or Less Likely?"

- **Is it more likely or less likely that it will snow tomorrow? Why?**
- **If a spinner is almost all red, is it more likely or less likely that a spin will land on red?**

Give children the materials for the game.

Describe the game and the directions. Lead children through the process of spinning, placing a tally mark in the appropriate section of the chart, and repeating the process 10 times. Make sure children can identify the animal they landed on the most often and the least often and why their results make sense. Then allow children to complete the game.

Describe another way to play: Have children take turns spinning. If the spinner lands on the hen, a player does not make a tally mark in the chart, but spins again. After 10 tallies, have children compare charts. If time permits, have children play another round and compare their results again.

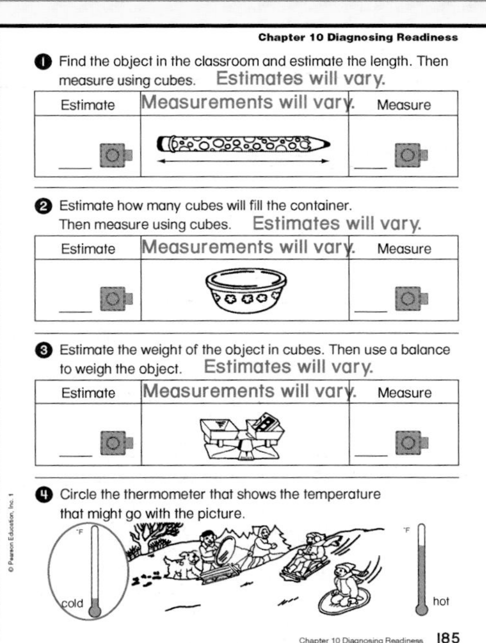

Chapter 10 Diagnosing Readiness

1. Find the object in the classroom and estimate the length. Then measure using cubes. Estimates will vary.

Estimate	Measurements will vary.	Measure
___		___

2. Estimate how many cubes will fill the container. Then measure using cubes. Estimates will vary.

Estimate	Measurements will vary.	Measure
___		___

3. Estimate the weight of the object in cubes. Then use a balance to weigh the object. Estimates will vary.

Estimate	Measurements will vary.	Measure
___		___

4. Circle the thermometer that shows the temperature that might go with the picture.

Chapter 10 Diagnosing Readiness 185

Item Analysis for Diagnosis and Intervention

Objective	Items	Student Book Pages*	Intervention System
Estimate the length and width of objects and verify by measuring in nonstandard units.	1	Kindergarten	D20
Estimate and measure capacity using nonstandard units.	2	Kindergarten	D20
Estimate the weight of objects and measure their weight in nonstandard units.	3	Kindergarten	D20
Explore temperature using comparative words and identify the thermometer as a tool for measuring temperature.	4	Kindergarten	D20

*For each lesson, there is a *Reteaching* activity in *Reaching All Learners* and a *Reteaching* master.

Math Leveled Literature Library

Sharks! (Average)★
Ginjer Clarke. New York: Grosset & Dunlap, 2001.
An informational book that compares sharks of all sizes.

10-1 Estimating, Measuring, and Comparing Length

Lesson Organizer

Quick Lesson Overview 

Objective Estimate, measure, and compare the lengths of objects using nonstandard units.

Math Understanding The length of an object can be described by comparing it to a defined unit of length.

Vocabulary Estimate, measure

Materials for Student Pages *(per child)* 15 connecting cubes; objects pictured on student pages or other similarly-sized classroom objects

Professional Development Note

Research Base

Young children begin to understand the measurement of length only when they see the need for standard and identical units. Then they must understand that any given unit can be either divided to create smaller units or multiplied to create larger units (National Research Council, 2001; Carpenter, 1975). This section starts by asking children to explore how to measure lengths with nonstandard units and then introduces both customary and metric standard units.

NCTM Standards

- Number and Operations
- Measurement

(For a complete correlation to the NCTM Standards and Grades Pre-K through 2 Expectations, see Pages 363G and 363H.)

Getting Started

Spiral Review

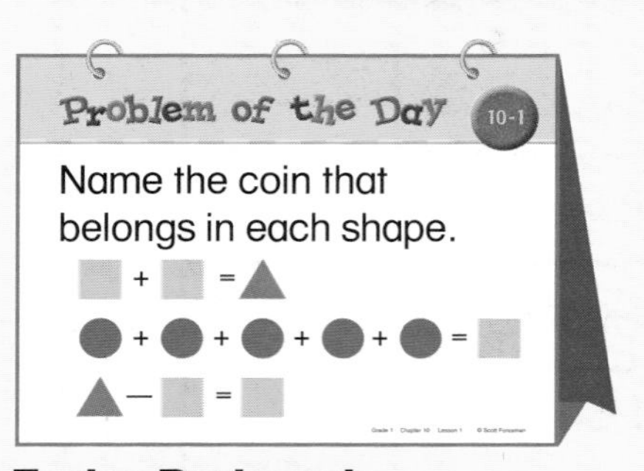

Topics Reviewed

- Coin values
- Addition
- Problem-Solving Strategy: Try, Check, and Revise

Answer Each circle is a penny, each square is a nickel, and each triangle is a dime.

Spiral Review and Test Prep 10-1

1. What is the number?
   1 less than 40 is ____.
   Ⓐ 30 Ⓑ 39 Ⓒ 41 Ⓓ 50
2. How many ears are there? Count by twos.
   Ⓐ 8 Ⓑ 4 Ⓒ 2 Ⓓ 12
3. Count on. Then write how much money there is in all.
   37 ¢ in all
4. Circle the coins you need to buy two rings.
   20¢ each
   Check children's work. They should circle coins that total 40¢.

Use with Lesson 10-1 115

Available as a transparency and as a blackline master

Topics Reviewed

1. 1 More, 1 Less; 10 More, 10 Less
2. Using Skip Counting
3.–4. Counting Dimes, Nickels, and Pennies

Investigating the Concept

How Long Is It?

15–20 MIN | Kinesthetic | Small Group

Materials *(per child)* 10 connecting cubes; classroom objects

What to Do

- Display two connecting cubes. Point out that they are the same size. Explain that the cubes can be used to measure how long or how tall something is.
- Tell children that they can estimate before they measure with cubes. Record children's estimates for the length of a calculator. Have children make cube trains and measure the calculator from end to end. Tell them to use the word *about* for a measure that is not an exact number of cubes.
- Have small groups estimate and measure with other small classroom items.

Ongoing Assessment

- **Reasoning Estimate how many cubes long an eraser is.** *(Answers will vary.)*
- **Would it take more cubes to measure a sneaker or an eraser? Explain.** *(A sneaker; because a sneaker is longer than an eraser)*

Reaching All Learners

Math Vocabulary

Estimate and Measure

10–15 MIN **Kinesthetic/Linguistic**

Materials *(per child)* Classroom objects; paper clips

- Give each child an object and some paper clips. Have children *estimate*–or predict, about how many paper clips it will take to measure the object. Have children record their estimates.
- Demonstrate how to measure by lining up paper clips next to the object and counting the paper clips. Have children measure their objects and compare the measurements to their estimates.
- Have children in the group exchange objects and repeat.

Access Content

English Language Learners

Understanding Fixed Units

10–15 MIN **Kinesthetic/Linguistic**

Materials *(per child)* Paper clips of different sizes; chalkboard eraser; classroom objects

- Have each child measure a chalkboard eraser by lining up paper clips. Each child should use a different size clip. Have partners compare their answers. **Were your answers the *same* or *different?***
- Next, have both partners use the same size clips. **Are your answers the *same* or *different?*** Discuss why the answers are the same.
- Repeat by measuring other objects in these two ways.

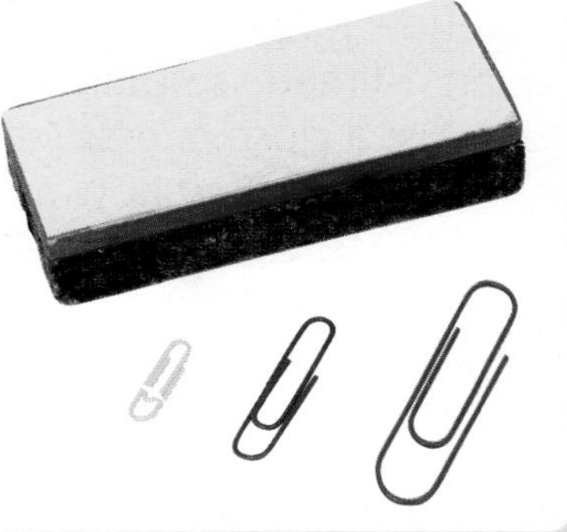

Reteaching

Comparing Length

5–10 MIN **Visual/Spatial**

Materials *(per child)* 4 classroom objects of varying lengths; connecting cubes

- Ask children to look at the objects and tell which one is the longest. **About how many cubes long is it?** Then have children tell which object is the shortest. Explain to children that their guesses are called *estimates*.
- Demonstrate how to confirm estimates by using connecting cubes to measure the objects.
- Have children order their objects from shortest to longest.

Math and Social Studies

Map Skills

10–15 MIN **Visual/Spatial**

Materials Classroom map of the United States; connecting cubes; small stickers or self-stick notes

- Put a sticker on the map near Los Angeles and another one near Dallas. Have children write their estimates for how many cubes it will take to measure the distance between the cities.
- Invite two children to connect cubes on the map between Los Angeles and Dallas. Have children compare their estimates to the actual measurement.
- Repeat, measuring the distances between other pairs of cities.

Los Angeles
Dallas

Objective Estimate, measure, and compare the lengths of objects using nonstandard units.

1 Warm Up

Activate Prior Knowledge Review the terms *longer* and *shorter.* Lay two items beside each other horizontally and compare their lengths. **Which is shorter? Which is longer?**

2 Teach

Learn!

Look at the picture together and explain that the girl is going to estimate, or predict, about how long the bug is. Assure children that an estimate is not intended to be exact, just a close guess. Tell them that we measure to find how many units long something is. Encourage children to use the word *about* when an object is not an exact length.

Ongoing Assessment

Talk About It

- **Why is it important that the cubes are all the same size?** *(So that* 3 cubes long *always means the same length)*
- **Why is it important that the ends of the bug line up with the ends of the cubes?** *(So that the measurement will be accurate)*

If children confuse an estimate with a measure,

then point out that an estimate is a guess made without the cubes and that a measurement is made using cubes.

Error Intervention

If children make errors when measuring,

then help them align the ends of the items with the cubes. *(Also see* Reteaching, *Page 365B.)*

Think About It Take time to revisit and practice using comparative terms. Discuss *long, longer, longest; short, shorter, shortest.*

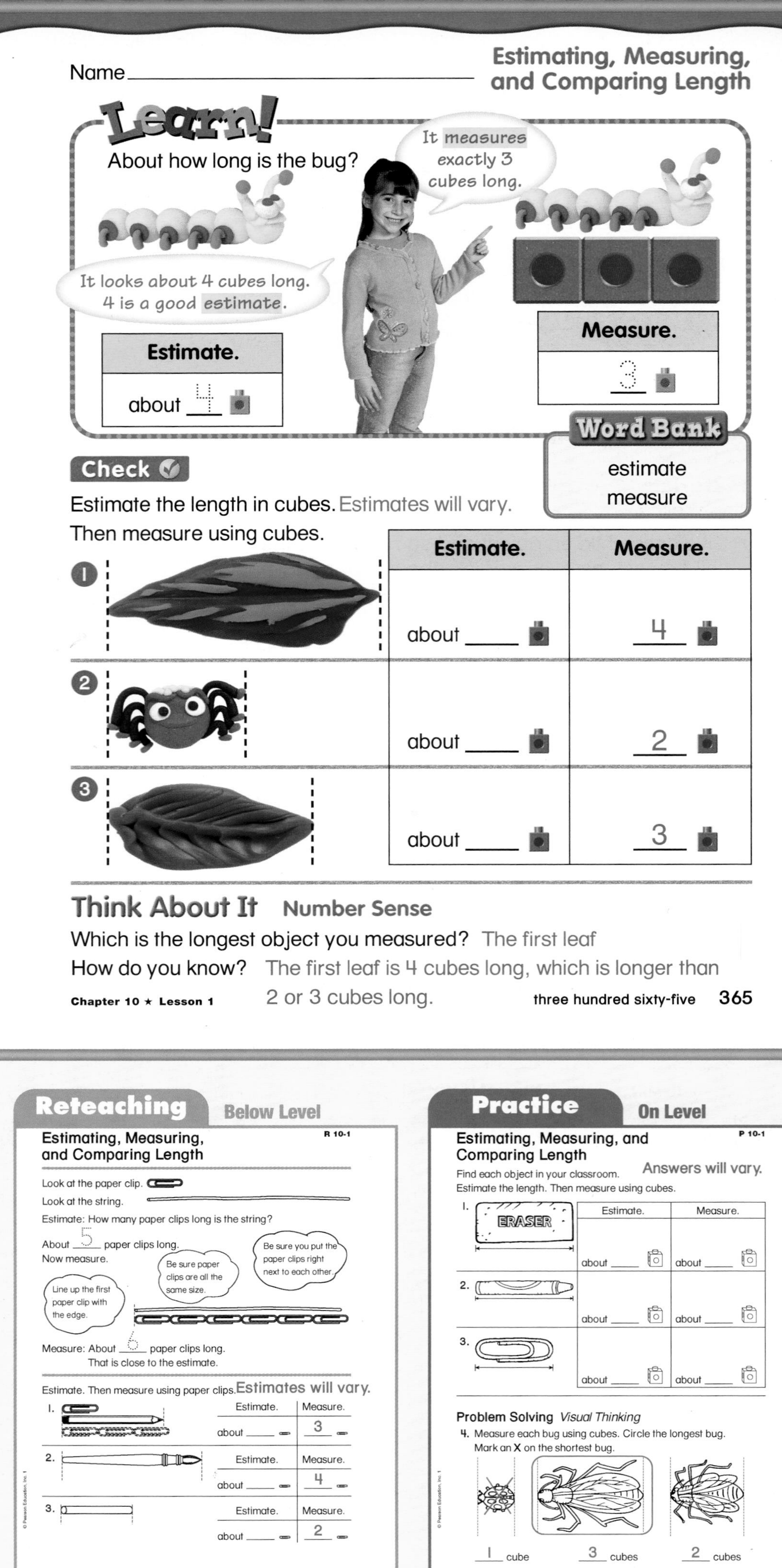

Name ______________________

Estimating, Measuring, and Comparing Length

Learn!

About how long is the bug?

Estimate.	Measure.
about 4 cubes	3 cubes

Word Bank
estimate
measure

Check

Estimate the length in cubes. Estimates will vary.
Then measure using cubes.

	Estimate.	Measure.
1	about ___	4
2	about ___	2
3	about ___	3

Think About It Number Sense

Which is the longest object you measured? The first leaf

How do you know? The first leaf is 4 cubes long, which is longer than 2 or 3 cubes long.

Chapter 10 ★ Lesson 1 three hundred sixty-five 365

Reteaching Below Level

Estimating, Measuring, and Comparing Length R 10-1

Look at the paper clip.
Look at the string.
Estimate: How many paper clips long is the string?
About 5 paper clips long.
Now measure.

Measure: About 6 paper clips long.
That is close to the estimate.

Estimate. Then measure using paper clips. Estimates will vary.

	Estimate.	Measure.
1.	about ___	3
2.	about ___	4
3.	about ___	2

Use with Lesson 10-1. 115

Practice On Level

Estimating, Measuring, and Comparing Length P 10-1

Find each object in your classroom. Answers will vary.
Estimate the length. Then measure using cubes.

	Estimate.	Measure.
1. ERASER	about ___	about ___
2.	about ___	about ___
3.	about ___	about ___

Problem Solving *Visual Thinking*

4. Measure each bug using cubes. Circle the longest bug. Mark an X on the shortest bug.

1 cube   3 cubes   2 cubes

Use with Lesson 10-1. 115

Practice

Find each object in your classroom.
Estimate the length in cubes. Answers will vary.
Then measure using cubes.

	Estimate.	Measure.
4	about ___ cubes	about ___ cubes
5	about ___ cubes	about ___ cubes
6	about ___ cubes	about ___ cubes
7	about ___ cubes	about ___ cubes

Problem Solving Visual Thinking

8. Measure each turtle using cubes. Circle the longest turtle. Mark an **X** on the shortest turtle.

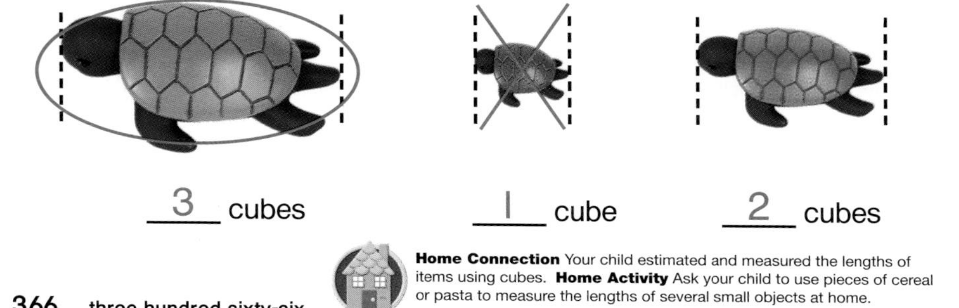

3 cubes   1 cube   2 cubes

Home Connection Your child estimated and measured the lengths of items using cubes. **Home Activity** Ask your child to use pieces of cereal or pasta to measure the lengths of several small objects at home.

Enrichment Above Level

How Long is It?

E 10-1 DATA

Find each object listed on the graph.
Use cubes to measure each object.
Color one square for each cube you use.

Object	Measurement in Cubes
Crayon	
Pencil	
Glue Stick	
Paint Brush	
	1 2 3 4 5 6 7 8 9 10

Use the graph to answer the questions.

1. Which object is the longest? Check children's graphs.
2. Which object is the shortest? Check children's graphs.
3. Which is longer, the paint brush or the pencil? Check children's graphs.
4. Which is shorter, the crayon or the glue stick? Check children's graphs.

Use with Lesson 10-1 115

Problem Solving

Estimating, Measuring, and Comparing Length

PS 10-1

Measure each object using cubes.
Color the longest object red.
Color the shortest object blue.

1. Answer may vary. about 4 cubes — blue, orange: Answer may vary. about 3 cubes
red: about 6 cubes Answer may vary.

2. John wants to put the objects into this box. In which space does each thing go? Write the name.

pencil	crayon
pen	

Use with Lesson 10-1. 115

3 Practice

Before children do Exercises 4–7, help them find the objects needed. Remind children to estimate first and then to measure.

Reading Assist: Make Judgments Ask children to make judgments about which attributes of an object are measurable and which are not. **Can you measure this crayon's length? its color? its texture? its thickness?**

Leveled Practice

Below Level Work with a partner.

On Level Work individually to complete all exercises.

Above Level After doing Exercises 4–7, circle the longest object and cross out the shortest object.

Early Finishers Ask children to find small classroom objects to measure using connecting cubes.

4 Assess

Journal Idea Have children trace a pencil and a crayon on paper and measure each with connecting cubes. Tell children to record the lengths of the pencil and crayon. Then ask children to circle the longer object.

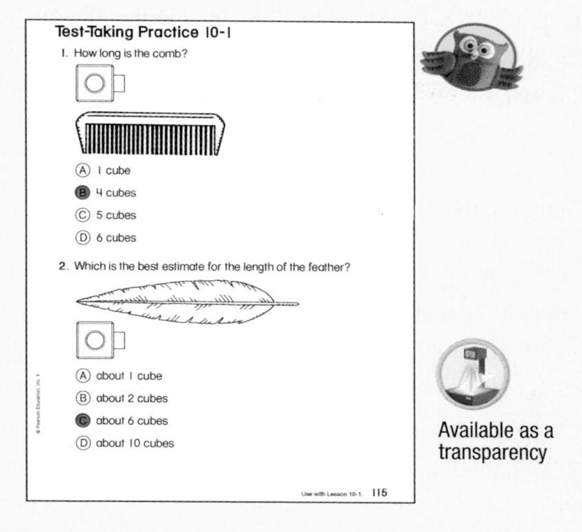
Test-Taking Practice 10-1

1. How long is the comb?
(A) 1 cube
(B) 4 cubes
(C) 5 cubes
(D) 6 cubes

2. Which is the best estimate for the length of the feather?
(A) about 1 cube
(B) about 2 cubes
(C) about 6 cubes
(D) about 10 cubes

Use with Lesson 10-1. 115

Available as a transparency

Reading for Math Success

Purpose Show children how to apply the reading skill, *Draw Conclusions,* to their math work. Help prepare children for the problem-solving strategy lesson, *Use Logical Reasoning,* which follows.

Using Student Page 367

Reading Skills and Math Understanding When children draw conclusions as they read, they form opinions or make decisions based on facts and details in the text along with what they already know. When children draw conclusions about measurement in a math problem, they use what they have read in the problem along with what they know about the lengths of different objects.

Model the Process Tell children that they will read a measurement problem and use the information in the problem along with what they know about the length of an object to solve it. **When I read a problem that asks me if more paper clips or connecting cubes were used to measure an object, I use the measurements given in the problem to solve it. I compare the numbers to find out which number is greater.**

Guide the Activity Have children read the sentences at the top of the page. Then guide them to compare the number of paper clips to the number of cubes used to measure the object in each exercise. Stress to children that they want to circle the unit that Sharon used more of to measure each object.

Think About It Discuss children's answers about why it always took more cubes than paper clips to measure each object. Guide children to draw the conclusion that since a connecting cube is shorter than a paper clip, it takes more shorter units than longer units to measure each object.

Reading for Math Success

Name ____________________

Draw Conclusions

Sharon measured 3 objects using paper clips and cubes.
Here is what each object measured.

about 3 paper clips
about 5 cubes

1. What did she use **more** of to measure the grasshopper?

Circle your answer. more paper clips or more cubes (circled)

about 2 paper clips
about 3 cubes

2. What did she use **more** of to measure the twig?

Circle your answer. more paper clips or more cubes (circled)

about 4 paper clips
about 7 cubes

3. What did she use **more** of to measure the feather?

Circle your answer. more paper clips or more cubes (circled)

Think About It Reasoning

Why do you think it took more cubes than paper clips to measure every object? Because a cube is smaller than a paper clip

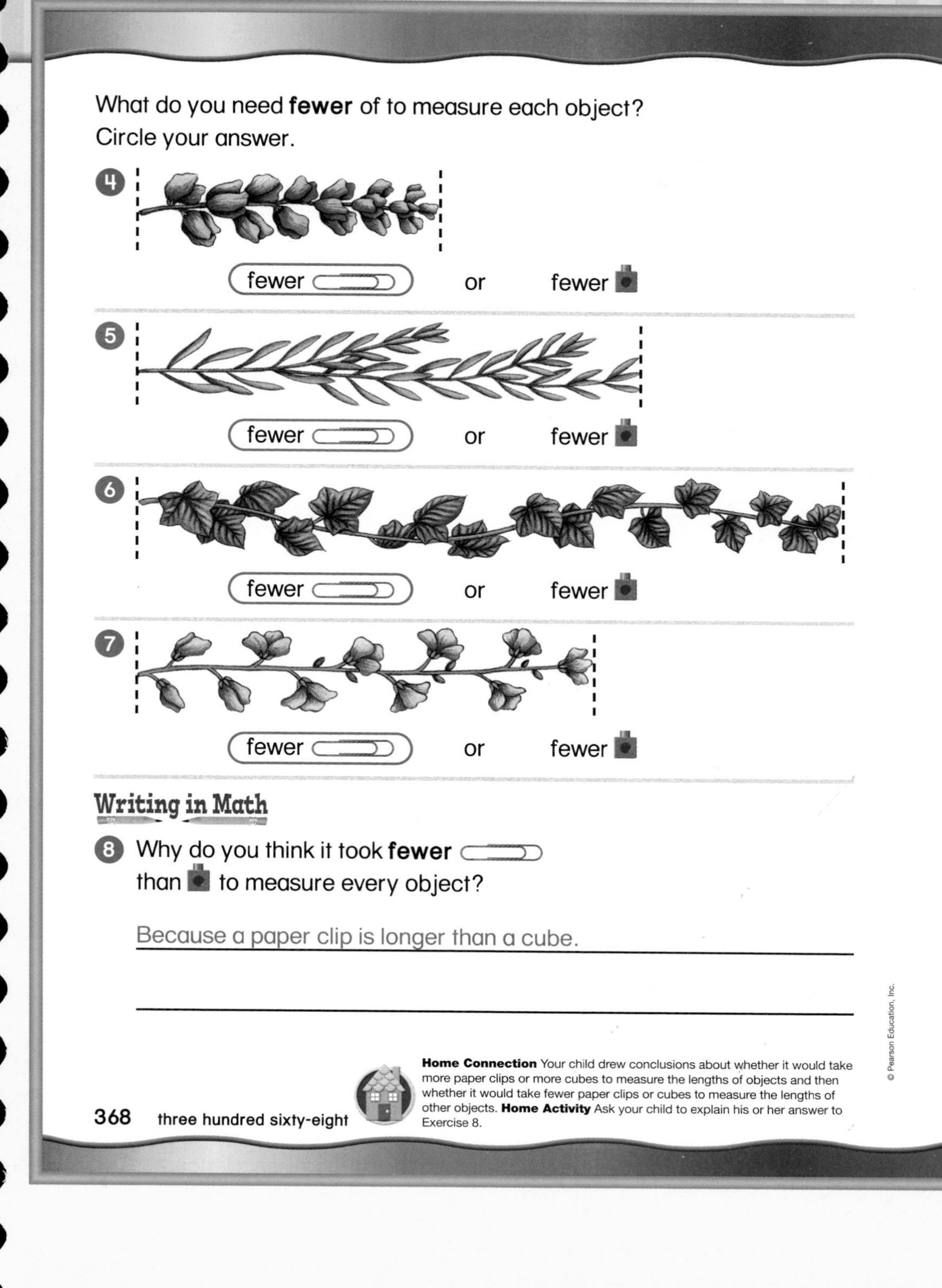

What do you need **fewer** of to measure each object?
Circle your answer.

4 fewer [paper clip] or fewer [cube]

5 fewer [paper clip] or fewer [cube]

6 fewer [paper clip] or fewer [cube]

7 fewer [paper clip] or fewer [cube]

Writing in Math

8 Why do you think it took **fewer** [paper clip] than [cube] to measure every object?

Because a paper clip is longer than a cube.

Home Connection Your child drew conclusions about whether it would take more paper clips or more cubes to measure the lengths of objects and then whether it would take fewer paper clips or cubes to measure the lengths of other objects. **Home Activity** Ask your child to explain his or her answer to Exercise 8.

368 three hundred sixty-eight

© Pearson Education, Inc.

Using Student Page 368

Have children independently read the directions at the top of the page. Remind children to use the measurements given in each exercise to determine whether fewer cubes or fewer paper clips were used to measure each object.

When children have completed Exercises 4–8, have them compare their answers with other children in the class.

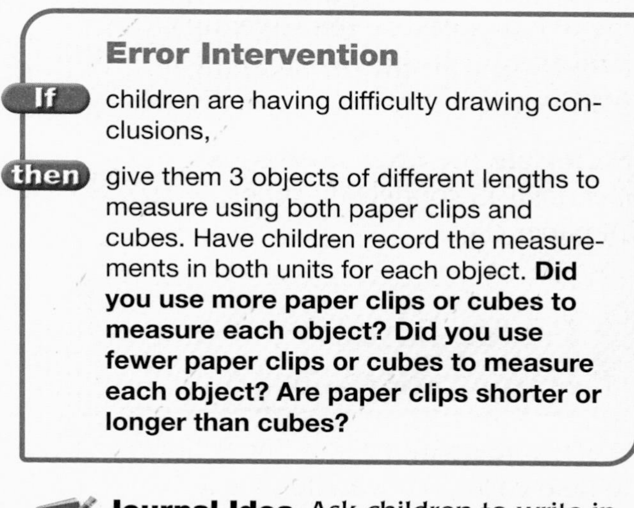

Error Intervention

If children are having difficulty drawing conclusions,

then give them 3 objects of different lengths to measure using both paper clips and cubes. Have children record the measurements in both units for each object. **Did you use more paper clips or cubes to measure each object? Did you use fewer paper clips or cubes to measure each object? Are paper clips shorter or longer than cubes?**

Journal Idea Ask children to write in their own words the conclusions that they were able to draw by completing the exercises. Encourage them to use drawings as part of their journal entries.

Use Logical Reasoning

Lesson Organizer

Quick Lesson Overview

Objective Solve problems by using logical reasoning.

Math Understanding The longer the unit of measure, the fewer units it takes to measure the length of an object.

Materials for Student Pages *(per child)* 15 connecting cubes; 15 paper clips

Professional Development Note

Math Background It is important to help children articulate why it takes fewer of the longer units and more of the shorter units to measure the same object. When comparing, children may want to say that it takes more of the longer unit because they associate the term *more* with the idea of *longer.*

NCTM Standards

- Measurement

(For a complete correlation to the NCTM Standards and Grades Pre-K through 2 Expectations, see Pages 363G and 363H.)

Getting Started

Spiral Review

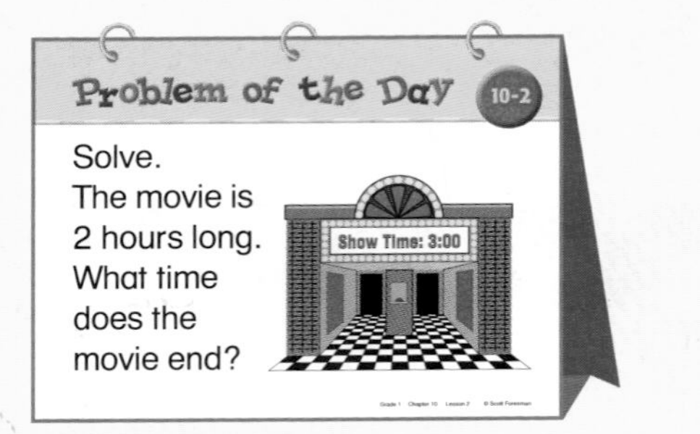

Topics Reviewed

- Elapsed time
- Problem-Solving Skill: Use Data from a Picture

Answer The movie ends at 5:00. Two hours after 3:00 is 5:00.

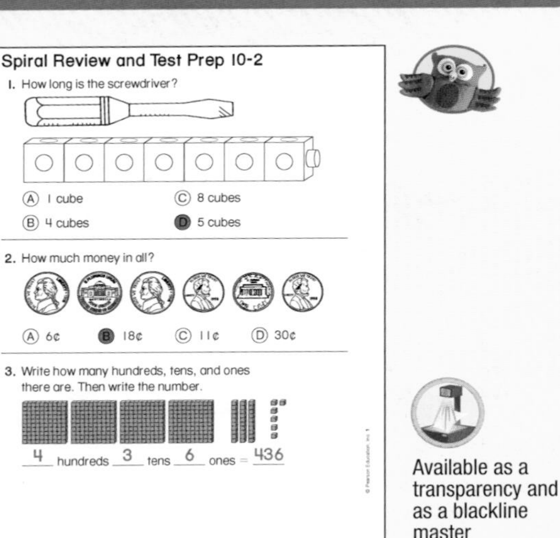

Available as a transparency and as a blackline master

Topics Reviewed

1. Estimating, Measuring, and Comparing Length
2. Nickel and Penny
3. Hundreds

Investigating the Concept

More or Fewer

Materials *(per child)* 10 jumbo paper clips; 10 connecting cubes; pencil

What to Do

- Compare the length of a paper clip to the length of a connecting cube. **Which is longer?** *(Paper clip)* Have children predict whether it will take *more* clips or *more* cubes to measure the length of a pencil. Have one child measure the pencil using paper clips. Record the measurement. Then ask another child to measure the same pencil using cubes. Record the measurement and compare the numbers.
- Have children predict whether it will take *fewer* clips or *fewer* cubes to measure a crayon. Ask children to measure a crayon with paper clips and cubes to find out.

Ongoing Assessment

- **Reasoning Does it take *fewer* connecting cubes or *fewer* clips to measure a crayon? Why?** *(Fewer clips; because they are longer)*
- **Would it take *more* cubes or *more* clips to measure a sheet of paper? Why?** *(More cubes; because they are shorter)*

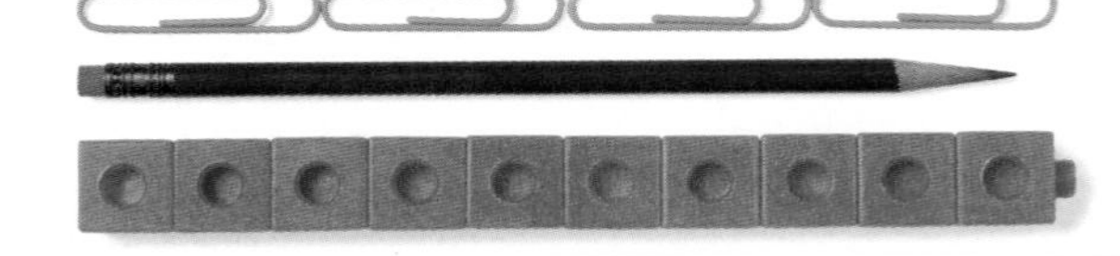

Reaching All Learners

Oral Language in Math

Walking to Problem Solve

10–15 MIN **Kinesthetic/Linguistic** WHOLE CLASS

- Explain that you need to measure the distance across the classroom in steps and want to find the person who can walk across the room with the fewest steps.
- Invite a child to walk across the room while counting his or her steps. Write the number of steps on the board.
- Ask another child to do the same but first to think about how to take fewer steps.
- Discuss how taking longer steps means taking fewer steps.

Extend Language

English Language Learners

Understanding More and Fewer

10–15 MIN **Auditory/Linguistic**

PAIRS

Materials *(per pair)* Paper clips; 2 index cards labeled "more" and "fewer"

- Review the meanings of *more* and *fewer.*
- Make two unequal piles of paper clips on the table. Invite a child to place the index cards in front of the appropriate piles of paper clips. Then have the child use *more* or *fewer* in a sentence.
- One child makes two different piles of paper clips. The partner puts cards in front of the piles and says a sentence. Then partners switch roles.

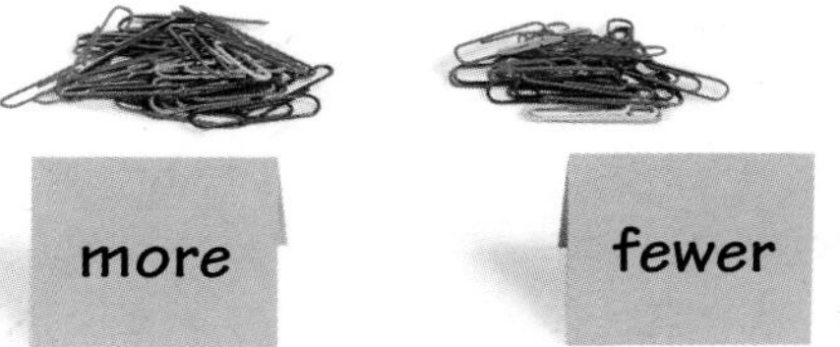

Reteaching

Comparing Measurements

10–15 MIN **Kinesthetic** SMALL GROUP

Materials *(per group)* Assorted small classroom objects of differing lengths, such as paper clips, crayons, and connecting cubes

- Demonstrate how to measure length by lining up several of one object as a measurement unit. Children use their measurement units to measure the length of the same flat surface, such as a tabletop.
- Have children compare measurements. **Which measurement unit was used least in measuring? Which was used most? Why?**
- Repeat, measuring a different piece of furniture or object. Help children to conclude that the longer the measurement unit, the fewer the units that will be needed to measure something.

Advanced Learners

Thinking About Measurement

15–20 MIN **Logical/Mathematical**

WHOLE CLASS

- Ask children which measuring object they would use if they wanted to measure the distance around the classroom. **Which tool would take the fewest number to measure the distance around?**
- Have children think about how many of each kind of object they would need to use to measure the distance from wall to wall.
- Discuss whether they would need to measure each wall to get the total distance around the classroom. **Why or why not?**
- Have children try out their solutions.

Objective Solve problems by using logical reasoning.

1 Warm Up

Activate Prior Knowledge Review how to compare lengths. Show the class a small object and a piece of chalk. **Is this object longer or shorter than my chalk?** Repeat with other classroom items.

2 Teach

Learn!

Read through the problem-solving steps together: Read and Understand, Plan and Solve, Look Back and Check.

Ongoing Assessment

Talk About It

- **What do you need to find out?** *(Whether it takes more paper clips or more cubes to measure the shoe)*
- **Which plan can you use to solve the problem?** *(Use reasoning to predict that since the cubes are shorter than the paper clips, it will take more cubes to measure the shoe.)*

If children have difficulty laying the paper clips end to end to check their predictions,

then have them hook the paper clips in chains.

Check

Error Intervention

If children make errors when deciding whether they would use more cubes or more paper clips,

then discuss the relative sizes of the cubes and clips and remind children that they will use more of the smaller unit. *(Also see Reteaching, Page 369B.)*

Think About It Ask: **Which are longer, straws or paper clips?** *(Drinking straws)* Guide children to conclude that the longer the unit of measure, the fewer the units that will be needed.

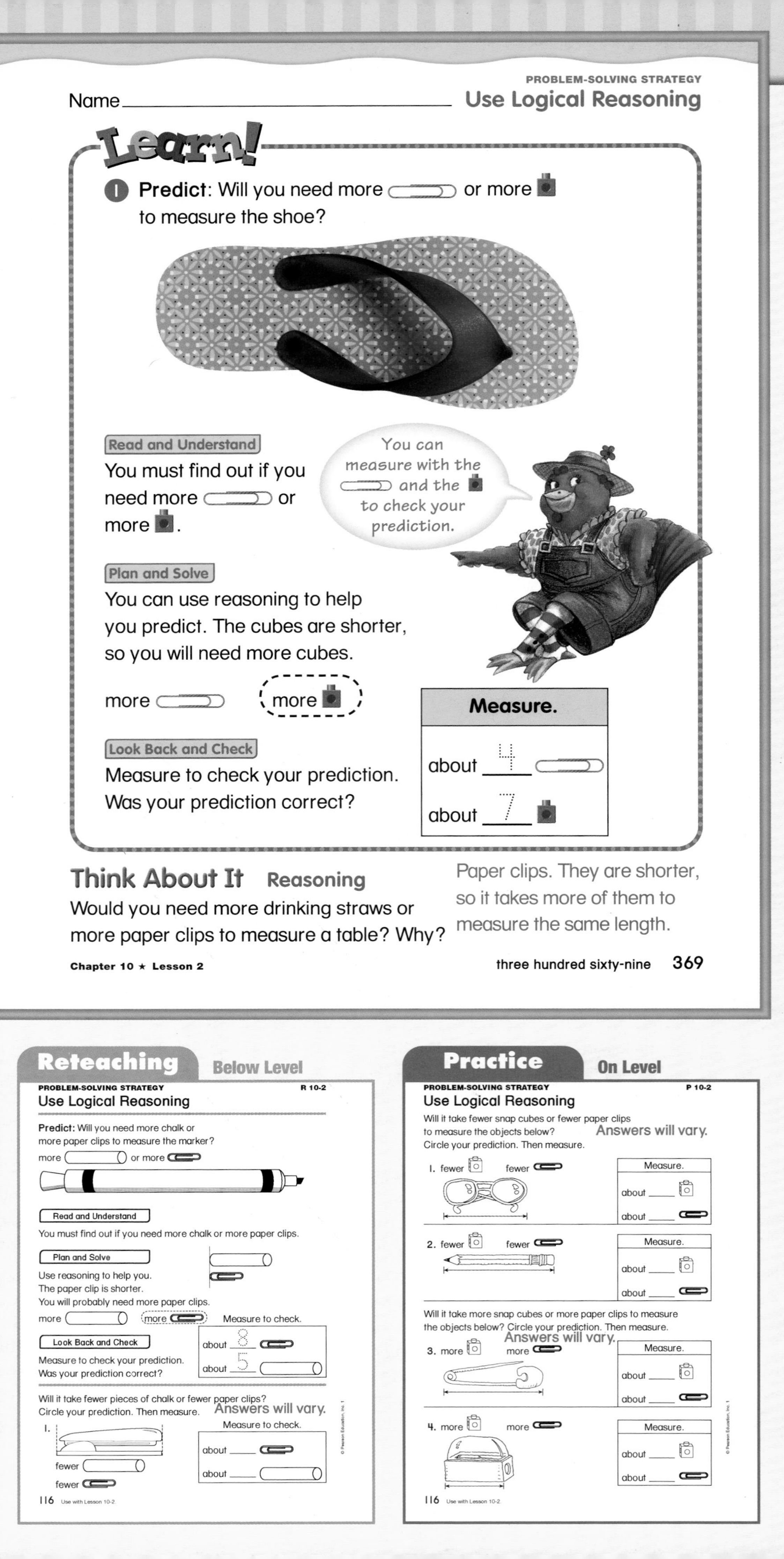

PROBLEM-SOLVING STRATEGY

Name ____________________ **Use Logical Reasoning**

Learn!

1 **Predict**: Will you need more paper clips or more cubes to measure the shoe?

Read and Understand
You must find out if you need more paper clips or more cubes.

Plan and Solve
You can use reasoning to help you predict. The cubes are shorter, so you will need more cubes.

more paper clips   (more cubes)

Look Back and Check
Measure to check your prediction. Was your prediction correct?

Measure.
about 4 paper clips
about 7 cubes

Think About It Reasoning
Would you need more drinking straws or more paper clips to measure a table? Why? *Paper clips. They are shorter, so it takes more of them to measure the same length.*

Chapter 10 ★ Lesson 2   three hundred sixty-nine 369

Reteaching Below Level

PROBLEM-SOLVING STRATEGY R 10-2
Use Logical Reasoning

Predict: Will you need more chalk or more paper clips to measure the marker?
more chalk or more paper clips

Read and Understand
You must find out if you need more chalk or more paper clips.

Plan and Solve
Use reasoning to help you.
The paper clip is shorter.
You will probably need more paper clips.
more chalk (more paper clips) Measure to check.

Look Back and Check
Measure to check your prediction.
Was your prediction correct?
about 8 paper clips
about 5 chalk

Will it take fewer pieces of chalk or fewer paper clips?
Circle your prediction. Then measure. *Answers will vary.*
1. fewer chalk / fewer paper clips — Measure to check. about ___ paper clips, about ___ chalk

116 Use with Lesson 10-2

Practice On Level

PROBLEM-SOLVING STRATEGY P 10-2
Use Logical Reasoning

Will it take fewer snap cubes or fewer paper clips to measure the objects below? *Answers will vary.*
Circle your prediction. Then measure.

1. fewer cubes fewer paper clips — Measure. about ___ cubes, about ___ paper clips
2. fewer cubes fewer paper clips — Measure. about ___ cubes, about ___ paper clips

Will it take more snap cubes or more paper clips to measure the objects below? Circle your prediction. Then measure. *Answers will vary.*

3. more cubes more paper clips — Measure. about ___ cubes, about ___ paper clips
4. more cubes more paper clips — Measure. about ___ cubes, about ___ paper clips

116 Use with Lesson 10-2

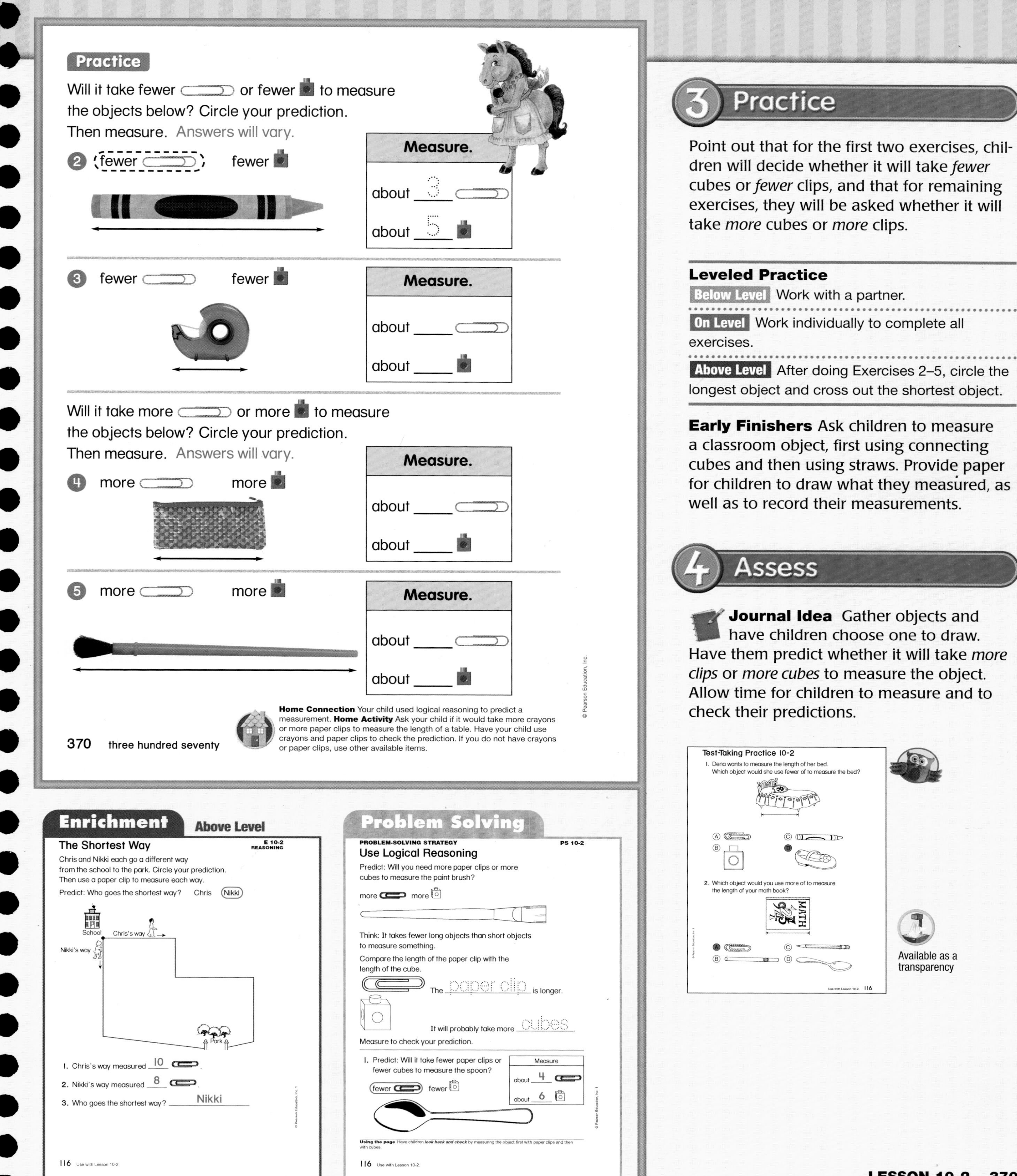

Practice

Will it take fewer [paper clips] or fewer [cubes] to measure the objects below? Circle your prediction. Then measure. Answers will vary.

2 (fewer [paper clips]) fewer [cubes]

Measure.
about 3 [paper clips]
about 5 [cubes]

3 fewer [paper clips] fewer [cubes]

Measure.
about ____ [paper clips]
about ____ [cubes]

Will it take more [paper clips] or more [cubes] to measure the objects below? Circle your prediction. Then measure. Answers will vary.

4 more [paper clips] more [cubes]

Measure.
about ____ [paper clips]
about ____ [cubes]

5 more [paper clips] more [cubes]

Measure.
about ____ [paper clips]
about ____ [cubes]

Home Connection Your child used logical reasoning to predict a measurement. **Home Activity** Ask your child if it would take more crayons or more paper clips to measure the length of a table. Have your child use crayons and paper clips to check the prediction. If you do not have crayons or paper clips, use other available items.

Enrichment Above Level

The Shortest Way

E 10-2 REASONING

Chris and Nikki each go a different way from the school to the park. Circle your prediction. Then use a paper clip to measure each way.

Predict: Who goes the shortest way? Chris (Nikki)

1. Chris's way measured 10 [paper clips].
2. Nikki's way measured 8 [paper clips].
3. Who goes the shortest way? Nikki

Problem Solving

PROBLEM-SOLVING STRATEGY PS 10-2

Use Logical Reasoning

Predict: Will you need more paper clips or more cubes to measure the paint brush?

more [paper clips] more [cubes]

Think: It takes fewer long objects than short objects to measure something.

Compare the length of the paper clip with the length of the cube.

The paper clip is longer.

It will probably take more cubes.

Measure to check your prediction.

1. Predict: Will it take fewer paper clips or fewer cubes to measure the spoon?

(fewer [paper clips]) fewer [cubes]

Measure
about 4 [paper clips]
about 6 [cubes]

Using the page Have children ***look back and check*** by measuring the object first with paper clips and then with cubes.

3 Practice

Point out that for the first two exercises, children will decide whether it will take *fewer* cubes or *fewer* clips, and that for remaining exercises, they will be asked whether it will take *more* cubes or *more* clips.

Leveled Practice

Below Level Work with a partner.

On Level Work individually to complete all exercises.

Above Level After doing Exercises 2–5, circle the longest object and cross out the shortest object.

Early Finishers Ask children to measure a classroom object, first using connecting cubes and then using straws. Provide paper for children to draw what they measured, as well as to record their measurements.

4 Assess

Journal Idea Gather objects and have children choose one to draw. Have them predict whether it will take *more clips* or *more cubes* to measure the object. Allow time for children to measure and to check their predictions.

Test-Taking Practice 10-2

1. Dena wants to measure the length of her bed. Which object would she use fewer of to measure the bed?

Ⓐ [paper clip] Ⓒ [crayon]
Ⓑ [cube] Ⓓ [shoe] (filled)

2. Which object would you use more of to measure the length of your math book?

Ⓐ [paper clip] (filled) Ⓒ [pencil]
Ⓑ [straw] Ⓓ [spoon]

Available as a transparency

10-3 Estimating and Measuring with Inches

Lesson Organizer

Quick Lesson Overview

Objective Estimate and measure the lengths of objects to the nearest inch using a ruler.

Math Understanding An inch is a standard unit used to measure length.

Vocabulary Inch

Materials for Student Pages *(per child)* Inch ruler; objects pictured on student pages or other similarly-sized classroom objects

Professional Development Note

How Children Learn Math Some children may have a difficult time counting units on a ruler when they first try. Help children make the transition from nonstandard units to standard units by first using strips cut from the Inch Grid (Teaching Tool 8) and then counting inches on a ruler.

NCTM Standards

- Number and Operations
- Measurement

(For a complete correlation to the NCTM Standards and Grades Pre-K through 2 Expectations, see Pages 363G and 363H.)

Getting Started

Spiral Review

Problem of the Day 10-3

Solve.
Betty cut her pizza into 6 pieces.
She took 2 pieces. How many more pieces could Betty take?

Topics Reviewed

- Addition and subtraction
- Problem-Solving Skill: One-Step Problem

Answer Betty can take 4 more pieces; 6 − 2 = 4, and 2 + 4 = 6.

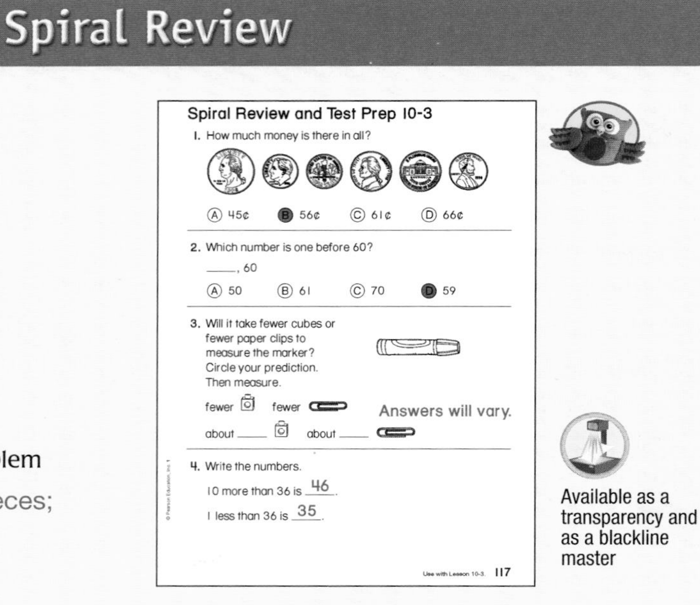

Spiral Review and Test Prep 10-3

1. How much money is there in all?

Ⓐ 45¢ Ⓑ 56¢ Ⓒ 61¢ Ⓓ 66¢

2. Which number is one before 60?

____, 60

Ⓐ 50 Ⓑ 61 Ⓒ 70 Ⓓ 59

3. Will it take fewer cubes or fewer paper clips to measure the marker? Circle your prediction. Then measure.

fewer ▢ fewer ▭ Answers will vary.

about ____ ▢ about ____ ▭

4. Write the numbers.

10 more than 36 is 46.

1 less than 36 is 35.

Use with Lesson 10-3. 117

Available as a transparency and as a blackline master

Topics Reviewed

1. Counting Sets of Coins
2. Before, After, and Between
3. Use Logical Reasoning
4. 1 More, 1 Less; 10 More, 10 Less

Investigating the Concept

Inches on a Ruler

15–20 MIN **Kinesthetic** PAIRS

Materials *(per pair)* 1-inch tile from Inch Grid (Teaching Tool 8); 12-inch ruler; small classroom objects

What to Do

- Ask one partner to place the square tile on top of the ruler, making sure that the end of the square meets the end mark, the 0, on the ruler. Help children see that one tile measures 1 inch on the ruler. Explain that an inch is a unit used to measure length. Point out the inches on the ruler.
- Draw a 9-inch line on the board. Ask children to estimate the length of the line. Show children how to measure it, lining up the end mark of the ruler with one end of the line. Then ask partners to estimate, measure, and record the lengths of other objects.

Ongoing Assessment

- **Number Sense** **How many inches are marked on the ruler you are using?** *(Answers will vary.)*
- **Do you think that your pencil is shorter than 1 inch or longer than 1 inch?** *(Longer than 1 inch)*

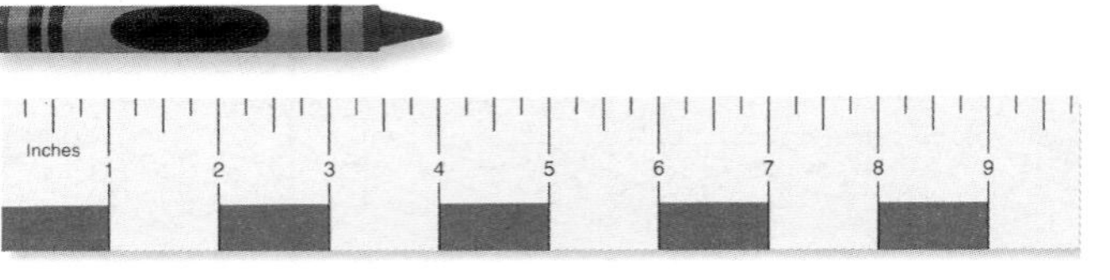

Reaching All Learners

Math Vocabulary

Measuring in Inches

10–15 MIN **Kinesthetic/Linguistic**

Materials Classroom objects; *(per child)* 12-inch ruler

- Draw a chart on the board. List each object in the first column. Label the second column "Estimate" and the third column "Measure."
- Demonstrate how to estimate inches using a thumb.
- Have children use their thumbs to estimate the length of each classroom object. Write their estimates in the chart.
- Identify inches on the ruler. Help children use rulers to measure each object in inches. Ask children to fill in inch measurements in the "Measure" column. Then have them compare the estimates to the measurements.

Access Content

English Language Learners

Understanding Inches

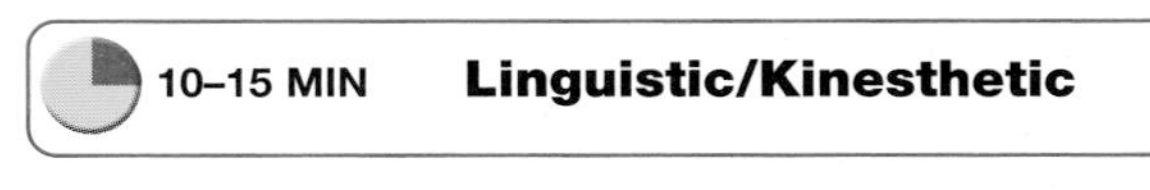

10–15 MIN **Linguistic/Kinesthetic**

Materials *(per pair)* 12-inch ruler; assorted classroom objects, some of which measure exactly 1 inch; 3 index cards labeled "shorter than 1 inch," "1 inch," and "longer than 1 inch"

- Have children work in pairs to measure their objects with a ruler.
- Invite children to determine which objects are shorter than 1 inch, 1 inch, or longer than 1 inch and have them place the objects into the three groups. Ask children to label each of the groups.

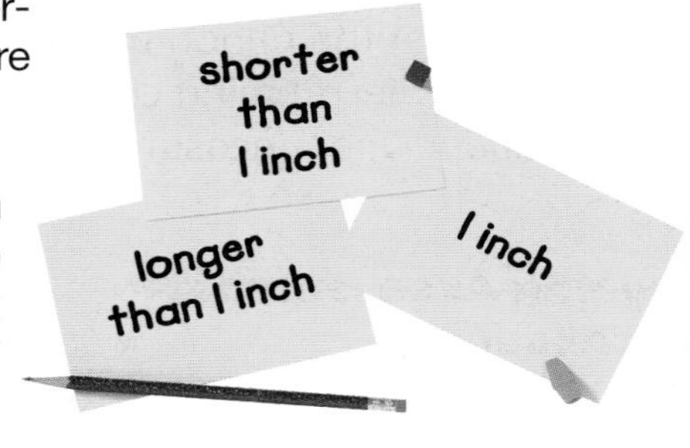

Reteaching

Ruler Practice

10–15 MIN **Kinesthetic**

PAIRS

Materials *(per pair)* 12-inch ruler; 1-inch squares from Inch Grid (Teaching Tool 8); classroom objects

- Demonstrate how to measure an object by lining up 1-inch squares alongside the object. Write the measurement in inches on the board.
- Then show how you can measure the same object using a 12-inch ruler. **Why do you get the same answer?**
- Have pairs work together to measure different objects in both ways and to compare the answers.

Math and Health

How Tall Am I?

15–20 MIN **Kinesthetic**

Materials Chart paper; tape; marker; 12-inch rulers

- Tape a piece of chart paper to the wall. Mark a line for each child's height on the paper.
- **What do you think will happen to your height in 1 month? in six months?**
- Take measurements monthly throughout the year. As each measurement is recorded, have children calculate their growth in inches and compare their actual growth to their predictions.

Objective Estimate and measure the lengths of objects to the nearest inch using a ruler.

1 Warm Up

Activate Prior Knowledge Review how to estimate and measure length using nonstandard units. Have children work in pairs to estimate and measure classroom objects using crayons.

2 Teach

Learn!

Call attention to the ruler and the ribbon at the top of the student page. Explain that an inch is a unit used to measure length. Help children see that the ribbon measures about 1 inch on the ruler. Remind children to use the term *about* when measurements are not exact.

Ongoing Assessment

Talk About It

- **Do you think that 1 inch is a good estimate for the length of your thumb? Why?** *(Yes; a thumb is about as long as the ribbon, and the ribbon measures about 1 inch.)*
- **Which other objects are about 1 inch long?** *(Sample answers: Paper clip, eraser, coat button)*

If children have difficulty estimating the length of their thumbs,

then have them use an inch tile to help.

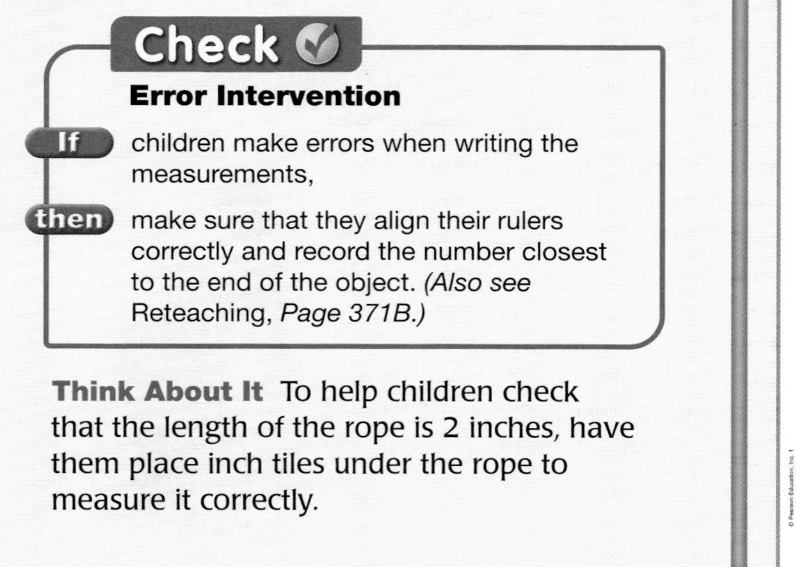

Check

Error Intervention

If children make errors when writing the measurements,

then make sure that they align their rulers correctly and record the number closest to the end of the object. *(Also see* Reteaching, *Page 371B.)*

Think About It To help children check that the length of the rope is 2 inches, have them place inch tiles under the rope to measure it correctly.

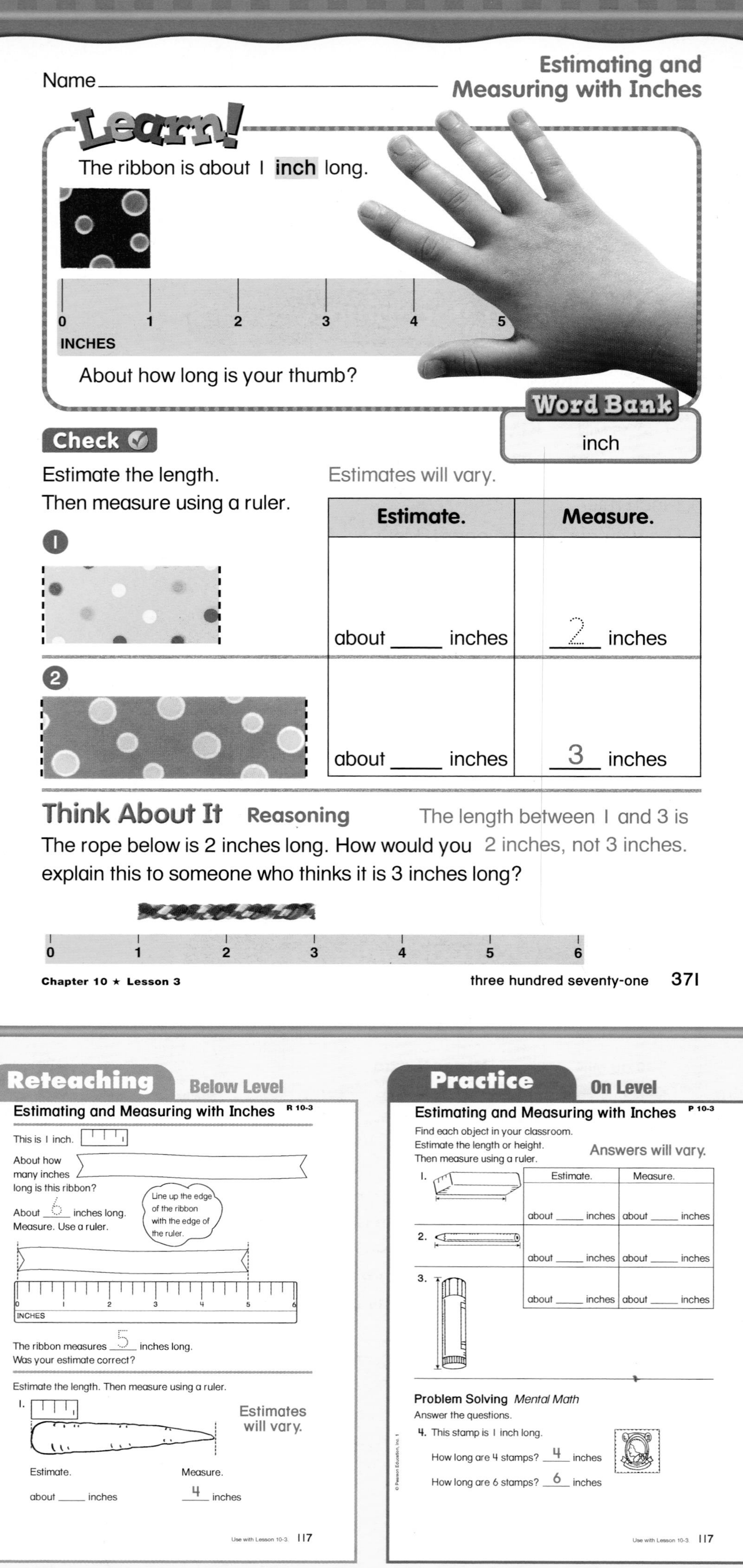

Name ____________________

Estimating and Measuring with Inches

Learn!

The ribbon is about 1 inch long.

About how long is your thumb?

Word Bank
inch

Check

Estimate the length.
Then measure using a ruler.

Estimates will vary.

	Estimate.	Measure.
1	about ____ inches	2 inches
2	about ____ inches	3 inches

Think About It Reasoning

The rope below is 2 inches long. How would you explain this to someone who thinks it is 3 inches long?

The length between 1 and 3 is 2 inches, not 3 inches.

Chapter 10 ★ Lesson 3 three hundred seventy-one 371

Reteaching Below Level

Estimating and Measuring with Inches R 10-3

This is 1 inch.

About how many inches long is this ribbon?

About 6 inches long.
Measure. Use a ruler.

Line up the edge of the ribbon with the edge of the ruler.

The ribbon measures 5 inches long.
Was your estimate correct?

Estimate the length. Then measure using a ruler.

1. Estimates will vary.

Estimate. about ____ inches

Measure. 4 inches

© Pearson Education, Inc. 1

Use with Lesson 10-3. 117

Practice On Level

Estimating and Measuring with Inches P 10-3

Find each object in your classroom.
Estimate the length or height.
Then measure using a ruler.

Answers will vary.

	Estimate.	Measure.
1.	about ____ inches	about ____ inches
2.	about ____ inches	about ____ inches
3.	about ____ inches	about ____ inches

Problem Solving *Mental Math*

Answer the questions.

4. This stamp is 1 inch long.

How long are 4 stamps? 4 inches

How long are 6 stamps? 6 inches

© Pearson Education, Inc. 1

Use with Lesson 10-3. 117

Practice

Find each object in your classroom. Estimate the length or height. Then measure using a ruler. Answers will vary.

	Estimate.	Measure.
3	about ____ inches	about ____ inches
4	about ____ inches	about ____ inches
5	about ____ inches	about ____ inches
6	about ____ inches	about ____ inches

Problem Solving Mental Math

7 Answer the questions.

This [bead] is 1 inch long.

How long are 3 [beads]? 3 inches

How long are 5 [beads]? 5 inches

Home Connection Your child estimated and then measured objects using inches. **Home Activity** Ask your child to estimate how many inches his or her shoe will measure. Then have your child check the estimate by measuring with a ruler.

Enrichment Above Level

The Inchworm E 10-3 VISUAL THINKING

Each move the inchworm makes is 1 inch long.
The path the inchworm made is shown.
Draw another path the inchworm could have made.
Make it equal in length to the path in the box.

1. Check that children's drawings are 6 inches.

2. Check that children's drawings are 8 inches.

Use with Lesson 10-3. 117

Problem Solving

Estimating and Measuring with Inches PS 10-3

This ▭ is 1 inch long. Read each story.
Estimate where the cut should be and draw a blue line. Then measure using a ruler and draw a red line.

Estimates will vary.

1. Dan is making a bookmark. He needs a piece of paper 4 inches long.

2. Rita needs a piece of ribbon 6 inches long.

3. Sally needs a string 5 inches long.

4. Ken is stringing beads for a necklace.
Each bead is 1 inch long.
How long is the necklace after Ken strings 5 beads?
5 inches
How long is the necklace after he strings 11 beads?
11 inches

Use with Lesson 10-3. 117

3 Practice

For Exercises 3–6, provide actual items for children to measure.

Reading Assist: Make Judgments Ask children to make a judgment about what they need to know in order to estimate the length in inches of each object in Exercises 3–6.

Leveled Practice

Below Level Use inch tiles and rulers to complete Exercises 3–6.

On Level Complete all exercises as written.

Above Level After completing Exercise 6, find an object that is about the same height.

Early Finishers Distribute pencils of three different lengths. Ask children to draw the pencils and then to measure each with a ruler.

4 Assess

Journal Idea Challenge children to find and measure three small objects in the room. Then have them list the objects in order from shortest to longest.

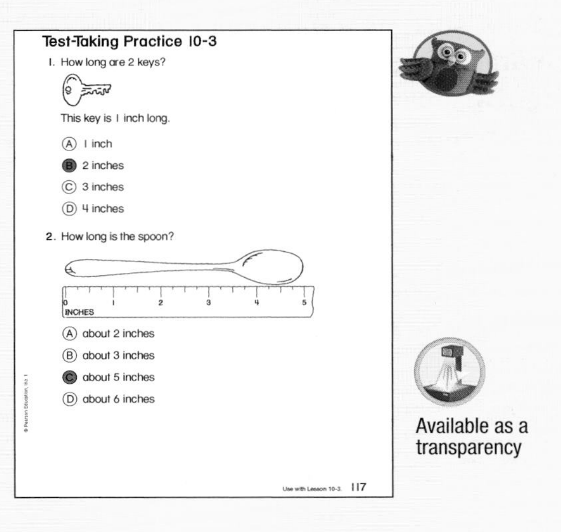

Test-Taking Practice 10-3

1. How long are 2 keys?
This key is 1 inch long.
Ⓐ 1 inch
● 2 inches
Ⓒ 3 inches
Ⓓ 4 inches

2. How long is the spoon?
Ⓐ about 2 inches
Ⓑ about 3 inches
● about 5 inches
Ⓓ about 6 inches

Use with Lesson 10-3. 117

Available as a transparency

10-4 Estimating and Measuring with Feet

Lesson Organizer

Quick Lesson Overview 

Objective Estimate and measure the length or height of objects to the nearest foot using a 12-inch ruler.

Math Understanding A foot is a 12-inch standard unit used to measure length.

Vocabulary Foot (feet)

Materials for Student Pages *(per child)* 12-inch ruler; objects pictured on student pages or other similarly-sized classroom objects

Math Monsters Videos Use Episode 2: *Measurement* with or anytime after Lesson 10-4.

Professional Development Note

Math Background It is helpful to provide children with referents for different units, such as a paper clip for an inch and a folder for a foot, to help them visualize units of measure when estimating lengths.

NCTM Standards

- Number and Operations
- Measurement

(For a complete correlation to the NCTM Standards and Grades Pre-K through 2 Expectations, see Pages 363G and 363H.)

Getting Started

Spiral Review

Problem of the Day 10-4

Ellen drew a square.
Ellen's shape has 1 more side than which of these shapes?

Shape A Shape B Shape C

Topics Reviewed
- Plane shapes
- Problem-Solving Skill: One-Step Problem

Answer Shape B; a square has one more side than a triangle.

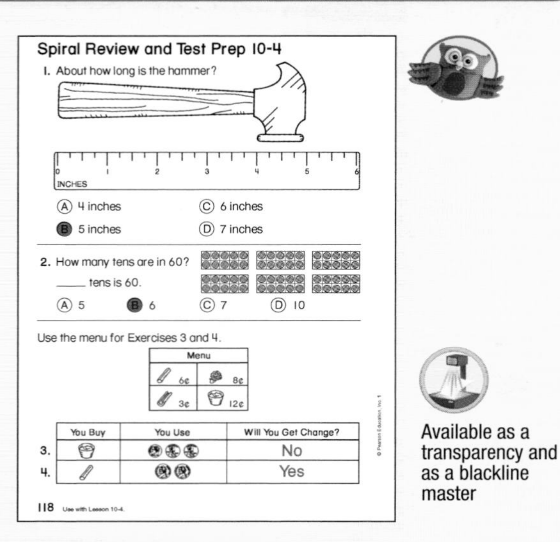

Spiral Review and Test Prep 10-4

1. About how long is the hammer?

INCHES

Ⓐ 4 inches Ⓒ 6 inches
Ⓑ 5 inches Ⓓ 7 inches

2. How many tens are in 60?

____ tens is 60.

Ⓐ 5 Ⓑ 6 Ⓒ 7 Ⓓ 10

Use the menu for Exercises 3 and 4.

	You Buy	You Use	Will You Get Change?
3.			No
4.			Yes

118

Available as a transparency and as a blackline master

Topics Reviewed
1. Estimating and Measuring with Inches
2. Numbers Made with Tens
3–4. Use Data from a Table

Investigating the Concept

How Many Feet?

Materials *(per pair)* 12-inch ruler

What to Do

- Point out the 12 inches on the ruler and explain that 12 inches is a measure we call 1 foot.
- Have children name things in the room that they think are about 1 foot in length or width. List their ideas on the board. Ask pairs to find an object that is about 1 foot long and to use their rulers to check their estimates.
- Demonstrate how to measure objects that are at least 2 feet long. Emphasize that the word *feet* is used to refer to more than 1 foot.

Ongoing Assessment

- **Reasoning Is a notebook about 1 inch or about 1 foot long? How do you know?** *(1 foot; 1 inch is too small to be the length of a notebook.)*
- **How many inches are equal to 1 foot?** *(12 inches)*

Reaching All Learners

Math Vocabulary

Inches or Feet?

10–15 MIN **Kinesthetic/Linguistic**

Materials 12-inch ruler; chart paper; marker

- Hold up a ruler and use it to show children 1 inch and 1 foot.
- Have children list classroom items that they can measure. For each item, ask the class if it would be better to measure the item in inches or in feet.
- As an item is mentioned, have a child measure it and report whether the class was correct in its choice.

Inches	Feet
pencil	bookcase
pen	chalkboard
book	door
eraser	

Activate Prior Knowledge/Build Background

English Language Learners

12 Inches = 1 Foot

Materials *(per pair)* 12-inch ruler; 1-inch squares cut from Inch Grid (Teaching Tool 8); folder

- Review how to measure objects using inches.
- Have pairs use the 1-inch squares to measure the longer side of a folder. **How many do you need?** *(About 12)*
- Hold up a ruler. Have children measure the folder using the 12-inch ruler. **How many rulers do you need?** *(1)*
- **How many 1-inch squares do you need to equal the length of the ruler?** *(12)*
- Explain that 12 inches is the same as a measure called 1 *foot.*

Reteaching

Putting Feet in Order

10–15 MIN **Kinesthetic**

Materials *(per group)* 12-inch ruler

- Make a list of classroom items, such as table, folder, bookcase, desk, bulletin board.
- Remind children that a ruler is 1 *foot* long and that *feet* means more than 1 foot.
- Show children how to use a ruler to measure length.
- Have children work in groups to measure each item and to write measurements on the list. Ask children to order the objects by size, draw pictures, and label them.

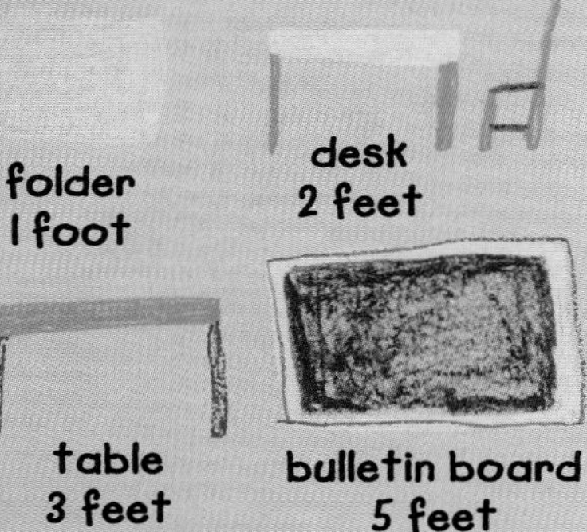

Students with Special Needs

Less Than 1 Foot/More Than 1 Foot

10–15 MIN **Kinesthetic**

Materials *(per pair)* 12-inch ruler; crayons

- Help pairs of children make lists of classroom objects and furniture to measure.
- Read the list with children and circle the items that they estimate are more than 1 foot long or 1 foot high.
- Review how to use a ruler. Invite children to move around the room using their rulers to measure the listed objects. Have children check that their circled items are in fact more than 1 foot long/high.

Objective Estimate and measure the length or height of objects to the nearest foot using a 12-inch ruler.

1 Warm Up

Activate Prior Knowledge Review how to estimate and measure using inches. Measure three different-sized crayons. Remind children to match one end of the ruler with one end of the crayon and to record the number closest to the other end of the crayon.

2 Teach

Learn!

Distribute 12-inch rulers. Explain that 12 inches is a measure that we call a foot. Note that the ruler shown on the student page is not really the size of a 12-inch ruler. Then introduce the term *feet* and demonstrate how to use the ruler to measure objects longer than 1 foot.

Ongoing Assessment

Talk About It

- **Which is the longer unit of measure: a foot or an inch?** *(A foot)* **How do you know?** *(It takes 12 inches to make 1 foot.)*
- **If I measure 1 foot and 1 foot, what is the total measure that I have?** *(2 feet)*

If children confuse the terms *foot* and *feet*,

then make a chart that says "1 foot, 2 feet, 3 feet, 4 feet, 5 feet" and read it together.

Check

Error Intervention

If children make errors when measuring,

then have them mark each foot that they measure with tape and check their counting. *(Also* see Reteaching, *Page 373B.)*

Think About It Discuss why it would be a good idea to measure long distances with the longer unit of measure.

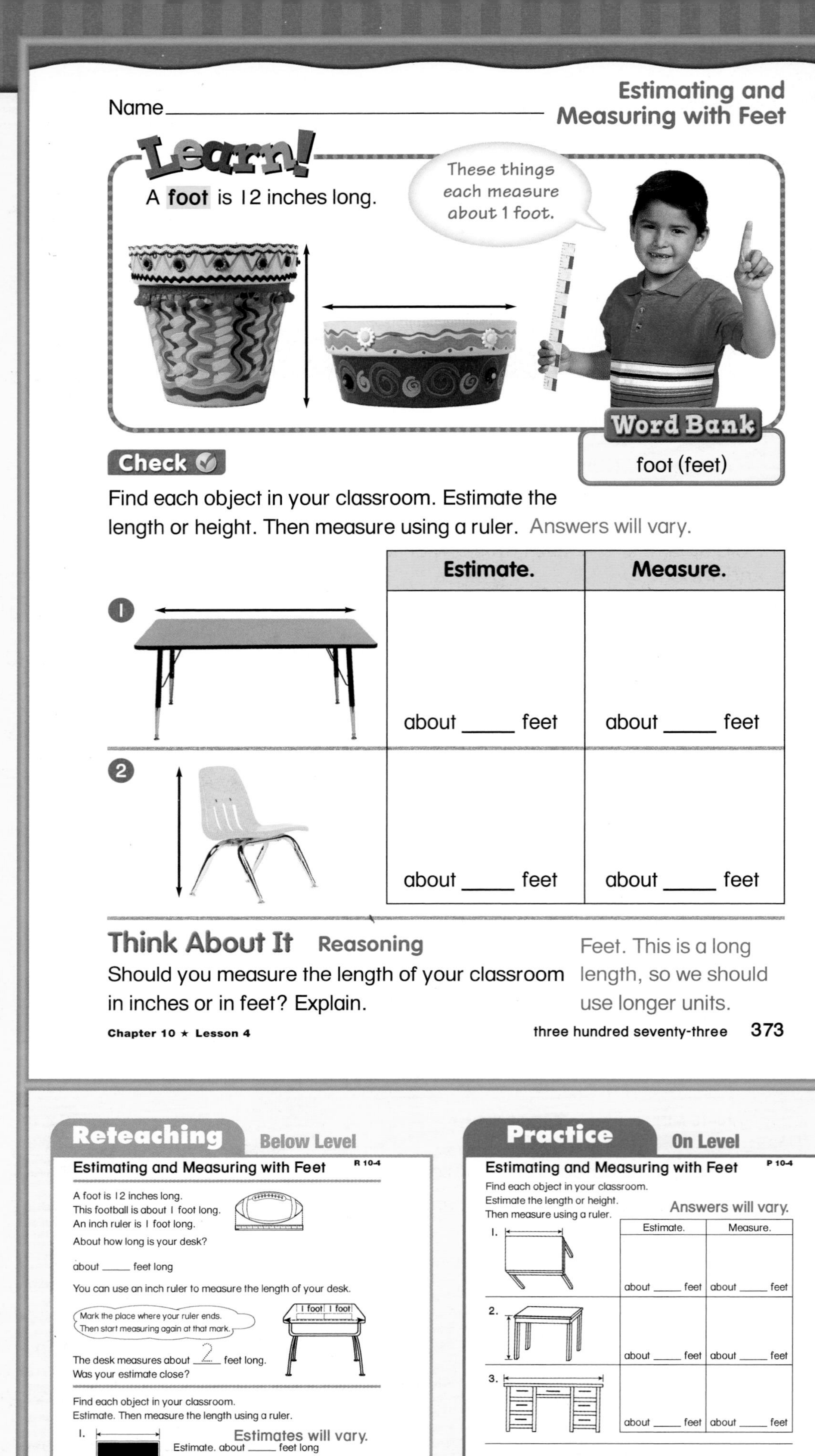

Name ____________________

Estimating and Measuring with Feet

Learn!

A **foot** is 12 inches long.

Word Bank

foot (feet)

Check

Find each object in your classroom. Estimate the length or height. Then measure using a ruler. Answers will vary.

	Estimate.	Measure.
1	about ____ feet	about ____ feet
2	about ____ feet	about ____ feet

Think About It Reasoning

Should you measure the length of your classroom in inches or in feet? Explain.

Feet. This is a long length, so we should use longer units.

Chapter 10 ★ Lesson 4   three hundred seventy-three   373

Reteaching Below Level

Estimating and Measuring with Feet R 10-4

A foot is 12 inches long.
This football is about 1 foot long.
An inch ruler is 1 foot long.
About how long is your desk?

about _____ feet long

You can use an inch ruler to measure the length of your desk.

The desk measures about __2__ feet long.
Was your estimate close?

Find each object in your classroom.
Estimate. Then measure the length using a ruler.

Estimates will vary.

1. Estimate. about _____ feet long
Measure. about _____ feet long

2. Estimate. about _____ feet long
Measure. about _____ feet long

© Pearson Education, Inc. 1

118 Use with Lesson 10-4.

Practice On Level

Estimating and Measuring with Feet P 10-4

Find each object in your classroom.
Estimate the length or height.
Then measure using a ruler.

Answers will vary.

	Estimate.	Measure.
1.	about _____ feet	about _____ feet
2.	about _____ feet	about _____ feet
3.	about _____ feet	about _____ feet

Problem Solving *Reasonableness*

4. About how long might each object be?
Circle the better estimate.

about 3 inches (about 3 feet) | about 2 inches (about 2 feet)

5. Draw a box around the shorter object.

© Pearson Education, Inc. 1

118 Use with Lesson 10-4.

Practice

Find each object in your classroom.
Estimate the length or height.
Then measure using a ruler. Answers will vary.

	Estimate.	Measure.
3	about ____ feet	about ____ feet
4	about ____ feet	about ____ feet
5 1+1=2	about ____ feet	about ____ feet

Problem Solving Reasonableness

About how tall might each object be?

6 Circle the better estimate.

(about 4 feet) (circled)
about 4 inches

about 5 inches
(about 5 feet) (circled)

7 Draw a box around the taller object.

Home Connection Your child estimated and then measured items using a ruler. **Home Activity** Ask your child to find an item in the house that is about 4 feet long. Together, measure the item.

3 Practice

Remind children that they will be estimating and then using a ruler to measure each item.

Reading Assist: Vocabulary Take this opportunity to distinguish between the meanings of *foot* and *feet*. Use each word in a sentence. Have children tell whether the word refers to a unit of measure or to a body part.

Leveled Practice

Below Level Work in pairs.

On Level Work individually to complete all exercises.

Above Level Find another object that is about the same height as the bookshelf in Exercise 3.

Early Finishers Challenge children to measure their own feet using 12-inch rulers. Have each child record whether his or her foot is longer or shorter than the ruler.

4 Assess

Journal Idea Have children draw three things they might measure using inches and three things they might measure using feet.

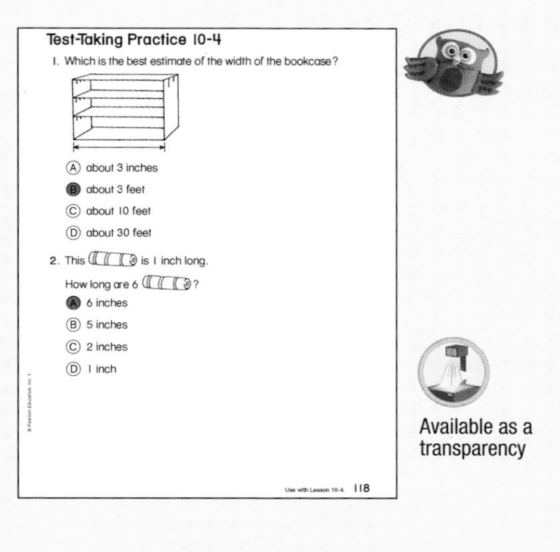

Test-Taking Practice 10-4

1. Which is the best estimate of the width of the bookcase?

Ⓐ about 3 inches
● about 3 feet
Ⓒ about 10 feet
Ⓓ about 30 feet

2. This is 1 inch long.
How long are 6 ?

● 6 inches
Ⓑ 5 inches
Ⓒ 2 inches
Ⓓ 1 inch

Use with Lesson 10-4. 118

Available as a transparency

Enrichment Above Level

A Foot or More? E 10-4 VISUAL THINKING

Follow each line. Is it longer or shorter than a foot?
Estimate, then measure. Use a ruler. Estimates will vary.

	Estimate	Measure
1.	longer / shorter	longer / (shorter)
2.	longer / shorter	(longer) / shorter
3.	longer / shorter	(longer) / shorter

118 Use with Lesson 10-4.

Problem Solving

Estimating and Measuring with Feet PS 10-4

Estimate the length or height. Answers will vary.
Then ask a friend to help you measure using a ruler.

1. How tall are you?
Stand next to a wall.
Have a friend mark your height to measure.
Estimate: I am about ____ feet tall.
Measure: I am ____ feet tall.

2. What is the length of a friend's arm?
Have your friend hold up his or her arm to measure.
Estimate:
My friend's arm is about ____ feet.
Measure:
My friend's arm is ____ feet.

3. About how tall might each object be?
Circle the better estimate.
(about 10 feet) about 10 inches
(about 3 feet) about 3 inches

4. Circle the object that is shorter.

118 Use with Lesson 10-4.

10-5 Estimating and Measuring with Centimeters

Lesson Organizer

Quick Lesson Overview

Objective Estimate and measure the length of objects in centimeters using a ruler.

Math Understanding A centimeter is a standard unit used to measure length.

Vocabulary Centimeter

Materials for Student Pages
(per child) Centimeter ruler; objects pictured on student pages or other similarly-sized classroom objects

Professional Development Note

How Children Learn Math
Centimeters are very small units for young children to count and use for measuring. Some children may need help understanding what 1 centimeter is and should be given many opportunities to compare the lengths of small objects to 1 centimeter.

NCTM Standards

- Number and Operations
- Measurement

(For a complete correlation to the NCTM Standards and Grades Pre-K through 2 Expectations, see Pages 363G and 363H.)

Getting Started

Spiral Review

Problem of the Day 10-5

Martin and Jill are reading the same book. Martin is near the middle and is on page 20. Jill is near the end. What page could she be on?

Topics Reviewed

- Number sense
- Problem-Solving Strategy: Use Logical Reasoning

Answer Accept reasonable answers. Since page 20 is the near the middle of the book, there are about 40 pages in the book. Jill could be on any page from 35 to 45.

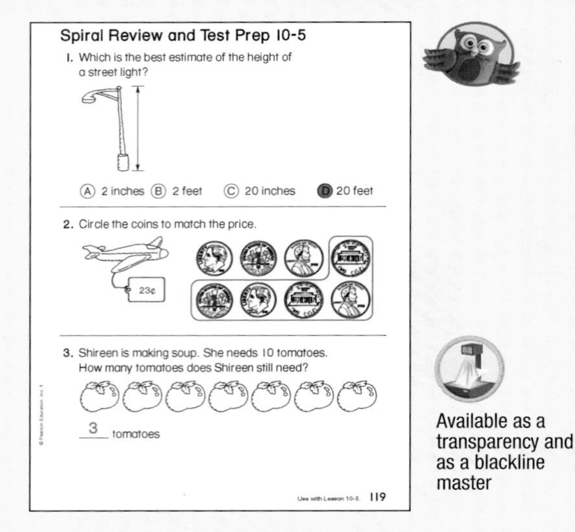
Spiral Review and Test Prep 10-5

1. Which is the best estimate of the height of a street light?

Ⓐ 2 inches Ⓑ 2 feet Ⓒ 20 inches Ⓓ 20 feet

2. Circle the coins to match the price.

23¢

3. Shireen is making soup. She needs 10 tomatoes. How many tomatoes does Shireen still need?

3 tomatoes

Use with Lesson 10-5. 119

Available as a transparency and as a blackline master

Topics Reviewed

1. Estimating and Measuring with Feet
2. Dime
3. Sums of 10

Investigating the Concept

Centimeters on a Ruler

15–20 MIN | Kinesthetic | PAIRS

Materials *(per pair)* Centimeter Grid (Teaching Tool 7); centimeter ruler; scissors; assorted small classroom objects

What to Do

- Explain that a centimeter is a unit used to measure length. Have children cut out and place a 1-centimeter square on the ruler. **Which numbers on the ruler are at each end of the square?** *(0 and 1)*
- Compare the centimeter squares to the ruler. Point out that each square measures 1 centimeter on the centimeter ruler.
- Remind children to use the term *about* when an object is not an exact number of centimeters. Have pairs of children measure assorted objects.

Ongoing Assessment

- **Reasoning** **Why would it be difficult to write with a pencil that was 3 centimeters long?** *(It would be too small to hold.)*
- **Would an ant be about 1 centimeter long or about 8 centimeters long?** *(About 1 centimeter long)*

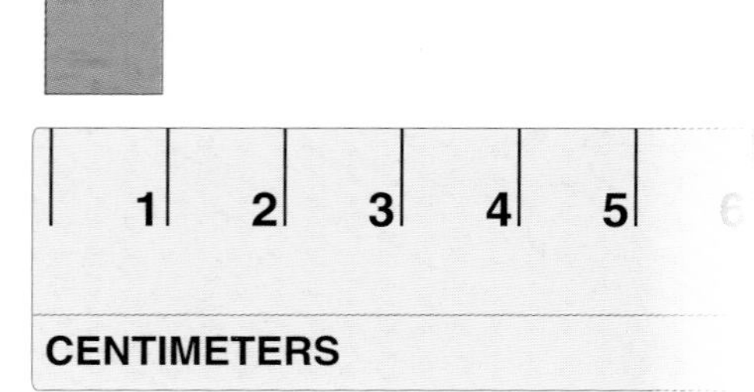

Reaching All Learners

Oral Language in Math

Comparing Measurements

10–15 MIN **Kinesthetic**

Materials *(per child)* Classroom objects of any size; string cut into 30-centimeter pieces

- Give each child an object and a length of string.
- Have children compare the length of the object to the length of string. Explain that the string is 30 centimeters long.
- Discuss whether the string is too long, too short, or just right. **Is the object longer than, shorter than, or equal to 30 centimeters?**
- Have children trade objects and repeat the activity.

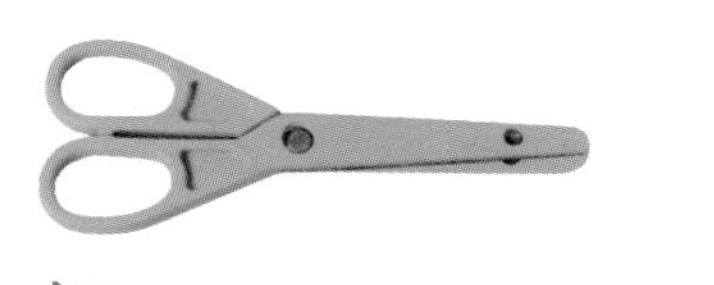

Activate Prior Knowledge/Build Background

English Language Learners

Closest To

10–15 MIN **Kinesthetic/Linguistic**

Materials Centimeter ruler; small objects; 3 index cards labeled "centimeter," "inch," and "foot"

- Remind children that they have measured objects in *inches* and *feet.* Explain that *centimeters* are even smaller units.
- Distribute various objects. Have children work together to measure the objects and to decide if they are *about* 1 centimeter, 1 inch, or 1 foot.
- Have children place the objects next to the card with the correct label.

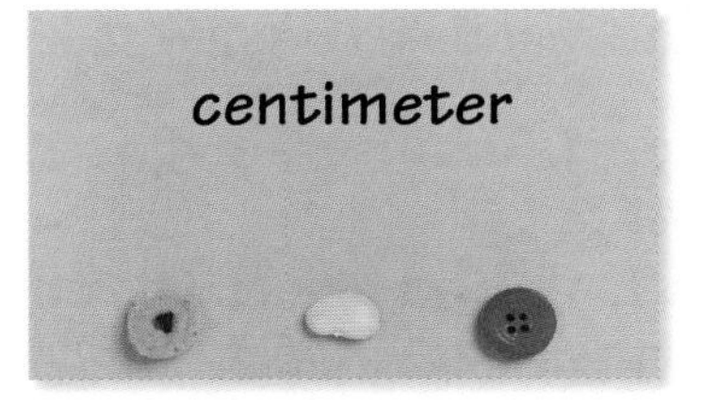

Reteaching

Ordering by Centimeters

10–15 MIN **Kinesthetic**

INDIVIDUAL

Materials *(per child)* Small classroom objects of varying sizes; centimeter ruler

- Distribute rulers and help children identify 1 centimeter. Demonstrate how to use the ruler to measure something in centimeters.
- Have children measure a variety of small objects in centimeters and put them in order from shortest to longest.
- Show children how use their rulers to draw lines the length of each object.

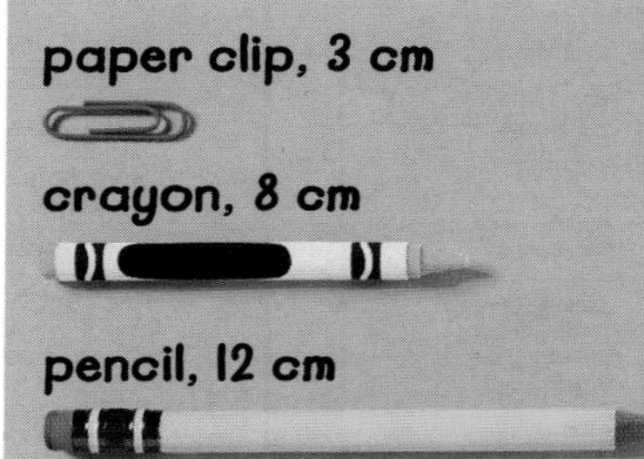

Advanced Learners

Mapping to Scale

15–20 MIN **Logical/Mathematical**

PAIRS

Materials *(per pair)* Centimeter ruler; 12-inch ruler

- Tell children that they are going to draw a map of the classroom.
- Explain that maps use small units of measure to represent objects measured in larger units.
- Have pairs measure the length of the classroom in feet.
- Show children how to draw one side of the room on paper. Explain how to make each centimeter on paper equal to 1 foot in the classroom.
- Repeat with all sides of the room.

Objective Estimate and measure the length of objects in centimeters using a ruler.

1 Warm Up

Activate Prior Knowledge Review how to use an inch ruler. Invite volunteers to use rulers to draw lines on the board that are about 1 inch, 6 inches, and 1 foot long.

2 Teach

Learn!

Give children centimeter rulers. Explain that a centimeter is a unit of measure. Note that a centimeter is smaller than an inch. Demonstrate how to use a centimeter ruler to measure small objects. Discuss *about* how long the blueberry measures and about how long the mandarin orange section measures.

Ongoing Assessment

Talk About It

- **How long is an object if its end is near 8 on the ruler?** *(About 8 centimeters long)*
- **Why do we say that the orange section is *about* 3 centimeters long?** *(It is very close to 3 centimeters, but not exactly 3 centimeters.)*

If children have difficulty measuring the blueberry and the orange section,

then have them work with partners.

Check

Error Intervention

If children make errors measuring,

then make sure they are lining up their rulers correctly when they measure. *(Also see* Reteaching, *Page 375B.)*

Think About It Discuss things that are longer than 1 centimeter. Extend the conversation by having children identify things in the room that are between 2 and 10 centimeters long.

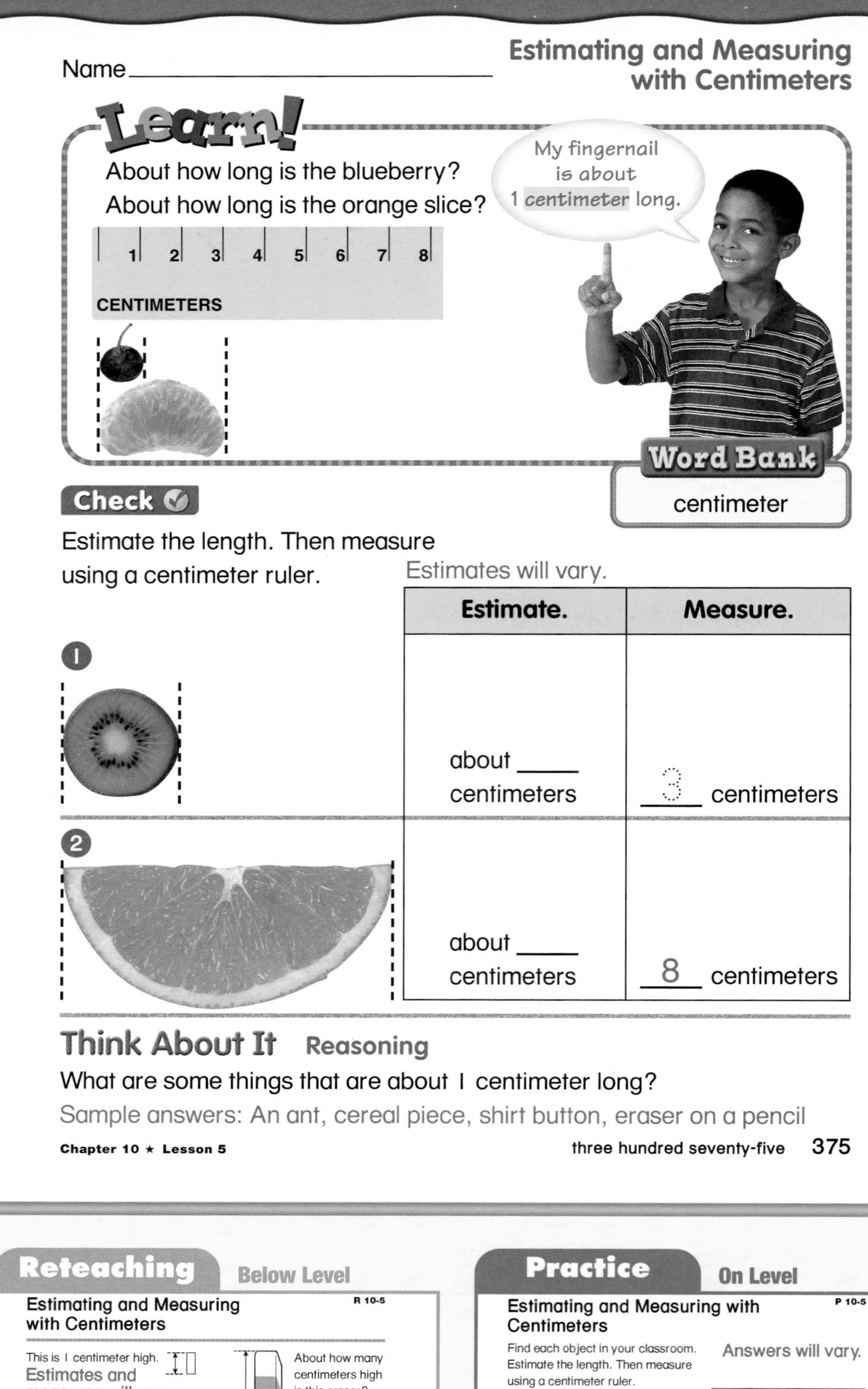

Name ______________________

Estimating and Measuring with Centimeters

Learn!

About how long is the blueberry?
About how long is the orange slice?

Word Bank
centimeter

Check

Estimate the length. Then measure using a centimeter ruler. Estimates will vary.

	Estimate.	Measure.
1	about ____ centimeters	3 centimeters
2	about ____ centimeters	8 centimeters

Think About It Reasoning

What are some things that are about 1 centimeter long?
Sample answers: An ant, cereal piece, shirt button, eraser on a pencil

Chapter 10 ★ Lesson 5 three hundred seventy-five 375

Reteaching Below Level

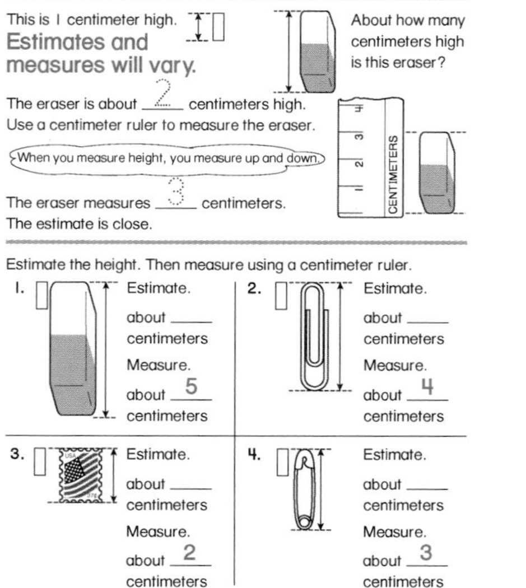

Estimating and Measuring with Centimeters R 10-5

This is 1 centimeter high.
Estimates and measures will vary.

About how many centimeters high is this eraser?

The eraser is about 2 centimeters high.
Use a centimeter ruler to measure the eraser.

When you measure height, you measure up and down.

The eraser measures 3 centimeters.
The estimate is close.

Estimate the height. Then measure using a centimeter ruler.

1. Estimate. about ____ centimeters. Measure. about 5 centimeters
2. Estimate. about ____ centimeters. Measure. about 4 centimeters
3. Estimate. about ____ centimeters. Measure. about 2 centimeters
4. Estimate. about ____ centimeters. Measure. about 3 centimeters

© Pearson Education, Inc. 1

Use with Lesson 10-5. 119

Practice On Level

Estimating and Measuring with Centimeters P 10-5

Find each object in your classroom. Estimate the length. Then measure using a centimeter ruler. Answers will vary.

	Estimate.	Measure.
1.	about ____ centimeters	about ____ centimeters
2.	about ____ centimeters	about ____ centimeters
3.	about ____ centimeters	about ____ centimeters

Problem Solving *Reasonableness*

Are these objects taller or shorter than 10 centimeters? Circle the better choice.

4. (taller than 10 centimeters) shorter than 10 centimeters
5. taller than 10 centimeters (shorter than 10 centimeters)

© Pearson Education, Inc. 1

Use with Lesson 10-5. 119

Practice

Find each object in your classroom. Estimate the length.
Then measure using a centimeter ruler. Answers will vary.

	Estimate.	Measure.
3	about ____ centimeters	about ____ centimeters
4	about ____ centimeters	about ____ centimeters
5	about ____ centimeters	about ____ centimeters
6	about ____ centimeters	about ____ centimeters

Problem Solving Reasonableness

Are these objects taller or shorter than 10 centimeters?
Circle the better choice.

7. (taller than 10 centimeters) shorter than 10 centimeters

8. taller than 10 centimeters (shorter than 10 centimeters)

Home Connection Your child estimated and then measured objects using a centimeter ruler. **Home Activity** Have your child collect small objects and then ask him or her to measure the objects using a centimeter ruler.

Enrichment Above Level

Measure It! E 10-5 ESTIMATION

This is 5 centimeters long.

Estimate if each length is more or less than 5 centimeters. Color a balloon to show your answer.
Then measure.

	More than 5 centimeters	Less than 5 centimeters	Measure
1.			6 centimeters
2.			4 centimeters
3.			2 centimeters
4.			6 centimeters
5.			4 centimeters

Use with Lesson 10-5. 119

Problem Solving

Estimating and Measuring with Centimeters PS 10-5

Draw lines from the star to each dot by the animals. Then answer the questions. Use a centimeter ruler to measure. Sample answers given.

Start here.

1. Estimate which pet is 10 centimeters from the star. Then measure. Was your estimate correct? cat — yes no
2. Estimate which pet is 2 centimeters from the star. Then measure. Was your estimate correct? hamster — yes no
3. Estimate which pet is 6 centimeters from the star. Then measure. Was your estimate correct? bird — yes no

Use with Lesson 10-5. 119

3 Practice

Consider having children work in pairs or small groups for Exercises 3–6.

Reading Assist: Compare and Contrast Have children compare and contrast a centimeter square and an inch square.

Leveled Practice

Below Level Use centimeter squares to make estimates before doing Exercises 3–6.

On Level Complete all exercises as written.

Above Level After completing Exercise 6, find an object that is about the same length as the object pictured.

Early Finishers Have children find objects that they estimate are shorter than 10 centimeters and measure to check their estimates.

4 Assess

Journal Idea Help children draw a line 10 centimeters long. Have them mark off each centimeter on the line to make a ruler. Invite children to draw a caterpillar above the ruler that is 6 centimeters long.

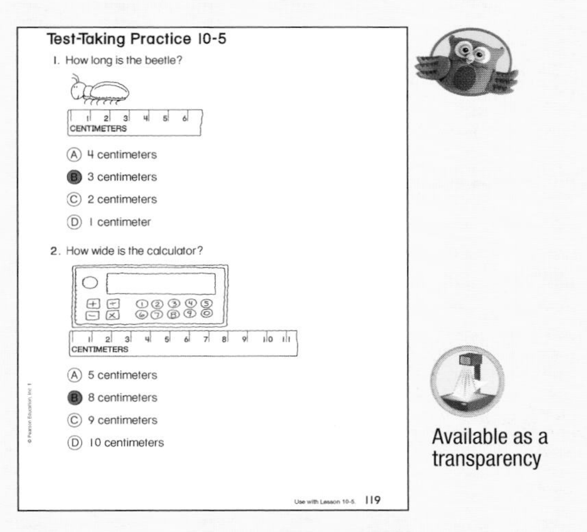
Test-Taking Practice 10-5

1. How long is the beetle?

(A) 4 centimeters
(B) 3 centimeters
(C) 2 centimeters
(D) 1 centimeter

2. How wide is the calculator?

(A) 5 centimeters
(B) 8 centimeters
(C) 9 centimeters
(D) 10 centimeters

Use with Lesson 10-5. 119

Available as a transparency

10-6 Understanding Perimeter

Lesson Organizer

Quick Lesson Overview 

Objective Find the distance around a shape using inches.

Math Understanding The distance around a shape (perimeter) can be measured by combining the measurements of each of the sides of the shape.

Math Background Children will use the same principles they used when measuring length to measure perimeter. That process includes choosing a unit, comparing the unit to the object being measured, and then recording the number of units.

NCTM Standards

- Measurement
- Geometry

(For a complete correlation to the NCTM Standards and Grades Pre-K through 2 Expectations, see Pages 363G and 363H.)

Getting Started

Spiral Review

Problem of the Day 10-6

Who am I?

My number is less than 5 + 5.
My number is greater than 7 − 1.

Ellen 11 | Juan 6 | May 8

Topics Reviewed

- Addition and subtraction
- Problem-Solving Strategy: Try, Check, and Revise

Answer May; May is number 8, which is both less than 5 + 5, or 10, and greater than 7 − 1, or 6.

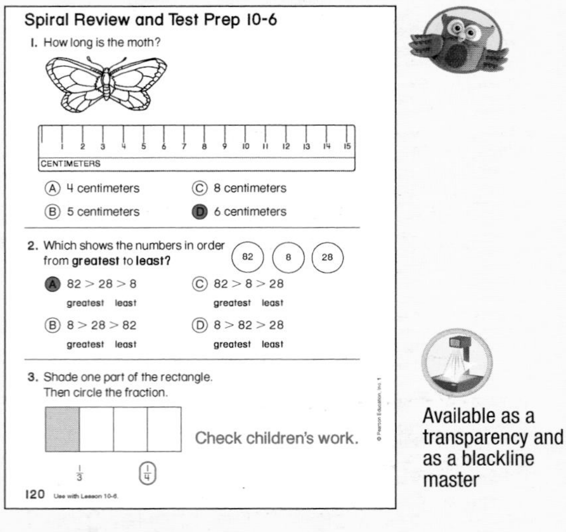

Spiral Review and Test Prep 10-6

1. How long is the moth?

CENTIMETERS

Ⓐ 4 centimeters Ⓒ 8 centimeters
Ⓑ 5 centimeters Ⓓ 6 centimeters

2. Which shows the numbers in order from **greatest** to **least**? 82 8 28

Ⓐ 82 > 28 > 8 greatest least
Ⓒ 82 > 8 > 28 greatest least
Ⓑ 8 > 28 > 82 greatest least
Ⓓ 8 > 82 > 28 greatest least

3. Shade one part of the rectangle. Then circle the fraction.

Check children's work.

$\frac{1}{3}$ $\frac{1}{4}$

120

Available as a transparency and as a blackline master

Topics Reviewed

1. Estimating and Measuring with Centimeters
2. Ordering Three Numbers
3. Counting Dimes and Nickels
4. Thirds and Fourths

Investigating the Concept

Counting Units Around

Materials *(per child)* Inch Grid (Teaching Tool 8); crayons

What to Do

- Model how to color in a shape that is 3 inches × 3 inches.
- Demonstrate how to count the number of inches on each side of the colored shape. Together, count as you go to determine that there are 12 inches around the shape.
- Repeat the activity with a variety of different shapes.

Ongoing Assessment

- **Can you draw a different shape that also measures 12 inches around? Explain.** *(Yes; one example is a 4 inch × 2 inch rectangle.)*
- **Reasoning What would happen if you measured each of the sides in centimeters instead of inches?** *(The measurement around the shape would be a much larger number.)*

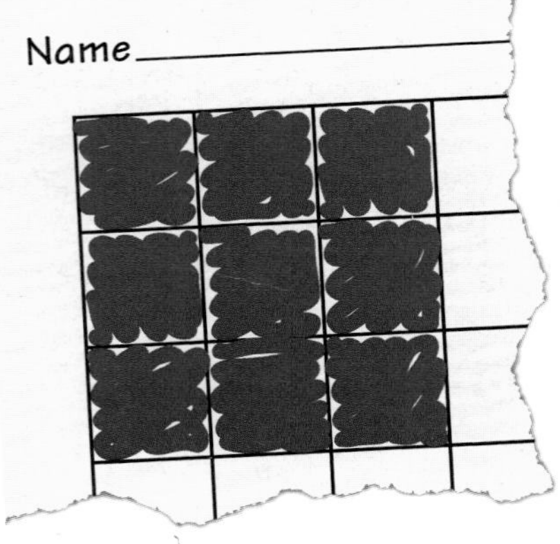

Reaching All Learners

Oral Language in Math

Understanding Perimeter

10–15 MIN **Linguistic/Kinesthetic**

- Explain distance around by inviting children to act as the units of measure to form the perimeter of a shape.
- Show children how to hold hands with their arms outstretched rigidly to make a shape, such as a square.
- **How many units does it take to make our shape? How many units are around the square?** *(The same number as there are children)*
- Repeat with different numbers of children and different shapes.

Access Content

English Language Learners

Going Around

10–15 MIN **Linguistic/Kinesthetic**

- Help children understand the term *around* by playing games in which children follow the direction to go around a circle.
- Play "Duck, Duck, Goose."
- One child goes around a circle of children, tapping each child and saying "Duck."
- When the child says "Goose," the child tapped must run around the circle in the same direction as "the tapper."
- "The tapper" tries to reach the empty space without being caught.

Reteaching

How Far Around?

10–15 MIN **Visual/Spatial**

PAIRS

Materials *(per pair)* 14 1-inch squares cut from Inch Grid (Teaching Tool 8)

- Have one child use up to 14 1-inch squares to create a shape on the table.
- Invite the partner to measure the perimeter of the shape by counting the number of units around the shape.
- Have children alternate the jobs of making shapes and finding the perimeter.

Math and Art

Making a Picture Frame

10–15 MIN **Visual/Spatial**

Materials *(per child)* Small photograph; construction paper; 12-inch ruler; glue

- Explain that when you make a frame for a piece of art, you have to think about the distance around the picture.
- Help children use the ruler to draw a rectangle around the photograph placed in the center of the construction paper.
- Children can make decorative frames around the outer edges of the rectangles. Then they can glue their photos inside the rectangles.
- Display the framed photos on a bulletin board.

Objective Find the distance around a shape using inches.

1 Warm Up

Activate Prior Knowledge Review the term *around.* Ask children to listen and follow directions, such as: **Walk around your chair. Hop around your desk. Take baby steps around my desk.**

2 Teach

Learn!

Demonstrate how to use the marks along each side of the shape to find how many inches long each side is. Then ask children to tell how many inches there are all the way around the shape. *(10)*

Ongoing Assessment

Talk About it

- **How do you measure the distance around the shape?** *(Count the number of inches on each of the sides of the shape.)*
- **How could you measure the number of inches around a shape if there were no marks on the shape?** *(Use an inch ruler to measure each of the sides.)*

If children do not recognize that each of the ends of the rectangle measures 1 inch,

then have them measure each end with an inch ruler.

Check

Error Intervention

If children cannot keep track of the count,

then ask them first to write the number for each side. *(Also see* Reteaching, *Page 377B.)*

Think About It Challenge children to measure around each shape using a centimeter ruler. **How do the centimeter measurements compare to the inch measurements?** *(It takes more centimeters than inches to measure around each shape.)*

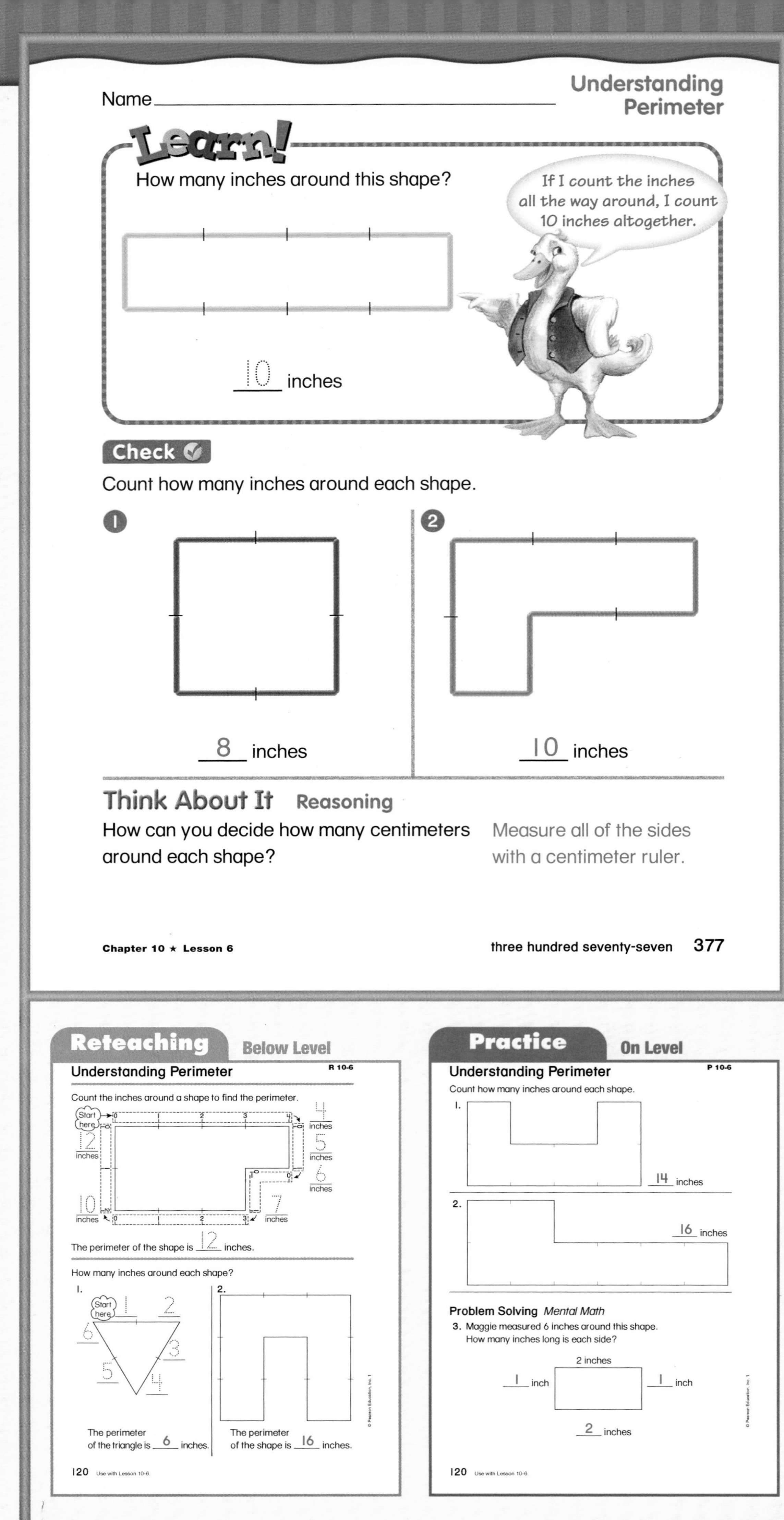

Name ____________

Understanding Perimeter

Learn!

How many inches around this shape?

10 inches

Check

Count how many inches around each shape.

1. 8 inches

2. 10 inches

Think About It Reasoning

How can you decide how many centimeters around each shape?

Measure all of the sides with a centimeter ruler.

Chapter 10 ★ Lesson 6 three hundred seventy-seven 377

Reteaching Below Level

Understanding Perimeter R 10-6

Count the inches around a shape to find the perimeter.

The perimeter of the shape is 12 inches.

How many inches around each shape?

1. The perimeter of the triangle is 6 inches.

2. The perimeter of the shape is 16 inches.

120 Use with Lesson 10-6.

Practice On Level

Understanding Perimeter P 10-6

Count how many inches around each shape.

1. 14 inches

2. 16 inches

Problem Solving *Mental Math*

3. Maggie measured 6 inches around this shape. How many inches long is each side?

120 Use with Lesson 10-6.

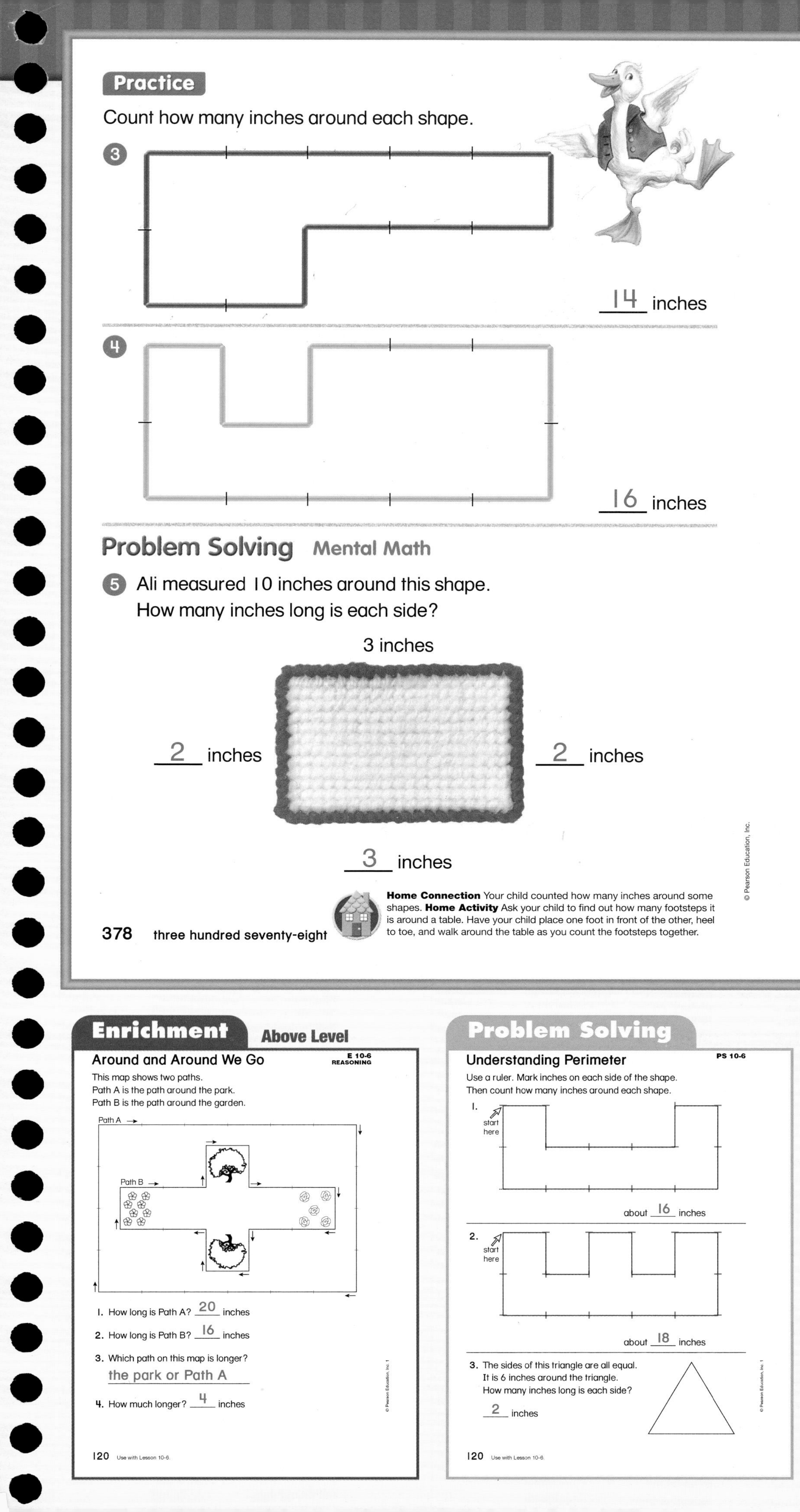

Practice

Count how many inches around each shape.

3. 14 inches

4. 16 inches

Problem Solving Mental Math

5. Ali measured 10 inches around this shape. How many inches long is each side?

3 inches

2 inches 2 inches

3 inches

Home Connection Your child counted how many inches around some shapes. **Home Activity** Ask your child to find out how many footsteps it is around a table. Have your child place one foot in front of the other, heel to toe, and walk around the table as you count the footsteps together.

Enrichment Above Level

Around and Around We Go — E 10-6 REASONING

This map shows two paths.
Path A is the path around the park.
Path B is the path around the garden.

1. How long is Path A? 20 inches
2. How long is Path B? 16 inches
3. Which path on this map is longer? the park or Path A
4. How much longer? 4 inches

Problem Solving

Understanding Perimeter — PS 10-6

Use a ruler. Mark inches on each side of the shape.
Then count how many inches around each shape.

1. start here — about 16 inches
2. start here — about 18 inches
3. The sides of this triangle are all equal. It is 6 inches around the triangle. How many inches long is each side? 2 inches

3 Practice

Have children use a ruler to check their answers for Exercise 5.

Reading Assist: Summarize Ask children to summarize the procedure to follow to measure the distance around a shape.

Leveled Practice

Below Level Work in pairs to complete all exercises.

On Level Do all exercises individually as written.

Above Level Measure the shapes in Exercises 3 and 4 in centimeters and record findings.

Early Finishers Distribute copies of the Inch Grid (Teaching Tool 8). Have children color a 4×4 shape. Then ask children to tell how many inches around it is. *(16 units)*

4 Assess

Journal Idea Give children copies of the Inch Grid (Teaching Tool 8). Have them outline and color shapes that are 10 inches around.

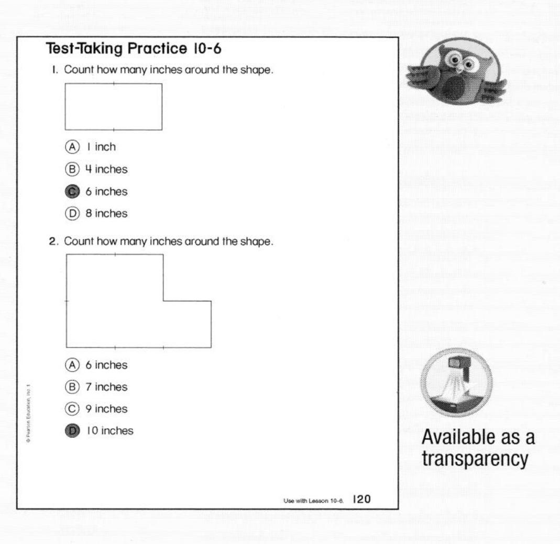

Test-Taking Practice 10-6

1. Count how many inches around the shape.
   - Ⓐ 1 inch
   - Ⓑ 4 inches
   - Ⓒ 6 inches
   - Ⓓ 8 inches
2. Count how many inches around the shape.
   - Ⓐ 6 inches
   - Ⓑ 7 inches
   - Ⓒ 9 inches
   - Ⓓ 10 inches

Use with Lesson 10-6. 120

Available as a transparency

PROBLEM-SOLVING SKILL 10-7

Look Back and Check

Lesson Organizer

Quick Lesson Overview

Objective Look back and check is a strategy that can help confirm the solution to a problem.

Math Understanding The area of a shape can be measured by placing square units on the shape and counting how many fit.

Materials for Student Pages *(per child)* 9 connecting cubes

Professional Development Note

How Children Learn Math
Children may not be ready to use the terms *perimeter* and *area,* but they are able to understand the difference between finding the distance around a shape and finding the number of squares that will cover a shape. Take this opportunity to emphasize the differences in procedures followed to find each measure.

NCTM Standards

- Measurement
- Geometry

(For a complete correlation to the NCTM Standards and Grades Pre-K through 2 Expectations, see Pages 363G and 363H.)

Getting Started

Spiral Review

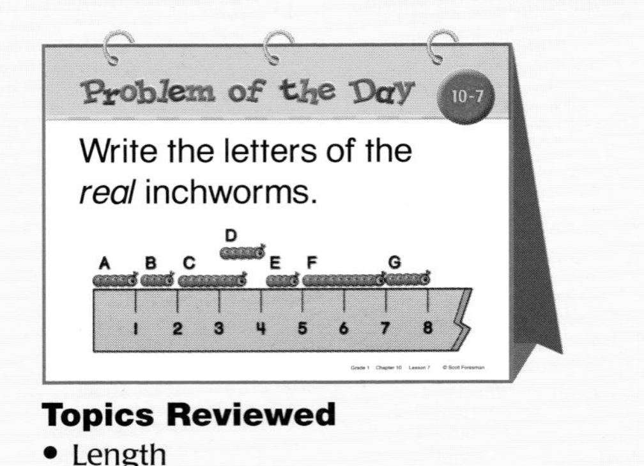

Topics Reviewed

- Length
- Problem-Solving Skill: Use Data from a Picture

Answer Worms A, D, and G measure exactly 1 inch long, so they are the real inchworms.

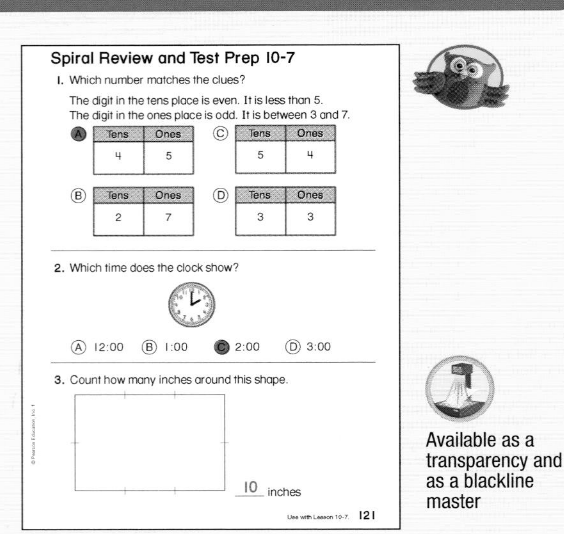

Spiral Review and Test Prep 10-7

1. Which number matches the clues?
The digit in the tens place is even. It is less than 5.
The digit in the ones place is odd. It is between 3 and 7.

Ⓐ

Tens	Ones
4	5

Ⓒ

Tens	Ones
5	4

Ⓑ

Tens	Ones
2	7

Ⓓ

Tens	Ones
3	3

2. Which time does the clock show?
Ⓐ 12:00 Ⓑ 1:00 Ⓒ 2:00 Ⓓ 3:00

3. Count how many inches around this shape.
10 inches

Use with Lesson 10-7. 121

Available as a transparency and as a blackline master

Topics Reviewed

1. Expanded Form
2. Telling and Writing Time to the Hour
3. Understanding Perimeter

Investigating the Concept

How Many Square Units?

20–25 MIN **Kinesthetic** SMALL GROUP

Materials *(per group)* 9 connecting cubes; colored paper that measures 3 cubes × 3 cubes

What to Do

- Distribute a colored paper square to each group. Ask children to hold a connecting cube. **This cube is a square unit. How many cubes will cover the shape?** Write "6 cubes" and " 9 cubes" on the board.
- Demonstrate how to cover the shape with cubes and count to find that 9 cubes will cover the shape. Have a volunteer circle the correct answer on the board.
- Have children follow along as you remove each cube and count again.

Ongoing Assessment

- **Number Sense Why does it make more sense to answer "9 cubes" than to answer "6 cubes"?** *(Because 6 is too few)*
- **What could you do to check to see if your answer is correct?** *(Sample response: Lift up the cubes and count again.)*

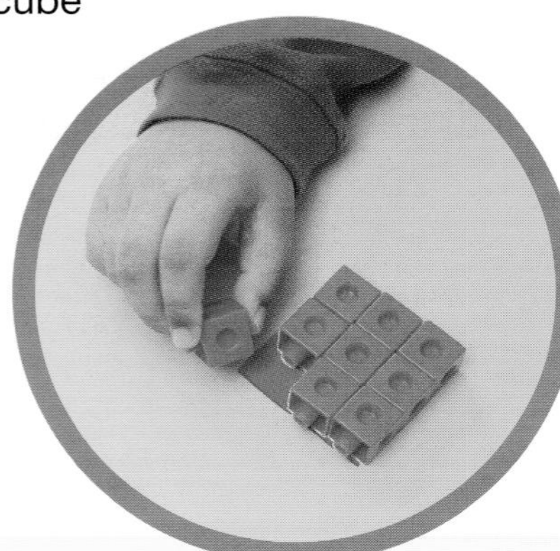

Reaching All Learners

Oral Language in Math

Guess and Check Square Units

10–15 MIN **Kinesthetic**

Materials *(per pair)* Connecting cubes; drawing paper

- Assemble connecting cubes into a shape. Place the shape on paper and trace around it. Remove all of the cubes. Have children guess how many cubes will be needed to cover the shape. Children can verify their guesses by covering the shape again with cubes.
- Have each child make a shape with connecting cubes and trace it on paper. The partner guesses how many cubes were used and then uses cubes to check the guess.

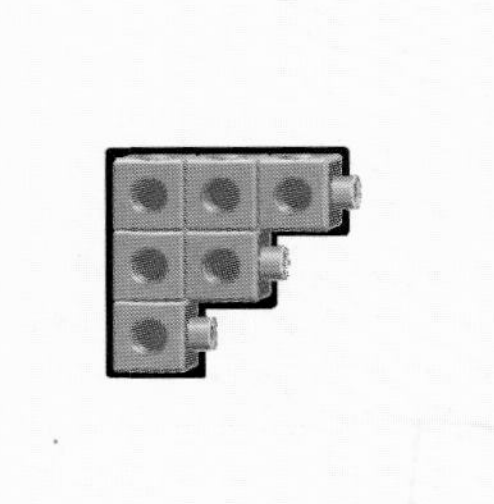

Access Content

English Language Learners

Understanding Square Units

5–10 MIN **Linguistic/Kinesthetic**

Materials *(per group)* Connecting cubes; counters; index cards with drawings of shapes made by tracing groups of connecting cubes

- Distribute a card to each group. Have children cover the shape using counters. **Are these counters *square units*? Can you completely cover the shape with the counters without overlapping them?**
- Have children take turns covering each of the shapes with cubes to find how many it takes to cover each shape.

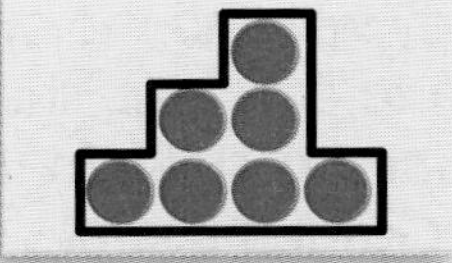

Reteaching

Connect the Dots to Make Square Units

10–15 MIN **Social/Cooperative**

Materials *(per pair)* Connecting cubes of two different colors; Dot Paper (Teaching Tool 18)

- Each child chooses a color of connecting cubes for the game.
- Children take turns drawing a line to connect two dots. A child whose line makes a complete square places his or her colored cube in the square and draws another line.
- When all of the squares are covered, children count their color cubes to see who has the most. Then have children add the number of cubes together to see how many there are in all.

Advanced Learners

Help Tile a Floor

10–15 MIN **Logical/Mathematical**

PAIRS

Materials *(per pair)* Inch Grid (Teaching Tool 8)

- Explain that Mr. Jones needs to put new tiles on the floor. The floor is 6 feet long and 3 feet wide.
- Ask children to use 1-inch tiles to represent tiles that are 1 foot square. **How many tiles will Mr. Jones need to tile the floor?** *(18)*
- Have children work together to draw a rectangle to represent Mr. Jones's floor and then to count the number of tiles needed to cover it.

Objective Look back and check is a strategy that can help confirm the solution to a problem.

1 Warm Up

Activate Prior Knowledge Review the meaning of the word *cover*. Have a volunteer cover a desk with napkins. Make sure that the napkins are placed edge to edge.

2 Teach

Learn!

Help children determine, after reading the problem at the top of the student page aloud, that they will find the number of cubes needed to cover the shape. Cover the shape with cubes as children follow using their cubes. Count the cubes together. Determine that 5 cubes is the answer that makes sense. Have children remove the cubes and recount to check their work.

Ongoing Assessment

Talk About It

- **How can you find out how many cubes will cover an index card?** *(Cover it with cubes and count them.)*
- **How can you decide whether your answer makes sense?** *(Sample response: Think about whether the number of cubes is too few or too many.)*

If children do not arrange the cubes correctly,

then explain that no part of the shape should be seen once the cubes cover it.

Check

Error Intervention

If children make errors counting the cubes,

then remind them to touch and count one cube at a time. *(Also see* Reteaching, *Page 379B.)*

Think About It Help children conclude that a penny is not a good measure for square units. **What shape is a penny? What shape is the flat surface of a cube?**

Name________________ PROBLEM-SOLVING SKILL

Look Back and Check

Learn!

How many cubes can you use to cover the shape?

3 are not enough. 5 cubes will cover the shape!

3 cubes

(5 cubes)

Does it make sense?

Check

How many cubes will cover each shape?
Circle the answer that makes sense.

1. (4 cubes) 8 cubes

2. 12 cubes (3 cubes)

Think About It Reasoning

Could you use pennies instead of cubes to cover the shapes above? Explain. No; pennies are not square.

Reteaching Below Level

PROBLEM-SOLVING SKILL R 10-7

Look Back and Check

How many triangle pattern blocks will cover this shape?
Check your answers to be sure they make sense.

Mai says 4 triangle pattern blocks will cover this shape.
Does her answer make sense?

Check. Put triangle blocks over the shape.

Circle the answer that makes sense.

4 pattern blocks (6 pattern blocks)

How many triangle pattern blocks will cover each shape?
Circle the answer that makes sense.

1. (5 pattern blocks) 8 pattern blocks

2. 10 pattern blocks (14 pattern blocks)

Practice On Level

PROBLEM-SOLVING SKILL P 10-7

Look Back and Check

How many cubes will cover each shape?
Circle the answer that makes sense.

1. (7 cubes) 12 cubes

2. 8 cubes (10 cubes)

Problem Solving *Visual Thinking*

3. Draw a different shape with the same number of square units.

Sample answer is given.

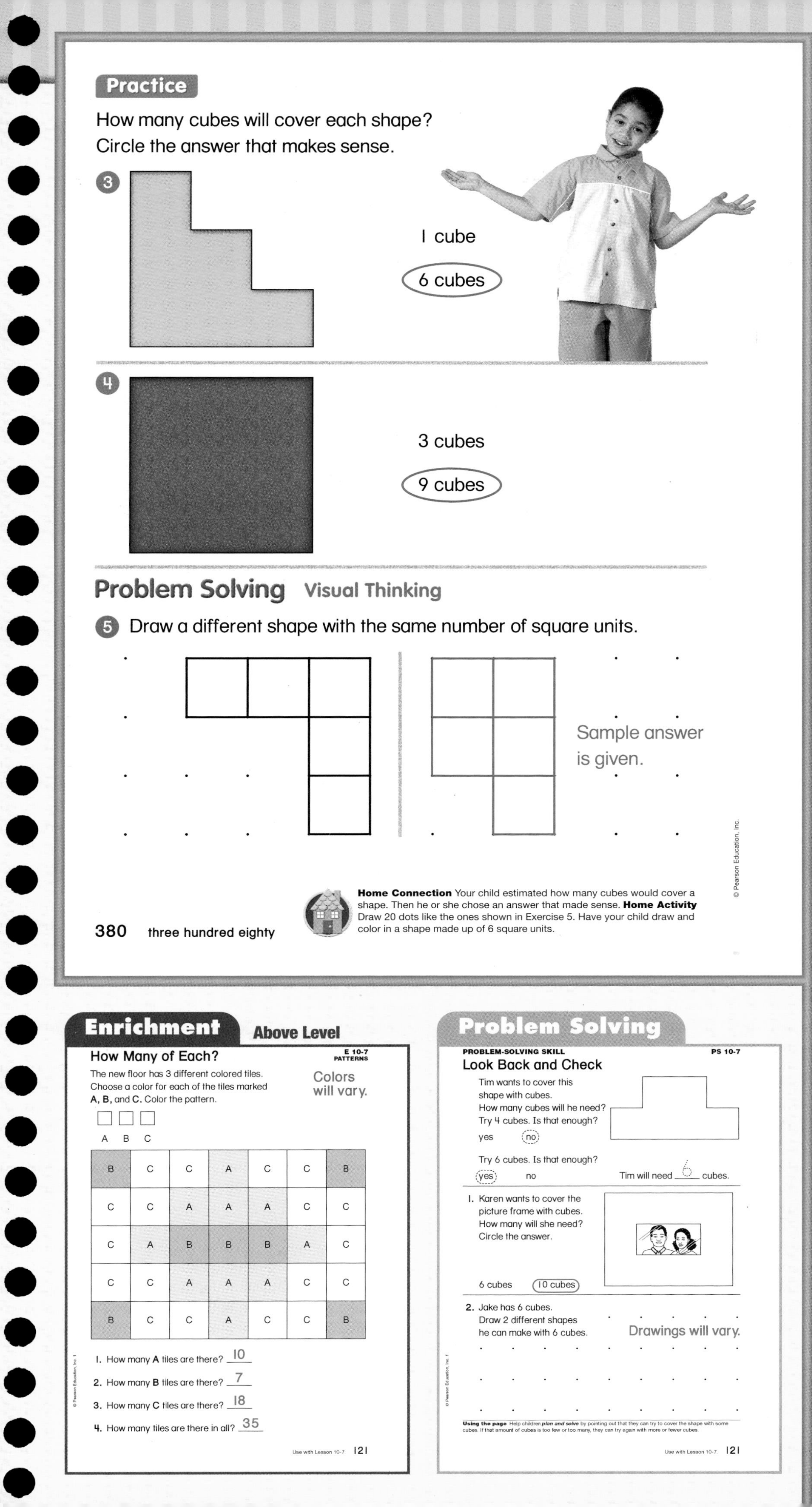

Practice

How many cubes will cover each shape?
Circle the answer that makes sense.

3. I cube / (6 cubes)

4. 3 cubes / (9 cubes)

Problem Solving Visual Thinking

5. Draw a different shape with the same number of square units.

Sample answer is given.

© Pearson Education, Inc.

Home Connection Your child estimated how many cubes would cover a shape. Then he or she chose an answer that made sense. **Home Activity** Draw 20 dots like the ones shown in Exercise 5. Have your child draw and color in a shape made up of 6 square units.

380 three hundred eighty

Enrichment Above Level

E 10-7 PATTERNS

How Many of Each?

The new floor has 3 different colored tiles. Choose a color for each of the tiles marked **A**, **B**, and **C**. Color the pattern.

Colors will vary.

A B C

B	C	C	A	C	C	B
C	C	A	A	A	C	C
C	A	B	B	B	A	C
C	C	A	A	A	C	C
B	C	C	A	C	C	B

1. How many **A** tiles are there? 10
2. How many **B** tiles are there? 7
3. How many **C** tiles are there? 18
4. How many tiles are there in all? 35

Use with Lesson 10-7 121

Problem Solving

PROBLEM-SOLVING SKILL PS 10-7

Look Back and Check

Tim wants to cover this shape with cubes.
How many cubes will he need?
Try 4 cubes. Is that enough?
yes (no)

Try 6 cubes. Is that enough?
(yes) no Tim will need 6 cubes.

1. Karen wants to cover the picture frame with cubes. How many will she need? Circle the answer.
6 cubes (10 cubes)

2. Jake has 6 cubes. Draw 2 different shapes he can make with 6 cubes.
Drawings will vary.

Using the page Help children *plan and solve* by pointing out that they can try to cover the shape with some cubes. If that amount of cubes is too few or too many, they can try again with more or fewer cubes.

Use with Lesson 10-7 121

3 Practice

After completing Exercises 3 and 4, have children compare the shapes.

Reading Assist: Compare and Contrast For Exercise 5, ask children how the shapes are alike and different. Guide them to see that although each drawing may be a different shape, they both contain the same number of square units.

Leveled Practice

Below Level Work in pairs to complete Exercises 3–5.

On Level Complete all exercises as written.

Above Level Draw a shape that has more square units than those in Exercise 5.

Early Finishers Have children make a shape using cubes and then count to see how many square units it measures. Have them repeat the procedure with different shapes.

4 Assess

Journal Idea Have children use their connecting cubes to draw a shape that contains exactly 10 cubes.

Test-Taking Practice 10-7

1. How many cubes will cover the shape? Which answer makes sense?

(A) I cube (C) 7 cubes
(B) 3 cubes (D) 10 cubes

2. Which shape has the same number of square units?

Use with Lesson 10-7 121

Available as a transparency

Diagnostic Checkpoint

Purpose Provide assessment of children's progress to date by checking their understanding of key content covered in the previous section.

Vocabulary Review

You may wish to review these terms before assigning the page:

centimeter A metric unit used to measure length: 100 centimeters equal 1 meter. *(pp 375–376)*

estimate To give an approximate rather than an exact answer *(pp. 365–366)*

foot (feet) A customary unit used to measure length: 1 foot equals 12 inches. Also an ancient Egyptian unit of measure equal to a human foot *(pp. 373–374)*

inch A customary unit used to measure length: 12 inches equal 1 foot. *(pp. 371–372)*

measure To find the size, quantity, or capacity of something *(pp. 365–366)*

Activities for this section are available in the Math Vocabulary Kit.

Name ______________________

Estimate the length. Then measure using cubes. Estimates will vary.

1

Estimate.	Measure.
about ____	3

Estimate the length. Then measure using an inch ruler.

2

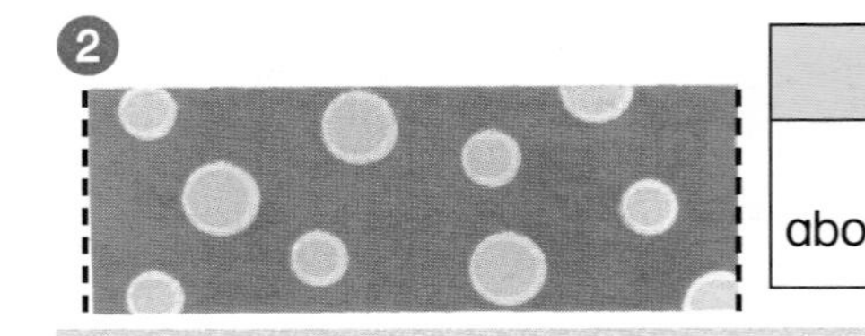

Estimate.	Measure.
about ____ inches	3 inches

Estimate the length. Then measure using a centimeter ruler.

3

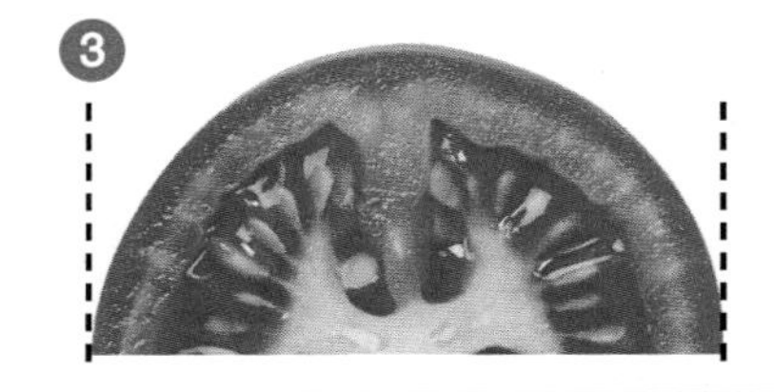

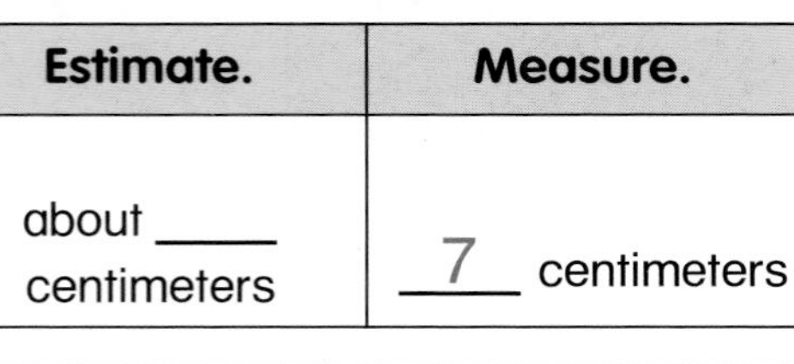

Estimate.	Measure.
about ____ centimeters	7 centimeters

Count how many inches around this shape.

4

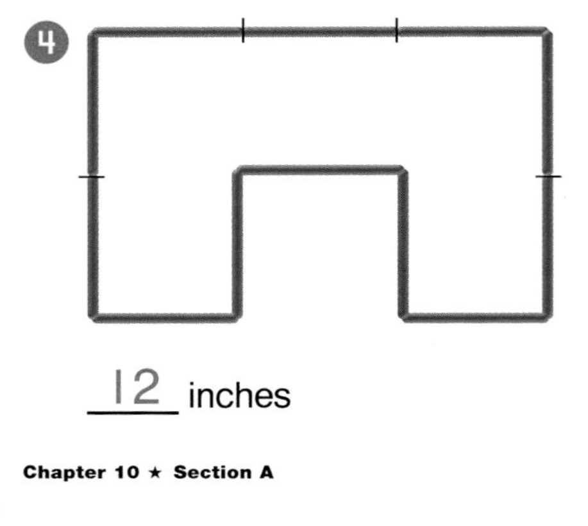

12 inches

Write how many cubes will cover this shape.

5

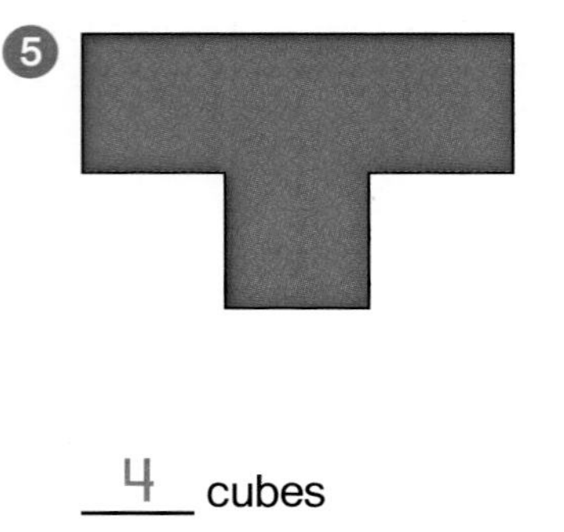

4 cubes

Item Analysis for Diagnosis and Intervention

Objective	Items	Student Book Pages*	Intervention System
Estimate, measure, and compare the lengths of objects using nonstandard units.	1	365–366	D21
Estimate and measure the lengths of objects to the nearest inch using a ruler.	2	371–372	D22
Estimate and measure the length of objects in centimeters using a ruler.	3	375–376	D23
Find the distance around a shape using inches.	4	377–378	D23
Look back and check is a strategy that can help confirm the solution to a problem.	5	379–380	E14

*For each lesson, there is a *Reteaching* activity in *Reaching All Learners* and a *Reteaching* master.

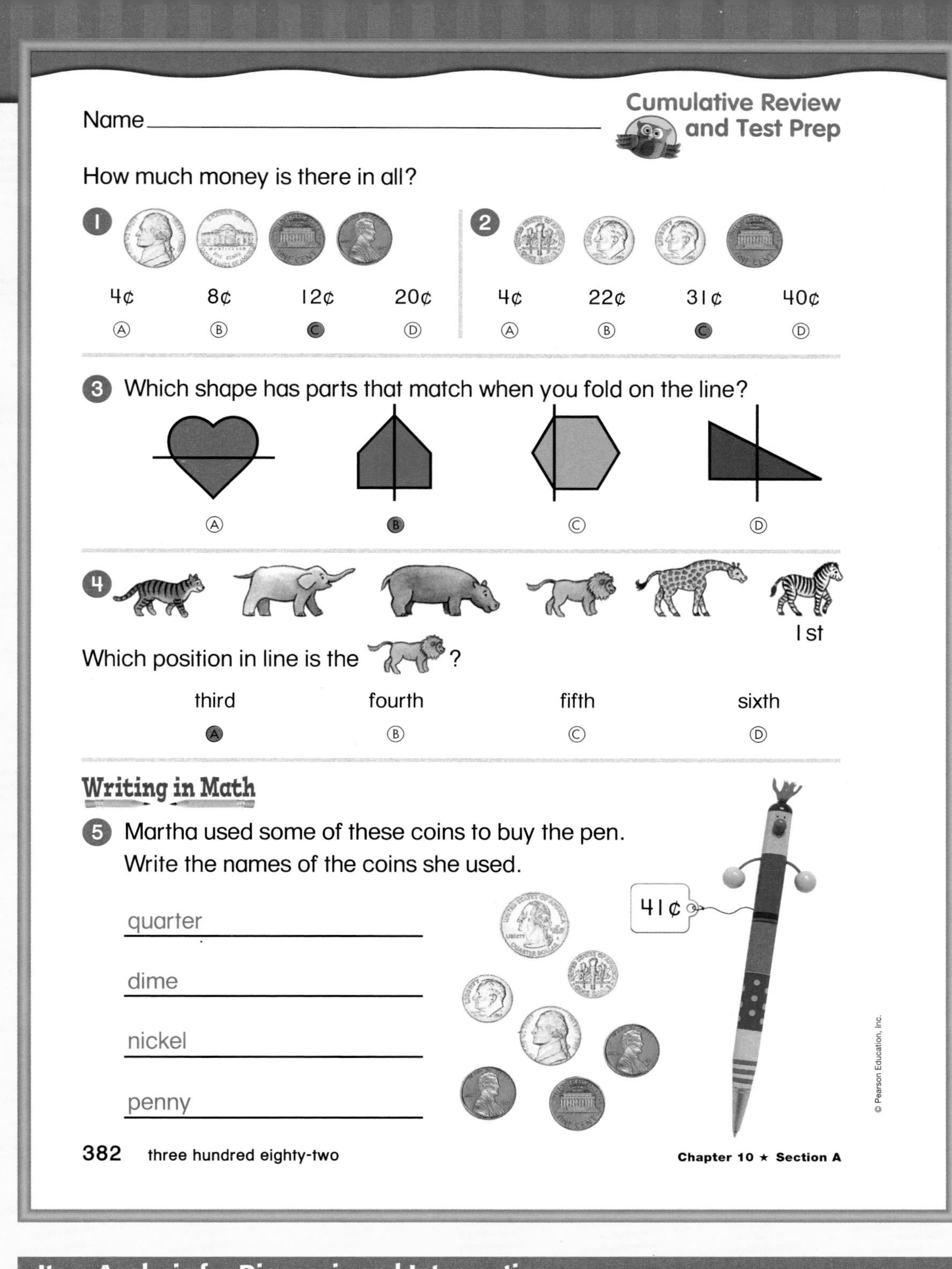
Name ______________________

Cumulative Review and Test Prep

How much money is there in all?

1 4¢ Ⓐ 8¢ Ⓑ 12¢ Ⓒ 20¢ Ⓓ

2 4¢ Ⓐ 22¢ Ⓑ 31¢ Ⓒ 40¢ Ⓓ

3 Which shape has parts that match when you fold on the line?

Ⓐ Ⓑ Ⓒ Ⓓ

4 1st

Which position in line is the ?

third Ⓐ fourth Ⓑ fifth Ⓒ sixth Ⓓ

Writing in Math

5 Martha used some of these coins to buy the pen.
Write the names of the coins she used.

41¢

quarter

dime

nickel

penny

© Pearson Education, Inc.

382 three hundred eighty-two

Chapter 10 ★ Section A

Cumulative Review and Test Prep

Purpose Provide children with a review of math concepts. Items appear as they would on a standardized test so children become familiar with that format.

Item Analysis for Diagnosis and Intervention

Objective	Items	Student Book Pages*	Intervention System
Identify the value of a group of nickels and pennies through 25¢.	1	331–332	A33
Identify the value of a group of dimes and pennies through 99¢.	2	333–334	A34
Identify objects that show symmetry and draw lines of symmetry.	3	171–172	D52
Use ordinals through twentieth to identify position.	4	267–268	A18
Identify a dollar bill, a dollar coin, a half-dollar coin, and combinations of coins worth amounts up to $1.00.	5	347–348	A38, A39

*For each lesson, there is a *Reteaching* activity in *Reaching All Learners* and a *Reteaching* master.

10-8

Estimating, Measuring, and Comparing Capacity

Lesson Organizer

Quick Lesson Overview

Objective Estimate, measure, and compare the capacities of containers.

Math Understanding The capacity of a container can be described by comparing it to that of a defined unit of capacity.

Vocabulary Cup

Materials for Student Pages
(per pair) Measuring cup; rice; containers pictured on student pages or other similarly-sized containers

Professional Development Note

Research Base

Whatever the attribute being measured, the available research evidence suggests that children learn to measure through a sequence that starts with recognizing that there is a measurable property, moves through making direct physical comparisons among objects that have that property, and then concludes with determining an appropriate unit to use to measure the property (Wilson & Rowland, 1993; Hiebert, 1984). This section helps children through this sequence for measuring capacity, weight, and temperature and introduces the standard units for those measurements.

NCTM Standards

- Measurement

(For a complete correlation to the NCTM Standards and Grades Pre-K through 2 Expectations, see Pages 363G and 363H.)

Getting Started

Spiral Review

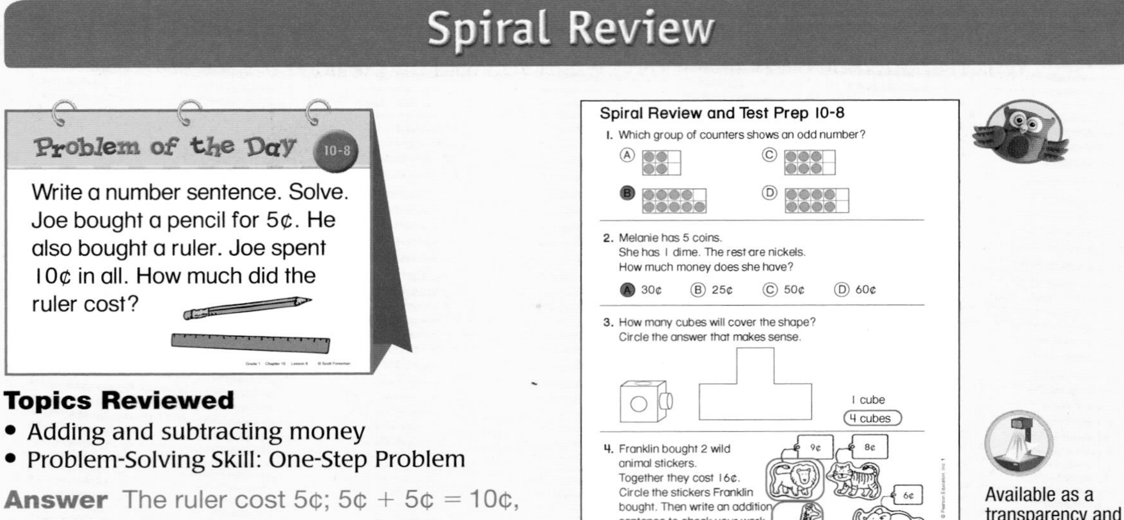

Problem of the Day 10-8

Write a number sentence. Solve.
Joe bought a pencil for 5¢. He also bought a ruler. Joe spent 10¢ in all. How much did the ruler cost?

Topics Reviewed
- Adding and subtracting money
- Problem-Solving Skill: One-Step Problem

Answer The ruler cost 5¢; 5¢ + 5¢ = 10¢, and 10¢ − 5¢ = 5¢.

Spiral Review and Test Prep 10-8

1. Which group of counters shows an odd number?
   (A) (B) (C) (D)
2. Melanie has 5 coins.
   She has 1 dime. The rest are nickels.
   How much money does she have?
   (A) 30¢ (B) 25¢ (C) 50¢ (D) 60¢
3. How many cubes will cover the shape?
   Circle the answer that makes sense.
   1 cube
   4 cubes
4. Franklin bought 2 wild animal stickers.
   Together they cost 16¢.
   Circle the stickers Franklin bought. Then write an addition sentence to check your work.
   9 ¢ + 7 ¢ = 16 ¢
   9¢ 8¢ 6¢ 7¢

122 Use with Lesson 10-8.

Available as a transparency and as a blackline master

Topics Reviewed
1. Odd and Even Numbers
2. Counting Dimes and Nickels
3. Look Back and Check
4. Try, Check, and Revise

Investigating the Concept

How Much Will It Hold?

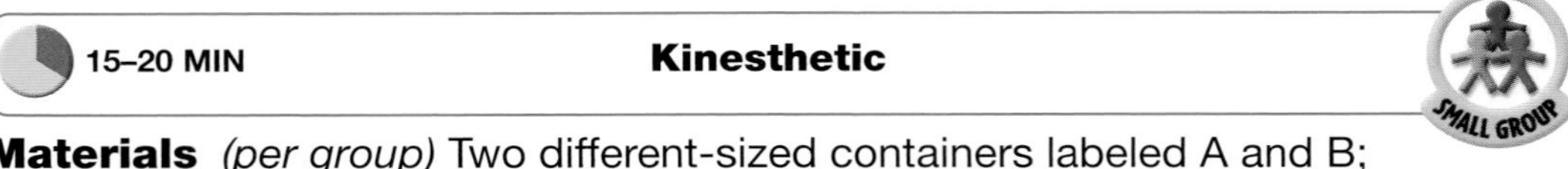

Materials *(per group)* Two different-sized containers labeled A and B; ladle; rice

What to Do

- Show children two different-sized containers. Ask children to suggest a way to use the ladle to see how much each container holds.
- Have children estimate about how many ladles of rice each container will hold. Model filling a container and counting each ladle as it is poured into the container. Compare the estimate to the measure and then identify the container that holds more.

Ongoing Assessment

- **Reasoning How can you use the ladle to figure out how much a container holds?** *(Fill the container with ladles of rice and count how many it holds.)*
- **Why does it take more ladles of rice to fill Bowl B than Bowl A?** *(Because Bowl B is larger and holds more)*

Reaching All Learners

Oral Language in Math

Talking About Capacity

5–10 MIN **Logical/Mathematical** 

Materials 3 containers of different shapes and sizes; rice or sand; measuring cup

- Show children the three containers and have them guess which container will hold the most. **How many cups will it hold?**
- Children should vote for the containers they think have the greatest capacity and the smallest capacity.
- Tally the votes and write down the most popular guesses for the number of cups that each will hold.
- Fill the containers, having children count along with you. Compare the actual capacities to children's guesses.

Access Content

English Language Learners

Words That Mean *Capacity*

5–10 MIN **Auditory/Visual/Spatial** 

Materials *(per group)* Connecting cubes; containers of various sizes

- Show children two containers, one of which is larger than the other. Count as you put connecting cubes into each container. Hold up the containers. **Which one *holds* more? Which one *holds* less?**
- Have children choose two containers and pose the same questions to the group.
- Have children fill the containers to check their answers.

Reteaching

Comparing Capacities

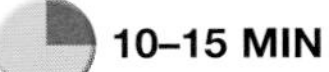 10–15 MIN **Kinesthetic**

Materials *(per group)* Rice; different-sized containers; large mixing spoon

- Have students work together to guess how many spoonfuls of rice each container will hold. Record children's estimates on the board.
- Have children fill the containers to capacity with rice using the mixing spoon, counting and recording the number of spoonfuls used. Have children put the containers in order according to capacity.
- Help children compare the actual measurements to their estimates.

Math and Science

Filling Flower Pots

10–15 MIN **Kinesthetic**

Materials *(per child)* Potting soil; plastic spoons; different-sized containers to use as planters; seeds

- Have each child choose a container. Each child should estimate how many spoonfuls of soil will be needed to fill the container. Write each child's estimate on the board.
- Have each child fill his or her container with soil, counting each spoonful.
- After children have filled their containers with soil, invite them to plant seeds. Water the plants as needed.

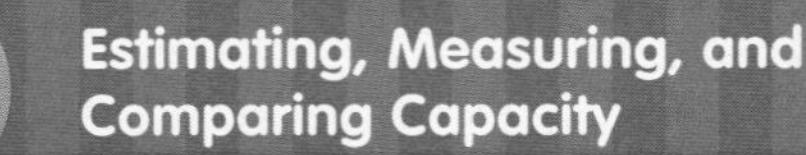

Objective Estimate, measure, and compare the capacities of containers.

1 Warm Up

Activate Prior Knowledge Review the terms *more, less, most,* and *least.* Display two piles of cubes. Have volunteers predict which pile has more and which has less. Children count the cubes to check their predictions. Then compare the three piles using the terms *most* and *least.*

2 Teach

Together, look at the top of the student page. Explain that the child first estimates how many cups of rice the bowl can hold. Then she fills the bowl, counting each cup of rice that she adds. Note that the estimate was about 3 cups and the measure was about 5 cups.

Ongoing Assessment

Talk About It

- **How did the girl check her estimate?** *(She counted how many cups of rice filled the bowl.)*
- **Was 3 a good estimate for the number of cups that will fill the bowl? Explain.** *(Yes; because it is close to 5, the actual measurement)*

If children confuse an estimate with a measure,

then point out that an estimate is made without cups of rice and a measure is made with them.

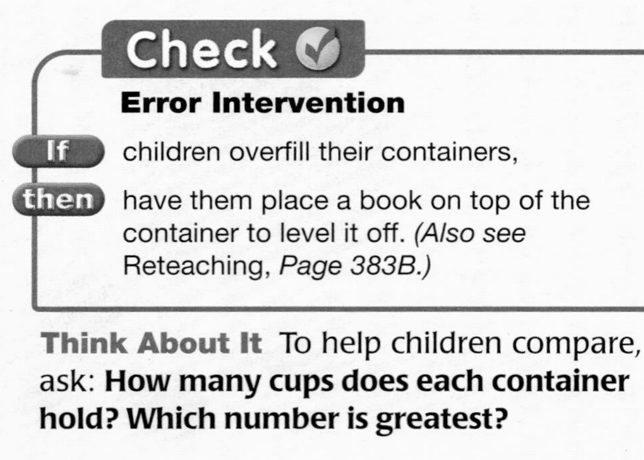

Check

Error Intervention

If children overfill their containers,

then have them place a book on top of the container to level it off. *(Also see* Reteaching, *Page 383B.)*

Think About It To help children compare, ask: **How many cups does each container hold? Which number is greatest?**

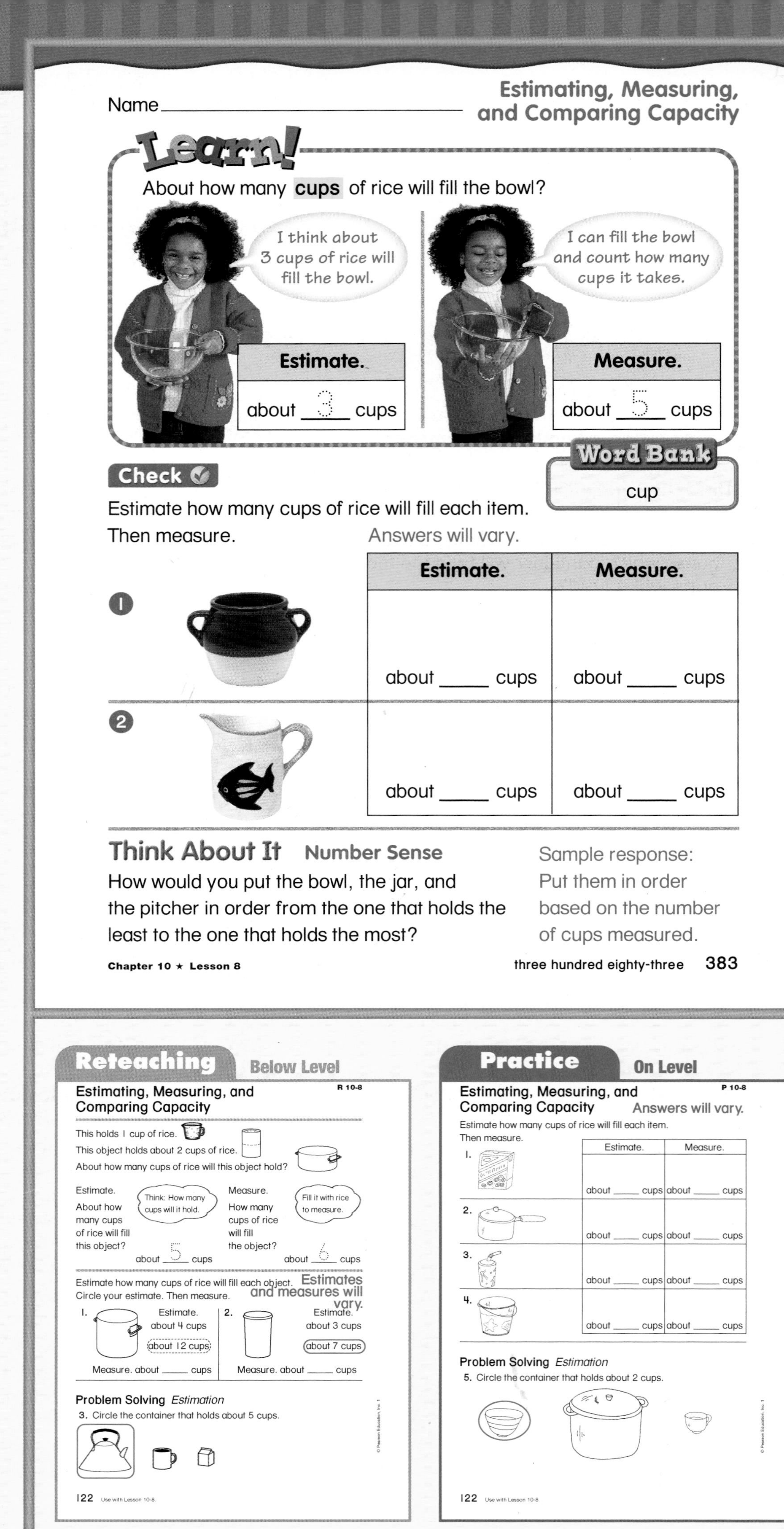

Name ______________________

Estimating, Measuring, and Comparing Capacity

Learn!

About how many **cups** of rice will fill the bowl?

Estimate.	Measure.
about 3 cups	about 5 cups

Word Bank

cup

Check

Estimate how many cups of rice will fill each item. Then measure.

Answers will vary.

	Estimate.	Measure.
1	about ____ cups	about ____ cups
2	about ____ cups	about ____ cups

Think About It Number Sense

How would you put the bowl, the jar, and the pitcher in order from the one that holds the least to the one that holds the most?

Sample response: Put them in order based on the number of cups measured.

Chapter 10 ★ Lesson 8

three hundred eighty-three 383

Reteaching Below Level

Estimating, Measuring, and Comparing Capacity R 10-8

This holds 1 cup of rice.

This object holds about 2 cups of rice.

About how many cups of rice will this object hold?

Estimate. About how many cups of rice will fill this object? (Think: How many cups will it hold.) about 5 cups

Measure. How many cups of rice will fill the object? (Fill it with rice to measure.) about 6 cups

Estimate how many cups of rice will fill each object. Circle your estimate. Then measure. Estimates and measures will vary.

1. Estimate. about 4 cups / (about 12 cups) Measure. about ____ cups

2. Estimate. about 3 cups / (about 7 cups) Measure. about ____ cups

Problem Solving *Estimation*

3. Circle the container that holds about 5 cups.

122 Use with Lesson 10-8

Practice On Level

Estimating, Measuring, and Comparing Capacity P 10-8

Answers will vary.

Estimate how many cups of rice will fill each item. Then measure.

	Estimate.	Measure.
1.	about ____ cups	about ____ cups
2.	about ____ cups	about ____ cups
3.	about ____ cups	about ____ cups
4.	about ____ cups	about ____ cups

Problem Solving *Estimation*

5. Circle the container that holds about 2 cups.

122 Use with Lesson 10-8

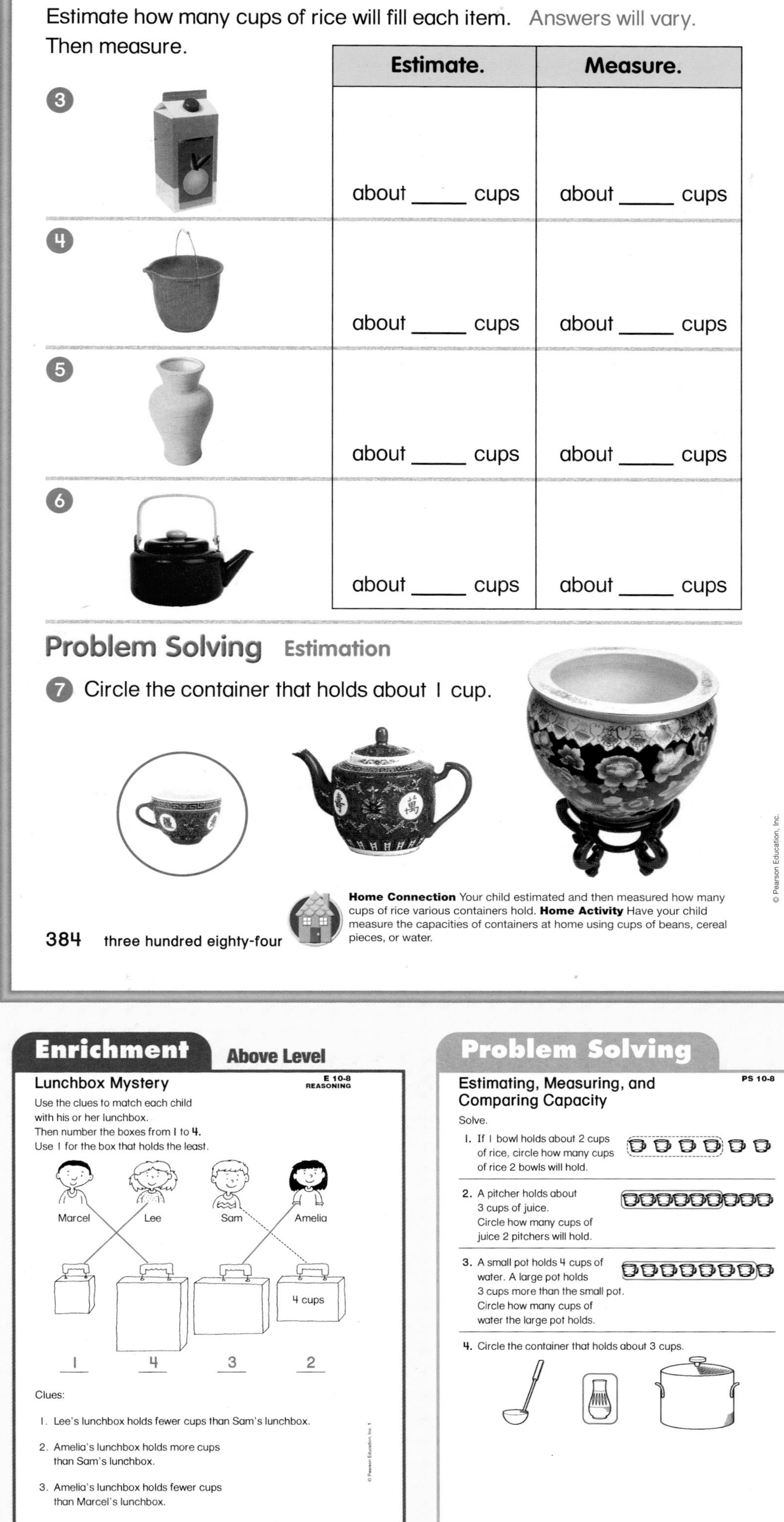

Practice

Estimate how many cups of rice will fill each item. Answers will vary.
Then measure.

	Estimate.	Measure.
3	about ____ cups	about ____ cups
4	about ____ cups	about ____ cups
5	about ____ cups	about ____ cups
6	about ____ cups	about ____ cups

Problem Solving Estimation

7. Circle the container that holds about 1 cup.

Home Connection Your child estimated and then measured how many cups of rice various containers hold. **Home Activity** Have your child measure the capacities of containers at home using cups of beans, cereal pieces, or water.

© Pearson Education, Inc.

384 three hundred eighty-four

Enrichment Above Level

Lunchbox Mystery — E 10-8 REASONING

Use the clues to match each child with his or her lunchbox.
Then number the boxes from 1 to 4.
Use 1 for the box that holds the least.

Marcel, Lee, Sam, Amelia

4 cups

1 4 3 2

Clues:

1. Lee's lunchbox holds fewer cups than Sam's lunchbox.
2. Amelia's lunchbox holds more cups than Sam's lunchbox.
3. Amelia's lunchbox holds fewer cups than Marcel's lunchbox.

122 Use with Lesson 10-8

Problem Solving

Estimating, Measuring, and Comparing Capacity — PS 10-8

Solve.

1. If 1 bowl holds about 2 cups of rice, circle how many cups of rice 2 bowls will hold.
2. A pitcher holds about 3 cups of juice. Circle how many cups of juice 2 pitchers will hold.
3. A small pot holds 4 cups of water. A large pot holds 3 cups more than the small pot. Circle how many cups of water the large pot holds.
4. Circle the container that holds about 3 cups.

122 Use with Lesson 10-8

3 Practice

Remind children to estimate before they use cups of rice to measure.

Leveled Practice

Below Level Work in pairs to complete all exercises.

On Level Complete all exercises individually.

Above Level Estimate how many cups each container in Exercise 7 will hold.

Early Finishers Provide catalogs and scissors. Have children cut out three pictures of containers. Ask children to paste the pictures onto a piece of paper, label the one that holds the most, and label the one that holds the least.

4 Assess

Journal Idea Have children draw a container that holds about 1 cup of rice.

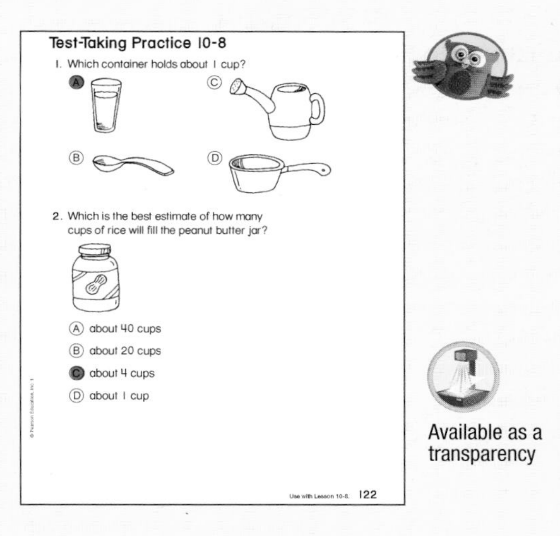

Test-Taking Practice 10-8

1. Which container holds about 1 cup?

Ⓐ Ⓑ Ⓒ Ⓓ

2. Which is the best estimate of how many cups of rice will fill the peanut butter jar?

Ⓐ about 40 cups
Ⓑ about 20 cups
Ⓒ about 4 cups
Ⓓ about 1 cup

Use with Lesson 10-8 122

Available as a transparency

10-9

Cups, Pints, and Quarts

Lesson Organizer

Quick Lesson Overview 

Objective Compare the capacities of cups, pints, and quarts.

Math Understanding Cups, pints, and quarts are standard units used to measure capacity.

Vocabulary Cup, pint, quart

Professional Development Note

Effective Questioning Techniques
As children complete the exercises in this lesson, ask questions that encourage them to explain their reasoning and thinking. Such questions might include: **Why do you think the orange juice container holds more than 1 cup? How did you decide that the milk glass holds less than 1 quart?**

NCTM Standards

- Measurement

(For a complete correlation to the NCTM Standards and Grades Pre-K through 2 Expectations, see Pages 363G and 363H.)

Getting Started

Spiral Review

Problem of the Day 10-9

Solve.
There are 3 boys and some girls on the swings. Five children in all are on the swings. How many girls are on the swings?

Topics Reviewed

- Addition and subtraction
- Problem-Solving Skill: One-Step Problem

Answer There are 2 girls on the swings; $5 - 3 = 2$, and $3 + 2 = 5$.

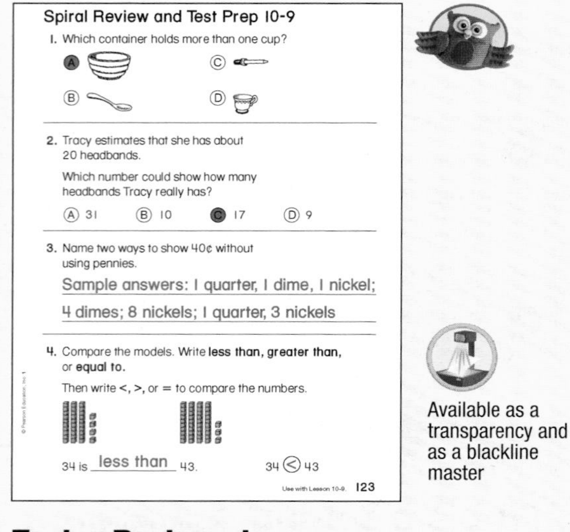

Spiral Review and Test Prep 10-9

1. Which container holds more than one cup?
Ⓐ Ⓑ Ⓒ Ⓓ

2. Tracy estimates that she has about 20 headbands.
Which number could show how many headbands Tracy really has?
Ⓐ 31 Ⓑ 10 Ⓒ 17 Ⓓ 9

3. Name two ways to show 40¢ without using pennies.
Sample answers: 1 quarter, 1 dime, 1 nickel; 4 dimes; 8 nickels; 1 quarter, 3 nickels

4. Compare the models. Write **less than, greater than,** or **equal to.**
Then write <, >, or = to compare the numbers.
34 is less than 43. 34 < 43

123

Available as a transparency and as a blackline master

Topics Reviewed
1. Estimating, Measuring, and Comparing Capacity **2.** Estimating with Groups of 10 **3.** Counting Sets of Coins **4.** Comparing Numbers: Greater Than, Less Than, Equal

Investigating the Concept

Cups, Pints, and Quarts

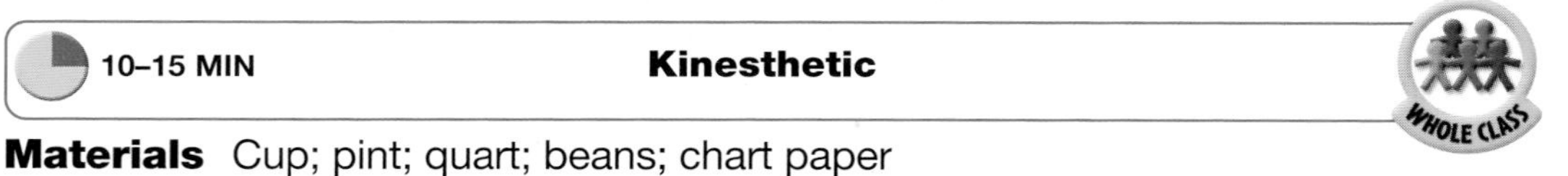

Materials Cup; pint; quart; beans; chart paper

What to Do

- Display a cup, a pint, and a quart container. Explain that cup, pint, and quart are units of measure that tell how much a container holds.
- Invite children to use beans to find how many cups fill 1 pint and 1 quart. Also have children find how many pints fill 1 quart. Record the class findings on a chart. Lead children to conclude that 1 pint holds more than 1 cup, and 1 quart holds more than 1 pint or 1 cup.
- Ask children to name things that might be measured in cups, pints, and quarts.

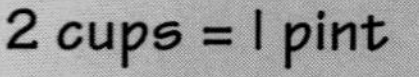
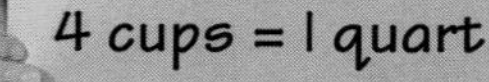

Ongoing Assessment

- **Reasoning Which holds more: 2 pints or 2 quarts?** *(2 quarts)*
- **Does a teaspoon hold more or less than 1 cup?** *(Less than 1 cup)*

Reaching All Learners

Reading in Math

Compare Containers

10–15 MIN **Linguistic/Kinesthetic**

Materials *(per group)* Cup; pint; quart

- Write the following words on the board: "cup, pint, quart."
- Let children fill the cup container with water. Then have children use the cup to fill the other containers. Have children record how many cupfuls were needed in each case.
- Then have children fill in the blanks in these statements:

  1 pint holds ___ cups.
  1 quart holds ___ cups.
  1 quart holds ___ pints.

Activate Prior Knowledge/Build Background

English Language Learners

Words for Measuring

5–10 MIN **Linguistic/Kinesthetic**

Materials *(per group)* Cup; pint; quart; rice or lentils

- Display the cup. **This is a cup.** Write the word on the board as children pronounce it with you. Repeat with the pint and the quart.
- Ask children to estimate how many cups will fit into the quart container. "I estimate that ___ cups will fit into the quart."
- Let children test their estimates. Repeat to find how many cups fill 1 pint and how many pints fill 1 quart.

Reteaching

Let's Measure

15–20 MIN **Visual/Spatial/Kinesthetic**

Materials *(per group)* Cup; pint; quart; empty containers, such as 8-ounce milk glass, quart juice container, cup yogurt container, pint frozen yogurt container

- Point to the glass. **How much will this glass hold: 1 cup, 1 pint, or 1 quart?**
- Pour water from the cup to the glass to demonstrate that an 8-ounce milk glass holds 1 cup.
- Continue this procedure with the other containers. Have volunteers do the measuring.

Math and Health

How Many Glasses?

15–20 MIN **Visual/Spatial**

Materials *(per group)* Chart paper; markers; stickers

- Have children complete a picture graph titled "How Many Glasses a Day?" that illustrates the amounts of three liquids the class had in one day.
- Under the headings "Water," "Milk," and "Orange Juice," have each child put stickers to show how many cups of these liquids he or she had the previous day.
- Calculate how many quarts of water, milk, and orange juice the class had altogether.

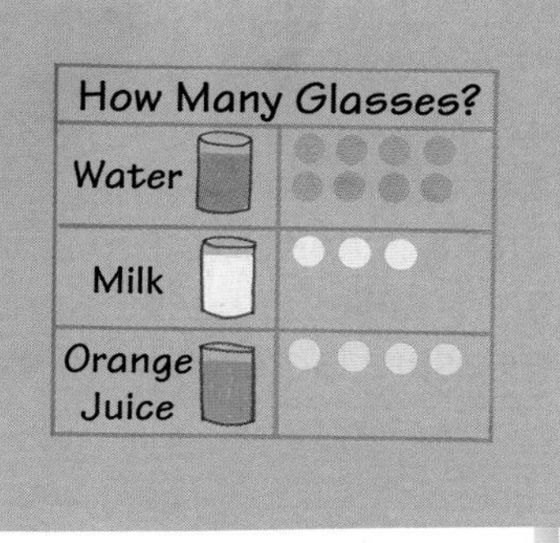

Objective Compare the capacities of cups, pints, and quarts.

1 Warm Up

Activate Prior Knowledge Review how to compare the capacity of containers. Display three different-sized empty containers. Have children put them in order from the one that holds the *most* to the one that holds the *least.*

2 Teach

Learn!

Direct children's attention to the measures shown on the student page. Explain that a cup, a pint, and a quart are units used to measure how much a container will hold. Lead children to conclude that 1 pint holds more than 1 cup and that 1 quart holds more than 1 pint or 1 cup.

Ongoing Assessment

Talk About It

- **If you have a cup, a pint, and a quart, which one holds the most?** *(A quart)*
- **How can you tell if a container can hold about 1 cup of water?** *(Possible response: If the container holds about 1 cup, the container will be nearly full but will not overflow.)*

If children do not understand the relative sizes,

then have them pour water or rice from a cup to a pint to a quart.

Check

Error Intervention

If children choose the incorrect estimate,

then remind them that a cup holds the least and a quart holds the most. *(Also see* Reteaching, *Page 385B.)*

Think About It Help children understand that it is better to use smaller units to measure smaller capacities and larger units to measure larger capacities.

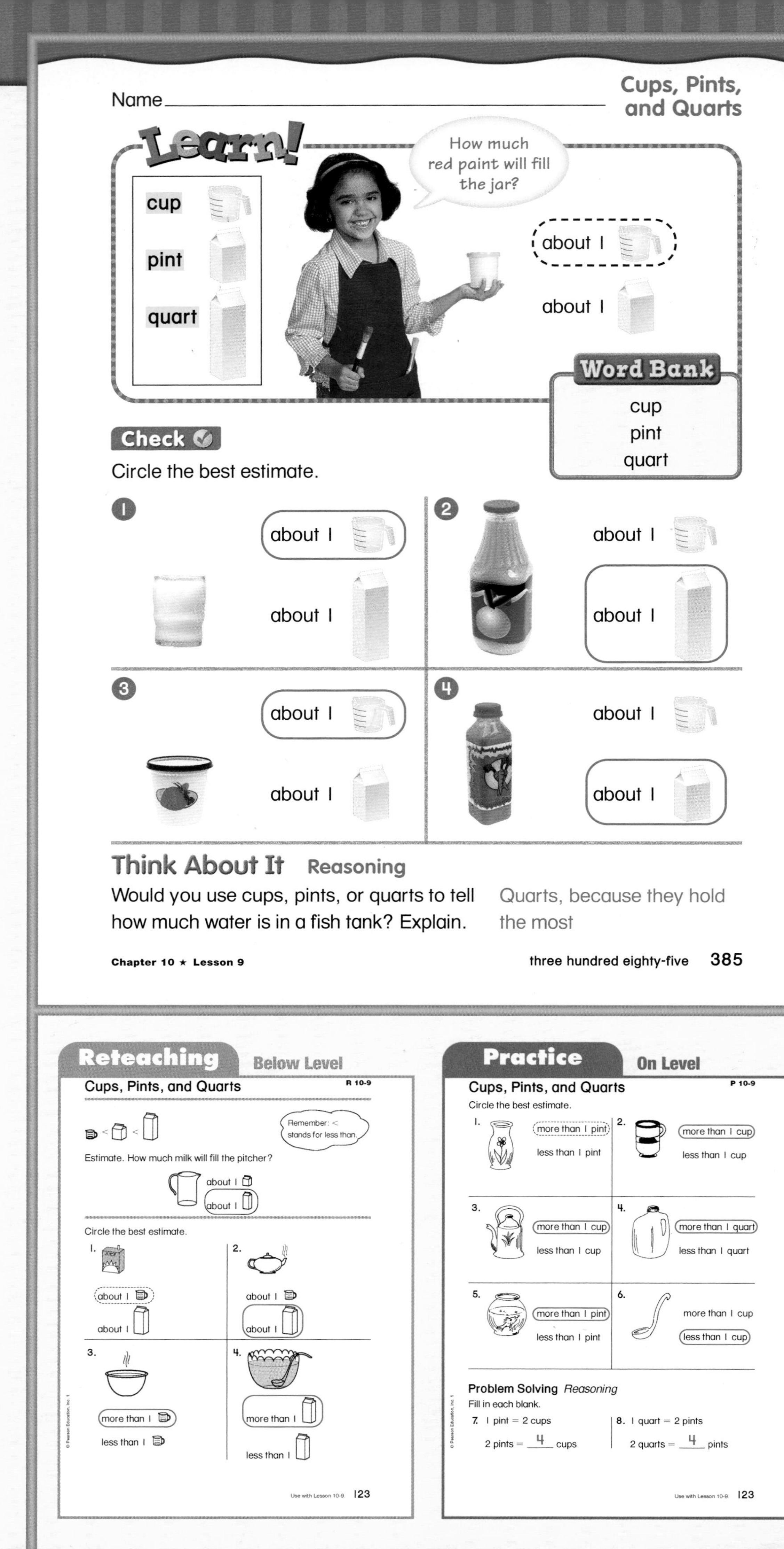
Name ____________________

Cups, Pints, and Quarts

Learn!

cup
pint
quart

How much red paint will fill the jar?

about 1 [cup]
about 1 [pint]

Word Bank
cup
pint
quart

Check

Circle the best estimate.

1. about 1 [cup] (circled) / about 1 [pint]
2. about 1 [cup] / about 1 [quart] (circled)
3. about 1 [cup] (circled) / about 1 [pint]
4. about 1 [cup] / about 1 [pint] (circled)

Think About It Reasoning

Would you use cups, pints, or quarts to tell how much water is in a fish tank? Explain. *Quarts, because they hold the most*

Chapter 10 ★ Lesson 9 — three hundred eighty-five 385

Reteaching Below Level

Cups, Pints, and Quarts R 10-9

Remember: < stands for less than.

Estimate. How much milk will fill the pitcher?

about 1 / about 1 (circled)

Circle the best estimate.

1. about 1 (circled) / about 1
2. about 1 / about 1 (circled)
3. more than 1 (circled) / less than 1
4. more than 1 (circled) / less than 1

Use with Lesson 10-9. 123

Practice On Level

Cups, Pints, and Quarts P 10-9

Circle the best estimate.

1. more than 1 pint (circled) / less than 1 pint
2. more than 1 cup (circled) / less than 1 cup
3. more than 1 cup (circled) / less than 1 cup
4. more than 1 quart (circled) / less than 1 quart
5. more than 1 pint (circled) / less than 1 pint
6. more than 1 cup / less than 1 cup (circled)

Problem Solving *Reasoning*

Fill in each blank.

7. 1 pint = 2 cups
2 pints = 4 cups

8. 1 quart = 2 pints
2 quarts = 4 pints

Use with Lesson 10-9. 123

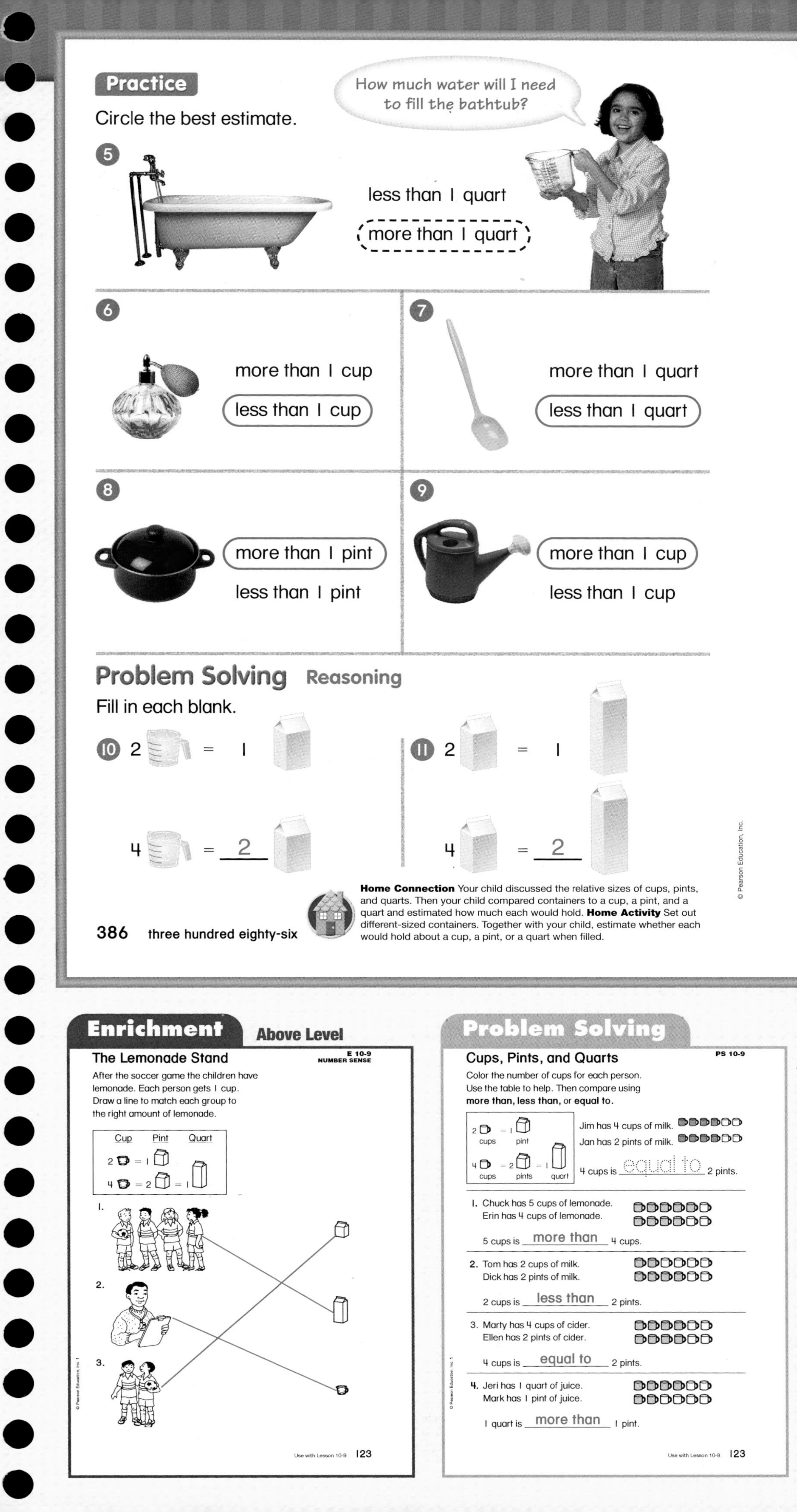

Practice

Circle the best estimate.

5. less than 1 quart / **(more than 1 quart)**

6. more than 1 cup / **(less than 1 cup)**

7. more than 1 quart / **(less than 1 quart)**

8. **(more than 1 pint)** / less than 1 pint

9. **(more than 1 cup)** / less than 1 cup

Problem Solving Reasoning

Fill in each blank.

10. 2 cups = 1 pint
 4 cups = 2 pints

11. 2 pints = 1 quart
 4 pints = 2 quarts

Home Connection Your child discussed the relative sizes of cups, pints, and quarts. Then your child compared containers to a cup, a pint, and a quart and estimated how much each would hold. **Home Activity** Set out different-sized containers. Together with your child, estimate whether each would hold about a cup, a pint, or a quart when filled.

386 three hundred eighty-six

Enrichment Above Level

The Lemonade Stand E 10-9 NUMBER SENSE

After the soccer game the children have lemonade. Each person gets 1 cup. Draw a line to match each group to the right amount of lemonade.

Cup Pint Quart
2 cups = 1 pint
4 cups = 2 pints = 1 quart

1.
2.
3.

Use with Lesson 10-9. 123

Problem Solving

Cups, Pints, and Quarts PS 10-9

Color the number of cups for each person. Use the table to help. Then compare using **more than, less than,** or **equal to.**

2 cups = 1 pint
4 cups = 2 pints = 1 quart

Jim has 4 cups of milk.
Jan has 2 pints of milk.
4 cups is equal to 2 pints.

1. Chuck has 5 cups of lemonade.
 Erin has 4 cups of lemonade.
 5 cups is more than 4 cups.

2. Tom has 2 cups of milk.
 Dick has 2 pints of milk.
 2 cups is less than 2 pints.

3. Marty has 4 cups of cider.
 Ellen has 2 pints of cider.
 4 cups is equal to 2 pints.

4. Jeri has 1 quart of juice.
 Mark has 1 pint of juice.
 1 quart is more than 1 pint.

Use with Lesson 10-9. 123

3 Practice

For Exercises 5–9, remind children of the relative sizes of each container.

Leveled Practice

Below Level Work in pairs to complete all exercises.

On Level Complete all exercises individually.

Above Level For each container shown in Exercises 5–9, draw another container that holds about the same amount.

Early Finishers Assign partners. Have children work together to write a list of things they might find in a refrigerator that may be measured in cups, pints, and quarts.

4 Assess

Journal Idea Ask children to draw a picture that shows a cup of apple juice, a pint of orange juice, and a quart of milk. Have them label their drawings with the words *cup, pint,* and *quart.*

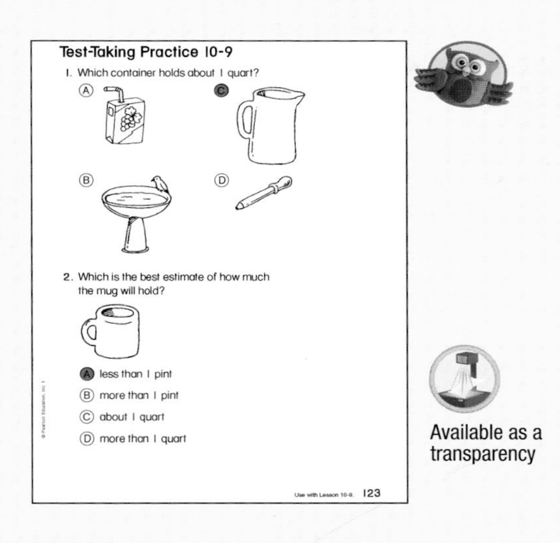

Test-Taking Practice 10-9

1. Which container holds about 1 quart?
 (A) (B) (C) (D)

2. Which is the best estimate of how much the mug will hold?
 (A) less than 1 pint
 (B) more than 1 pint
 (C) about 1 quart
 (D) more than 1 quart

Use with Lesson 10-9. 123

Available as a transparency

10-10 Liters

Lesson Organizer

Quick Lesson Overview 

Objective Compare the capacity of containers to one liter.

Math Understanding A liter is a standard unit used to measure capacity.

Vocabulary Liter

Professional Development Note

Effective Questioning Techniques Children will be asked to compare a given container to a 1-liter container, without actually measuring. It will be helpful to ask questions that encourage children to make logical choices. **Does the container look smaller than the 1- liter container? Does it look larger? Do you think it holds more than 1 liter or less than 1 liter?**

NCTM Standards

- Measurement

(For a complete correlation to the NCTM Standards and Grades Pre-K through 2 Expectations, see Pages 363G and 363H.)

Getting Started

Spiral Review

Problem of the Day 10-10

Write a number sentence. Then Solve. There are 10 big dogs and 3 small dogs. How many more big dogs are there than small dogs?

Topics Reviewed

- Subtraction
- Problem-Solving Strategy: Write a Number Sentence

Answer Answer 10 − 3 = ___; there are 7 more big dogs.

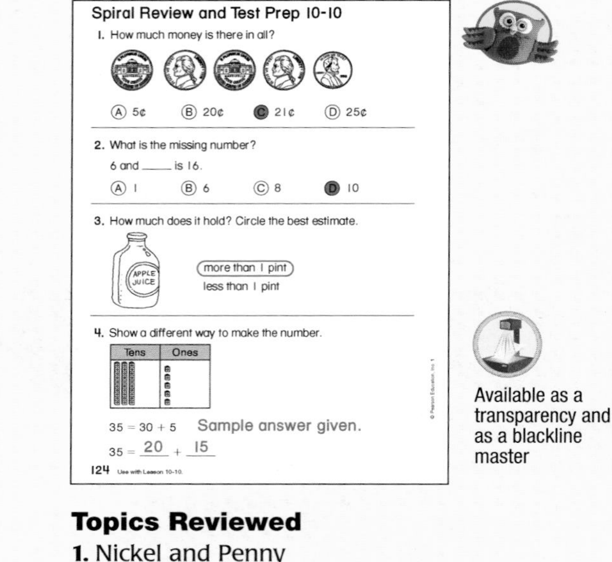

Spiral Review and Test Prep 10-10

1. How much money is there in all?

Ⓐ 5¢ Ⓑ 20¢ Ⓒ 21¢ Ⓓ 25¢

2. What is the missing number?

6 and ___ is 16.

Ⓐ 1 Ⓑ 6 Ⓒ 8 Ⓓ 10

3. How much does it hold? Circle the best estimate.

more than 1 pint

less than 1 pint

4. Show a different way to make the number.

Tens	Ones

35 = 30 + 5 Sample answer given.

35 = 20 + 15

124

Available as a transparency and as a blackline master

Topics Reviewed

1. Nickel and Penny
2. Numbers to 19
3. Cups, Pints, and Quarts
4. Ways to Make Numbers

Investigating the Concept

Liters

10–15 MIN **Visual/Spatial** WHOLE CLASS

Materials Liter, pint, and quart; colored water

What to Do

- Display a 1-liter container. Explain that a liter is a unit used to measure how much a container holds.
- Place the 1-liter container next to the pint. Ask children to estimate whether a liter will hold more or less than 1 pint. *(More)* Check by filling the pint and pouring the water into the liter. Then display a quart. Ask children to estimate whether a liter will hold more or less than 1 quart. *(Less)* Check by filling the liter and pouring it into the quart container.

Ongoing Assessment

- **Reasoning How can you tell if a container holds more than 1 liter?** *(By its size; a bigger container will hold more.)*
- **Would you buy a cup of juice or a liter of juice to serve yourself and two friends?** *(A liter, because it would hold more juice)*

Reaching All Learners

Oral Language in Math

More, Less, or the Same?

10–15 MIN | **Visual/Spatial** | WHOLE CLASS

Materials Liter bottle

- Show children the liter bottle and explain that the container holds 1 liter of liquid.
- Ask children to look around the classroom to find some containers that hold less than 1 liter. Then have them locate items that hold more than 1 liter and containers that hold about 1 liter.
- Discuss how children might test their ideas about the capacities of the containers.

Extend Language

English Language Learners

Speaking of Containers

5–10 MIN | **Auditory/Linguistic** | SMALL GROUP

Materials *(per group)* Cup; pint; quart; liter container

- Hold up the liter bottle. **This bottle holds 1 liter.** Then hold up another container. **This container holds (more, less, the same) as 1 liter.**
- Have each member of the group choose two containers to compare, describing them following the language pattern you demonstrated.

Reteaching

Remember the Liter

10–15 MIN | **Visual/Spatial** | SMALL GROUP

Materials *(per group)* Liter bottle; bowl with capacity larger than 1 liter; teacup; bucket; pictures of containers that hold water

- As children watch, fill up the liter bottle with water and empty it into the larger container or a sink.
- Ask children to recall the amount of water that was needed to fill up the liter bottle before they decide whether the objects (or the objects pictured) hold less than or more than 1 liter.

Math and Music

Liter Orchestra

15–20 MIN | **Kinesthetic/Auditory** | SMALL GROUP

Materials *(per group)* Cup; 4 identical 1-liter glass jars or bottles

- Have volunteers fill the first liter bottle with 1 cup of water, a second with 2 cups of water, the third with 3 cups, and the fourth with 4 cups.
- Line up the bottles in order from least to greatest amounts of water.
- Challenge children to make music by blowing across the top of the bottles or by lightly striking the bottles with pencils.

Objective Compare the capacity of containers to one liter.

1 Warm Up

Activate Prior Knowledge Review cups, pints, and quarts. Ask children to solve such riddles as: **I hold more than 1 cup and less than 1 quart. What am I?** *(Pint)*

2 Teach

Learn!

Focus on the pictures at the top of the student page. Explain that a liter is a unit used to measure how much a container holds. If you wish, show children a 1-liter container, a 1-pint container, and a 1-gallon container. Have children compare the containers and determine that the smaller one holds less than 1 liter and the larger one holds more than 1 liter.

Ongoing Assessment

Talk About It

- **How can you tell that the glass at the top of the student page holds less than 1 liter?** *(It is smaller than the liter bottle.)*
- **Explain what helps you decide whether a container holds more or less than 1 liter.** *(A container that is larger than 1 liter will hold more, and a container that is smaller will hold less.)*

If children have difficulty comparing the pictures,

then have them refer to the containers you used in the demonstration.

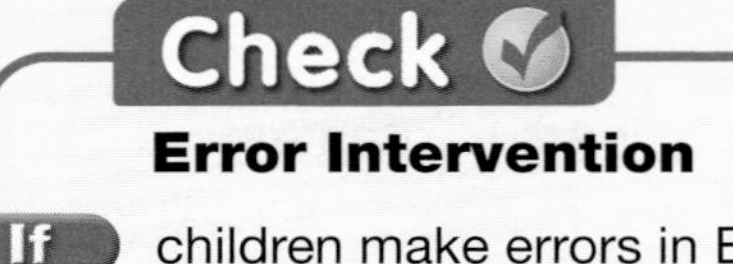

Check

Error Intervention

If children make errors in Exercises 1–4,

then refer them to the pictures at the top of the student page. *(Also see* Reteaching, *Page 387B.)*

Think About It You may wish to show children two 2-liter bottles to help them answer the question.

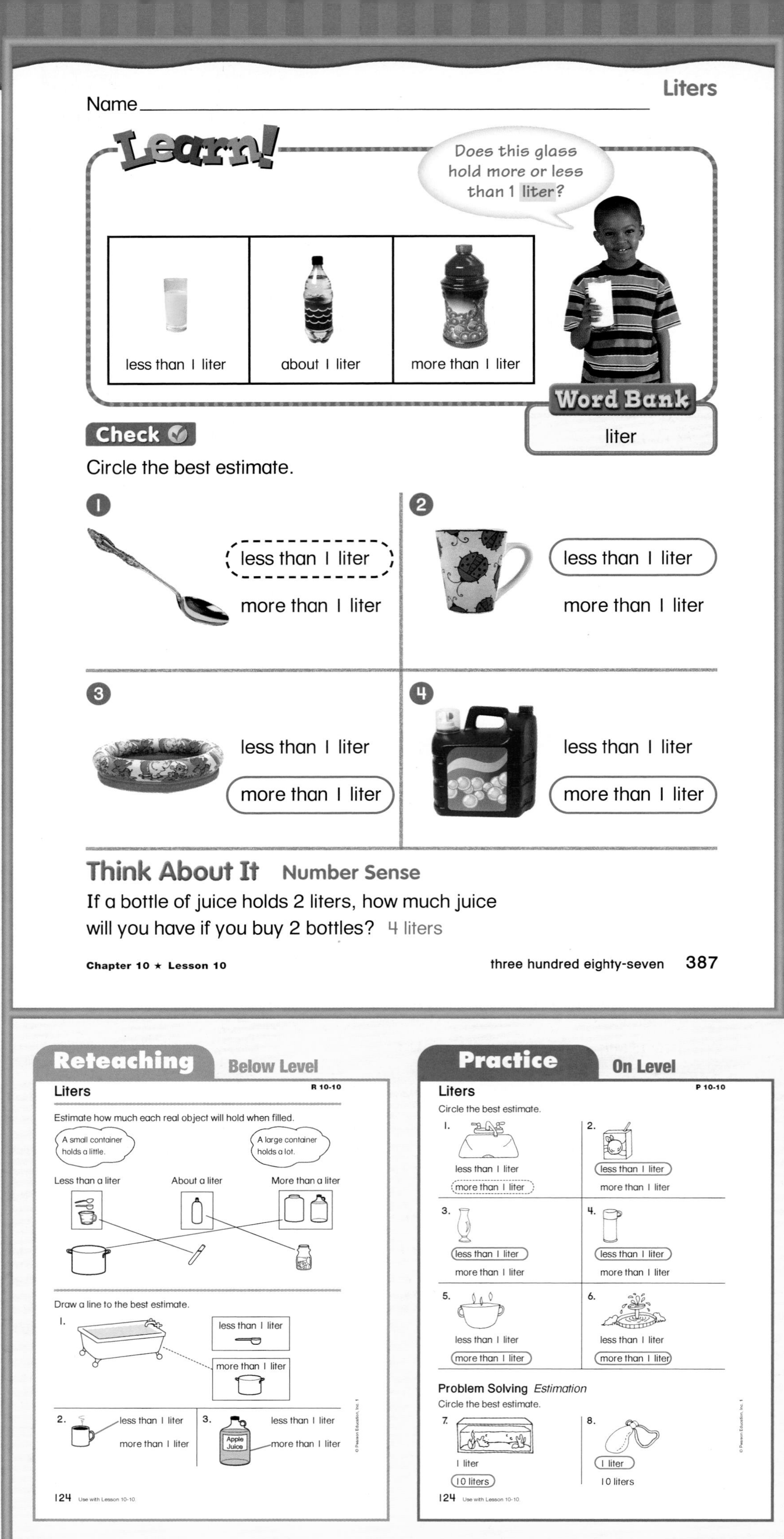

Name ____________________ **Liters**

Learn!

Does this glass hold more or less than 1 liter?

less than 1 liter	about 1 liter	more than 1 liter

Word Bank
liter

Check

Circle the best estimate.

1. less than 1 liter / more than 1 liter
2. less than 1 liter / more than 1 liter
3. less than 1 liter / more than 1 liter
4. less than 1 liter / more than 1 liter

Think About It Number Sense

If a bottle of juice holds 2 liters, how much juice will you have if you buy 2 bottles? 4 liters

Chapter 10 ★ Lesson 10 — three hundred eighty-seven 387

Reteaching Below Level

Liters R 10-10

Estimate how much each real object will hold when filled.

A small container holds a little. — A large container holds a lot.

Less than a liter — About a liter — More than a liter

Draw a line to the best estimate.

1. less than 1 liter / more than 1 liter
2. less than 1 liter / more than 1 liter
3. less than 1 liter / more than 1 liter

Apple Juice

124 Use with Lesson 10-10.

Practice On Level

Liters P 10-10

Circle the best estimate.

1. less than 1 liter / more than 1 liter
2. less than 1 liter / more than 1 liter
3. less than 1 liter / more than 1 liter
4. less than 1 liter / more than 1 liter
5. less than 1 liter / more than 1 liter
6. less than 1 liter / more than 1 liter

Problem Solving *Estimation*

Circle the best estimate.

7. 1 liter / 10 liters
8. 1 liter / 10 liters

124 Use with Lesson 10-10.

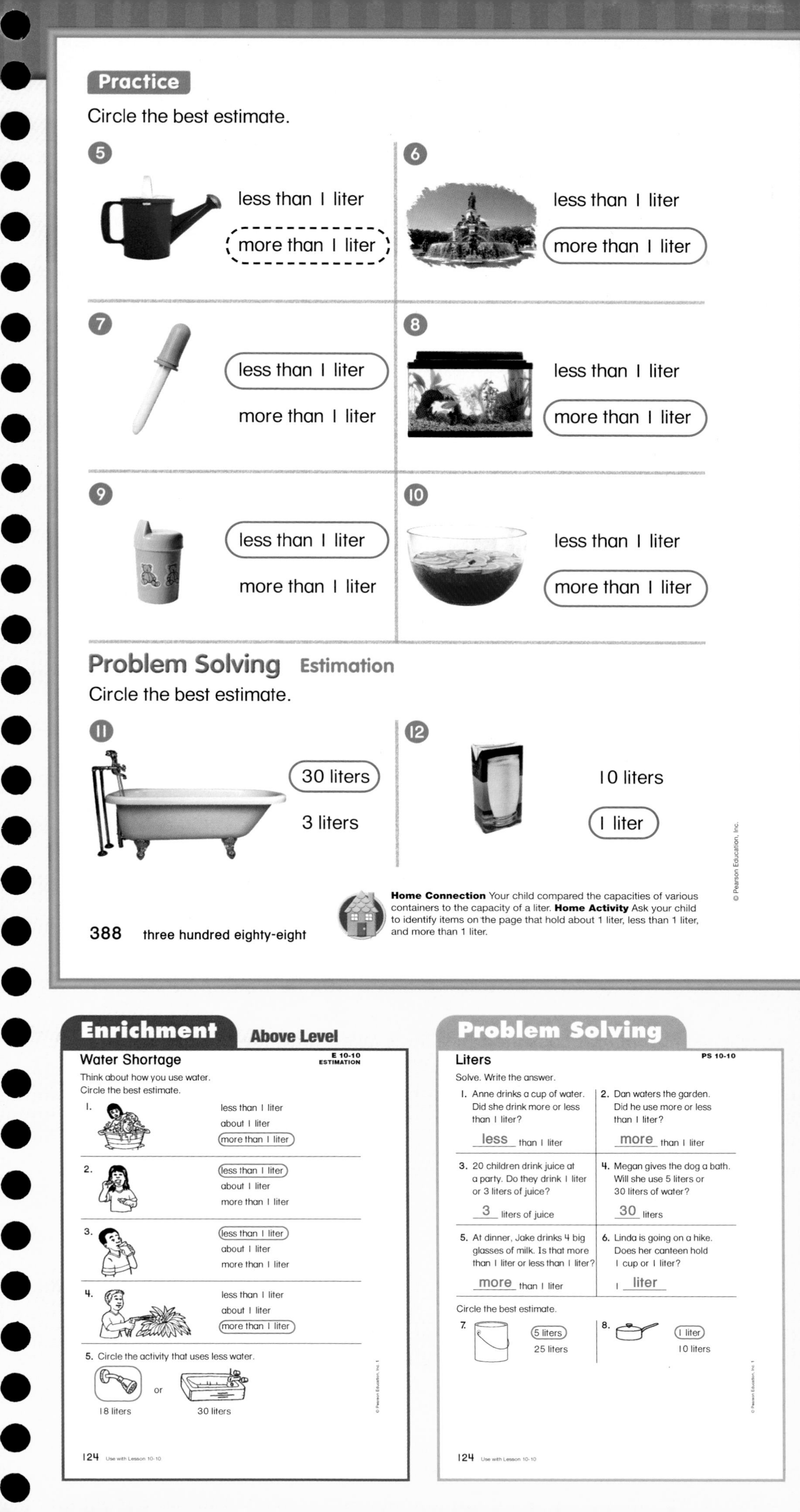

Practice

Circle the best estimate.

5. less than 1 liter / (more than 1 liter)

6. less than 1 liter / (more than 1 liter)

7. (less than 1 liter) / more than 1 liter

8. less than 1 liter / (more than 1 liter)

9. (less than 1 liter) / more than 1 liter

10. less than 1 liter / (more than 1 liter)

Problem Solving Estimation

Circle the best estimate.

11. (30 liters) / 3 liters

12. 10 liters / (1 liter)

Home Connection Your child compared the capacities of various containers to the capacity of a liter. **Home Activity** Ask your child to identify items on the page that hold about 1 liter, less than 1 liter, and more than 1 liter.

388 three hundred eighty-eight

Enrichment Above Level

Water Shortage E 10-10 ESTIMATION

Think about how you use water.
Circle the best estimate.

1. less than 1 liter / about 1 liter / (more than 1 liter)
2. (less than 1 liter) / about 1 liter / more than 1 liter
3. (less than 1 liter) / about 1 liter / more than 1 liter
4. less than 1 liter / about 1 liter / (more than 1 liter)

5. Circle the activity that uses less water.
18 liters or 30 liters

124 Use with Lesson 10-10

Problem Solving

Liters PS 10-10

Solve. Write the answer.

1. Anne drinks a cup of water. Did she drink more or less than 1 liter? less than 1 liter
2. Dan waters the garden. Did he use more or less than 1 liter? more than 1 liter
3. 20 children drink juice at a party. Do they drink 1 liter or 3 liters of juice? 3 liters of juice
4. Megan gives the dog a bath. Will she use 5 liters or 30 liters of water? 30 liters
5. At dinner, Jake drinks 4 big glasses of milk. Is that more than 1 liter or less than 1 liter? more than 1 liter
6. Linda is going on a hike. Does her canteen hold 1 cup or 1 liter? 1 liter

Circle the best estimate.

7. (5 liters) / 25 liters
8. (1 liter) / 10 liters

124 Use with Lesson 10-10

3 Practice

Keep the containers that you used in the demonstration displayed for children to refer to as they complete Exercises 5–10.

Leveled Practice

Below Level Use the pictures at the top of Student Page 387 to complete Exercises 5–10.

On Level Do all exercises as written.

Above Level For each exercise, draw a second container for which the answer would be the same.

Early Finishers Assign partners. Provide each pair with a spoon and a 1-liter container. Have children estimate and measure how many spoonfuls of water it will take to fill the liter.

4 Assess

Journal Idea Provide three containers, one of which is a 1-liter bottle. Have children draw them and label them "Holds less than 1 liter," "Holds more than 1 liter," and "Holds about 1 liter."

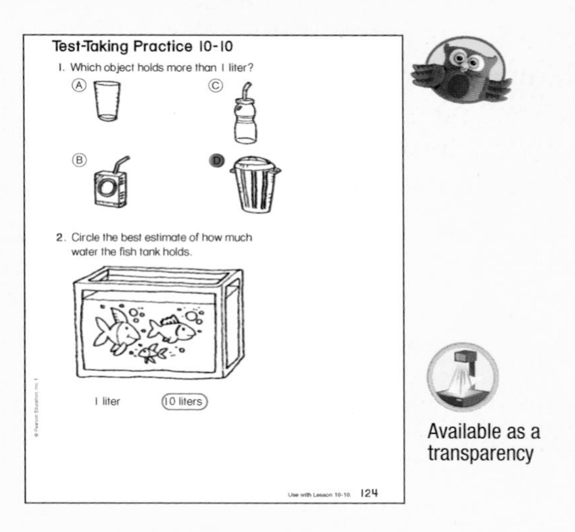

Test-Taking Practice 10-10

1. Which object holds more than 1 liter?
Ⓐ Ⓑ Ⓒ Ⓓ

2. Circle the best estimate of how much water the fish tank holds.
1 liter (10 liters)

Use with Lesson 10-10 124

Available as a transparency

10-11 Estimating, Measuring, and Comparing Weight

Lesson Organizer

Quick Lesson Overview

Objective Estimate, measure, and compare the weights of different objects.

Math Understanding You can tell how heavy or light an object is by using a balance scale to measure its weight.

Materials for Student Pages *(per child)* Balance; 25 connecting cubes; objects pictured on student pages or other similarly-sized classroom objects

Professional Development Note

Managing Instruction Children should have several opportunities to use the balance to see what it looks like when two objects weigh the same amount and when they do not. For this reason, you may wish to have children work in small groups to share the materials.

NCTM Standards

- Number and Operations
- Measurement

(For a complete correlation to the NCTM Standards and Grades Pre-K through 2 Expectations, see Pages 363G and 363H.)

Getting Started

Spiral Review

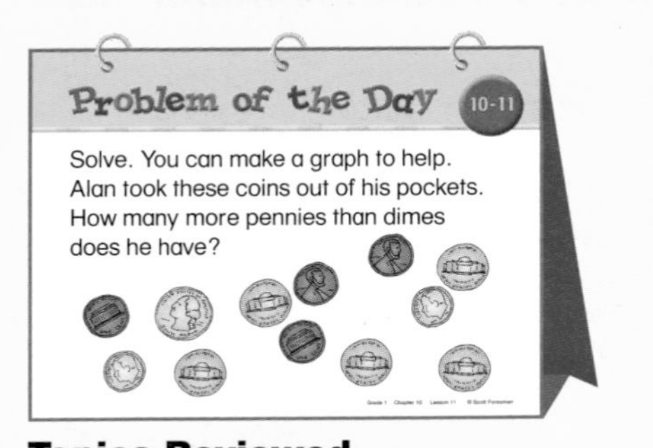
Problem of the Day 10-11

Solve. You can make a graph to help.
Alan took these coins out of his pockets.
How many more pennies than dimes does he have?

Topics Reviewed

- Pictographs and bar graphs
- Problem-Solving Strategy: Make a Graph

Answer Check children's graphs. Since Alan has 4 pennies and 2 dimes, he has 2 more pennies than dimes.

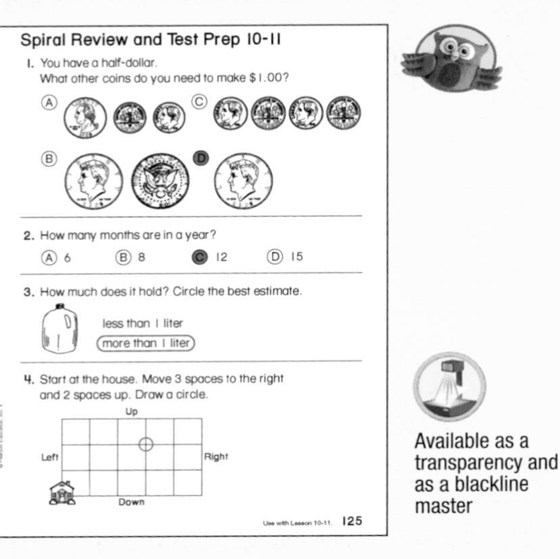
Spiral Review and Test Prep 10-11

1. You have a half-dollar.
What other coins do you need to make $1.00?
Ⓐ Ⓑ Ⓒ Ⓓ

2. How many months are in a year?
Ⓐ 6 Ⓑ 8 Ⓒ 12 Ⓓ 15

3. How much does it hold? Circle the best estimate.
less than 1 liter
more than 1 liter

4. Start at the house. Move 3 spaces to the right and 2 spaces up. Draw a circle.

Use with Lesson 10-11. 125

Available as a transparency and as a blackline master

Topics Reviewed

1. Half-Dollar and Dollar
2. Months of the Year
3. Liters
4. Coordinate Grids

Investigating the Concept

How Heavy Is It?

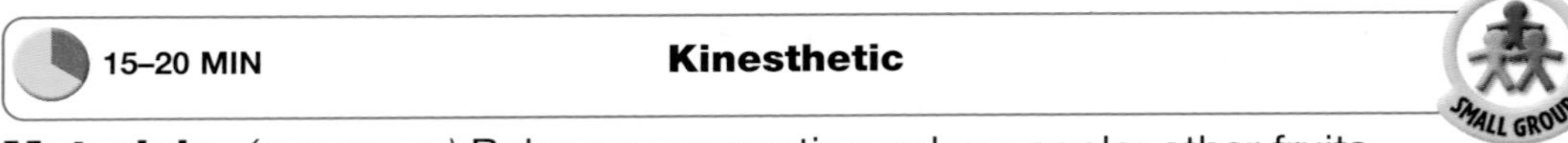

Materials *(per group)* Balance; connecting cubes; apple; other fruits

What to Do

- Ask children how many cubes they think it will take to balance an apple on the balance. Record children's estimates on the board.
- Use the balance as you demonstrate how to add one cube at a time until both sides are even. Compare the measure to the estimates.
- Have groups weigh different fruits, keeping a record of their estimates and measures. Discuss what happens to the scale when one object is heavier and one is lighter.

Ongoing Assessment

- **Number Sense Which was the lightest of the fruits that you weighed? the heaviest?** *(Answers will vary.)*
- **How can you tell whether an apple is heavier than a pear?** *(Put an apple on one side and a pear on the other side of a balance. The heavier fruit will be lower than the lighter fruit.)*

Reaching All Learners

Reading in Math

Drawing Conclusions

10–15 MIN **Linguistic**

Materials Balance; 20 pennies; notepaper pad; rubber stamp

- Tell children that you are going to weigh some things. **Watch what I am doing and tell me what conclusions you can draw.**
- Put the pad of notepaper on one side of the scale and add pennies to the other side until the scale balances.
- Help children draw conclusions about the paper pad such as, "The paper pad weighs ___ pennies."

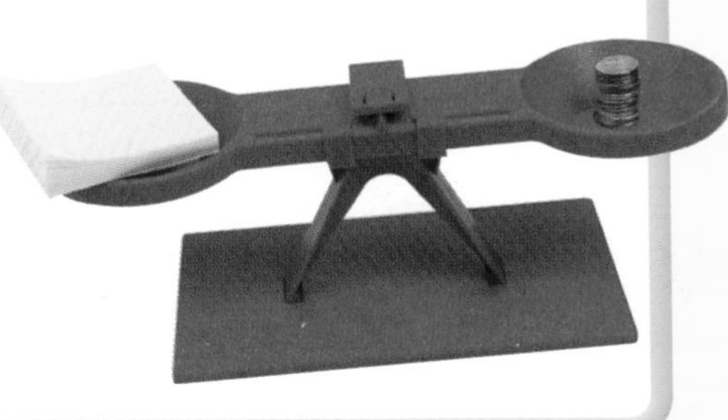

Access Content

English Language Learners

Does It Balance?

10–15 MIN **Linguistic/Kinesthetic**

Materials *(per group)* Balance; connecting cubes

- Point to the balance scale. **This is a balance.**
- Put the same number of cubes on both sides of the balance scale so that it balances.
- **The scale is in *balance.* Both sides are even.** Write the word *"balance"* on the board.
- Have children take turns putting cubes on the balance and saying either, "both sides balance" or "the sides do not balance. This side is heavier."

Reteaching

More Cubes?

10–15 MIN **Visual/Spatial**

SMALL GROUP

Materials *(per group)* Balance; connecting cubes; small toys

- Have a volunteer place a toy on one side of the balance. Explain that when both sides are even, the items weigh the same, and the scale balances.
- Ask children to guess about how many cubes will balance the toy. Write the number on the board.
- Each time a cube is added, ask: **Does it balance yet?**
- When the sides balance, have a volunteer compare the number of cubes to the estimate.

Math and Physical Education

Seesaw Balance

15–20 MIN **Kinesthetic/Linguistic**

PAIRS

- For this outdoor activity, have pairs of children try to balance their weights on a seesaw so that the seesaw is perfectly level.
- Gather the children after playtime.
- **What happened when only one person was on the seesaw? Why did one end go down and one end go up?**
- Discuss what children did and how weight affects balancing the seesaw.
- Have children compare the seesaw to the balance they use to compare weights of objects in the classroom.

10-11 Estimating, Measuring, and Comparing Weight

Objective Estimate, measure, and compare the weights of different objects.

1 Warm Up

Activate Prior Knowledge Review places where scales are used to weigh things. Have children give examples, such as a baby at the doctor's office or vegetables at the supermarket.

2 Teach

Learn!

Demonstrate how to weigh an object using connecting cubes and a balance. Place a calculator on one side of the scale and add one cube at a time until the scale balances. Determine that it takes about 10 cubes to balance the calculator. Complete the student page together, using the balance to show each answer.

Ongoing Assessment

Talk About it

- **How can you tell how many cubes an object weighs?** *(Count the cubes it takes to balance the scale.)*
- **What would happen if you added 10 more cubes to the balance after the sides were even?** *(The side with added cubes would be heavier and lower; the other side would be lighter and higher.)*

If children have difficulty using the balance,

then say the directions aloud: **Add one more** or **Stop.**

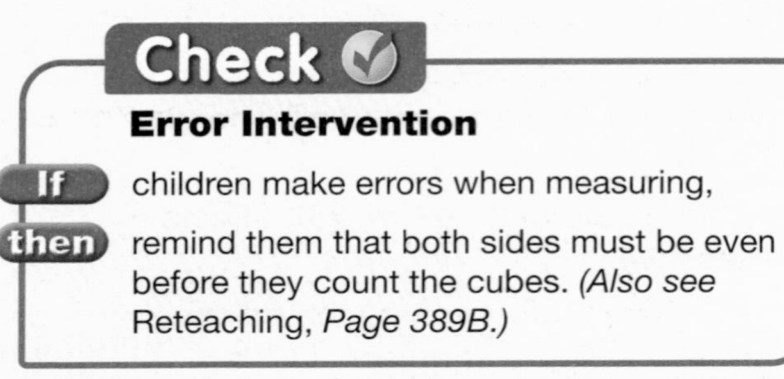

Check

Error Intervention

If children make errors when measuring,

then remind them that both sides must be even before they count the cubes. *(Also see Reteaching, Page 389B.)*

Think About It Ask children if they can tell which object is heavier just by looking. Then ask them to compare the numbers.

Name ______________________

Estimating, Measuring, and Comparing Weight

Learn!

About how many cubes will it take to balance?

I used 11 cubes.

Check

Estimate how many cubes it will take to balance.
Then measure. *Answers will vary.*

	Estimate.	Measure.
1	about ____	about ____
2	about ____	about ____

Think About It Number Sense

Which is heavier, the eraser or the pencil case? How do you know? *Answers will vary based on the actual weight of each object.*

Reteaching Below Level

Estimating, Measuring, and Comparing Weight R 10-11

Does not balance.	Balances.	Does not balance.
The orange is heavier than 2 cubes.	9 cubes are as heavy as the orange.	20 cubes are heavier than the orange.

Estimate how many cubes it will take to balance.
Then measure. *Estimates and measures will vary.*

1. Estimate. about ____ Measure. about ____
2. Estimate. about ____ Measure. about ____
3. Estimate. about ____ Measure. about ____
4. Estimate. about ____ Measure. about ____

Practice On Level

Estimating, Measuring, and Comparing Weight P 10-11 *Answers will vary.*

Estimate how many cubes it will take to balance.
Then measure.

	Estimate.	Measure.
1.	about ____	about ____
2.	about ____	about ____
3.	about ____	about ____

Problem Solving *Number Sense*

4. Number the objects from lightest to heaviest.
Use 1 for the lightest and 4 for the heaviest.

3 4 2 1

Practice

Estimate how many cubes it will take to balance.
Then measure.

Answers will vary.

	Estimate.	Measure.
3	about ____ cube	about ____ cube
4	about ____ cube	about ____ cube
5	about ____ cube	about ____ cube

Problem Solving Number Sense

6. Number the animals from lightest to heaviest.
Use 1 for the lightest and 4 for the heaviest.

4

1

3

2

Home Connection Your child estimated and measured how many cubes it takes to balance an object on a balance scale. **Home Activity** Show your child an item in your home. Have your child find one item that is lighter and one item that is heavier.

3 Practice

For Exercise 6, suggest that children first find the lightest animal and write 1 below it.

Reading Assist: Vocabulary Ask children to suggest words that mean *heavier* and *lighter,* such as *weighs more* and *weighs less.*

Leveled Practice

Below Level Work in pairs.

On Level Do all exercises individually.

Above Level Draw another object in each exercise that is lighter than the object shown.

Early Finishers Invite children to draw an object that is heavier than a pencil but lighter than a book.

4 Assess

Journal Idea Ask children to draw three fruits of different sizes. Ask them to use *heaviest* to label the one that weighs the most and *lightest* to label the one that weighs the least.

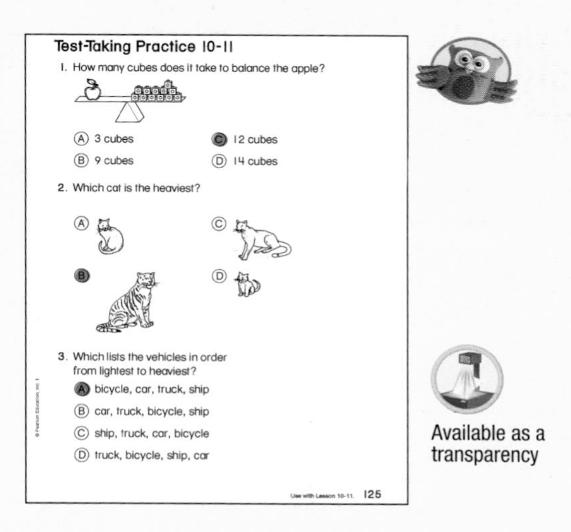

Test-Taking Practice 10-11

1. How many cubes does it take to balance the apple?

Ⓐ 3 cubes
Ⓑ 9 cubes
● 12 cubes
Ⓓ 14 cubes

2. Which cat is the heaviest?

Ⓐ Ⓑ Ⓒ Ⓓ

3. Which lists the vehicles in order from lightest to heaviest?

● bicycle, car, truck, ship
Ⓑ car, truck, bicycle, ship
Ⓒ ship, truck, car, bicycle
Ⓓ truck, bicycle, ship, car

Use with Lesson 10-11. 125

Available as a transparency

Enrichment Above Level

Balancing Act E 10-11 NUMBER SENSE

Put the number of cubes shown on the scale.
Find an object that will balance.
Draw the object on the right side of the scale.

1. Answers will vary.
2.
3.
4.
5.

Use with Lesson 10-11. 125

Problem Solving

Estimating, Measuring, and Comparing Weight PS 10-11

Does the first object weigh **more than, less than,** or **about the same as** the second object?
Circle your answer.

1. weighs ______ — (more than) / less than / about the same as
2. weighs ______ — more than / (less than) / about the same as
3. weighs ______ — more than / less than / (about the same as)
4. weighs ______ — more than / (less than) / about the same as

5. Number the objects from the lightest to heaviest.
Use 1 for the lightest and 4 for the heaviest.

2 4 3 1

Use with Lesson 10-11. 125

10-12 Pounds

Lesson Organizer

Quick Lesson Overview

Objective Compare the weights of objects to one pound.

Math Understanding A pound is a standard unit used to measure weight.

Vocabulary Pound

Professional Development Note

Effective Questioning Techniques
In this lesson, children will be asked to estimate whether an item weighs more or less than 1 pound. Encourage children, through your questioning, to discuss why they have chosen each estimate. Ask questions, such as: **Have you ever actually held this item in your hand? What about the size of this item led you to choose that estimate? What else do you know about this item that helped you choose the estimate?**

NCTM Standards

- Number and Operations
- Measurement

(For a complete correlation to the NCTM Standards and Grades Pre-K through 2 Expectations, see Pages 363G and 363H.)

Getting Started

Spiral Review

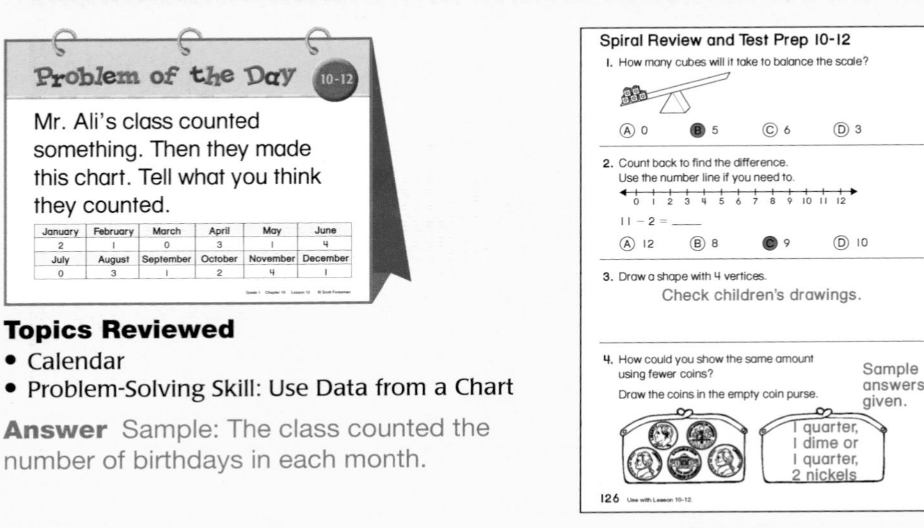

Problem of the Day 10-12

Mr. Ali's class counted something. Then they made this chart. Tell what you think they counted.

January	February	March	April	May	June
2	1	0	3	1	4
July	August	September	October	November	December
0	3	1	2	4	1

Spiral Review and Test Prep 10-12

1. How many cubes will it take to balance the scale?

Ⓐ 0 Ⓑ 5 Ⓒ 6 Ⓓ 3

2. Count back to find the difference. Use the number line if you need to.

0 1 2 3 4 5 6 7 8 9 10 11 12

11 − 2 = ____

Ⓐ 12 Ⓑ 8 Ⓒ 9 Ⓓ 10

3. Draw a shape with 4 vertices.

Check children's drawings.

4. How could you show the same amount using fewer coins? Draw the coins in the empty coin purse.

Sample answers given.

1 quarter, 1 dime or 1 quarter, 2 nickels

126 Use with Lesson 10-12.

Topics Reviewed

- Calendar
- Problem-Solving Skill: Use Data from a Chart

Answer Sample: The class counted the number of birthdays in each month.

Available as a transparency and as a blackline master

Topics Reviewed

1. Estimating, Measuring, and Comparing Weight
2. Counting Back Using a Number Line
3. Properties of Plane Shapes
4. Counting Sets of Coins

Investigating the Concept

More or Less Than a Pound?

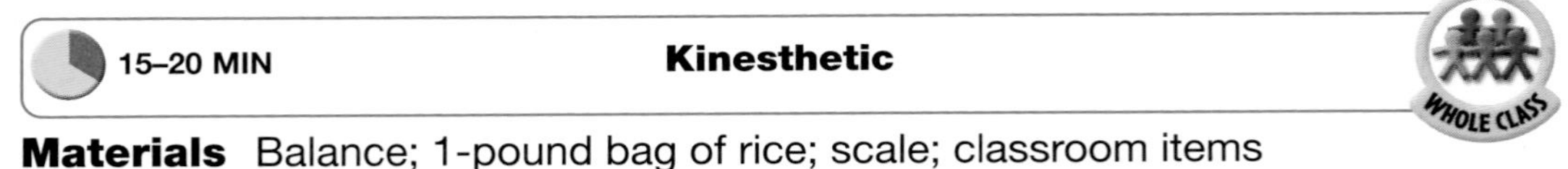

Materials Balance; 1-pound bag of rice; scale; classroom items

What to Do

- Pass around the 1-pound bag of rice. **A pound is a unit used to measure weight. This bag weighs 1 pound.**
- Demonstrate how to estimate whether a book weighs more than 1 pound or less than 1 pound. After children estimate, place the book and the rice on the balance to check their estimates.
- Have children continue estimating and measuring the weights of other classroom items. For each item, have children determine whether the weight is more or less than 1 pound.

Ongoing Assessment

- **Reasoning** **Name something that weighs less than 1 pound.** *(Sample responses: Button, pencil, eraser, connecting cube)*
- **Does a computer weigh more or less than 1 pound?** *(More)*

Reaching All Learners

Oral Language in Math

More, Less, the Same

5–10 MIN **Linguistic**

Materials Dictionary; straw; shoe; 1-pound box of cereal or crackers

- Show the items to the class. **Which item weighs 1 pound?** Show children the weight printed on the 1-pound box.
- Tell children that one item weighs more than 1 pound, or is heavier than 1 pound. Have children guess which one.
- Ask children to tell which item weighs less than a pound, or is lighter than a pound. **Which item weighs nearly the same as the box of cereal?**

Extend Language

English Language Learners

Lighter and Heavier

10–15 MIN **Linguistic/Kinesthetic**

- Play a game of "Lighter and Heavier" with the group.
- Choose pairs of items in the classroom for children to examine, such as a paper bag and a stapler. Select a child to pick out the item that is *heavier* or the one that is *lighter.*
- Continue until all of the children have had the opportunity to participate.
- Then have children arrange three or four of the items from lightest to heaviest.

Reteaching

What Weighs 1 Pound?

10–15 MIN **Kinesthetic**

Materials *(per group)* Balance; connecting cubes; 1-pound bag of rice; apple; 1-pound loaf of bread; stone or other heavy object

- Put the bag of rice on the scale. **This weighs 1 pound.**
- Add connecting cubes to the other side until they balance with the rice. **The cubes weigh 1 pound.**
- Remove the rice.
- Have children place, in turn, the apple, the stone, and the bread on the scale.
- **Why is this side lower, or higher, than the side with the cubes?** *(It weighs more, or less, than 1 pound.)*

Math and Social Studies

Pounds at the Grocery Store

15–20 MIN **Linguistic/Kinesthetic**

Materials *(per pair)* Empty cereal boxes and other packages; money

- Help children find the weights listed on the packages. Explain that just about everything at the grocery store is marked with its weight.
- Let children play grocery store by asking for groceries by package weight and by buying and selling the empty containers using the money.

Objective Compare the weights of objects to one pound.

1 Warm Up

Activate Prior Knowledge Review how to compare weights. Have children arrange sets of three objects in order from heaviest to lightest.

2 Teach

Talk about the balances shown at the top of the student page. Explain that a pound is a unit used to measure weight. You may wish to have children take turns lifting a 1-pound box of rice to feel how much 1 pound weighs. If possible, use a balance to show that an apple weighs less than 1 pound. Add more apples to show a weight that is more than 1 pound.

Ongoing Assessment

Talk About It

- **How can you decide whether a pencil weighs more or less than 1 pound without a balance?** *(By comparing its weight to something that weighs 1 pound)*
- **Which objects can you name that are probably lighter than 1 pound?** *(Sample responses: Stamp, eyeglasses, bracelet)*

If children have difficulty understanding why the pound of rice is lower on the balance than the apple,

then remind them that the heavier object is always lower on the balance.

Check

Error Intervention

If children make errors with *more* or *less*,

then ask them to hold the object in one hand and the pound in the other or to use the balance. *(Also see* Reteaching, *Page 391B.)*

Think About It Point out to children that even though the bags are the same size, they hold different objects, and a marble is much heavier than a piece of popcorn.

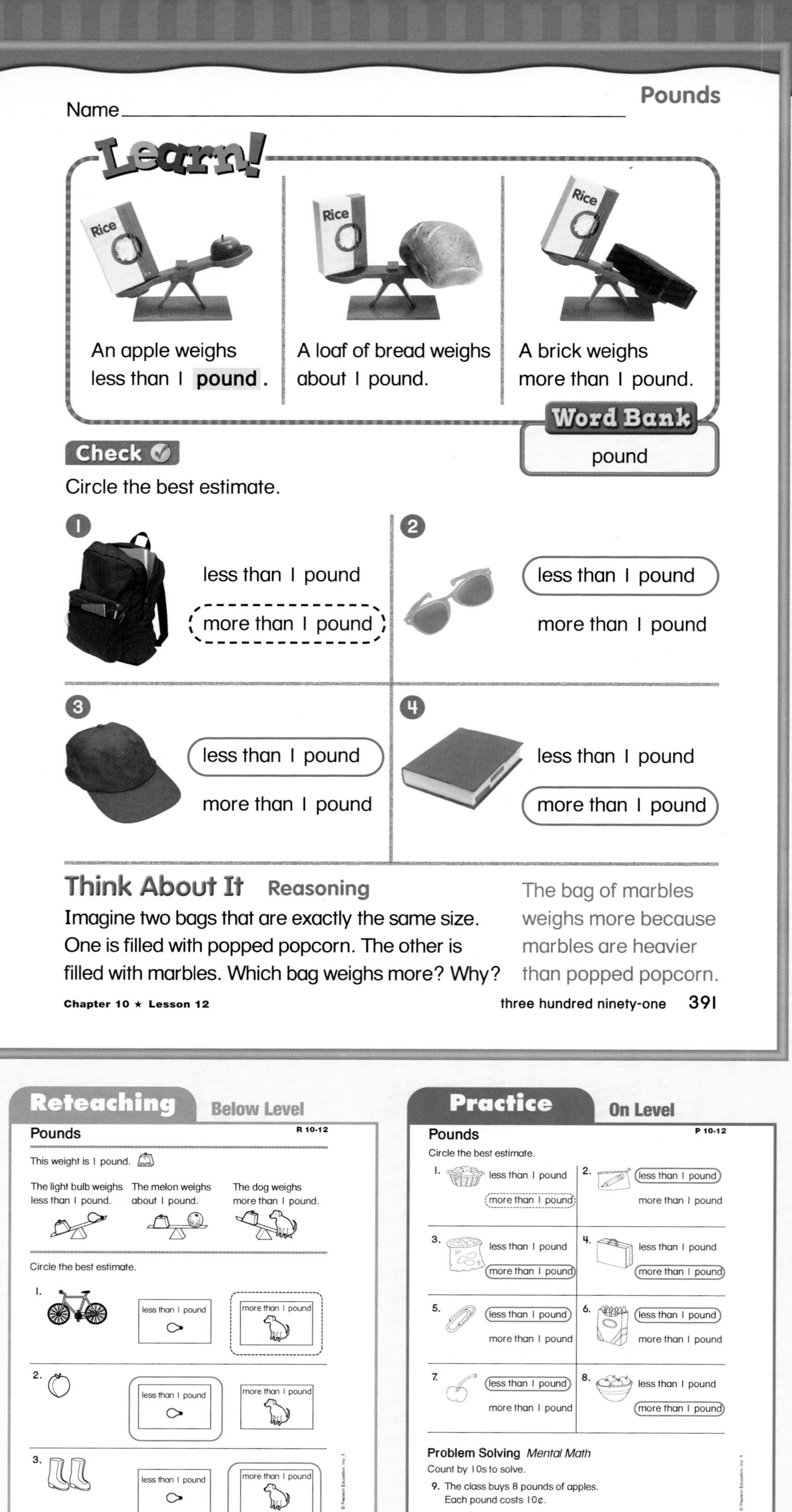

Name ____________________ Pounds

Learn!

An apple weighs less than 1 pound.

A loaf of bread weighs about 1 pound.

A brick weighs more than 1 pound.

Word Bank: pound

Check

Circle the best estimate.

1. less than 1 pound / more than 1 pound
2. less than 1 pound / more than 1 pound
3. less than 1 pound / more than 1 pound
4. less than 1 pound / more than 1 pound

Think About It Reasoning

Imagine two bags that are exactly the same size. One is filled with popped popcorn. The other is filled with marbles. Which bag weighs more? Why?

The bag of marbles weighs more because marbles are heavier than popped popcorn.

Chapter 10 ★ Lesson 12 three hundred ninety-one 391

Reteaching Below Level

Pounds R 10-12

This weight is 1 pound.

The light bulb weighs less than 1 pound. The melon weighs about 1 pound. The dog weighs more than 1 pound.

Circle the best estimate.

1. less than 1 pound / more than 1 pound
2. less than 1 pound / more than 1 pound
3. less than 1 pound / more than 1 pound

126 Use with Lesson 10-12

Practice On Level

Pounds P 10-12

Circle the best estimate.

1. less than 1 pound / more than 1 pound
2. less than 1 pound / more than 1 pound
3. less than 1 pound / more than 1 pound
4. less than 1 pound / more than 1 pound
5. less than 1 pound / more than 1 pound
6. less than 1 pound / more than 1 pound
7. less than 1 pound / more than 1 pound
8. less than 1 pound / more than 1 pound

Problem Solving *Mental Math*

Count by 10s to solve.

9. The class buys 8 pounds of apples. Each pound costs 10¢.

How much does the class pay? 80 ¢

126 Use with Lesson 10-12

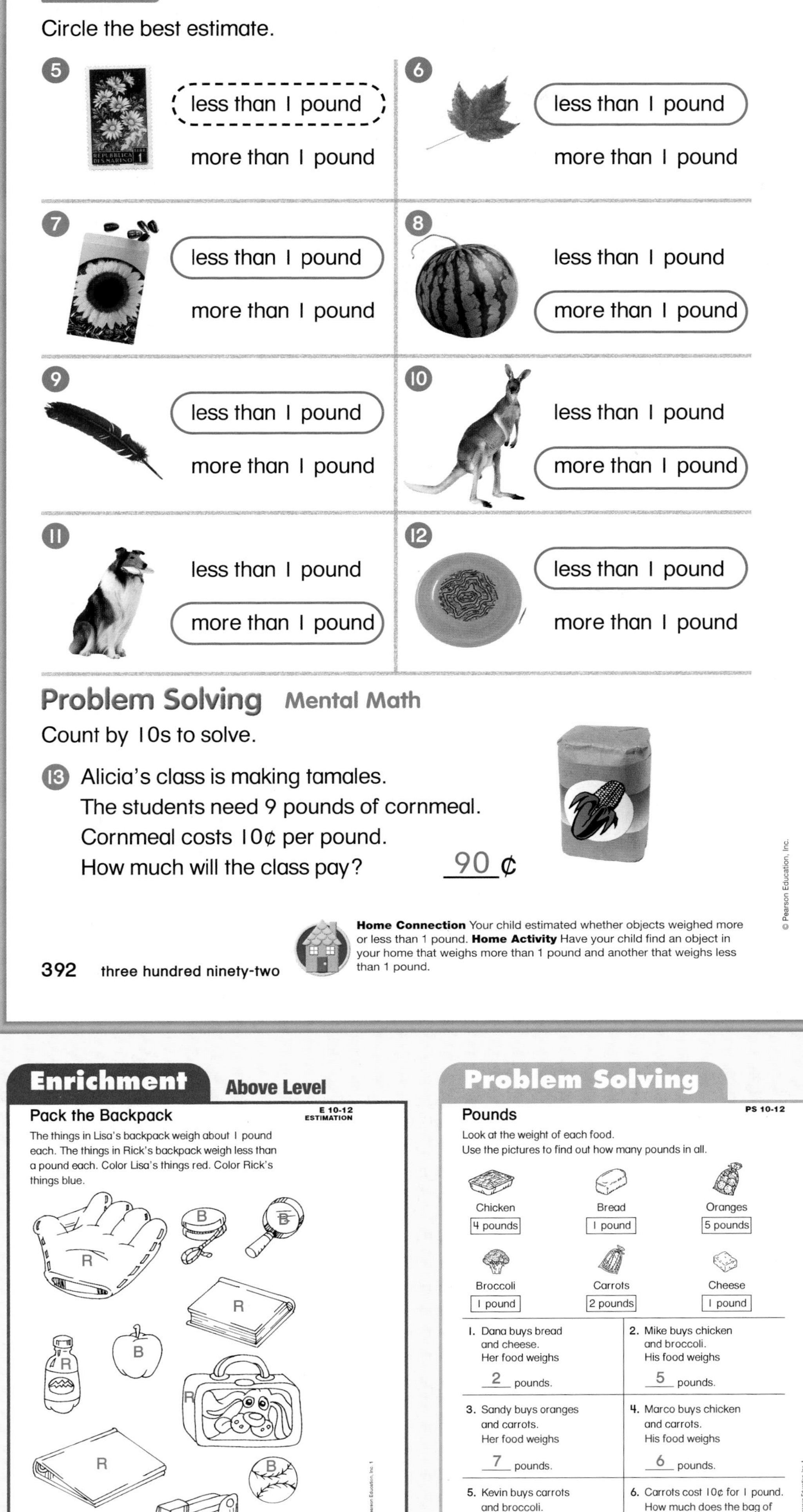

Practice

Circle the best estimate.

5. less than 1 pound / more than 1 pound
6. less than 1 pound / more than 1 pound
7. less than 1 pound / more than 1 pound
8. less than 1 pound / more than 1 pound
9. less than 1 pound / more than 1 pound
10. less than 1 pound / more than 1 pound
11. less than 1 pound / more than 1 pound
12. less than 1 pound / more than 1 pound

Problem Solving Mental Math

Count by 10s to solve.

13. Alicia's class is making tamales.
The students need 9 pounds of cornmeal.
Cornmeal costs 10¢ per pound.
How much will the class pay? 90 ¢

Home Connection Your child estimated whether objects weighed more or less than 1 pound. **Home Activity** Have your child find an object in your home that weighs more than 1 pound and another that weighs less than 1 pound.

Enrichment Above Level

Pack the Backpack E 10-12 ESTIMATION

The things in Lisa's backpack weigh about 1 pound each. The things in Rick's backpack weigh less than a pound each. Color Lisa's things red. Color Rick's things blue.

Problem Solving

Pounds PS 10-12

Look at the weight of each food.
Use the pictures to find out how many pounds in all.

Chicken	Bread	Oranges
4 pounds	1 pound	5 pounds
Broccoli	**Carrots**	**Cheese**
1 pound	2 pounds	1 pound

1. Dana buys bread and cheese. Her food weighs 2 pounds.
2. Mike buys chicken and broccoli. His food weighs 5 pounds.
3. Sandy buys oranges and carrots. Her food weighs 7 pounds.
4. Marco buys chicken and carrots. His food weighs 6 pounds.
5. Kevin buys carrots and broccoli. His food weighs 3 pounds.
6. Carrots cost 10¢ for 1 pound. How much does the bag of carrots shown above cost? 20 ¢

3 Practice

Have children draw a picture to solve Exercise 13.

Reading Assist: Main Idea Ask children to look at Exercise 5. Tell them that the main idea is that some things weigh less than 1 pound. Ask children to find other exercises that show this main idea. *(Exercises 6, 7, 9, and 12)*

Leveled Practice

Below Level Use dimes to solve Exercise 13.

On Level Do all exercises as written.

Above Level Write a story problem like the one in Exercise 13.

Early Finishers Ask children to fill a bag with classroom objects until they think it weighs about 1 pound. Children can then weigh the bag to check their estimates.

4 Assess

Journal Idea Have children draw five objects that are heavier than a feather, but lighter than their math book.

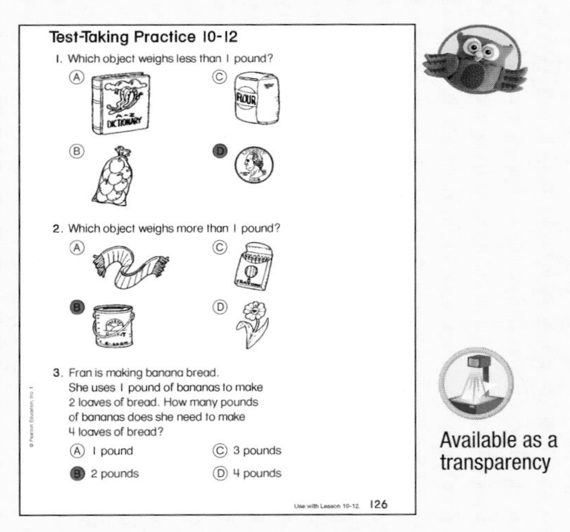

Test-Taking Practice 10-12

1. Which object weighs less than 1 pound?
Ⓐ Ⓑ Ⓒ Ⓓ

2. Which object weighs more than 1 pound?
Ⓐ Ⓑ Ⓒ Ⓓ

3. Fran is making banana bread. She uses 1 pound of bananas to make 2 loaves of bread. How many pounds of bananas does she need to make 4 loaves of bread?
Ⓐ 1 pound Ⓒ 3 pounds
Ⓑ 2 pounds Ⓓ 4 pounds

Use with Lesson 10-12. 126

Available as a transparency

10-13 Grams and Kilograms

Lesson Organizer

Quick Lesson Overview

Objective Select the appropriate unit for measuring, given the choice of grams or kilograms.

Math Understanding A gram and a kilogram are standard units used to measure weight; 1 kilogram is the same as 1,000 grams.

Vocabulary Gram, kilogram

Professional Development Note

How Children Learn Math Before doing the exercises on these student pages, have children take turns holding things that measure about 1 kilogram and things that measure about 1 gram so that they can feel the difference. Keep the objects available for those children who need to use them for reference throughout the lesson.

NCTM Standards

- Measurement

(For a complete correlation to the NCTM Standards and Grades Pre-K through 2 Expectations, see Pages 363G and 363H.)

Getting Started

Spiral Review

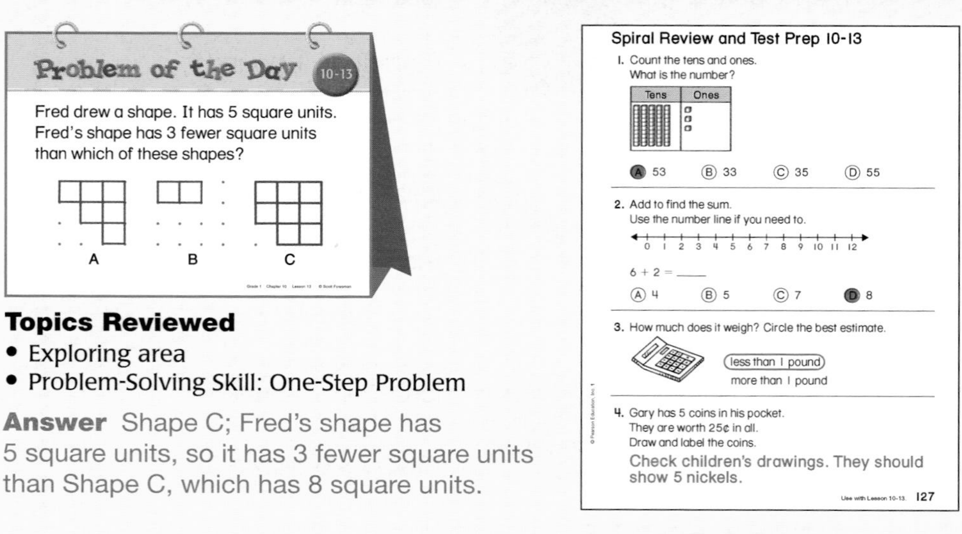

Problem of the Day 10-13

Fred drew a shape. It has 5 square units. Fred's shape has 3 fewer square units than which of these shapes?

A B C

Spiral Review and Test Prep 10-13

1. Count the tens and ones. What is the number?

Tens | Ones

(A) 53 (B) 33 (C) 35 (D) 55

2. Add to find the sum. Use the number line if you need to.

0 1 2 3 4 5 6 7 8 9 10 11 12

6 + 2 = ____

(A) 4 (B) 5 (C) 7 (D) 8

3. How much does it weigh? Circle the best estimate.

less than 1 pound

more than 1 pound

4. Gary has 5 coins in his pocket. They are worth 25¢ in all. Draw and label the coins.

Check children's drawings. They should show 5 nickels.

Use with Lesson 10-13. 127

Topics Reviewed
- Exploring area
- Problem-Solving Skill: One-Step Problem

Answer Shape C; Fred's shape has 5 square units, so it has 3 fewer square units than Shape C, which has 8 square units.

Available as a transparency and as a blackline master

Topics Reviewed
1. Tens and Ones
2. Adding Using a Number Line
3. Pounds
4. Quarter

Investigating the Concept

Grams or Kilograms

15–20 MIN **Visual/Spatial/Kinesthetic** WHOLE CLASS

Materials *(per child)* 2 index cards; jumbo paper clip; full quart of milk or juice

What to Do

- Explain that a gram and a kilogram are units used to measure how heavy something is. Pass around a jumbo paper clip to show something that measures about 1 gram, noting that it is very light. Do the same with a full quart of milk for a kilogram, noting that it is heavier than the gram.
- Have children write "gram" on one card and "kilogram" on the other card. Point to various objects around the room and ask children to show the card that tells the better unit to use to measure each object.

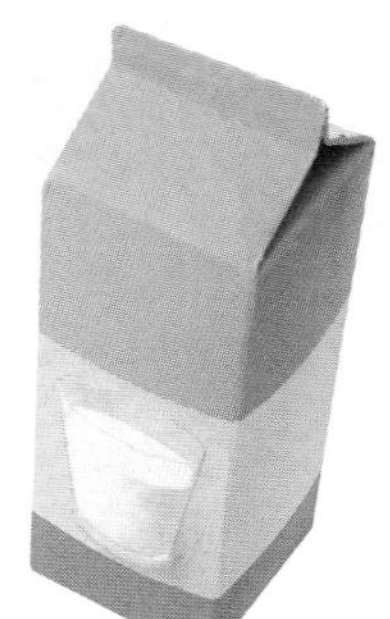

gram

kilogram

Ongoing Assessment

- **Reasoning Name something you would measure using grams.** *(Sample responses: Pencil, stamp, flower, paintbrush)*
- **Name something you would measure using kilograms.** *(Sample responses: Lamp, rabbit, chair)*

Reaching All Learners

Math Vocabulary

Make a Glossary

10–15 MIN **Linguistic**

Materials *(per group)* Chart paper; old magazines; scissors; glue

- Make an illustrated classroom glossary that summarizes terms used in measuring amounts: *pound, gram, kilogram* and *cup, pint, quart, liter.*
- Help children define the vocabulary words in such sentences as, "A loaf of bread weighs 1 pound."
- Invite children to illustrate their definitions with photographs from magazines.
- Display the glossary.

Activate Prior Knowledge/Build Background

English Language Learners

Kilograms and Pounds

10–15 MIN **Auditory/Linguistic**

Materials *(per group)* Balance; books

- Some children might be familiar with measures given in kilograms. Explain that a pound is another way to show how heavy something is.
- Encourage them to use this pattern: "How much does this book weigh? It measures ___ kilograms. It also weighs ___ pounds."
- Place a 1-kilogram book on one side of the scale and a 1-pound book on the other. Let children observe that a kilogram is heavier than a pound.

Reteaching

Light as a Cube, Heavy as a Book

10–15 MIN **Visual/Spatial** SMALL GROUP

Materials *(per group)* Connecting cube; heavy book; chart paper; marker

- Make a two-column chart. One column is headed "Use Grams" and has a picture of a connecting cube. The other is headed "Use Kilograms" and has a picture of a book.
- Have children compare the measures of the connecting cube and the book.
- Ask children to choose items in the classroom and tell whether they would be better measured in grams or in kilograms.
- Invite children to draw pictures of their objects in the correct columns of the chart.

Advanced Learners

How Many Grams in a Kilogram?

15–20 MIN **Logical/Mathematical** PAIRS

Materials *(per pair)* Sheets of paper; books

- Have a volunteer tell which is heavier, a gram or a kilogram.
- Explain that a kilogram is 1,000 grams.
- Challenge children to figure out how many objects it takes to make a kilogram. **If a sheet of paper measures about 1 gram, how many sheets of paper are needed to measure 1 kilogram in all?** *(1,000 sheets)*
- Have children work in pairs to discuss the solution to this problem and to write similar problems.

A leaf measures 1 gram.

How many leaves are needed to measure 3 kilograms in all?

Objective Select the appropriate unit for measuring, given the choice of grams or kilograms.

1 Warm Up

Activate Prior Knowledge Review the meanings of the terms *heavier* and *lighter.* Have children take turns holding two objects and comparing their weights.

2 Teach

Learn!

Explain that a gram and a kilogram are units used to measure how heavy something is. To demonstrate a gram weight, give each child a sheet of paper. Ask children to lift their math books to show 1 kilogram. Explain that we measure the weight of light things in grams and the weight of heavy things in kilograms.

Ongoing Assessment

Talk About It

- **What might measure about 1 gram?** *(Sample responses: Penny, button, stamp)*
- **Would you always measure small objects using grams? Explain.** *(No; because some small objects are heavy)*

If children do not understand the relative measures of a gram and a kilogram,

then provide other items of each measure for children to hold and compare.

Check

Error Intervention

If children make errors choosing units,

then suggest that they compare each object to the sheet of paper or to the math book. *(Also see* Reteaching, *Page 393B.)*

Think About It Ask children to think about a bag of feathers and a bag of rocks. **Which would you choose to measure the feathers?** *(Grams)* **the rocks?** *(Kilograms)*

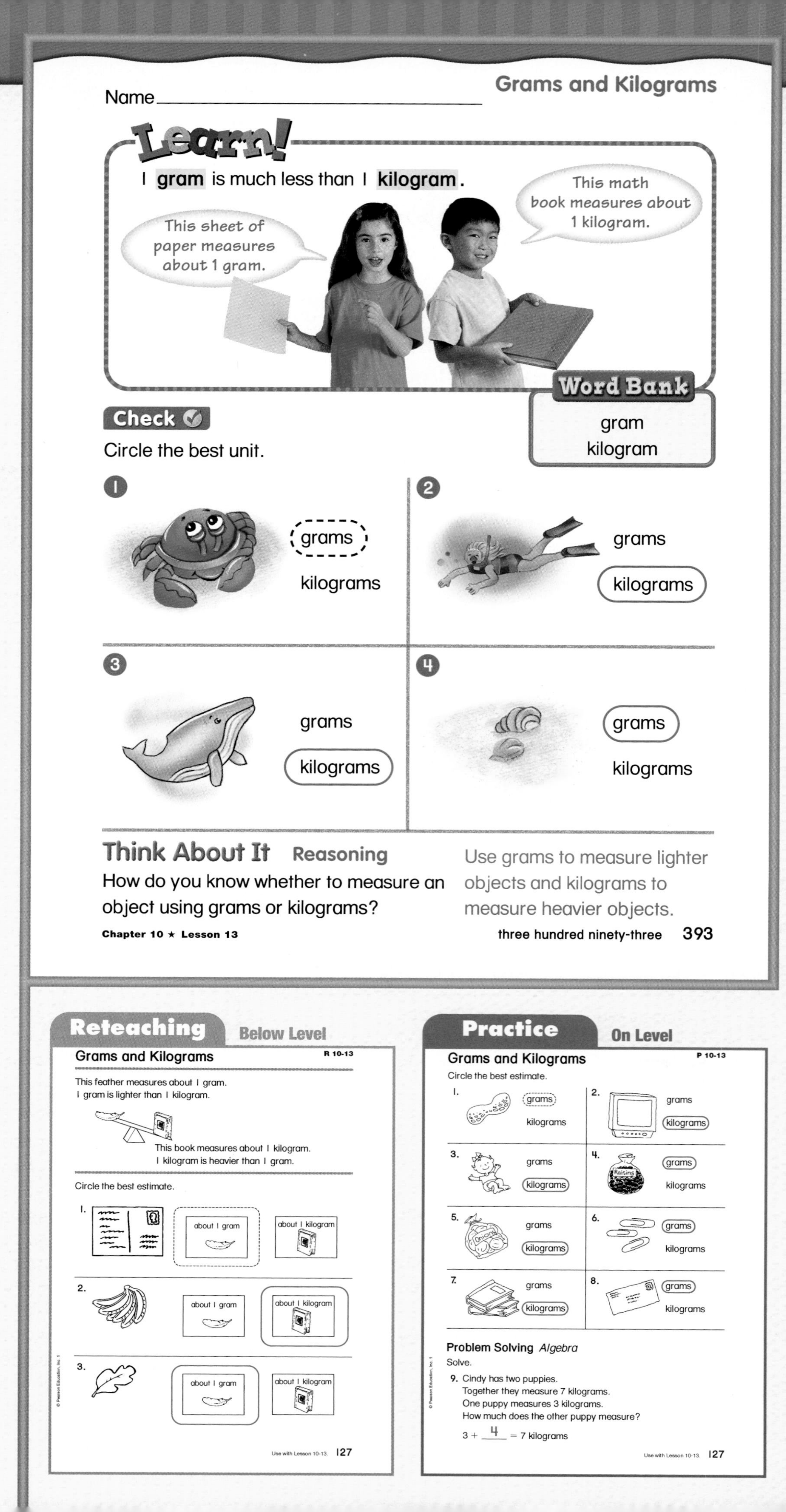

Name ____________

Grams and Kilograms

Learn!

I gram is much less than I kilogram.

Word Bank
gram
kilogram

Check

Circle the best unit.

1. grams / kilograms
2. grams / kilograms
3. grams / kilograms
4. grams / kilograms

Think About It Reasoning

How do you know whether to measure an object using grams or kilograms?

Use grams to measure lighter objects and kilograms to measure heavier objects.

Chapter 10 ★ Lesson 13 three hundred ninety-three 393

Reteaching Below Level

Grams and Kilograms R 10-13

This feather measures about I gram.
I gram is lighter than I kilogram.

This book measures about I kilogram.
I kilogram is heavier than I gram.

Circle the best estimate.

1. about I gram / about I kilogram
2. about I gram / about I kilogram
3. about I gram / about I kilogram

Use with Lesson 10-13. 127

Practice On Level

Grams and Kilograms P 10-13

Circle the best estimate.

1. grams / kilograms
2. grams / kilograms
3. grams / kilograms
4. grams / kilograms
5. grams / kilograms
6. grams / kilograms
7. grams / kilograms
8. grams / kilograms

Problem Solving *Algebra*

Solve.

9. Cindy has two puppies.
Together they measure 7 kilograms.
One puppy measures 3 kilograms.
How much does the other puppy measure?
3 + 4 = 7 kilograms

Use with Lesson 10-13. 127

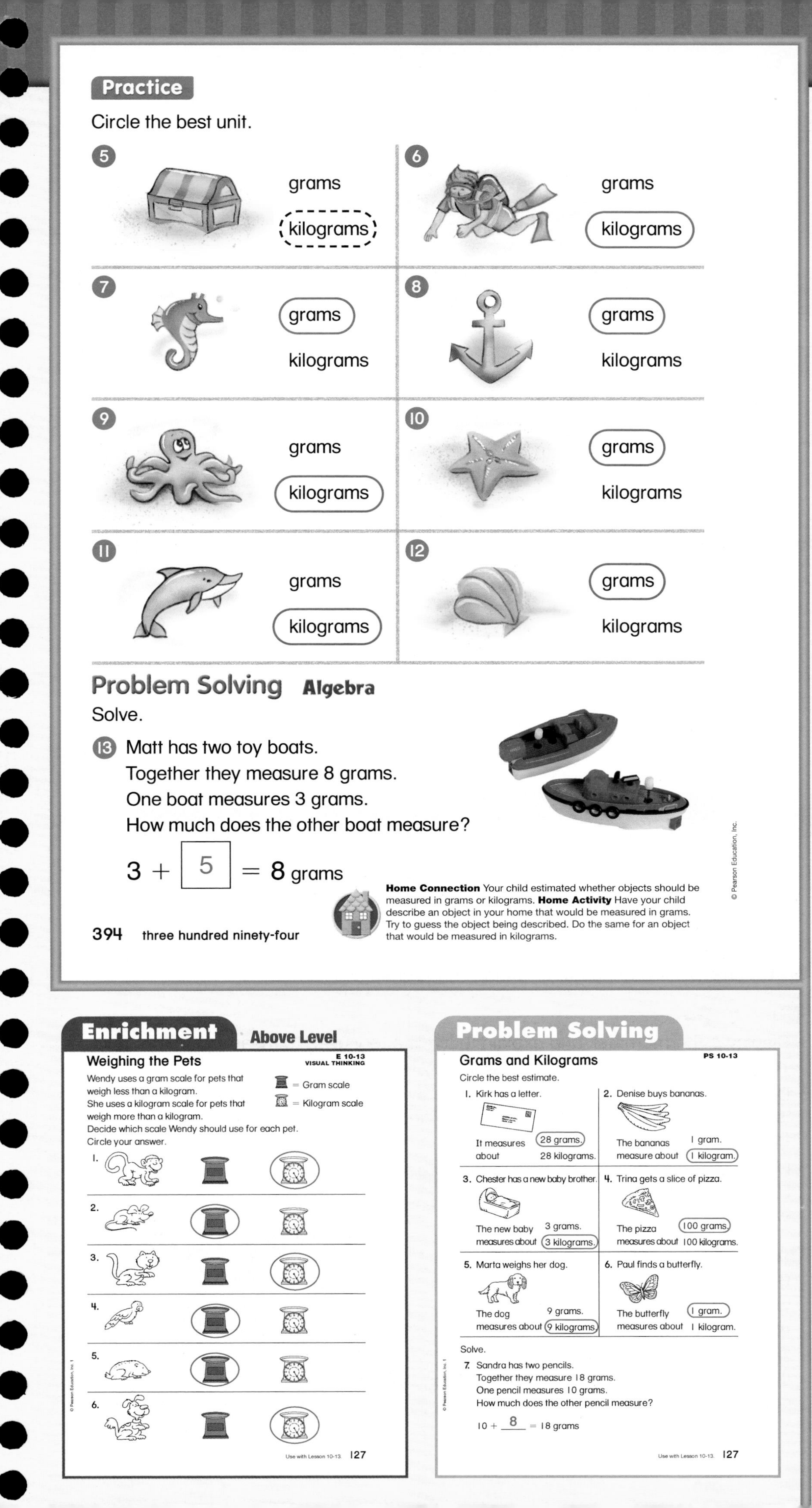

Practice

Circle the best unit.

5. grams / kilograms
6. grams / kilograms
7. grams / kilograms
8. grams / kilograms
9. grams / kilograms
10. grams / kilograms
11. grams / kilograms
12. grams / kilograms

Problem Solving **Algebra**

Solve.

13. Matt has two toy boats.
Together they measure 8 grams.
One boat measures 3 grams.
How much does the other boat measure?

$3 + \boxed{5} = 8$ grams

Home Connection Your child estimated whether objects should be measured in grams or kilograms. **Home Activity** Have your child describe an object in your home that would be measured in grams. Try to guess the object being described. Do the same for an object that would be measured in kilograms.

394 three hundred ninety-four

Enrichment Above Level

Weighing the Pets — E 10-13 VISUAL THINKING

Wendy uses a gram scale for pets that weigh less than a kilogram.
She uses a kilogram scale for pets that weigh more than a kilogram.
Decide which scale Wendy should use for each pet.
Circle your answer.

= Gram scale
= Kilogram scale

1.
2.
3.
4.
5.
6.

Use with Lesson 10-13. 127

Problem Solving

Grams and Kilograms — PS 10-13

Circle the best estimate.

1. Kirk has a letter. It measures about 28 grams. / 28 kilograms.
2. Denise buys bananas. The bananas measure about 1 gram. / 1 kilogram.
3. Chester has a new baby brother. The new baby measures about 3 grams. / 3 kilograms.
4. Trina gets a slice of pizza. The pizza measures about 100 grams. / 100 kilograms.
5. Marta weighs her dog. The dog measures about 9 grams. / 9 kilograms.
6. Paul finds a butterfly. The butterfly measures about 1 gram. / 1 kilogram.

Solve.

7. Sandra has two pencils.
Together they measure 18 grams.
One pencil measures 10 grams.
How much does the other pencil measure?

10 + 8 = 18 grams

Use with Lesson 10-13. 127

3 Practice

Discuss when to measure using grams and when to measure using kilograms. Children should conclude that lighter objects are measured in grams and heavier objects are measured in kilograms.

Leveled Practice

Below Level Work with a partner to complete all exercises.

On Level Complete all exercises as written.

Above Level For Exercises 5–12, draw other objects that weigh the same amount as those pictured.

Early Finishers Ask children to make a list of objects in the classroom that they would measure using grams.

4 Assess

Journal Idea Ask children to draw three things they might find at a grocery store that would be measured in kilograms.

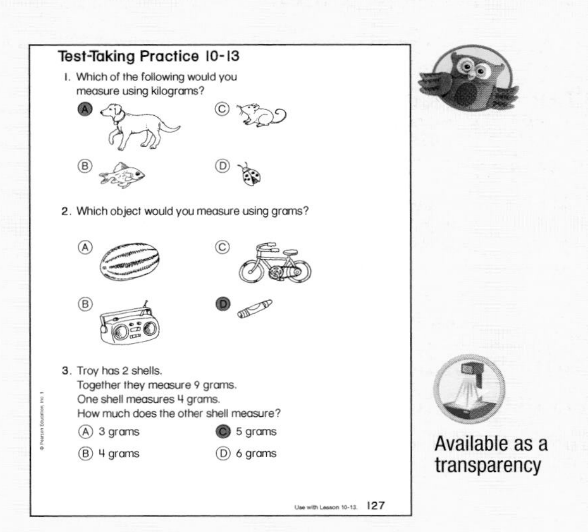

Test-Taking Practice 10-13

1. Which of the following would you measure using kilograms?
Ⓐ Ⓑ Ⓒ Ⓓ

2. Which object would you measure using grams?
Ⓐ Ⓑ Ⓒ Ⓓ

3. Troy has 2 shells.
Together they measure 9 grams.
One shell measures 4 grams.
How much does the other shell measure?
Ⓐ 3 grams Ⓑ 4 grams Ⓒ 5 grams Ⓓ 6 grams

Use with Lesson 10-13. 127

Available as a transparency

10-14 Measuring Temperature

Lesson Organizer

Quick Lesson Overview

Objective Compare temperatures on a thermometer and match them to activities or objects.

Math Understanding Temperature is a measure of how hot or cold something is.

Vocabulary Thermometer, temperature

Professional Development Note

Math Background Review measuring tools and the units they measure. Write the following chart on the board:

Tool	Units
ruler	inches, feet, centimeters
container	cups, pints, quarts, liters
balance	pounds, grams, kilograms

Tell children that in this lesson they will learn about the thermometer, which is used to measure temperature. Add *thermometer* and *degrees* to the chart.

NCTM Standards

- Measurement

(For a complete correlation to the NCTM Standards and Grades Pre-K through 2 Expectations, see Pages 363G and 363H.)

Getting Started

Spiral Review

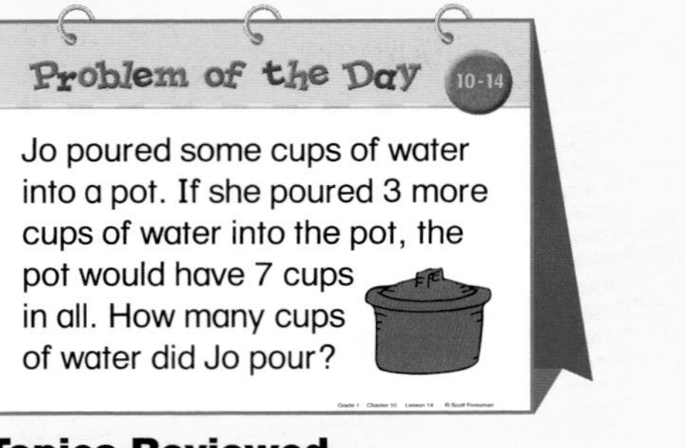

Problem of the Day 10-14

Jo poured some cups of water into a pot. If she poured 3 more cups of water into the pot, the pot would have 7 cups in all. How many cups of water did Jo pour?

Topics Reviewed

- Addition and subtraction
- Problem-Solving Skill: One-Step Problem

Answer Jo poured 4 cups of water into the pot; $3 + 4 = 7$, and $7 - 3 = 4$.

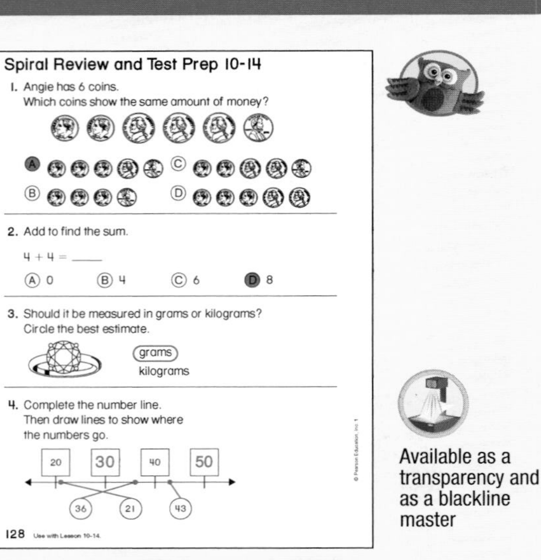

Spiral Review and Test Prep 10-14

1. Angie has 6 coins. Which coins show the same amount of money?

Ⓐ Ⓑ Ⓒ Ⓓ

2. Add to find the sum.

4 + 4 = ____

Ⓐ 0 Ⓑ 4 Ⓒ 6 Ⓓ 8

3. Should it be measured in grams or kilograms? Circle the best estimate.

grams
kilograms

4. Complete the number line. Then draw lines to show where the numbers go.

20 30 40 50

36 21 43

128 Use with Lesson 10-14.

© Pearson Education, Inc. 1

Available as a transparency and as a blackline master

Topics Reviewed

1. Counting Dimes, Nickels, and Pennies
2. Doubles
3. Grams and Kilograms
4. Number-Line Estimation: Numbers to 100

Investigating the Concept

Comparing Temperatures

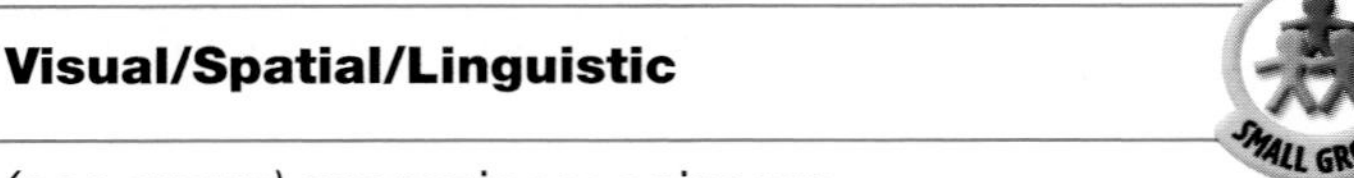

15–20 MIN **Visual/Spatial/Linguistic** SMALL GROUP

Materials Thermometer; *(per group)* magazines; scissors

What to Do

- Display a thermometer and explain that it is a tool used to measure temperature. Tell children that the temperature tells how hot or cold something is.
- Draw two thermometers on the board. Draw a red line that reaches 85°F. **85°F is a hot temperature.** Then draw a red line that reaches 30°F. **30°F is a cold temperature.**
- Discuss things that children might do outdoors on a hot day and on a cold day. Have groups cut out pictures to match each thermometer.

Ongoing Assessment

- **If you were building a snowman, would the temperature be about 20°F or about 90°F ?** *(About 20°F)*
- **Reasoning What happens to the red line as the temperature gets hotter?** *(It gets taller.)*

Reaching All Learners

Math and Literature

Seasons

5–10 MIN **Auditory/Linguistic**

Materials *Chicken Soup with Rice: A Book of Months* by Maurice Sendak (HarperCollins, 1962)

- Read aloud several poems (at least one poem for each season) from *Chicken Soup with Rice: A Book of Months* by Maurice Sendak.
- After children have had a chance to enjoy the poems, discuss what the weather is like during these months of the year.
- Have children suggest typical temperatures for a spring, summer, autumn, and winter month in your area.

Activate Prior Knowledge/Build Background

English Language Learners

What Is the Temperature?

10–15 MIN **Auditory/Linguistic**

Materials Thermometer; photographs of summer and winter scenes in a temperate climate

- Point to the thermometer. **A *thermometer* tells the *temperature.***
- Show the seasonal pictures. **In summer the *temperature* is about 80 *degrees.* Is that warm or cold? In winter it is about 20 *degrees.* Is that warm or cold?**
- Encourage children to describe activities they do outdoors during those seasons and in those temperatures.

Reteaching

Dressing for the Weather

10–15 MIN **Linguistic/Visual/Spatial**

Materials *(per group)* Pictures of articles of clothing appropriate for temperatures from 10°F to 100°F

- Draw a large thermometer on the board with temperatures from 10°F to 100°F. Write *Cold* next to the bottom of the thermometer, an upward facing arrow, and *Hot* at the top.
- Hold the picture of the mittens. Encourage children to tell you at which temperature they would wear this type of clothing.
- Continue by placing the other pictures next to the temperatures with which they correspond.

Math and Science

Measure Temperatures

15–20 MIN **Visual/Spatial**

Materials *(per group)* Thermometer; glass of water with ice cubes; glass of hot water; glass of lukewarm water

- Demonstrate how to use the thermometer to check the temperature of a glass of water.
- Then have children take turns using the thermometer to find the temperatures of each of the three glasses of water.
- Encourage children to compare their temperature readings to those of their classmates.
- Show children how to make a log of the temperatures by drawing the three glasses. Suggest that children check the temperatures every 10 minutes and record their findings in their log.

Objective Compare temperatures on a thermometer and match them to activities or objects.

1 Warm Up

Activate Prior Knowledge Review the four seasons. Encourage children to tell how to dress for each season and to name activities that people do in each season.

2 Teach

Learn!

Explain that temperature is a measure of how hot or cold something is. Identify a thermometer as the tool used to measure temperature in degrees. Demonstrate how to read the thermometers on the student page, both in Fahrenheit and in Celsius. Point out that the hotter the temperature, the taller the red line is on the thermometer and the colder the temperature, the shorter the red line.

Ongoing Assessment

Talk About It

- **If it is a snowy day, will the red line be tall or short on the thermometer? Explain.** *(Short; the colder the temperature, the shorter the line)*
- **Will the temperature be high or low if it is a good day for swimming outdoors?** *(High)*

If children have difficulty telling the temperature,

then draw an oversized thermometer and have children circle the number to read.

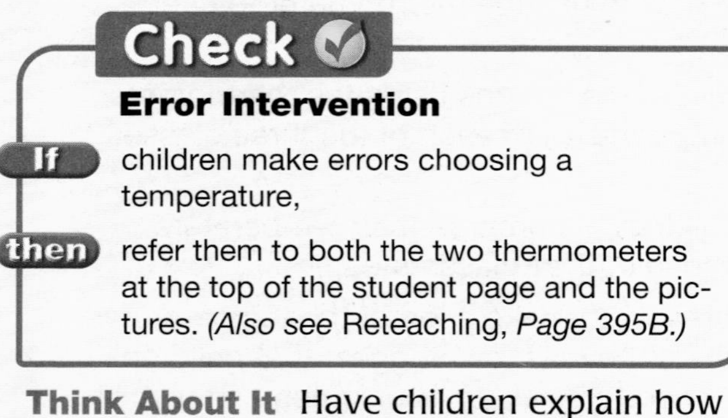

Check

Error Intervention

If children make errors choosing a temperature,

then refer them to both the two thermometers at the top of the student page and the pictures. *(Also see* Reteaching, *Page 395B.)*

Think About It Have children explain how they determined that a coat would not be needed.

Name ______________________ Measuring Temperature

Learn!

We can use a thermometer to measure the temperature.

°F 90 °C 32

°F 34 °C 1

Word Bank
thermometer
temperature

Check

Circle the thermometer that shows the temperature.

1. °F 38 °F 75
2. °C 6 °C 34
3. °F 85 °F 40
4. °C 32 °C 0

Think About It Reasoning

If this were the temperature outside today, would you need to wear a coat? Explain. °F 95

No; it is too hot to wear a coat.

Chapter 10 ★ Lesson 14 three hundred ninety-five 395

Reteaching Below Level

Measuring Temperature R 10-14

The colored part of a thermometer measures the temperature.
It tells how hot or how cold it is.

Not much of the colored part means cold.
A lot of the colored part means hot.

Circle the thermometer that shows the temperature.

1. 20 75
2. 2 34
3. 10 90
4. 0 40

128 Use with Lesson 10-14

Practice On Level

Measuring Temperature P 10-14

Circle the thermometer that shows the temperature.

1. 28°F 80°F
2. 0°C 40°C

Draw lines to match each picture to the temperature.

3. 42°C 1°C
4. 70°F 50°F

Problem Solving *Number Sense*

5. Number the thermometers from coldest to hottest. Use 1 for coldest and 3 for hottest.

1 3 2

128 Use with Lesson 10-14

Practice

Draw lines to match each picture to a temperature.

Problem Solving Number Sense

7 Number the thermometers from coldest to hottest.
Use **1** for the coldest and **3** for the hottest.

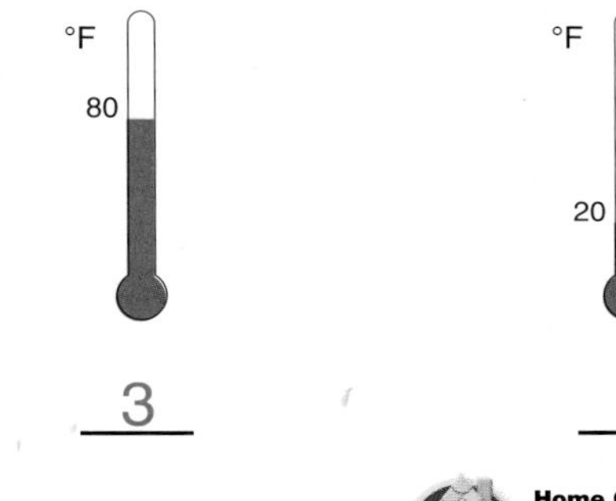

3 1 2

© Pearson Education, Inc.

Home Connection Your child used a thermometer to tell the temperature in various pictures. **Home Activity** Watch a weather report on TV with your child. Talk about the temperature and determine whether it will be hot or cold.

Enrichment Above Level

What Will I Wear? E 10-14 DECISION MAKING

Look at the thermometer.
Circle what you would wear.

1. 88°F 31°C
2. 32°F 0°C
3. 93°F 34°C
4. 45°F 7°C

© Pearson Education, Inc. 1

128 Use with Lesson 10-14.

Problem Solving

Measuring Temperature PS 10-14

Read each story. Circle the thermometer that shows the temperature.

1. It is winter. Cassie and her friend go ice skating. (°F °C 32 0) (°F °C 77 25)
2. John wears a jacket to go to his soccer game. (°F °C 95 35) (°F °C 50 10)
3. Kwame and Jake make a snowman. (°F °C 80 27) (°F °C 23 −5)
4. It is a warm sunny day. Jean has baseball practice. (°F °C 86 30) (°F °C 41 5)
5. It starts to snow. (°F °C 32 0) (°F °C 68 20)
6. It is summer. Frankie jumps into the pool. (°F °C 38 4) (°F °C 95 35)
7. Number the thermometers from coldest to hottest. Use 1 for the coldest and 3 for the hottest. (°C 27) (°C 38) (°C 15)
2 3 1

© Pearson Education, Inc. 1

128 Use with Lesson 10-14.

3 Practice

For Exercise 7, encourage children to decide which thermometer shows the coldest temperature first. Then they should decide which thermometer shows the hottest temperature.

Leveled Practice

Below Level Work in pairs to do Exercises 5–7.

On Level Complete all exercises as written.

Above Level Write the temperatures for Exercise 5 in order from hottest to coldest.

Early Finishers Have children copy the following temperatures from the board: 70°F, 30°F, 45°F, 10°F, 90°F. Ask children to rewrite the temperatures in order from coldest to hottest. Remind children that the coldest temperature is the lowest number.

4 Assess

Journal Idea Have children draw something they might do outdoors on a day when the temperature is 80°F and something they might do outdoors on a day when the temperature is 20°F.

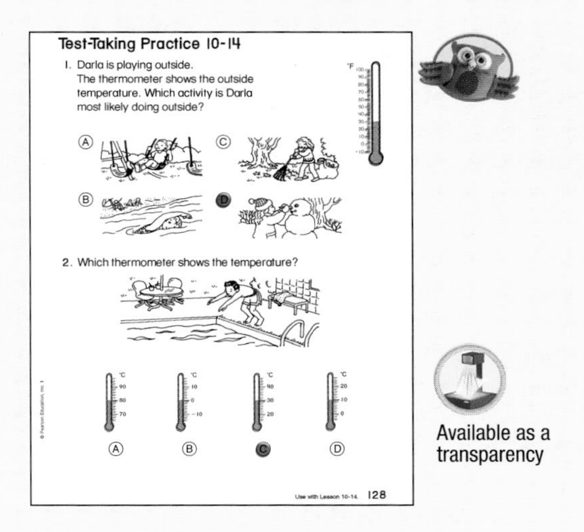
Test-Taking Practice 10-14

1. Darla is playing outside. The thermometer shows the outside temperature. Which activity is Darla most likely doing outside?
Ⓐ Ⓑ Ⓒ Ⓓ

2. Which thermometer shows the temperature?
Ⓐ Ⓑ Ⓒ Ⓓ

Use with Lesson 10-14. 128

Available as a transparency

Lesson Organizer

Quick Lesson Overview

Objective Identify appropriate tools for measuring length, weight, capacity, and temperature.

Math Understanding There are many ways to measure an object, and each way uses a different tool.

Professional Development Note

Math Background Talk with children about why we use measurement tools. Guide them to understand that using measurement tools increases accuracy. **How would you determine weight if you did not have a balance? Could you find out how much an object holds if you measured with different-sized cups?**

NCTM Standards

- Measurement

(For a complete correlation to the NCTM Standards and Grades Pre-K through 2 Expectations, see Pages 363G and 363H.)

Getting Started

Spiral Review

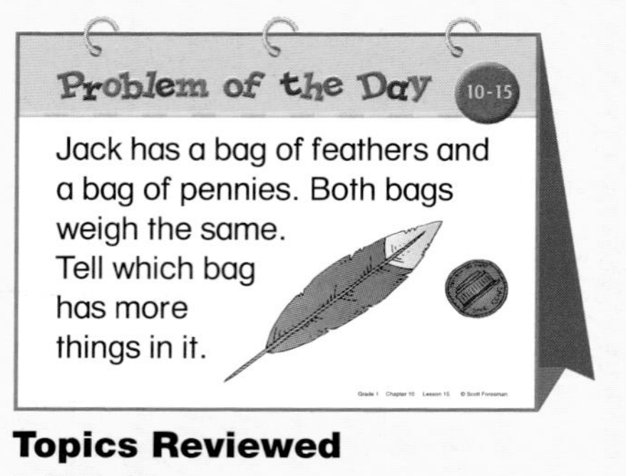

Problem of the Day 10-15

Jack has a bag of feathers and a bag of pennies. Both bags weigh the same. Tell which bag has more things in it.

Topics Reviewed

- Weight
- Problem-Solving Strategy: Use Logical Reasoning

Answer Feathers weigh less than pennies, so the bag of feathers has more things in it than the bag of pennies.

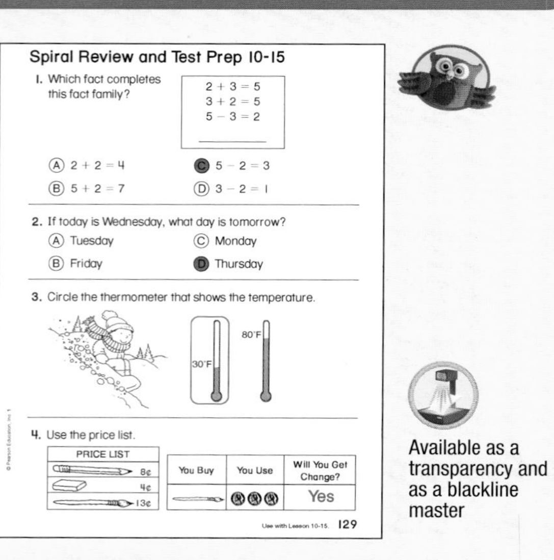

Spiral Review and Test Prep 10-15

1. Which fact completes this fact family?

$2 + 3 = 5$
$3 + 2 = 5$
$5 - 3 = 2$

(A) $2 + 2 = 4$ (C) $5 - 2 = 3$
(B) $5 + 2 = 7$ (D) $3 - 2 = 1$

2. If today is Wednesday, what day is tomorrow?

(A) Tuesday (C) Monday
(B) Friday (D) Thursday

3. Circle the thermometer that shows the temperature.

30°F 80°F

4. Use the price list.

PRICE LIST	
	8¢
	4¢
	13¢

You Buy	You Use	Will You Get Change?
		Yes

Use with Lesson 10-15. 129

Available as a transparency and as a blackline master

Topics Reviewed

1. Fact Families
2. Days of the Week
3. Temperature
4. Use Data from a Table

Investigating the Concept

Measure in More Than One Way

15–20 MIN **Kinesthetic/Logical/Mathematical** PAIRS

Materials *(per pair)* Classroom objects; ruler; balance; measuring cup; thermometer; construction paper; crayons

What to Do

- Model how to measure an object in more than one way. For example, you can measure the height of a vase, as well as its weight and capacity. If it contains water, the temperature of the water can be measured as well. Ask children to name the appropriate tool for each measurement.
- Provide each pair with measuring tools and an object to measure. Have children measure the object in as many ways as they can. Then have them work together to draw a picture to show each way. Invite children to share their work.

Ongoing Assessment

- **Reasoning Which different ways did you find to measure your object? Which tools did you use?** *(Answers will vary.)*
- **What could you measure using a thermometer?** *(Sample response: Water or air temperature)*

Reaching All Learners

Reading in Math

Word Match

5–10 MIN **Linguistic**

- Write the following words on the board in one column: "cold, long, heavy, tall, light, full, hot."
- Write these words in a second column: "balance, ruler, thermometer, quart."
- Read all of the words with children. Invite children to match each of the words in the first column with related words in the second column by drawing a line to connect them.
- Have children use the word pairs in sentences.

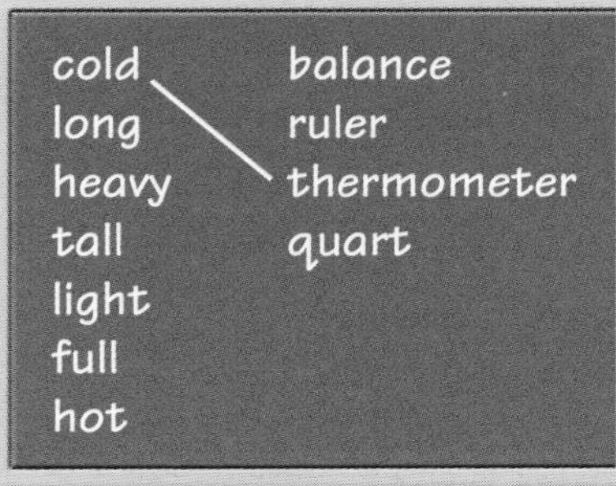

Access Content

English Language Learners

Measurement Charades

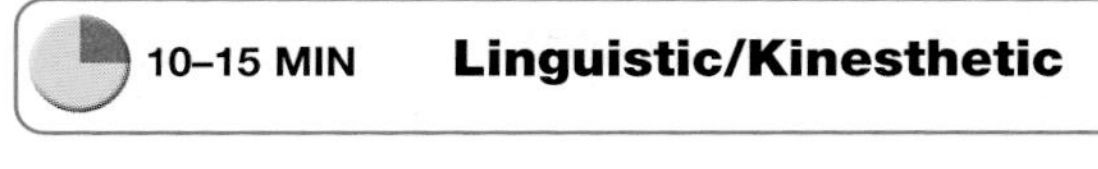

Materials *(per group)* Ruler; balance; measuring cup; thermometer

- Demonstrate how to act out the use of each measuring tool. Encourage children to offer suggestions for the actions.
- Pretend to shiver and put on a coat to have children choose the thermometer as the tool suggested by your actions.
- Give each child an opportunity to act out the use of a tool.

Reteaching

Pick a Tool

10–15 MIN **Linguistic/Kinesthetic**

SMALL GROUP

Materials Books; connecting cubes; water with ice cubes; pennies; other objects that can be measured by weight, length, height, and temperature; measuring cup; ruler; balance; thermometer

- Arrange the objects to be measured on one table and the measuring tools on another.
- Pick an object, such as the book, and a tool, such as the ruler.
- Measure the length of the book with the ruler and state the measurement.
- Have each child take a turn choosing an object and a tool.
- As each child measures using the tool, have the rest of the group tell which quality is being measured.

Math and Social Studies

Tools of the Trade

10–15 MIN **Linguistic**

- Talk about how people use different measuring tools to do their jobs.
- Discuss the tools that a professional cook would use: measuring cups, spoons, quart and pint containers.
- Make lists of the measuring tools a grocery store clerk, scientist, carpenter, doctor, and architect might use.
- You may wish to use the Internet to research careers that children find particularly interesting to learn more about the measuring tools used to do those jobs.

Objective Identify appropriate tools for measuring length, weight, capacity, and temperature.

1 Warm Up

Activate Prior Knowledge Review vocabulary. On the board, write the following words: "light, heavy, hot, cold, long, short, wide, tall." Ask children to use each word in a sentence. For example, "It is *hot* on a summer day."

2 Teach

Learn!

Discuss the picture at the top of the student page. Invite children to talk about the different ways the pitcher can be measured. Discuss each of the measuring tools and how it is used.

Ongoing Assessment

Talk About It

- **What else could you measure with a ruler?** *(Sample response: The length of a book)* **a cup?** *(Sample response: How much a bucket holds)* **a balance?** *(Sample response: How heavy a shoe is)* **a thermometer?** *(Sample response: How hot a cup of tea is)*

If children cannot think of objects for each tool,

then remind them that a ruler measures length, a balance measures weight, a thermometer measures temperature, and a cup measures how much an object will hold inside.

Error Intervention

If children have difficulty choosing a tool,

then read each question with them again, emphasizing the words *heavy*, *hot*, and *long*. *(Also see* Reteaching, *Page 397B.)*

Think About It Have children describe a pumpkin. **Which sizes do pumpkins come in? What shape is a pumpkin? What does it feel like? What is inside it?**

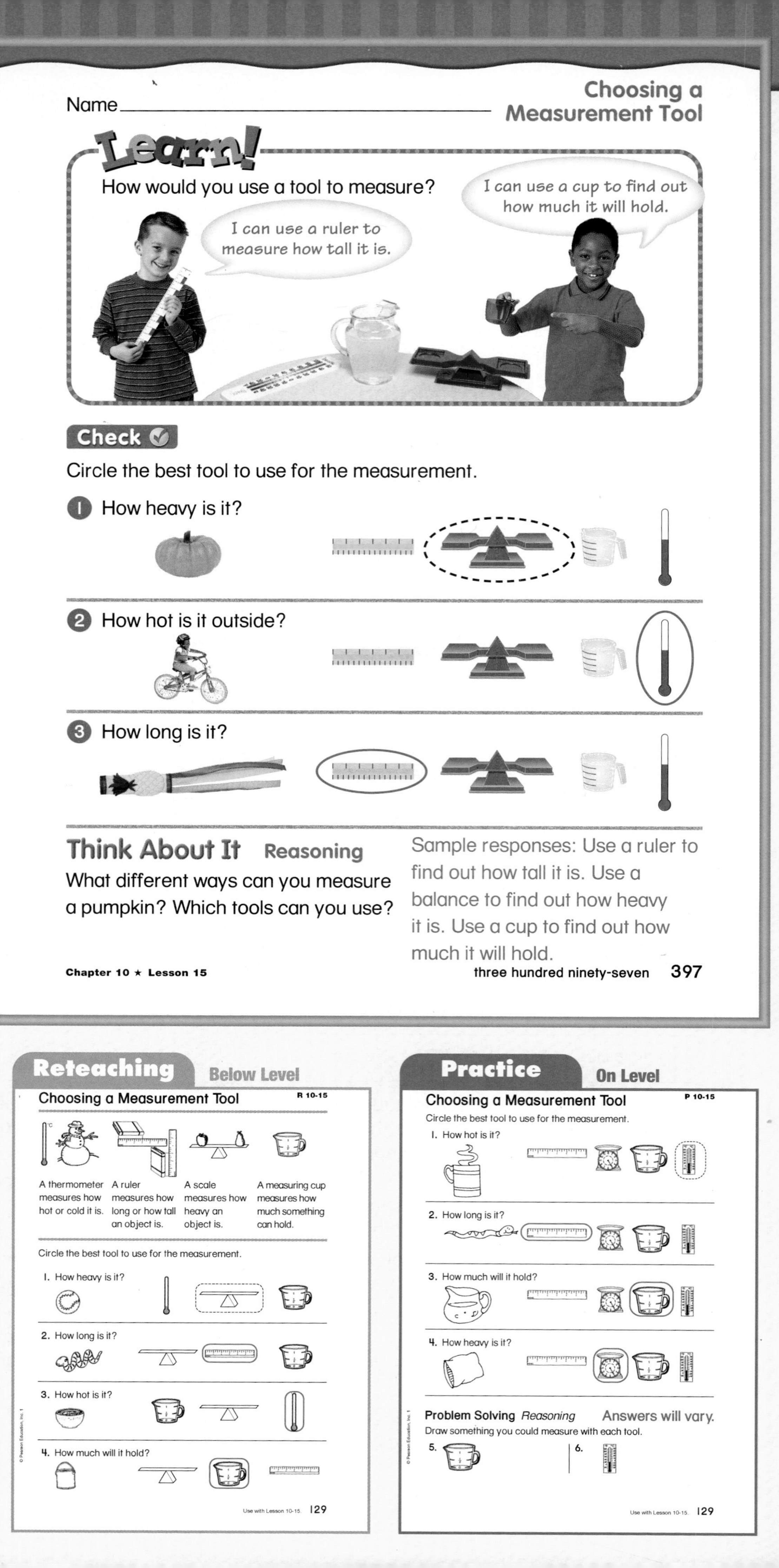

Name ______________________

Choosing a Measurement Tool

Learn!

How would you use a tool to measure?

Check

Circle the best tool to use for the measurement.

1. How heavy is it?
2. How hot is it outside?
3. How long is it?

Think About It Reasoning

What different ways can you measure a pumpkin? Which tools can you use?

Sample responses: Use a ruler to find out how tall it is. Use a balance to find out how heavy it is. Use a cup to find out how much it will hold.

Chapter 10 ★ Lesson 15 three hundred ninety-seven 397

Reteaching Below Level

Choosing a Measurement Tool R 10-15

A thermometer measures how hot or cold it is. A ruler measures how long or how tall an object is. A scale measures how heavy an object is. A measuring cup measures how much something can hold.

Circle the best tool to use for the measurement.

1. How heavy is it?
2. How long is it?
3. How hot is it?
4. How much will it hold?

Use with Lesson 10-15. 129

Practice On Level

Choosing a Measurement Tool P 10-15

Circle the best tool to use for the measurement.

1. How hot is it?
2. How long is it?
3. How much will it hold?
4. How heavy is it?

Problem Solving *Reasoning* Answers will vary.

Draw something you could measure with each tool.

5. 6.

Use with Lesson 10-15. 129

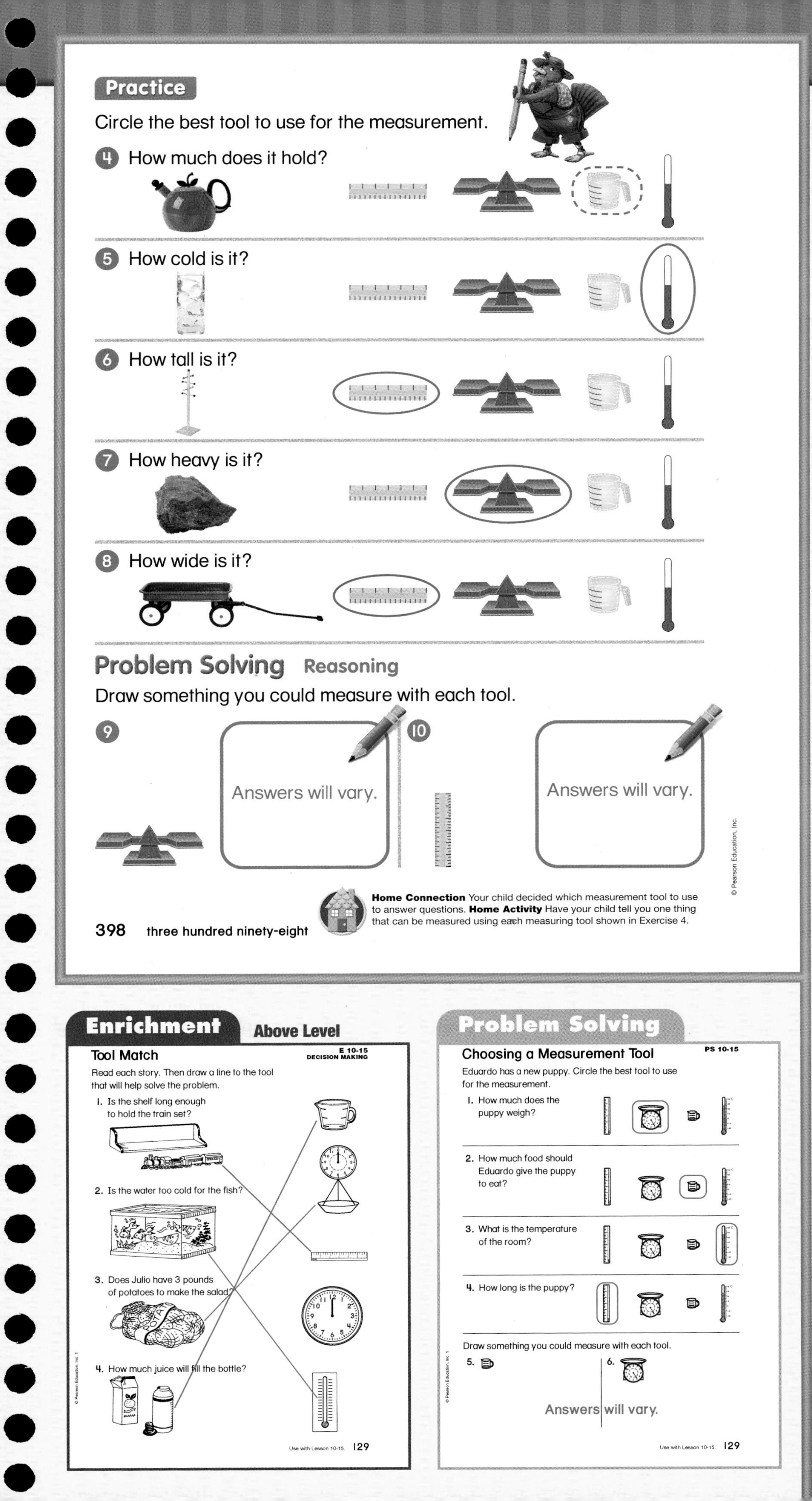

Practice

Circle the best tool to use for the measurement.

4. How much does it hold?
5. How cold is it?
6. How tall is it?
7. How heavy is it?
8. How wide is it?

Problem Solving Reasoning

Draw something you could measure with each tool.

9. Answers will vary.

10. Answers will vary.

Home Connection Your child decided which measurement tool to use to answer questions. **Home Activity** Have your child tell you one thing that can be measured using each measuring tool shown in Exercise 4.

Enrichment Above Level

Tool Match E 10-15 DECISION MAKING

Read each story. Then draw a line to the tool that will help solve the problem.

1. Is the shelf long enough to hold the train set?
2. Is the water too cold for the fish?
3. Does Julio have 3 pounds of potatoes to make the salad?
4. How much juice will fill the bottle?

Problem Solving

Choosing a Measurement Tool PS 10-15

Eduardo has a new puppy. Circle the best tool to use for the measurement.

1. How much does the puppy weigh?
2. How much food should Eduardo give the puppy to eat?
3. What is the temperature of the room?
4. How long is the puppy?

Draw something you could measure with each tool.

5. 6.

Answers will vary.

3 Practice

Have children continue to circle the best tool for each type of measurement. You may wish to read the questions with children before they complete any of the exercises.

Leveled Practice

Below Level Work in pairs to complete exercises.

On Level Complete all exercises individually.

Above Level Cross out any tools that cannot be used to measure the object.

Early Finishers Invite pairs of children to work together to create measurement-tool charts. Have them draw each tool across the top of a sheet of paper. Beneath, have children draw objects that can be measured using each tool. Post the charts and add to them as children identify new objects.

4 Assess

Journal Idea Draw a picture of a watermelon on the board. Have children draw and write ways they could measure it. Ask children to draw the tools they would use as well.

Test-Taking Practice 10-15

1. Which is the best tool to use to measure how heavy a dog is?

Ⓐ Ⓑ Ⓒ Ⓓ

2. Which is the best tool to use to measure how long a bus is?

Ⓐ Ⓑ Ⓒ Ⓓ

Available as a transparency

Diagnostic Checkpoint

Purpose Provide assessment of children's progress to date by checking their understanding of key content covered in the previous section.

Vocabulary Review

You may wish to review these terms before assigning the page:

cup A customary unit used to measure capacity *(pp. 383–386)*

gram A metric unit used to measure how heavy an object is: 1,000 grams equal 1 kilogram. *(pp. 393–394)*

kilogram A metric unit used to measure how heavy an object is: 1 kilogram equals 1,000 grams. *(pp. 393–394)*

liter A metric unit used to measure capacity: 1 liter equals 1,000 milliliters. *(pp. 387–388)*

pint A customary unit used to measure capacity: 1 pint equals 2 cups. *(pp. 385–386)*

pound A customary unit used to measure weight: 1 pound equals 16 ounces. *(pp. 391–392)*

quart A customary unit used to measure capacity: 1 quart equals 4 cups. *(pp. 385–386)*

temperature The degree of heat or cold *(pp. 395–396)*

thermometer An instrument used for measuring temperature *(pp. 395–396)*

Activities for this section are available in the Math Vocabulary Kit.

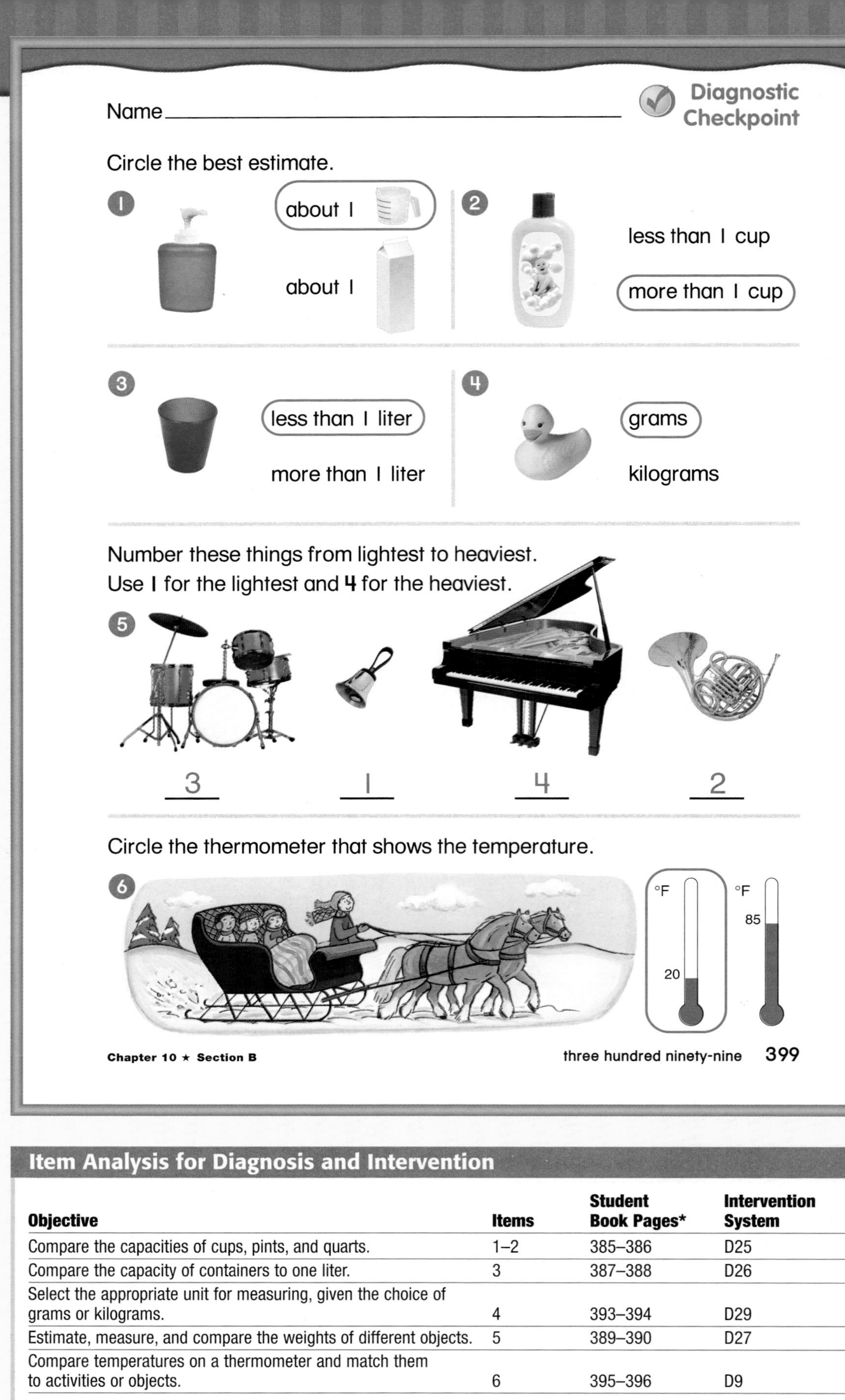
Name ______________________

Diagnostic Checkpoint

Circle the best estimate.

1 about I / about I

2 less than I cup / more than I cup

3 less than I liter / more than I liter

4 grams / kilograms

Number these things from lightest to heaviest.
Use I for the lightest and 4 for the heaviest.

5 3 I 4 2

Circle the thermometer that shows the temperature.

6

Chapter 10 ★ Section B

three hundred ninety-nine 399

Item Analysis for Diagnosis and Intervention

Objective	Items	Student Book Pages*	Intervention System
Compare the capacities of cups, pints, and quarts.	1–2	385–386	D25
Compare the capacity of containers to one liter.	3	387–388	D26
Select the appropriate unit for measuring, given the choice of grams or kilograms.	4	393–394	D29
Estimate, measure, and compare the weights of different objects.	5	389–390	D27
Compare temperatures on a thermometer and match them to activities or objects.	6	395–396	D9

*For each lesson, there is a *Reteaching* activity in *Reaching All Learners* and a *Reteaching* master.

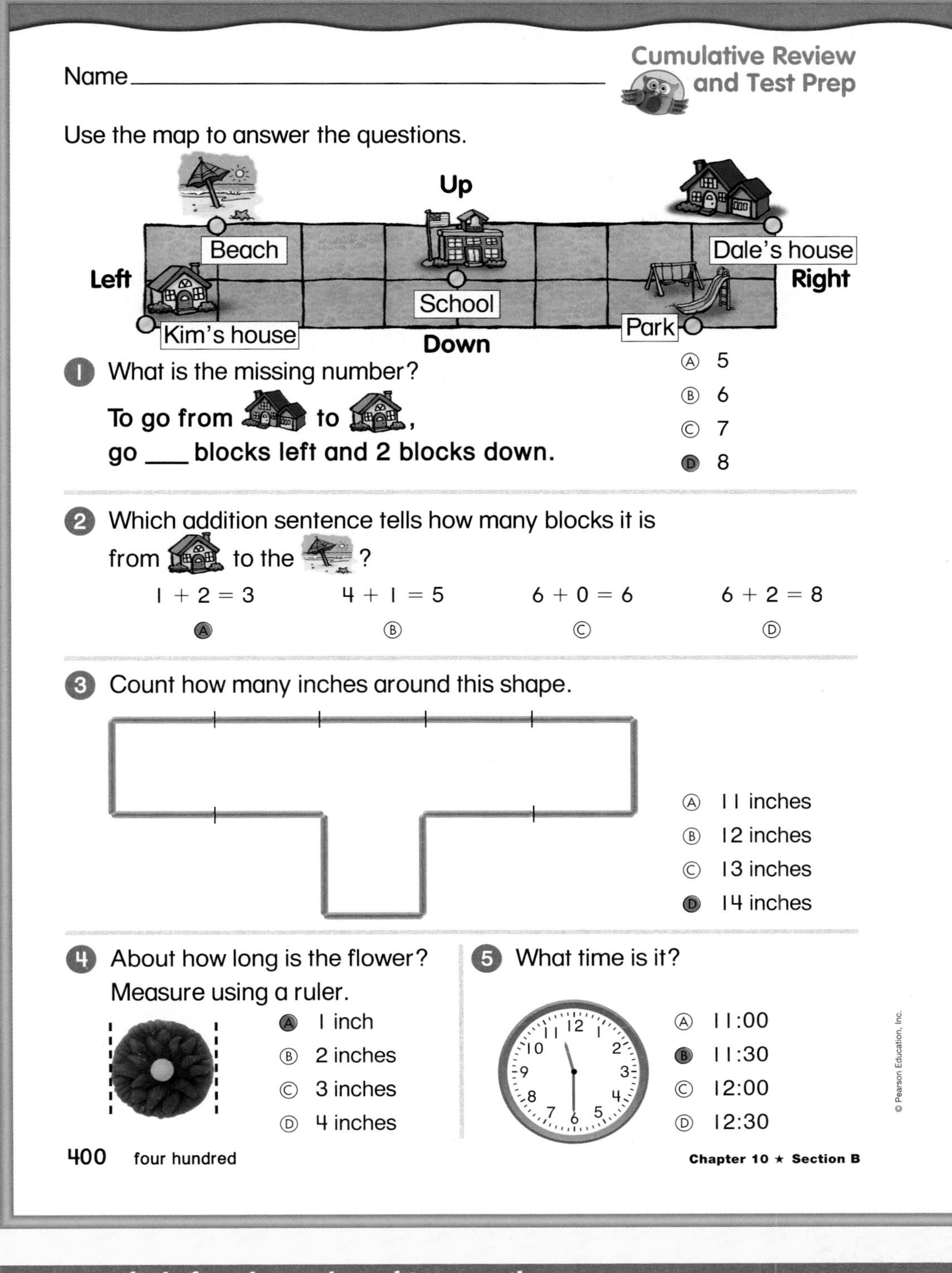

Name ____________________

Cumulative Review and Test Prep

Use the map to answer the questions.

1. What is the missing number?

   To go from [Dale's house] to [Kim's house],
   go ___ blocks left and 2 blocks down.

   Ⓐ 5
   Ⓑ 6
   Ⓒ 7
   Ⓓ 8

2. Which addition sentence tells how many blocks it is from [Kim's house] to the [Beach]?

   Ⓐ 1 + 2 = 3   Ⓑ 4 + 1 = 5   Ⓒ 6 + 0 = 6   Ⓓ 6 + 2 = 8

3. Count how many inches around this shape.

   Ⓐ 11 inches
   Ⓑ 12 inches
   Ⓒ 13 inches
   Ⓓ 14 inches

4. About how long is the flower? Measure using a ruler.

   Ⓐ 1 inch
   Ⓑ 2 inches
   Ⓒ 3 inches
   Ⓓ 4 inches

5. What time is it?

   Ⓐ 11:00
   Ⓑ 11:30
   Ⓒ 12:00
   Ⓓ 12:30

Cumulative Review and Test Prep

Purpose Provide children with a review of math concepts. Items appear as they would on a standardized test so children become familiar with that format.

Item Analysis for Diagnosis and Intervention

Objective	Items	Student Book Pages*	Intervention System
Identify the distance from one point to another on a grid by describing how far it is to the left, right, up, or down.	1	315–316	D68
Solve problems by using a map.	2	317–318	E3
Find the distance around a shape using inches.	3	377–378	D23
Estimate and measure the lengths of objects to the nearest inch using a ruler.	4	371–372	D22
Tell and write time to the half hour.	5	211–212	E30

*For each lesson, there is a *Reteaching* activity in *Reaching All Learners* and a *Reteaching* master.

10-16 Certain or Impossible

Lesson Organizer

Quick Lesson Overview

Objective Describe the likelihood of an event as certain or impossible.

Math Understanding An event that is certain to happen will always happen; an event that is impossible will never happen.

Vocabulary Certain, impossible

Materials for Student Pages
Crayons

Professional Development Note

Research Base

The topic of probability may be a challenge for the young learner. A recent study indicates that a sizable number of children in grades 1 through 3 had difficulty listing the outcomes of an experiment (Jones, et al, 1997, 1999). Two lessons which children will encounter in this section involve more or less likely events and whether an event is certain or impossible to happen. Children will need concrete representations to develop and support their understanding of these important probability beginnings.

NCTM Standards

- Data Analysis and Probability

(For a complete correlation to the NCTM Standards and Grades Pre-K through 2 Expectations, see Pages 363G and 363H.)

Getting Started

Spiral Review

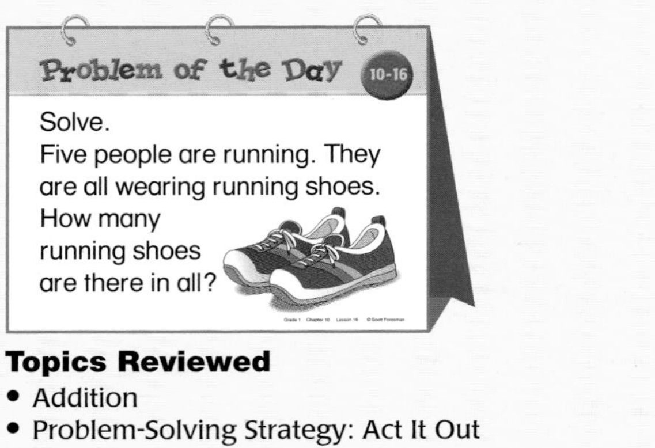

Topics Reviewed
- Addition
- Problem-Solving Strategy: Act It Out

Answer There are 2 + 2 + 2 + 2 + 2, or 10 running shoes in all.

Spiral Review and Test Prep 10-16

1. Which is the best tool to use to measure how much the vase holds?

2. Which coins show $1.00?

3. Write tally marks to show how many kittens and puppies there are. Write the totals.

		Total
Kittens	𝍸 II	7
Puppies	𝍸	5

4. Use the tally chart in Exercise 3 to answer the question.
How many more kittens than puppies are there? 2

130

Available as a transparency and as a blackline master

Topics Reviewed
1. Choosing a Measurement Tool
2. Half-Dollar and Dollar
3.–4. Using Tally Marks

Investigating the Concept

Certain or Impossible

Materials Clear plastic bag; connecting cubes in various colors

What to Do

- Fill a bag with 10 red connecting cubes. Have a child choose one cube. Explain that because there are only red cubes in the bag, you are certain to pick a red cube. Because there are no blue cubes in the bag, it is impossible to pick a blue cube.
- Repeat, filling the bag with different colors of cubes. Each time, ask children to use the word *certain* or *impossible* to describe a color picked from the bag.

Ongoing Assessment

- **If a bag has red, blue, and orange cubes, can you ever be certain of which color you will pick? Explain.** *(No; because there are 3 different colors of cubes in the bag)*
- **Reasoning What must be true of a bag of cubes from which it is impossible to pick blue?** *(There must be no blue cubes in the bag.)*

Reaching All Learners

Oral Language in Math

What Are the Chances?

10–15 MIN **Linguistic/Logical/Mathematical**

- Explain that when something is sure to happen, we say it is *certain*. Then explain that when something can never happen, we say it is *impossible*.
- Write a chart titled "What Are the Chances?" on the board. Add the column headings "Certain" and "Impossible."
- Use children's suggestions to create a class list of things that are certain and things that are impossible.

What Are the Chances?	
Certain	Impossible
Friday will follow Thursday.	Julio's dog will fly.

Extend Language

English Language Learners

Choose a Card

5–10 MIN **Auditory/Linguistic**

Materials *(per group)* Spinner Pattern (Teaching Tool 34); *(per child)* 2 index cards labeled *"certain"* and *"impossible"*

- Divide the spinner into 6 equal sections and label them with the numbers 1 through 6. Discuss the words *certain* and *impossible*. Have children pronounce the words.
- Show the spinner. **It is *certain* that the spinner will land on a number from 1 to 6. It is *impossible* for the spinner to land on 9.**
- Continue making *certain* and *impossible* statements about the spinner. Have children hold up the appropriate index card after each statement.

Reteaching

Ways to Show Numbers

5–10 MIN **Visual/Spatial/Linguistic**

- Draw two circles, each bisected by a line. In one circle, write 3 on one half and draw three dots on the other. In the second circle, write 5 on one half and draw five dots on the other.
- **What are two ways the circles show 3 and 5?** *(Numerals and dots)*
- Point toward the 3 circle. **If I point anywhere on the circle, is it *certain* or *impossible* that I will point to 3?** *(Certain)* **to 6?** *(Impossible)* Do the same with the other circle.

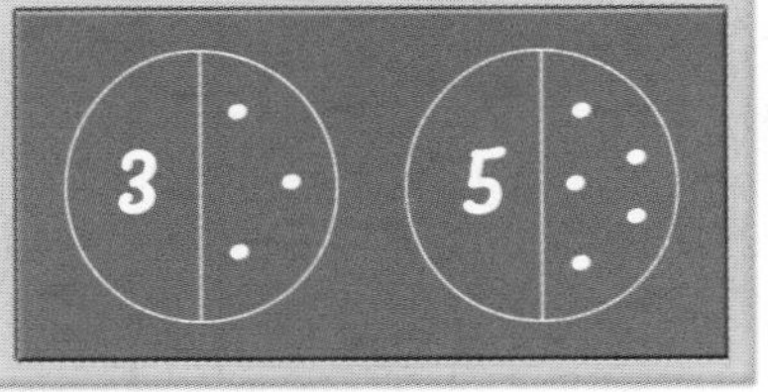

Math and Physical Education

Circle Hops

10–15 MIN **Auditory/Kinesthetic**

- Play a hopscotch-like game to reinforce the ideas of *certain* and *impossible.*
- Draw six chalk circles large enough for children to jump into. Each should have a number in it from 1 to 6.
- Have players follow your instructions and hop into the correct circle. For example, you might say: **Hop into the circle that is *certain* to contain a number greater than 4.**
- Continue the game by giving hopping instructions using the words *certain* and *impossible.*

Objective Describe the likelihood of an event as certain or impossible.

1 Warm Up

Activate Prior Knowledge Review daily events. Have children share events in nature that always happen, such as the sun rising each morning and setting each night.

2 Teach

Learn!

Look at the bowls at the top of the student page. Explain that it is certain that the boy will pick a green cube if he takes a cube from his bowl. It is impossible for the girl to pick a green cube from her bowl. There are not any green cubes in her bowl.

Ongoing Assessment

Talk About It

- **Why is the boy certain to pick a green cube?** *(There are only green cubes in his bowl.)*
- **Is the girl certain to pick a red cube? Explain.** *(No; there are yellow cubes and red cubes in her bowl. She could pick either.)*

If children have difficulty answering questions,

then have them use cubes.

Check

Error Intervention

If children confuse *certain* and *impossible,*

then give many real-world examples that correctly use the words. *(Also see* Reteaching, *Page 401B.)*

Think About It Ask: **Are all of the cubes red? Could you pick a green cube?** Help children understand that if there is even one green, you are not certain to pick red.

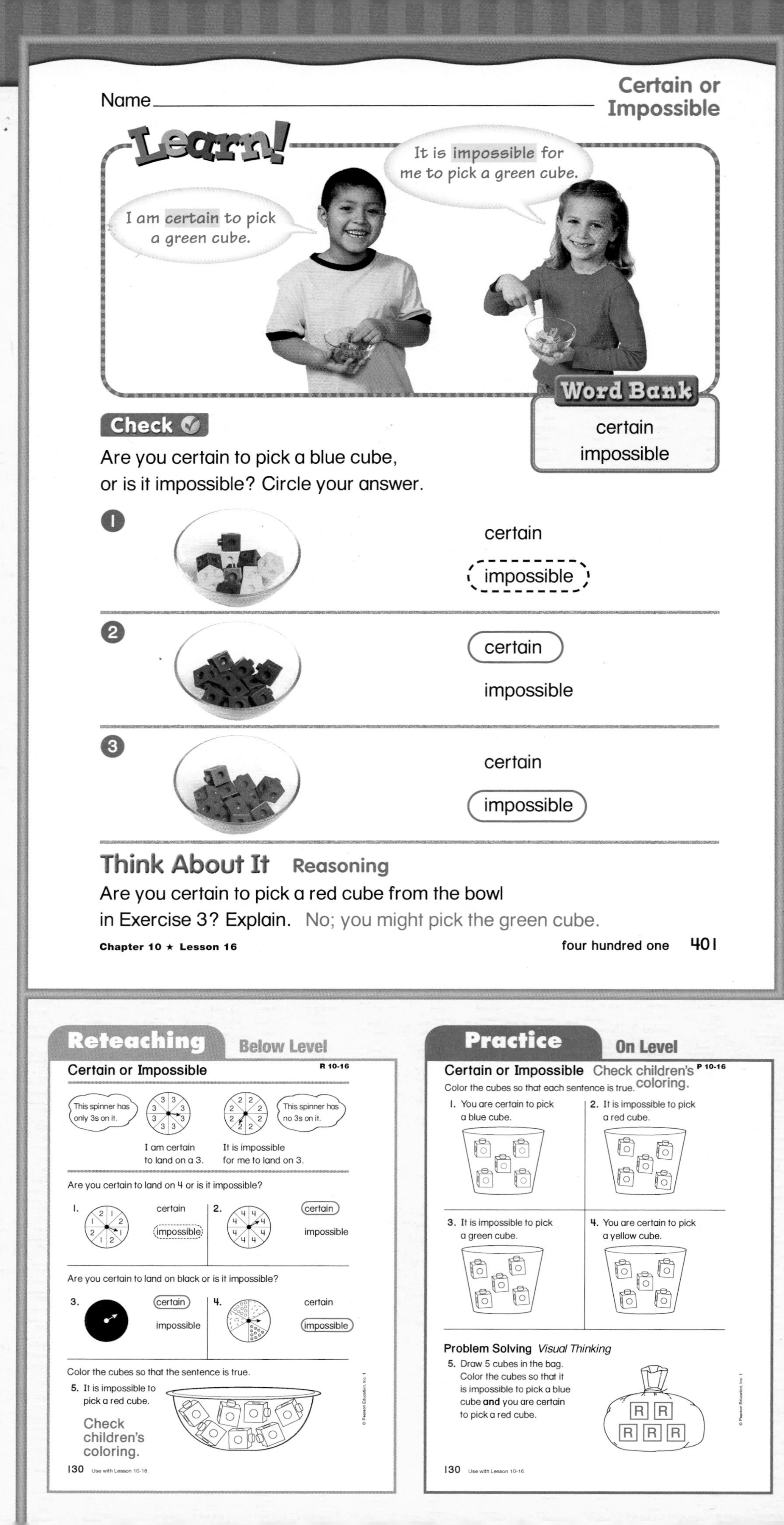

Name ____________________ Certain or Impossible

Learn!

I am certain to pick a green cube.

It is impossible for me to pick a green cube.

Word Bank: certain, impossible

Check

Are you certain to pick a blue cube, or is it impossible? Circle your answer.

1. certain / impossible (impossible circled)
2. certain / impossible (certain circled)
3. certain / impossible (impossible circled)

Think About It Reasoning

Are you certain to pick a red cube from the bowl in Exercise 3? Explain. No; you might pick the green cube.

Chapter 10 ★ Lesson 16 — four hundred one 401

Reteaching Below Level

Certain or Impossible R 10-16

This spinner has only 3s on it. I am certain to land on a 3.

This spinner has no 3s on it. It is impossible for me to land on 3.

Are you certain to land on 4 or is it impossible?

1. certain / impossible (impossible circled)
2. certain / impossible (certain circled)

Are you certain to land on black or is it impossible?

3. certain / impossible (certain circled)
4. certain / impossible (impossible circled)

Color the cubes so that the sentence is true.

5. It is impossible to pick a red cube. Check children's coloring.

130 Use with Lesson 10-16.

Practice On Level

Certain or Impossible P 10-16 Check children's coloring.

Color the cubes so that each sentence is true.

1. You are certain to pick a blue cube.
2. It is impossible to pick a red cube.
3. It is impossible to pick a green cube.
4. You are certain to pick a yellow cube.

Problem Solving *Visual Thinking*

5. Draw 5 cubes in the bag. Color the cubes so that it is impossible to pick a blue cube **and** you are certain to pick a red cube.

130 Use with Lesson 10-16.

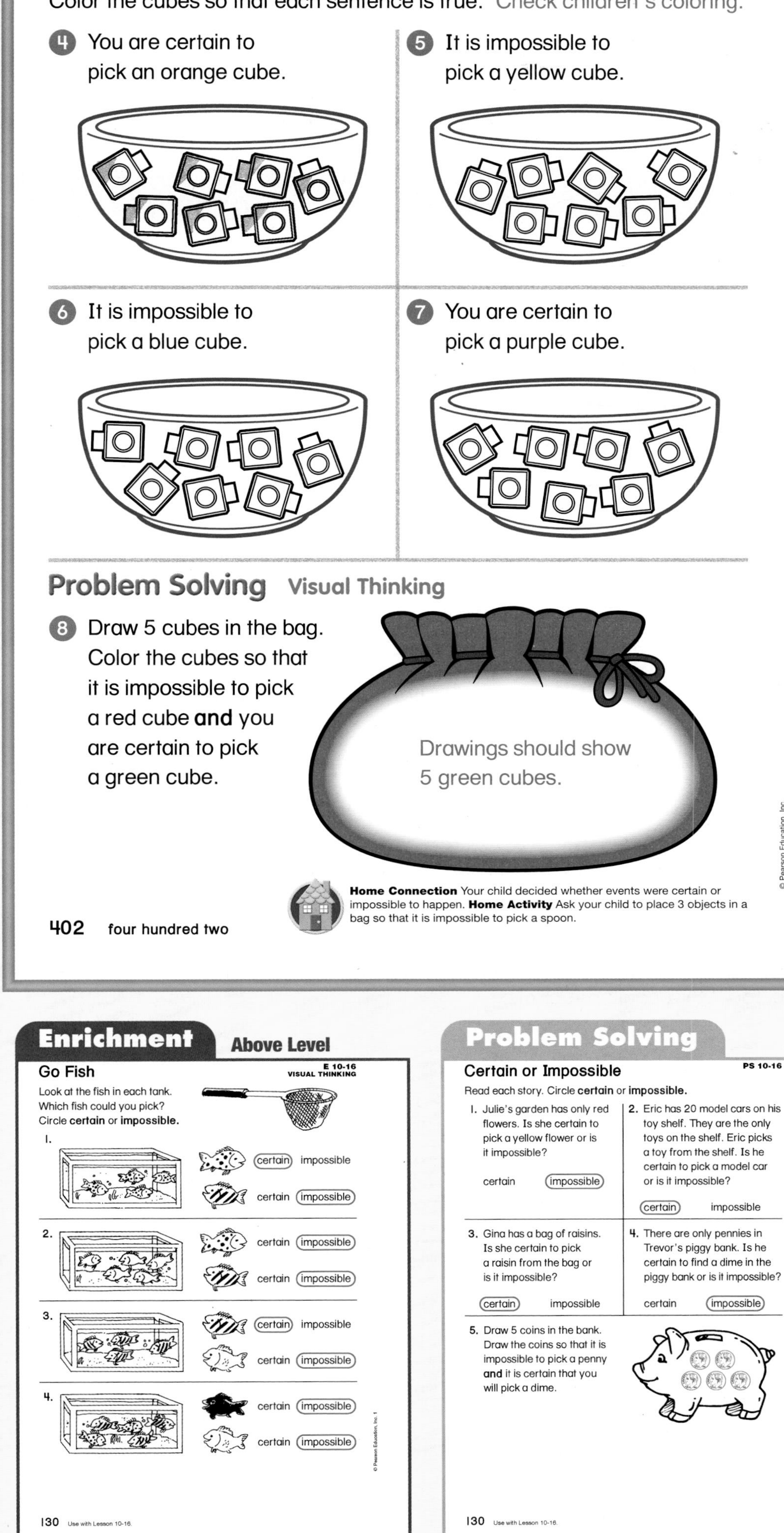

Practice

Color the cubes so that each sentence is true. Check children's coloring.

4. You are certain to pick an orange cube.
5. It is impossible to pick a yellow cube.
6. It is impossible to pick a blue cube.
7. You are certain to pick a purple cube.

Problem Solving Visual Thinking

8. Draw 5 cubes in the bag. Color the cubes so that it is impossible to pick a red cube **and** you are certain to pick a green cube.

Drawings should show 5 green cubes.

© Pearson Education, Inc.

Home Connection Your child decided whether events were certain or impossible to happen. **Home Activity** Ask your child to place 3 objects in a bag so that it is impossible to pick a spoon.

402 four hundred two

Enrichment Above Level

Go Fish — E 10-16 VISUAL THINKING

Look at the fish in each tank. Which fish could you pick? Circle **certain** or **impossible.**

1. (certain) impossible; certain (impossible)
2. certain (impossible); certain (impossible)
3. (certain) impossible; certain (impossible)
4. certain (impossible); certain (impossible)

130 Use with Lesson 10-16.

Problem Solving

Certain or Impossible — PS 10-16

Read each story. Circle **certain** or **impossible.**

1. Julie's garden has only red flowers. Is she certain to pick a yellow flower or is it impossible? certain (impossible)
2. Eric has 20 model cars on his toy shelf. They are the only toys on the shelf. Eric picks a toy from the shelf. Is he certain to pick a model car or is it impossible? (certain) impossible
3. Gina has a bag of raisins. Is she certain to pick a raisin from the bag or is it impossible? (certain) impossible
4. There are only pennies in Trevor's piggy bank. Is he certain to find a dime in the piggy bank or is it impossible? certain (impossible)
5. Draw 5 coins in the bank. Draw the coins so that it is impossible to pick a penny **and** it is certain that you will pick a dime.

130 Use with Lesson 10-16.

3 Practice

For Exercises 5 and 6, tell children that there are many possible correct answers.

Leveled Practice

Below Level Work with a partner to complete all exercises.

On Level Complete all exercises individually.

Above Level For Exercises 5 and 6, draw and color 6 more cubes so that the sentence is still true.

Early Finishers Assign partners. Have one child fill a clear bag with connecting cubes. The other child can tell which colors are certain or impossible to be picked.

4 Assess

Journal Idea Ask children to draw 4 circles that, if cut out and put in a bag, you would be certain to pick red. Then have them draw 4 other circles that would make it impossible for you to pick red from the bag.

Test-Taking Practice 10-16

1. From which bowl are you certain to pick a shaded cube? (A) (B) (C) (D)
2. From which bowl is it impossible for you to pick a shaded cube? (A) (B) (C) (D)

Use with Lesson 10-16. 130

Available as a transparency

10-17 More Likely or Less Likely

Lesson Organizer

Quick Lesson Overview 

Objective Describe the likelihood of an event as more likely or less likely.

Math Understanding An event that is more likely will occur more often than an event that is less likely.

Vocabulary More likely, less likely

Materials for Student Pages *(per pair)* Pencil; paper clip

Professional Development Note

Effective Questioning Techniques
As children use the statements *more likely* or *less likely* to predict the likelihood of spinning a given color, ask questions that encourage them to explain their reasoning. For example, you might ask: **Why do you think you are more likely to spin blue? Why do you think you are less likely to spin red? How might you test your prediction?**

NCTM Standards

- Data Analysis and Probability

(For a complete correlation to the NCTM Standards and Grades Pre-K through 2 Expectations, see Pages 363G and 363H.)

Getting Started

Spiral Review

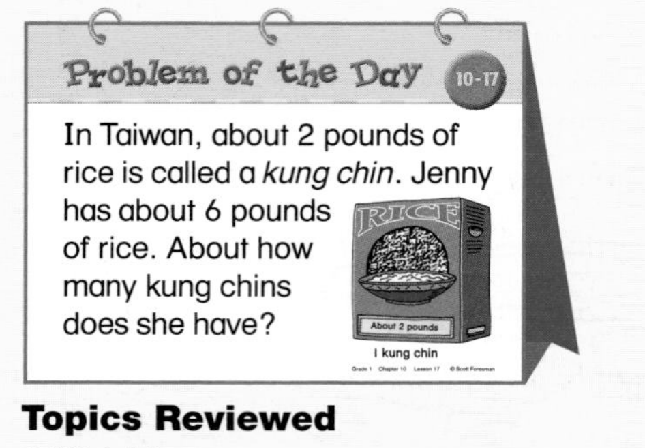

Problem of the Day 10-17

In Taiwan, about 2 pounds of rice is called a *kung chin*. Jenny has about 6 pounds of rice. About how many kung chins does she have?

Topics Reviewed
- Weight
- Addition
- Problem-Solving Skill: Use Data from a Story

Answer Since 2 + 2 + 2 = 6, Jenny has 3 groups of rice that are each about 2 pounds. Jenny has 3 *kung chins*.

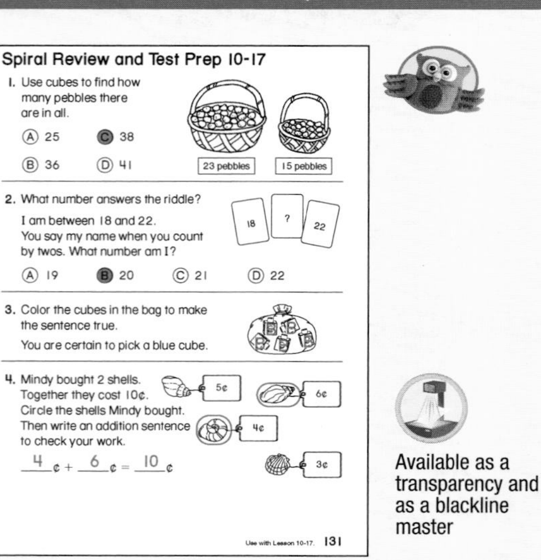

Spiral Review and Test Prep 10-17

1. Use cubes to find how many pebbles there are in all.
   Ⓐ 25 Ⓒ 38 Ⓑ 36 Ⓓ 41
   23 pebbles 15 pebbles
2. What number answers the riddle?
   I am between 18 and 22. You say my name when you count by twos. What number am I?
   Ⓐ 19 Ⓑ 20 Ⓒ 21 Ⓓ 22
3. Color the cubes in the bag to make the sentence true.
   You are certain to pick a blue cube.
4. Mindy bought 2 shells. Together they cost 10¢. Circle the shells Mindy bought. Then write an addition sentence to check your work.
   5¢ 6¢ 4¢ 3¢
   4 ¢ + 6 ¢ = 10 ¢

© Pearson Education, Inc. 1

Use with Lesson 10-17. 131

Available as a transparency and as a blackline master

Topics Reviewed
1. Use Objects
2. Before, After, and Between
3. Certain or Impossible
4. Try, Check, and Revise

Investigating the Concept

More or Less Likely

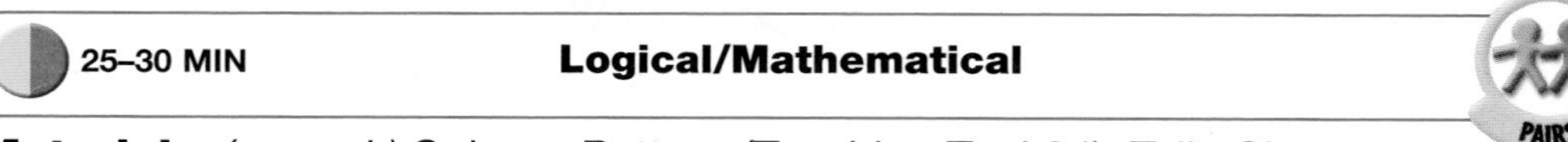

25–30 MIN **Logical/Mathematical** PAIRS

Materials *(per pair)* Spinner Pattern (Teaching Tool 34); Tally Chart (Teaching Tool 38); pencil; paper clip

What to Do

- Have children divide the spinner into fourths. Then have them color $\frac{3}{4}$ green and $\frac{1}{4}$ purple. Have children spin the spinner 20 times and record their results on the tally chart.
- Explain that because green was spun more often, it is *more likely* that green will be spun next. It is *less likely* that purple will be spun next.

Ongoing Assessment

- **Reasoning Can you be certain that you will spin green next? Explain.** *(No; because there is a chance you will spin purple)*
- **If you spin 10 more times, which color will you probably spin more?** *(Green)*

		Total
Green	𝍸 𝍸 𝍸	15
Purple	𝍸	5

Reaching All Learners

Reading in Math

Make Predictions

10–15 MIN **Logical/Mathematical**

Materials *(per group)* Bag; 8 red marbles; 2 blue marbles

- Explain that when we make a prediction, we use what we know to tell what is *more likely* or *less likely* to happen.
- Have children count the red marbles and the blue marbles and then find the total. Ask children to place the marbles in the bag and predict whether they are *more likely* to choose a red marble or a blue marble from the bag.
- Have children test their predictions.

English Language Learners

Extend Language

Let's Predict

5–10 MIN **Visual/Spatial/Linguistic**

Materials *(per group)* Picture of a sunny day; picture of a rainy day; other outdoor pictures cut from magazines

- Hold up the picture of the sunny day. **I *predict* it will not rain. What do you *predict?***
- Hold up the picture of the rainy day. **I predict people will wear raincoats. What do you predict?**
- Show other pictures that invite predictions and have children imitate your examples, saying sentences about the pictures in which they use the word *predict*.

Reteaching

Group Tally Chart

10–15 MIN **Logical/Mathematical**

Materials *(per group)* Box; 12 silver beads; 4 gold beads; Tally Chart (Teaching Tool 38)

- Mark a tally chart with the headings "Silver" and "Gold."
- Display the silver and gold beads and then put them into the box. **Are you *more likely* to get a silver bead or a gold bead?**
- After children make predictions, have a child select a bead, write a tally mark on the chart, and replace the bead. Repeat 20 times.
- **Look at the chart. Which color is *more likely* to be chosen next?**

Advanced Learners

Penny Toss

Materials *(per pair)* Penny; Tally Chart (Teaching Tool 38)

- Review the sides of a coin. Discuss whether it is *more likely* that heads or tails will result from a coin toss. **If you toss a penny 30 times, how many times will it show heads? tails?** Have children record their predictions.
- Have partners flip a coin 30 times and record the results on a tally chart.
- Have partners write a sentence that compares the results of the tally chart to their initial predictions.

		Totals
Heads	~~||||~~ ~~||||~~ ||||	14
Tails	~~||||~~ ~~||||~~ ~~||||~~		16

Objective Describe the likelihood of an event as more likely or less likely.

1 Warm Up

Activate Prior Knowledge Review tally marks. Have children make a tally chart to show how many classmates are wearing red, yellow, and blue.

2 Teach

Learn!

Discuss the picture at the top of the student page. Point out that because there is more green space on the spinner, the boy is more likely to spin green and less likely to spin purple. Before children complete the page, model how to spin the spinner and record its color.

Ongoing Assessment

Talk About It

- **If the spinner had more purple space than green space, which color would you be more likely to spin?** *(Purple)*
- **How do you predict which color you are less likely to spin?** *(The color that there is less of on the spinner)*

If children do not understand *more likely* and *less likely*,

then remind them that more of an item means more likely, and less of an item means less likely.

Check

Error Intervention

If children have difficulty predicting which color will be spun next,

then have them continue the experiment until they have a larger sample. *(Also see Reteaching, Page 403B.)*

Think About It Reassure children that a prediction will not always be correct. They should use what they have already spun to predict.

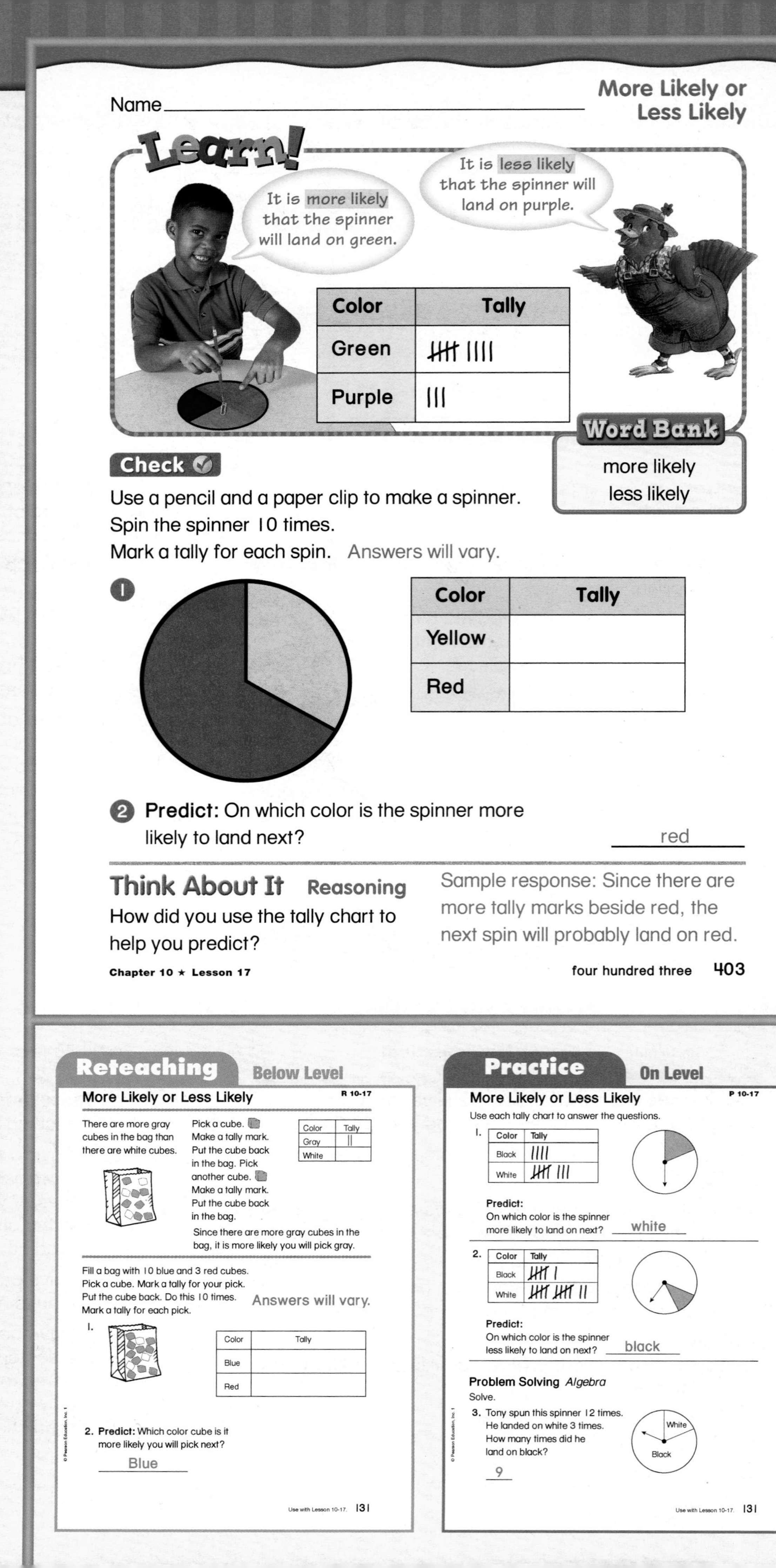

Name ____________________

More Likely or Less Likely

Learn!

Color	Tally
Green	HHT IIII
Purple	III

Word Bank
more likely
less likely

Check

Use a pencil and a paper clip to make a spinner.
Spin the spinner 10 times.
Mark a tally for each spin. Answers will vary.

1.

Color	Tally
Yellow	
Red	

2. **Predict:** On which color is the spinner more likely to land next? red

Think About It Reasoning
How did you use the tally chart to help you predict?

Sample response: Since there are more tally marks beside red, the next spin will probably land on red.

Chapter 10 ★ Lesson 17 — four hundred three 403

Reteaching Below Level

More Likely or Less Likely R 10-17

There are more gray cubes in the bag than there are white cubes.

Pick a cube. Make a tally mark. Put the cube back in the bag. Pick another cube. Make a tally mark. Put the cube back in the bag.

Color	Tally
Gray	II
White	

Since there are more gray cubes in the bag, it is more likely you will pick gray.

Fill a bag with 10 blue and 3 red cubes. Pick a cube. Mark a tally for your pick. Put the cube back. Do this 10 times. Mark a tally for each pick. Answers will vary.

1.

Color	Tally
Blue	
Red	

2. **Predict:** Which color cube is it more likely you will pick next? Blue

Use with Lesson 10-17. 131

Practice On Level

More Likely or Less Likely P 10-17

Use each tally chart to answer the questions.

1.

Color	Tally
Black	IIII
White	HHT III

Predict: On which color is the spinner more likely to land on next? white

2.

Color	Tally
Black	HHT I
White	HHT HHT II

Predict: On which color is the spinner less likely to land on next? black

Problem Solving *Algebra*
Solve.

3. Tony spun this spinner 12 times. He landed on white 3 times. How many times did he land on black? 9

Use with Lesson 10-17. 131

Practice

Use each tally chart to answer the questions.

Color	Tally
Green	𝍸 𝍸
Orange	𝍸

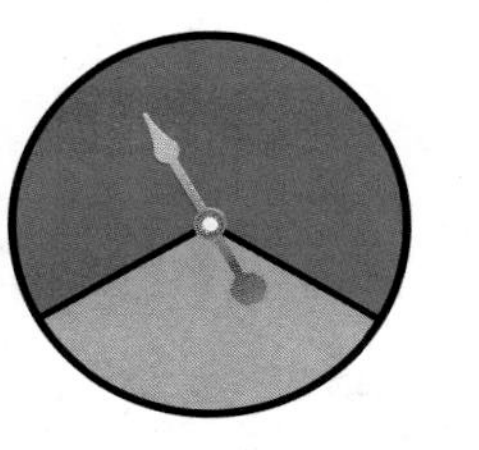

3 **Predict:** On which color is the spinner **more likely** to land next? green

Color	Tally
Blue	||||
Yellow	𝍸 ||||

4 **Predict:** On which color is the spinner **less likely** to land next? blue

Problem Solving **Algebra**

Solve.

5 Liz spun this spinner 11 times. She landed on blue 8 times. How many times did she land on red?

3 times

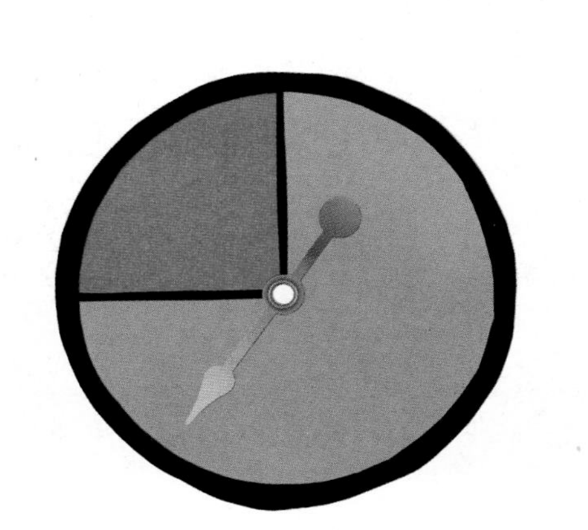

Home Connection Your child spun a spinner and predicted which color it would land on next. **Home Activity** Ask your child to explain how he or she made the predictions in Exercises 3 and 4.

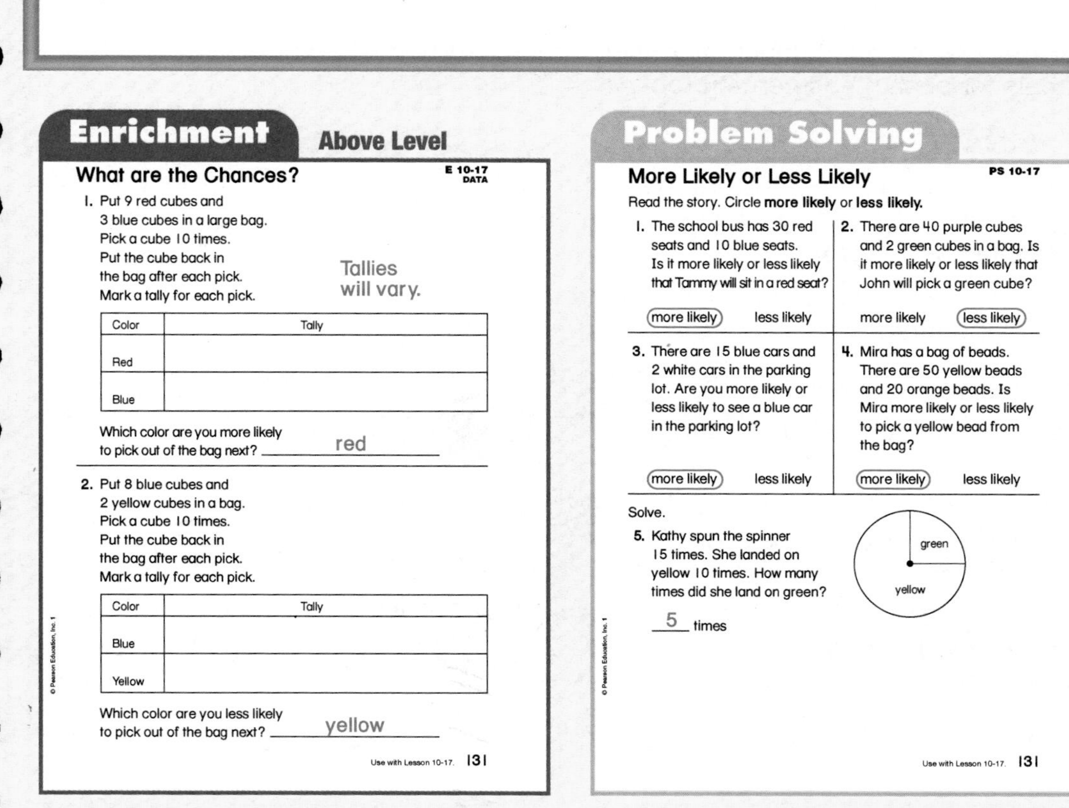

Enrichment — Above Level

What are the Chances? E 10-17 DATA

1. Put 9 red cubes and 3 blue cubes in a large bag. Pick a cube 10 times. Put the cube back in the bag after each pick. Mark a tally for each pick.

Tallies will vary.

Color	Tally
Red	
Blue	

Which color are you more likely to pick out of the bag next? red

2. Put 8 blue cubes and 2 yellow cubes in a bag. Pick a cube 10 times. Put the cube back in the bag after each pick. Mark a tally for each pick.

Color	Tally
Blue	
Yellow	

Which color are you less likely to pick out of the bag next? yellow

Use with Lesson 10-17. 131

Problem Solving

More Likely or Less Likely PS 10-17

Read the story. Circle **more likely** or **less likely**.

1. The school bus has 30 red seats and 10 blue seats. Is it more likely or less likely that Tammy will sit in a red seat? (more likely) less likely
2. There are 40 purple cubes and 2 green cubes in a bag. Is it more likely or less likely that John will pick a green cube? more likely (less likely)
3. There are 15 blue cars and 2 white cars in the parking lot. Are you more likely or less likely to see a blue car in the parking lot? (more likely) less likely
4. Mira has a bag of beads. There are 50 yellow beads and 20 orange beads. Is Mira more likely or less likely to pick a yellow bead from the bag? (more likely) less likely

Solve.

5. Kathy spun the spinner 15 times. She landed on yellow 10 times. How many times did she land on green? 5 times

green
yellow

Use with Lesson 10-17. 131

3 Practice

Explain that children will not be spinning the spinners for Exercises 3–5.

Leveled Practice

Below Level Work with a partner to complete all exercises.

On Level Work individually to complete all exercises.

Above Level Use a pencil and paper clip to spin each spinner 5 more times. Record a tally mark for each spin.

Early Finishers Have partners put yellow and green cubes in a bag so that a yellow cube is more likely to be picked. Then have children try picking and record what happens.

4 Assess

Journal Idea Have children draw a bag filled with cubes. Ask them to color the cubes so that it is less likely that a red cube will be chosen.

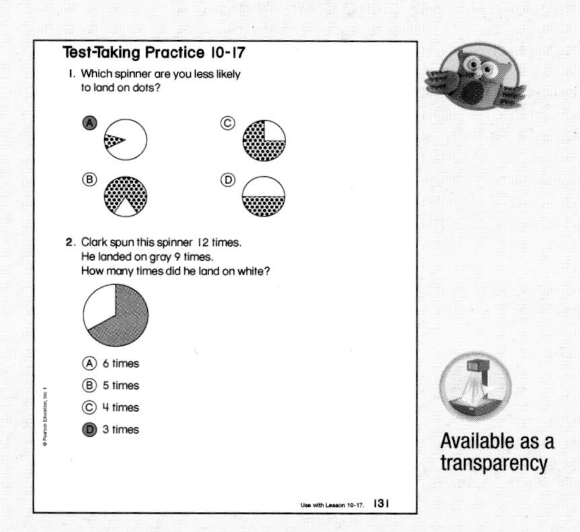

Test-Taking Practice 10-17

1. Which spinner are you less likely to land on dots?

Ⓐ Ⓑ Ⓒ Ⓓ

2. Clark spun this spinner 12 times. He landed on gray 9 times. How many times did he land on white?

Ⓐ 6 times
Ⓑ 5 times
Ⓒ 4 times
Ⓓ 3 times

Use with Lesson 10-17. 131

Available as a transparency

Stir-Fry It!

Lesson Organizer

Quick Lesson Overview

Objective Review and apply concepts, skills, and strategies learned in this and previous chapters.

Math Understanding Some real-world problems can be solved using known concepts, skills, and strategies.

Professional Development Note

Math Background Children apply what they know about measurement to solve new problems. If a child has difficulty solving a problem using a particular measure, determine whether the child does not understand the problem or whether he or she does not recall how to use the measure.

NCTM Standards

- Number and Operations
- Measurement

(For a complete correlation to the NCTM Standards and Grades Pre-K through 2 Expectations, see Pages 363G and 363H.)

Getting Started

Spiral Review

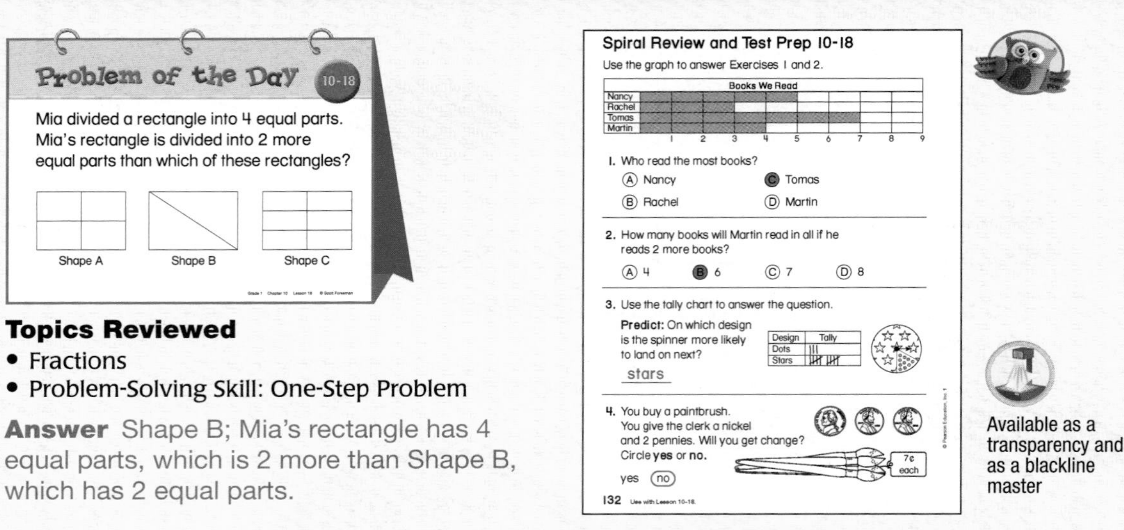

Problem of the Day 10-18

Mia divided a rectangle into 4 equal parts. Mia's rectangle is divided into 2 more equal parts than which of these rectangles?

Shape A Shape B Shape C

Spiral Review and Test Prep 10-18

Use the graph to answer Exercises 1 and 2.

Books We Read (Nancy, Rachel, Tomas, Martin; 1 2 3 4 5 6 7 8 9)

1. Who read the most books?
   (A) Nancy (B) Rachel (C) Tomas (D) Martin
2. How many books will Martin read in all if he reads 2 more books?
   (A) 4 (B) 6 (C) 7 (D) 8
3. Use the tally chart to answer the question.
   Predict: On which design is the spinner more likely to land on next? stars

Design	Tally
Dots	|||
Stars	~~||||~~ ~~||||~~

4. You buy a paintbrush. You give the clerk a nickel and 2 pennies. Will you get change? Circle **yes** or **no**.
   yes (no)
   7¢ each

132 Use with Lesson 10-18.

Topics Reviewed

- Fractions
- Problem-Solving Skill: One-Step Problem

Answer Shape B; Mia's rectangle has 4 equal parts, which is 2 more than Shape B, which has 2 equal parts.

Available as a transparency and as a blackline master

Topics Reviewed

1–2. Making Bar Graphs
3. More Likely or Less Likely
4. Use Data from a Table

Investigating the Concept

Review Measurement

Materials 12-inch ruler; centimeter ruler; cup; pint; quart; liter; index card labels for each measurement tool

What to Do

- Display the rulers and containers. Set out a label for each in random order on a desk or ledge. Discuss each standard measure and which kinds of things it might be used to measure.
- Have children take turns choosing a standard measure and matching it with its label.

cup pint quart liter inch ruler centimeter ruler

Ongoing Assessment

- **Reasoning Which things would you use a cup to measure?** *(Sample responses: Milk, juice, water, soup)*
- **How are the two rulers different?** *(One measures in inches, and one measures in centimeters.)*
- **What is alike about all of these objects?** *(They are all used to measure things.)*

Reaching All Learners

Reading in Math

Follow a Recipe

15–20 MIN **Linguistic/Kinesthetic**

Materials *(per group)* Paper towels; pan or bowl; cup; 12-inch ruler; tablespoon; paste

- Write the following recipe for papier-mâché:

  Papier-mâché
  Tear the paper towels in strips that are 1-inch wide.
  Put the strips in the pan.
  Cover the strips with about 1 cup of water.
  Let the paper soak for 1 day.
  When the paper is soft, mix in 2 tablespoons of paste.
  Now it's ready to use!
- Have children cover cardboard boxes and tubes to make constructions. When the buildings are dry, children may paint and display them.

Access Content

English Language Learners

I Am Thinking Of ...

5–10 MIN **Linguistic**

Materials *(per group)* 12-inch ruler; centimeter ruler; cup; pint; quart; liter

- Assemble the rulers and the measuring cups. Invite children to name the measuring tools with you.
- Play a guessing game in which children secretly select a measurement tool and give clues for others to guess which one they chose. Start the game by saying: **It is smaller than a pint.**
- Give each child a chance to give clues for the group to guess.

Reteaching

Party Preparations

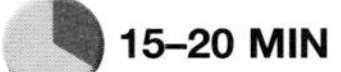

15–20 MIN **Kinesthetic**

Materials Cup; pint; quart; 12-inch rulers; construction paper; markers

- Assign committees to use measurements to make preparations for a class party. Have one group determine how many quarts of juice per table the class will need if each child drinks 1 cup of juice.
- Help another group measure paper to make decorative place cards, place mats, and table decorations. Have some children make invitations for special guests.

Math and Social Studies

Foods of Many Places

15–20 MIN **Linguistic/Kinesthetic**

WHOLE CLASS

- Discuss the types of food that children enjoy with their families. Help children make a list of their favorite dishes.
- Invite children to share how these dishes are made.
- Suggest that children ask their families to help them write down how to prepare the dishes, including measurement of ingredients, cooking temperature, and cooking time.
- Compile the recipes in a book and duplicate it for each child in the class.

Objective Review and apply concepts, skills, and strategies learned in this and previous chapters.

1 Warm Up

Activate Prior Knowledge Review how to make a tally chart. Write the following information on the board: "10 children like fried rice." "2 children do not like fried rice." "1 child has never eaten fried rice." Have children use the information to make a tally chart.

2 Teach

Explain to children that they will use what they know about measurement to solve the problems on Student Page 405. Read Exercise 1 aloud.

Ongoing Assessment

Talk About It

- **What do we need to find out?** *(Is 1 cup more than 1 quart or less than 1 quart?)*
- **What do we know?** *(A cup and a quart are units of capacity.)*
- **How can we solve this problem?** *(Compare the size of a cup to the size of a quart.)*
- **Is 1 cup more than 1 quart or less than 1 quart?** *(Less than 1 quart)*

If children cannot compare what the cup and the quart hold,

then fill a cup and a quart with rice and compare how much they hold.

Error Intervention

If children have difficulty reading the questions,

then read the questions aloud. *(Also see Reteaching, Page 405B.)*

Name ________________

PROBLEM-SOLVING APPLICATIONS
Stir-Fry It!

DK Dorling Kindersley

Chow mein is made by combining noodles and stir-fried vegetables.

Do You Know... that more people have soy sauce in their homes than have milk?

1. Lin is making chow mein. He needs 1 cup of dry noodles. Is 1 cup more than 1 quart or less than 1 quart?
   less than 1 quart
2. A chopstick measures about 10 inches long. Is 10 inches more than 1 centimeter or less than 1 centimeter?
   more than 1 centimeter
3. Is 10 inches more than 1 foot or less than 1 foot?
   less than 1 foot

Fun Fact! People started using chopsticks in China over 4,000 years ago.

Chapter 10 ★ Lesson 18 — four hundred five 405

Reteaching Below Level

Happy Birthday to You! E 10-18 DECISION MAKING

You are having a party.
6 friends are coming.

1. Circle how much juice you should buy.
2. There are 9 banana muffins and 3 blueberry muffins. Is it more likely or less likely that friends will get a blueberry muffin? Circle your answer. more likely / (less likely)
3. There are 7 party hats. Is it certain or impossible that each friend will get one? Circle your answer. (certain) / impossible
4. Each friend brings a gift. Tammy's gift is 10 centimeters long. Ray's gift is 10 inches long. Which gift is longer? Ray's gift
5. Your party begins at 1 o'clock. It will last 2 hours. Your party will end at 3:00.

132 Use with Lesson 10-18.

Practice On Level

PROBLEM-SOLVING APPLICATIONS P 10-18
Stir-Fry It!

Read each exercise. Solve.

1. Raffi and his dad are making bread. Raffi measures 1 cup of milk. Is 1 cup more than 1 pint or less than 1 pint?
   less than a pint
2. The bread pan measures 8 inches. Is the bread pan more than 1 foot long or less than 1 foot long?
   less than a foot long
3. What will Raffi's dad use to measure how hot the oven is? Circle your answer.
4. It takes a half hour to make chow mein. It takes 2 hours to make bread. Which takes longer to make?
   bread
5. Raffi wants to have milk to drink with his bread. Will he have more than 1 liter or less than 1 liter?
   less than a liter

Writing in Math Answers will vary.

6. Ask 10 children in your class if they prefer bagels or muffins. Make a tally chart to show their answers.

132 Use with Lesson 10-18.

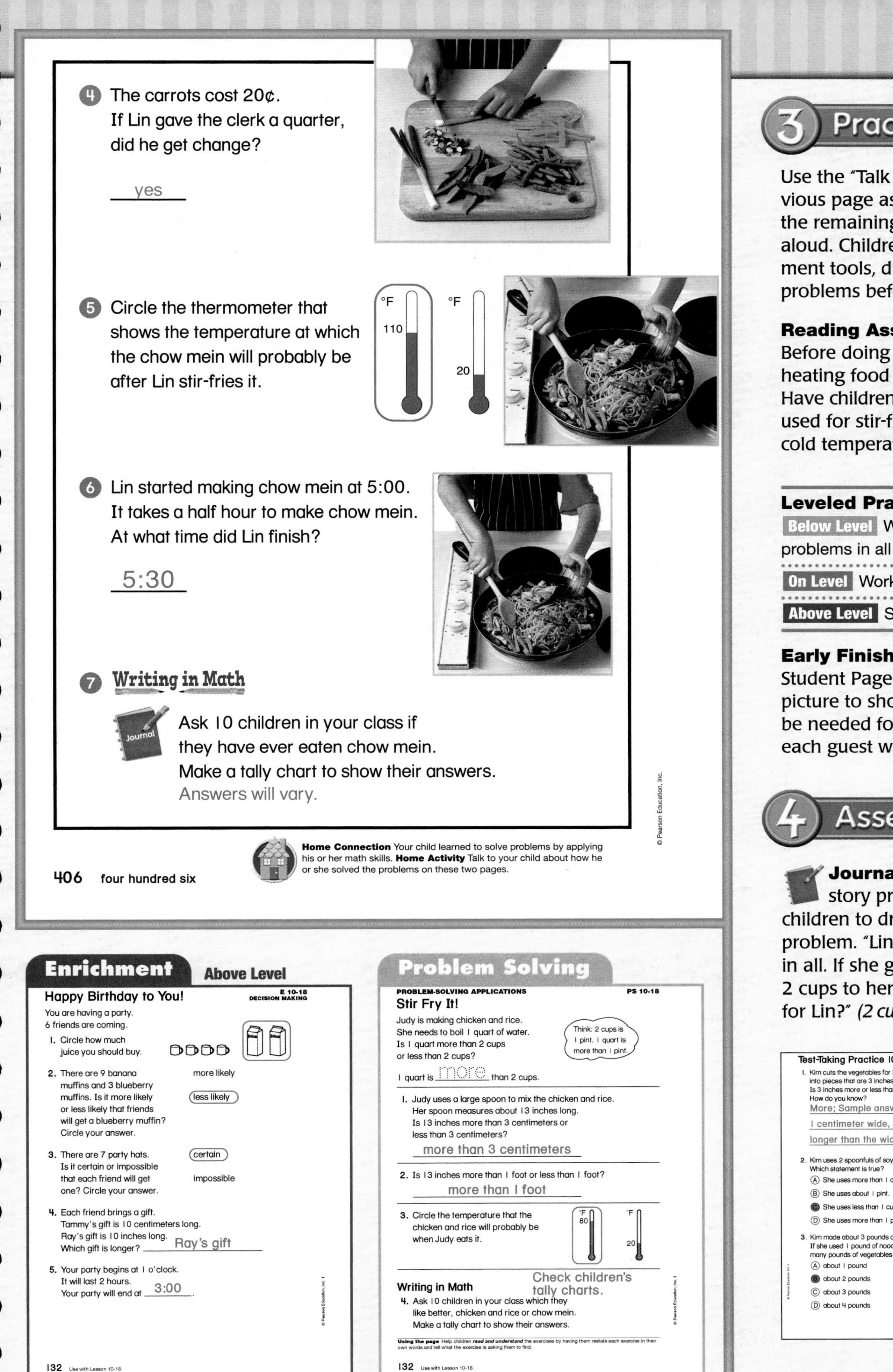

4. The carrots cost 20¢.
If Lin gave the clerk a quarter, did he get change?

yes

5. Circle the thermometer that shows the temperature at which the chow mein will probably be after Lin stir-fries it.

°F 110 (circled) °F 20

6. Lin started making chow mein at 5:00.
It takes a half hour to make chow mein.
At what time did Lin finish?

5:30

7. **Writing in Math**

Journal

Ask 10 children in your class if they have ever eaten chow mein.
Make a tally chart to show their answers.
Answers will vary.

Home Connection Your child learned to solve problems by applying his or her math skills. **Home Activity** Talk to your child about how he or she solved the problems on these two pages.

Enrichment — Above Level

Happy Birthday to You! E 10-18 DECISION MAKING

You are having a party.
6 friends are coming.

1. Circle how much juice you should buy.
2. There are 9 banana muffins and 3 blueberry muffins. Is it more likely or less likely that friends will get a blueberry muffin? Circle your answer. more likely / (less likely)
3. There are 7 party hats. Is it certain or impossible that each friend will get one? Circle your answer. (certain) / impossible
4. Each friend brings a gift. Tammy's gift is 10 centimeters long. Ray's gift is 10 inches long. Which gift is longer? Ray's gift
5. Your party begins at 1 o'clock. It will last 2 hours. Your party will end at 3:00.

132 Use with Lesson 10-18.

Problem Solving

PROBLEM-SOLVING APPLICATIONS PS 10-18

Stir Fry It!

Judy is making chicken and rice.
She needs to boil 1 quart of water.
Is 1 quart more than 2 cups or less than 2 cups?

Think: 2 cups is 1 pint. 1 quart is more than 1 pint.

1 quart is more than 2 cups.

1. Judy uses a large spoon to mix the chicken and rice. Her spoon measures about 13 inches long. Is 13 inches more than 3 centimeters or less than 3 centimeters?
more than 3 centimeters
2. Is 13 inches more than 1 foot or less than 1 foot?
more than 1 foot
3. Circle the temperature that the chicken and rice will probably be when Judy eats it.
°F 80 (circled) °F 20

Writing in Math

4. Ask 10 children in your class which they like better, chicken and rice or chow mein. Make a tally chart to show their answers.
Check children's tally charts.

Using the page Help children *read and understand* the exercises by having them restate each exercise in their own words and tell what the exercise is asking them to find.

132 Use with Lesson 10-18.

3 Practice

Use the "Talk About It" questions on the previous page as a guide to help children do the remaining exercises. Read each problem aloud. Children may use available measurement tools, draw pictures, or act out the problems before they write their answers.

Reading Assist: Make Predictions Before doing Exercise 5, remind children that heating food brings it to a high temperature. Have children predict whether a thermometer used for stir-fried food will show a hot or cold temperature.

Leveled Practice

Below Level Work with a partner to solve problems in all exercises.

On Level Work with a partner to solve Exercise 7.

Above Level Solve all problems independently.

Early Finishers Discuss the *Fun Fact* on Student Page 405. Have children draw a picture to show how many chopsticks will be needed for 8 guests, remembering that each guest will use 2. *(16)*

4 Assess

Journal Idea Write the following story problem on the board. Ask children to draw a picture to go with the problem. "Lin made 5 cups of chow mein in all. If she gives 1 cup to her brother and 2 cups to her sister, how much will be left for Lin?" *(2 cups)*

Test-Taking Practice 10-18

1. Kim cuts the vegetables for her chow mein into pieces that are 3 inches long. Is 3 inches more or less than 1 centimeter? How do you know?
More; Sample answer: My finger is about 1 centimeter wide, and 3 inches is much longer than the width of my finger.
2. Kim uses 2 spoonfuls of soy sauce in her chow mein. Which statement is true?
   - (A) She uses more than 1 quart.
   - (B) She uses about 1 pint.
   - (C) She uses less than 1 cup. (filled)
   - (D) She uses more than 1 pint.
3. Kim made about 3 pounds of chow mein. If she used 1 pound of noodles, about how many pounds of vegetables did she use?
   - (A) about 1 pound
   - (B) about 2 pounds (filled)
   - (C) about 3 pounds
   - (D) about 4 pounds

Use with Lesson 10-18. 132

Available as a transparency

Diagnostic Checkpoint

Purpose Provide assessment of children's progress to date by checking their understanding of key content covered in the previous section.

Vocabulary Review

You may wish to review these terms before assigning the page:

certain Definitely will happen *(pp. 401–402)*

impossible Cannot happen *(pp. 401–402)*

less likely Smaller chance that an event will happen than that it won't happen *(pp. 403–404)*

more likely Greater chance that an event will happen than that it won't happen *(pp. 403–404)*

Activities for this section are available in the Math Vocabulary Kit.

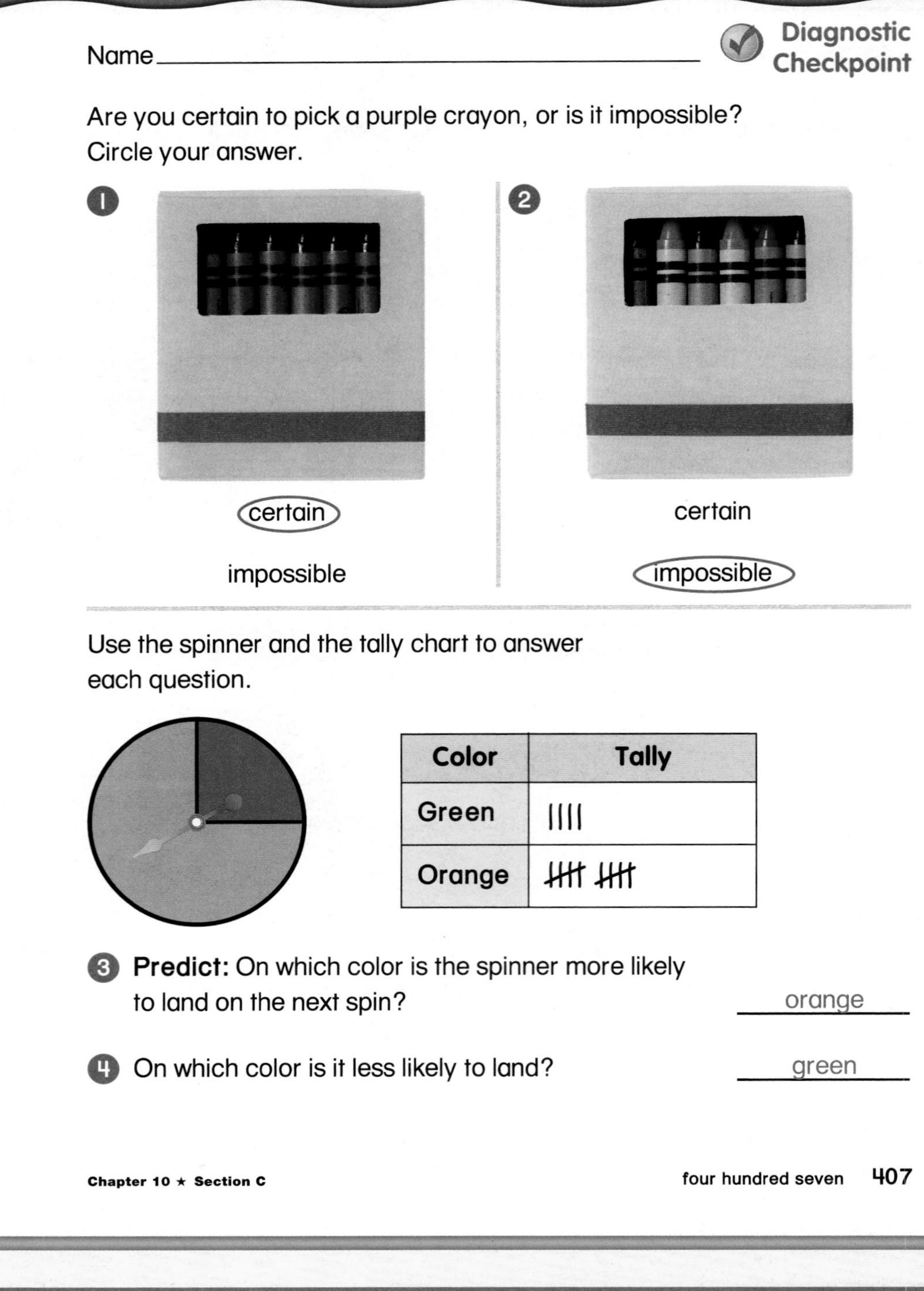

Name ______________________

Diagnostic Checkpoint

Are you certain to pick a purple crayon, or is it impossible? Circle your answer.

1. (certain) impossible

2. certain (impossible)

Use the spinner and the tally chart to answer each question.

Color	Tally
Green	||||
Orange	~~||||~~ ~~||||~~

3. **Predict:** On which color is the spinner more likely to land on the next spin? orange

4. On which color is it less likely to land? green

Chapter 10 ★ Section C

four hundred seven 407

Item Analysis for Diagnosis and Intervention

Objective	Items	Student Book Pages*	Intervention System
Describe the likelihood of an event as certain or impossible.	1–2	401–402	D69
Describe the likelihood of an event as more likely or less likely.	3–4	403–404	D69

*For each lesson, there is a *Reteaching* activity in *Reaching All Learners* and a *Reteaching* master.

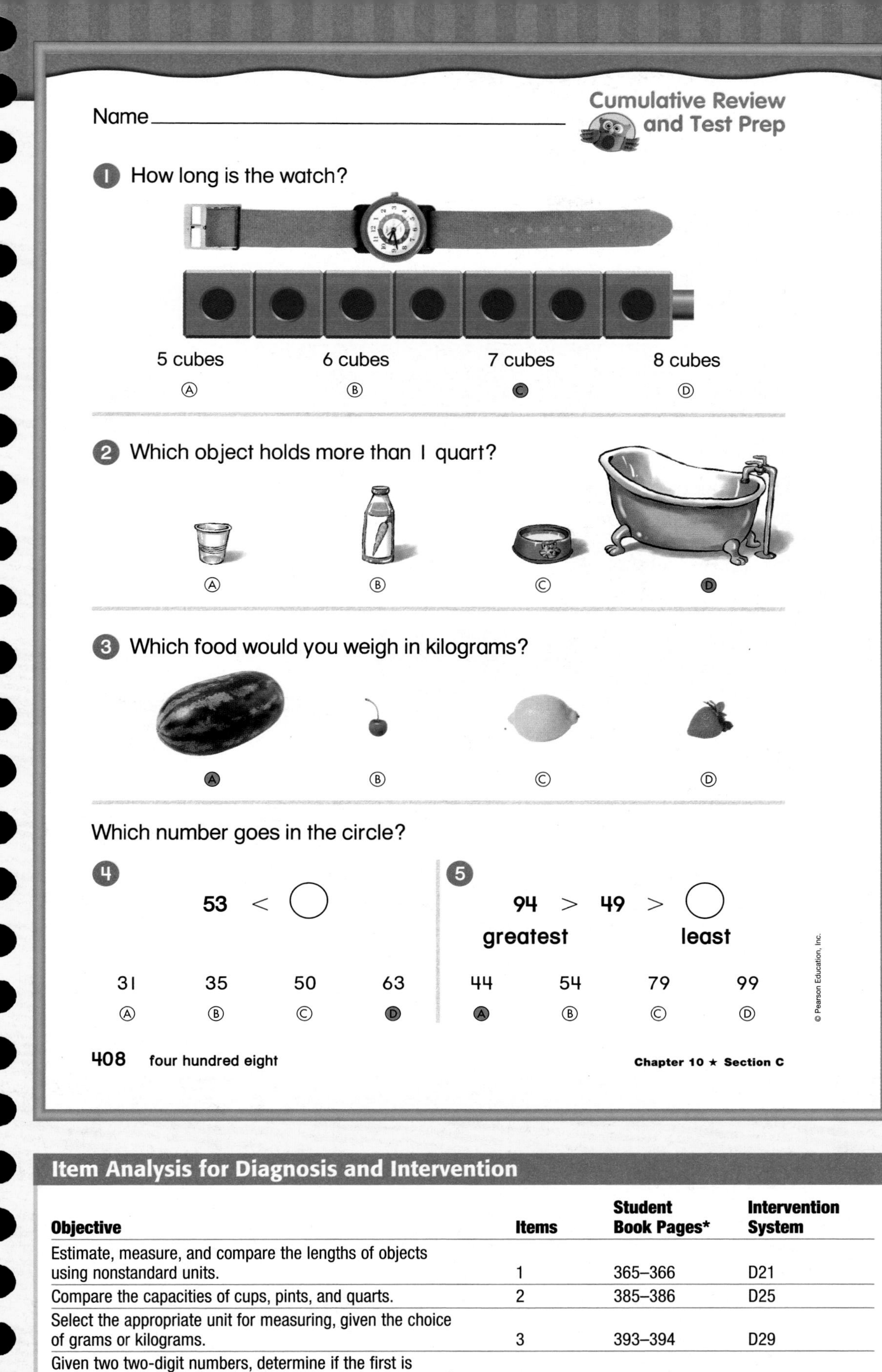

Item Analysis for Diagnosis and Intervention

Objective	Items	Student Book Pages*	Intervention System
Estimate, measure, and compare the lengths of objects using nonstandard units.	1	365–366	D21
Compare the capacities of cups, pints, and quarts.	2	385–386	D25
Select the appropriate unit for measuring, given the choice of grams or kilograms.	3	393–394	D29
Given two two-digit numbers, determine if the first is greater than, less than, or equal to the second.	4	297–298	A27
Given three two-digit numbers, order them from least to greatest or from greatest to least.	5	301–302	A29

*For each lesson, there is a *Reteaching* activity in *Reaching All Learners* and a *Reteaching* master.

Cumulative Review and Test Prep

Purpose Provide children with a review of math concepts. Items appear as they would on a standardized test so children become familiar with that format.

Enrichment

Purpose Provide children with related mathematical topics and applications beyond the basic chapter content.

Using Student Page 409

Remind children that they have already learned that they can measure using standard units, such as inches, as well as using nonstandard units, such as cubes or paper clips. Tell them that this page will show them that the length of an object can be measured using many types of units and that the measurement of an object depends upon the unit used to measure it.

Before having children work through the page, you may want to use rulers, crayons, and pencils to show how a measurement depends on the unit of measure. Have children measure their desks using an inch ruler and share their results. Point out that the results are the same for everyone. Then have children measure their desks using a pencil or a crayon and share their results again. Children may find that all of their measurements are not the same because their pencils and crayons are different lengths. Discuss with children why this makes sense. Repeat the process for measuring other classroom objects such as chairs or tables.

Once children are comfortable with the process, read the directions on the page and make sure children understand how to complete the exercises.

When measuring using paper clips, make sure children understand that they must lay them end to end without overlapping the clips or leaving spaces between them. For the Writing in Math feature, have children tell why it makes sense that different units of measure produce different measurements. Remind children that as units grow longer in length, fewer units are required to measure an object.

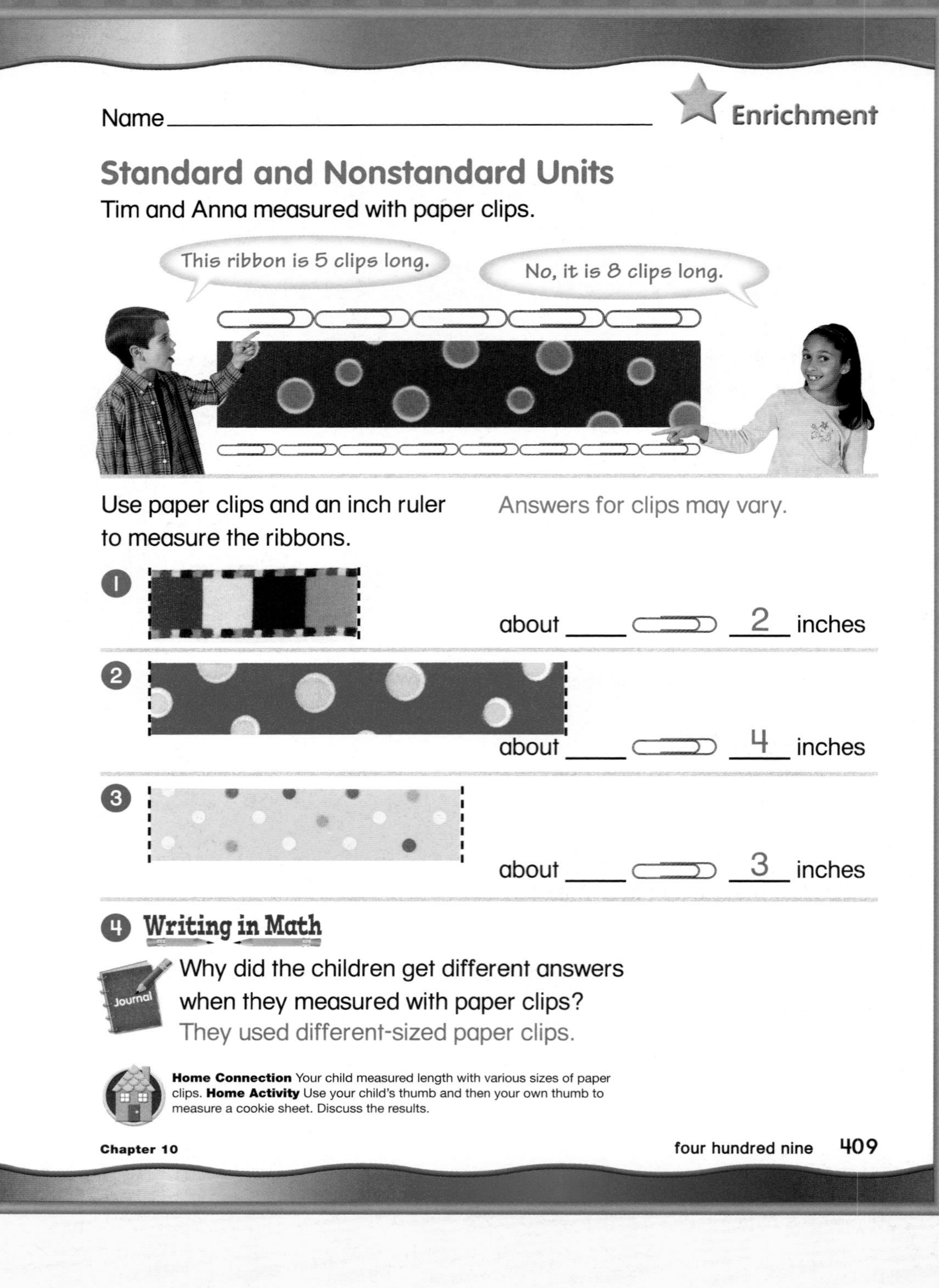

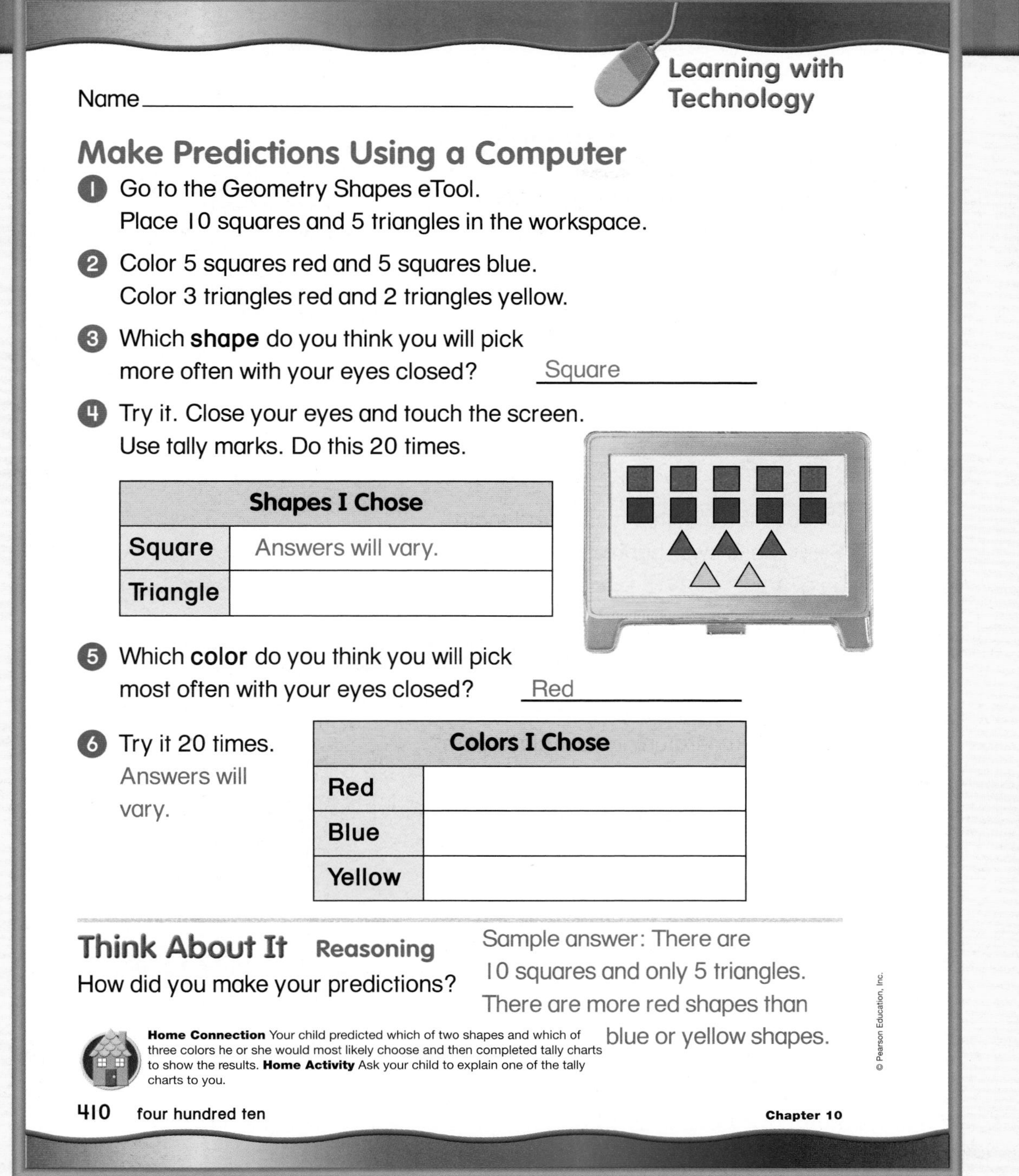
Name ______________________

Learning with Technology

Make Predictions Using a Computer

1. Go to the Geometry Shapes eTool.
   Place 10 squares and 5 triangles in the workspace.
2. Color 5 squares red and 5 squares blue.
   Color 3 triangles red and 2 triangles yellow.
3. Which **shape** do you think you will pick more often with your eyes closed? Square
4. Try it. Close your eyes and touch the screen.
   Use tally marks. Do this 20 times.

Shapes I Chose	
Square	Answers will vary.
Triangle	

5. Which **color** do you think you will pick most often with your eyes closed? Red
6. Try it 20 times.
   Answers will vary.

Colors I Chose	
Red	
Blue	
Yellow	

Think About It Reasoning
How did you make your predictions? Sample answer: There are 10 squares and only 5 triangles. There are more red shapes than blue or yellow shapes.

Home Connection Your child predicted which of two shapes and which of three colors he or she would most likely choose and then completed tally charts to show the results. **Home Activity** Ask your child to explain one of the tally charts to you.

410 four hundred ten Chapter 10

Learning with Technology

Purpose Use a computer program to perform a probability experiment.

Using Student Page 410

You will need the Shapes eTool for this computer activity.

Using your computer screen or an overhead projector, demonstrate how to add shapes to the workspace and how to color them.

When children are ready to begin, allow them some time to familiarize themselves with the computer tool. Have them practice putting shapes into the workspace and coloring the shapes. Remind children that it is important that they write down their predictions before they begin each experiment. For Exercise 4, children should place a tally mark in the chart next to the shape that is closest to their finger on the screen. For Exercise 6, children should place a tally mark in the chart next to the color of the shape that is closest to their finger on the screen.

Think About It Have children tell why they predicted that they would point to one shape or color over another. Guide children to realize that they had a greater chance of selecting a square because there were more squares than triangles on their screens and that they had a greater chance of selecting a red shape because there were more red shapes than blue or yellow shapes on their screens.

Test Talk

Purpose Teach children a particular test-taking strategy and help them become more comfortable with the language and format used on standardized tests.

Using Student Page 411

This page is designed to give children practice in understanding test questions.

Children often have difficulty on standardized tests not because they haven't been introduced to the concept or skill being tested, but because they fail to understand what they are being asked to do or how they are being asked to do it. This page can help with both the what and the how.

Discuss the question in Exercise 1. You might ask a volunteer to indicate the length of his or her math book. Then ask the class to explain why an inch ruler is the tool in the answer choices that makes sense for measuring length.

Have children complete Exercise 2 independently. When they have finished, ask children to identify what each tool in the answer choices is used to measure. *(Sample answers: A thermometer is used to measure temperature; a centimeter ruler is used to measure length or width; a balance scale is used to measure weight; and a one-liter container is used to measure capacity.)* Then discuss why a thermometer is the correct answer.

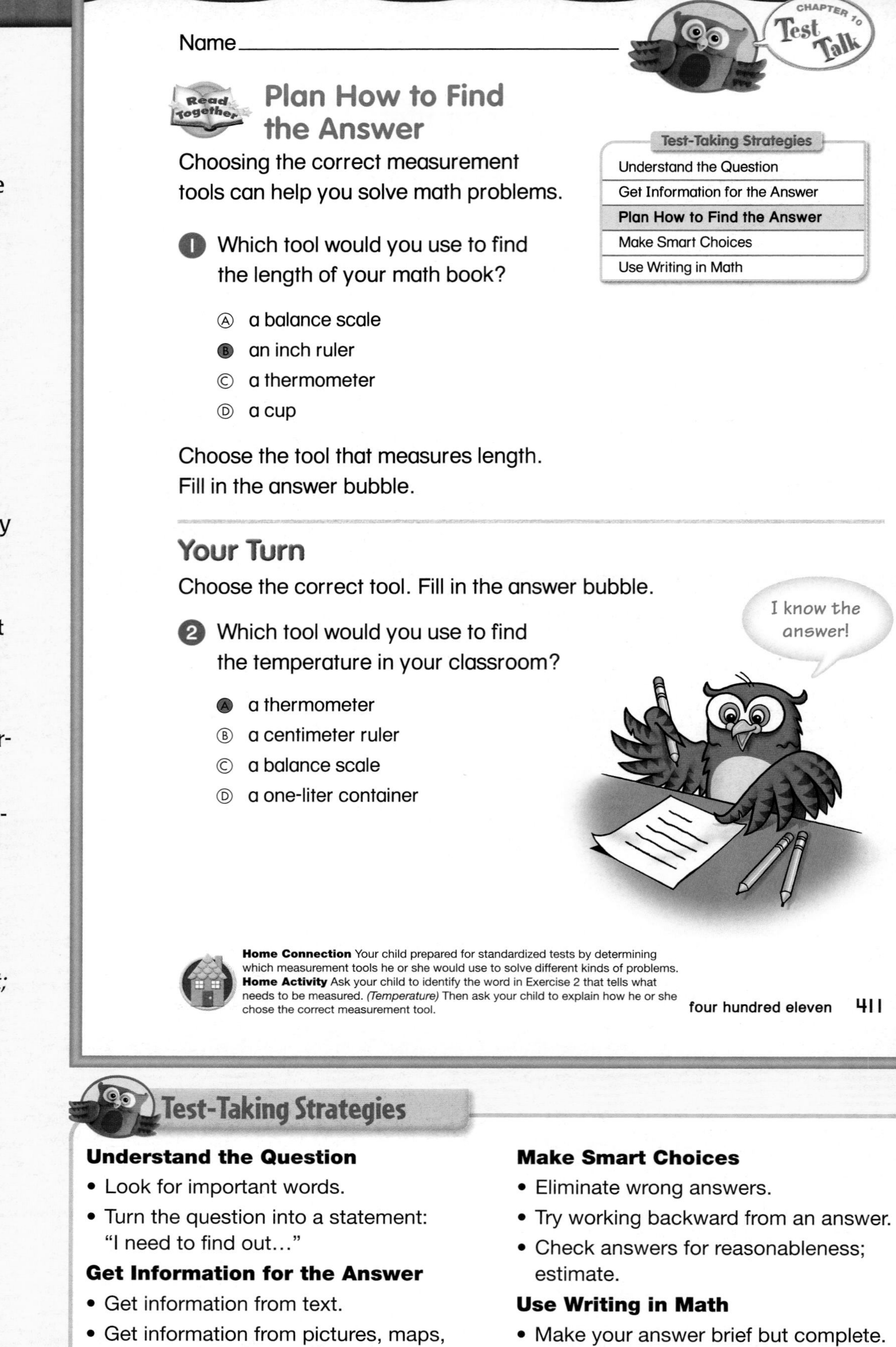

Name ______________________

CHAPTER 10 Test Talk

Read Together

Plan How to Find the Answer

Choosing the correct measurement tools can help you solve math problems.

Test-Taking Strategies
Understand the Question
Get Information for the Answer
Plan How to Find the Answer
Make Smart Choices
Use Writing in Math

1. Which tool would you use to find the length of your math book?

   Ⓐ a balance scale
   Ⓑ an inch ruler
   Ⓒ a thermometer
   Ⓓ a cup

Choose the tool that measures length. Fill in the answer bubble.

Your Turn

Choose the correct tool. Fill in the answer bubble.

2. Which tool would you use to find the temperature in your classroom?

   Ⓐ a thermometer
   Ⓑ a centimeter ruler
   Ⓒ a balance scale
   Ⓓ a one-liter container

Home Connection Your child prepared for standardized tests by determining which measurement tools he or she would use to solve different kinds of problems. **Home Activity** Ask your child to identify the word in Exercise 2 that tells what needs to be measured. *(Temperature)* Then ask your child to explain how he or she chose the correct measurement tool.

four hundred eleven 411

Test-Taking Strategies

Understand the Question
- Look for important words.
- Turn the question into a statement: "I need to find out…"

Get Information for the Answer
- Get information from text.
- Get information from pictures, maps, diagrams, tables, graphs.

Plan How to Find the Answer
- Think about problem-solving skills and strategies.
- Choose computation methods.

Make Smart Choices
- Eliminate wrong answers.
- Try working backward from an answer.
- Check answers for reasonableness; estimate.

Use Writing in Math
- Make your answer brief but complete.
- Use words from the problem and use math terms accurately.
- Describe steps in order.
- Draw pictures to explain your thinking.

Name ____________________

Discover Math in Your World

Discovery Channel School

Read Together

Light as a Feather?

Can you pick up an elephant? No way!
Some things are very heavy.
Others are very light.
How would you weigh a feather?

Measuring Weight

1. Work in a group. Choose something light to weigh.
2. Put your object on one side of a balance scale.
3. On the other side of the scale, add seeds or beans one at a time until the scale balances.
4. Record the weight of your object on a separate sheet of paper.
5. Repeat Steps 1–4 using two other light objects.

Take It to the NET
Video and Activities
www.scottforesman.com

Home Connection Your child weighed light objects by using a balance scale and seeds or beans. **Home Activity** Ask your child to explain how he or she found the weight of one of the objects.

Take It to the NET
Video and Activities
www.scottforesman.com

The video includes pre-viewing and post-viewing questions.
A Discovery Channel Blackline Master is also provided.

Discover Math in Your World

Purpose Help children connect math content to everyday applications.

Using Student Page 412

In this activity, children will learn to use a balance to compare the weights of light objects such as a flower petal and a feather.

Show children two classroom objects, such as a pencil and a desk. **Which object is heavy?** *(The desk)* **Which object is light?** *(The pencil)* Remind children that the weight of an object can be measured by using a balance.

Read through the paragraph at the top of the page and ask children to identify the objects in the pictures. **Which objects are light?** *(The feathers, the shells, the starfish, and the rice)* **Which object is heavy?** *(The elephant)* **About how much does each object weigh?** *(Accept reasonable answers.)*

Read through the directions with children and have them work in groups to measure objects using a balance. Circulate to help groups, if necessary. When finished, ask: **Which object weighs the most? Which object weighs the least? Do any of the objects weigh the same amount?**

Note: Before children begin using a balance, you might want to review how to use it. Point out that the scale is called a "balance" because both sides are the same height when the weights on both sides are equal. Children want to determine the weight of an object by balancing the scale with a number of seeds, rice, or beans that have the same weight. Point out that it would not be possible to weigh a very heavy object, such as an elephant, on the scale without breaking it.

Chapter Test

Purpose Assess children's progress by checking their understanding of the concepts and skills covered in Chapter 10. Use as a review, practice test, or chapter test.

MindPoint Quiz Show CD-ROM Use *MindPoint Quiz Show* for additional practice on Chapter 10.

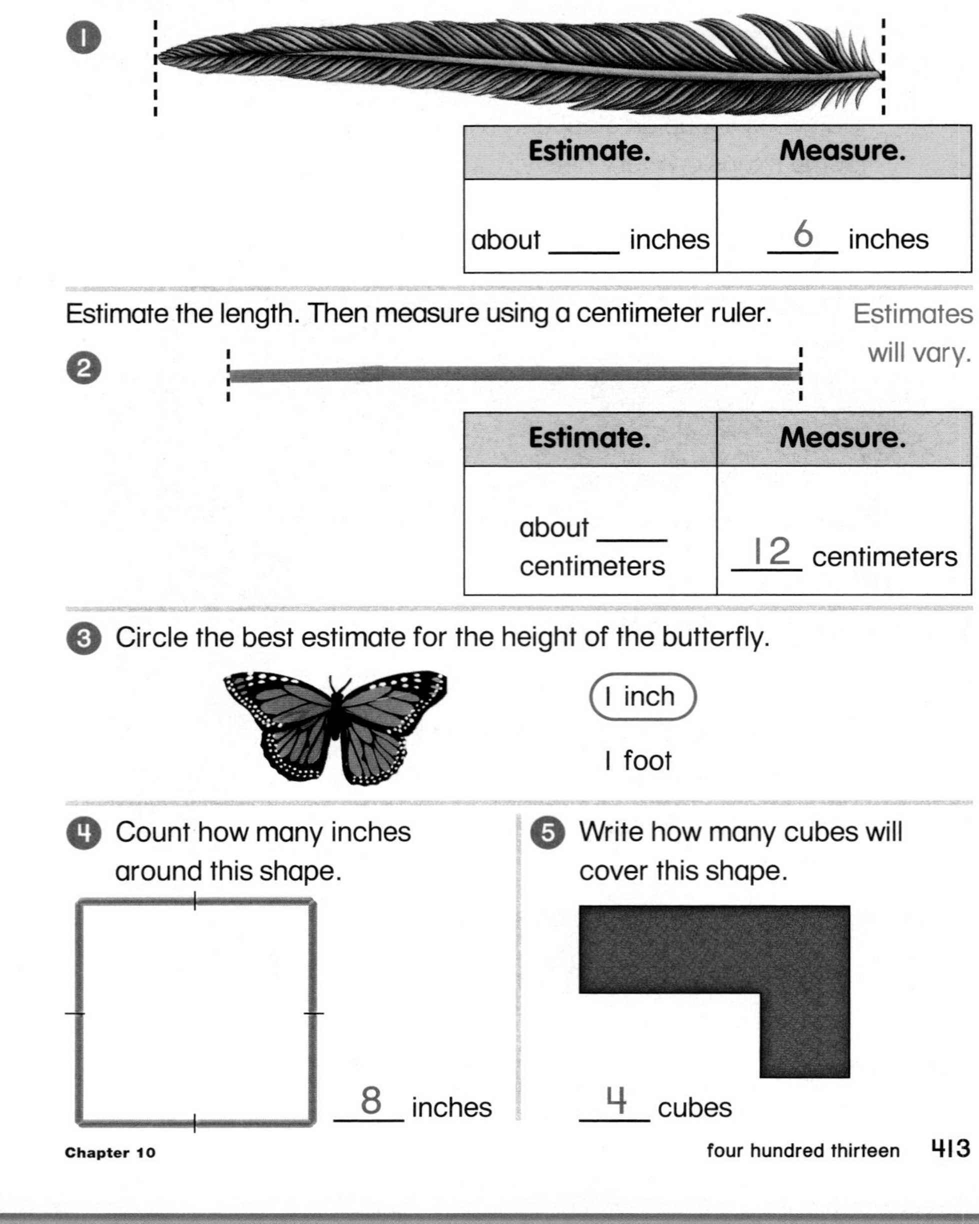

Name ______________________ Chapter Test

Estimate the length. Then measure using an inch ruler. Estimates will vary.

1

Estimate.	Measure.
about ____ inches	6 inches

Estimate the length. Then measure using a centimeter ruler. Estimates will vary.

2

Estimate.	Measure.
about ____ centimeters	12 centimeters

3 Circle the best estimate for the height of the butterfly.

(1 inch)

1 foot

4 Count how many inches around this shape.

8 inches

5 Write how many cubes will cover this shape.

4 cubes

Chapter 10 four hundred thirteen 413

Item Analysis for Diagnosis and Intervention

Objective	Items	Student Book Pages*	Intervention System
Estimate and measure the lengths of objects to the nearest inch using a ruler.	1	371–372	D22
Estimate and measure the length of objects in centimeters using a ruler.	2	375–376	D23
Estimate and measure the length or height of objects to the nearest foot using a 12-inch ruler.	3	373–374	D22
Find the distance around a shape using inches.	4	377–378	D23
Look back and check is a strategy that can help confirm the solution to a problem.	5	379–380	E14

*For each lesson, there is a *Reteaching* activity in *Reaching All Learners* and a *Reteaching* master.

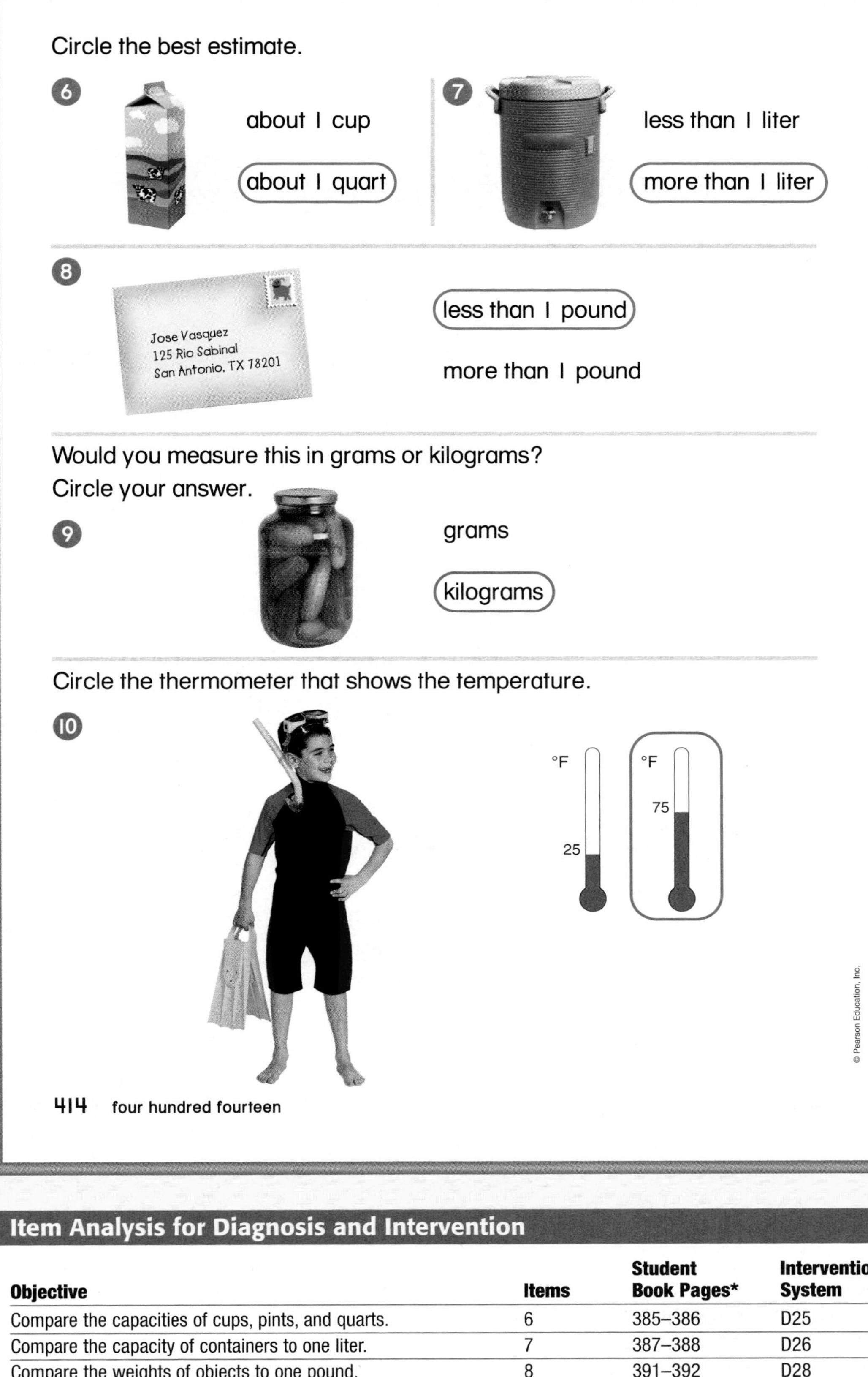

Circle the best estimate.

6 about 1 cup / **(about 1 quart)**

7 less than 1 liter / **(more than 1 liter)**

8 **(less than 1 pound)** / more than 1 pound

Would you measure this in grams or kilograms?
Circle your answer.

9 grams / **(kilograms)**

Circle the thermometer that shows the temperature.

10

Item Analysis for Diagnosis and Intervention

Objective	Items	Student Book Pages*	Intervention System
Compare the capacities of cups, pints, and quarts.	6	385–386	D25
Compare the capacity of containers to one liter.	7	387–388	D26
Compare the weights of objects to one pound.	8	391–392	D28
Select the appropriate unit for measuring, given the choice of grams or kilograms.	9	393–394	D29
Compare temperatures on a thermometer and match them to activities or objects.	10	395–396	D9

*For each lesson, there is a *Reteaching* activity in *Reaching All Learners* and a *Reteaching* master.

Assessment Sourcebook

These additional assessment options may be found in the *Assessment Sourcebook:*

- Chapter 10 Free-Response Test (Forms A and B)
- Chapter 10 Multiple-Choice Test (Forms C and D)
- Chapter 10 Performance Assessment

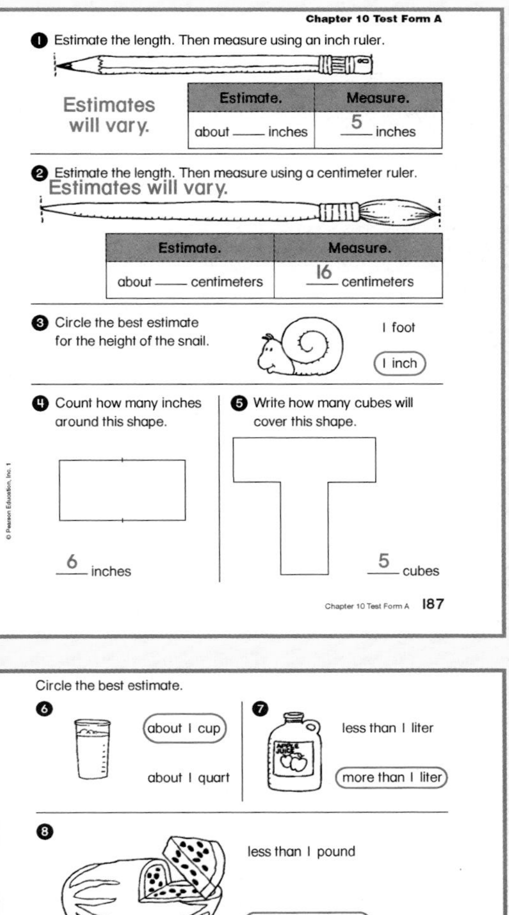

Chapter 10 Test Form A

1 Estimate the length. Then measure using an inch ruler.

Estimates will vary.

Estimate.	Measure.
about ___ inches	5 inches

2 Estimate the length. Then measure using a centimeter ruler.

Estimates will vary.

Estimate.	Measure.
about ___ centimeters	16 centimeters

3 Circle the best estimate for the height of the snail. 1 foot / (1 inch)

4 Count how many inches around this shape. 6 inches

5 Write how many cubes will cover this shape. 5 cubes

© Pearson Education, Inc. 1

Chapter 10 Test Form A 187

Circle the best estimate.

6 (about 1 cup) / about 1 quart

7 less than 1 liter / (more than 1 liter)

8 less than 1 pound / (more than 1 pound)

9 Would you measure this in grams or kilograms? Circle your answer. (grams) / kilograms

10 Circle the thermometer that shows the temperature.

°F 30 °F 90

© Pearson Education, Inc. 1

188 Chapter 10 Test Form A

Cumulative Review and Test Prep

Purpose Provide children with a review of math concepts. Items on page 414A appear as they would on a standardized test so children become familiar with that format.

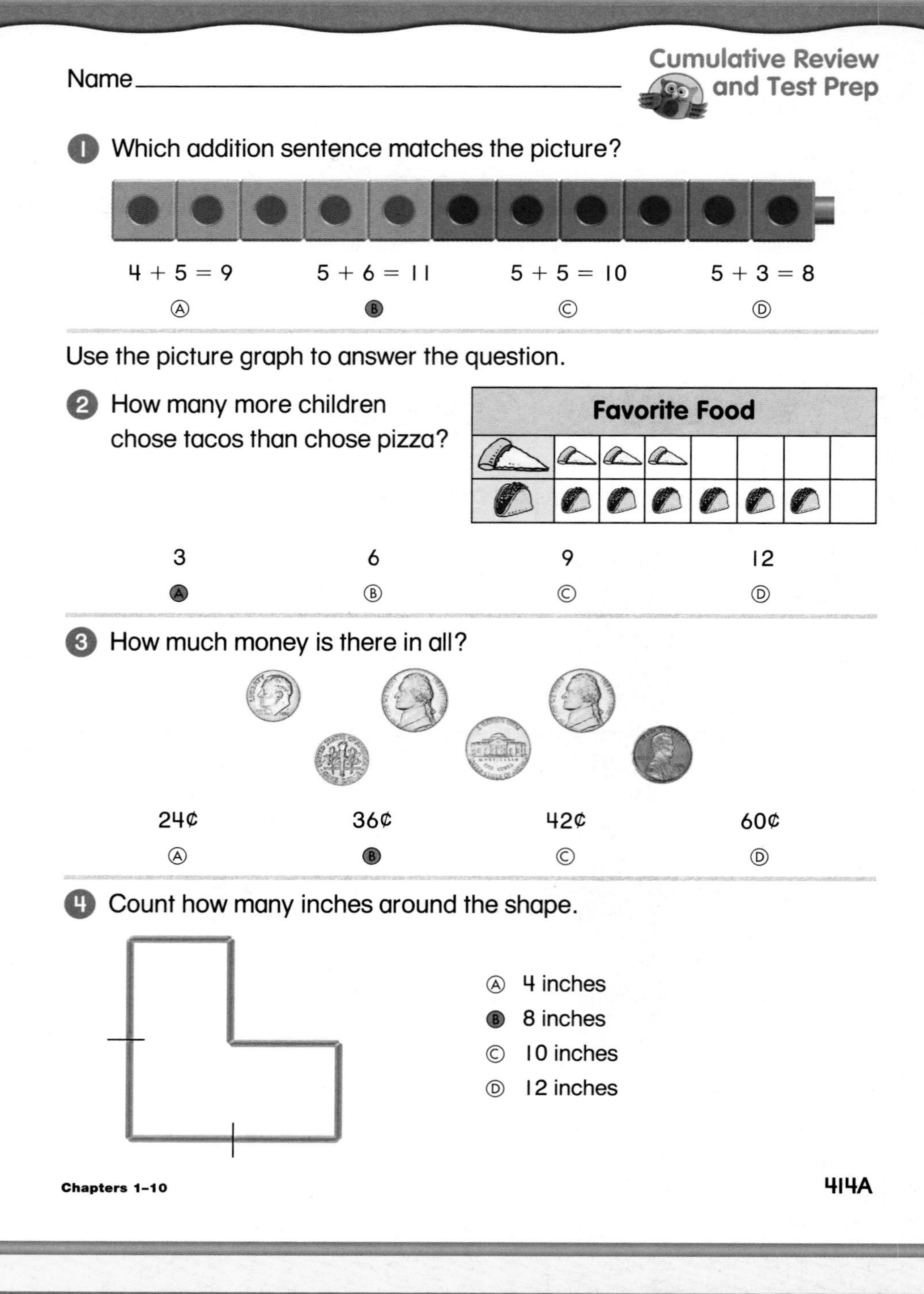

Item Analysis for Diagnosis and Intervention

Objective	Review Items	Student Book Pages*	Intervention System
Use doubles facts to learn doubles-plus-1 facts.	1	105–106	B22
Collect data and organize it into a bar graph.	2	311–312	D66
Identify the value of a group of dimes, nickels, and pennies through 99¢.	3	337–338	A35
Find the distance around a shape using inches.	4	377–378	D23

*For each lesson, there is a *Reteaching* activity in *Reaching All Learners* and a *Reteaching* master.

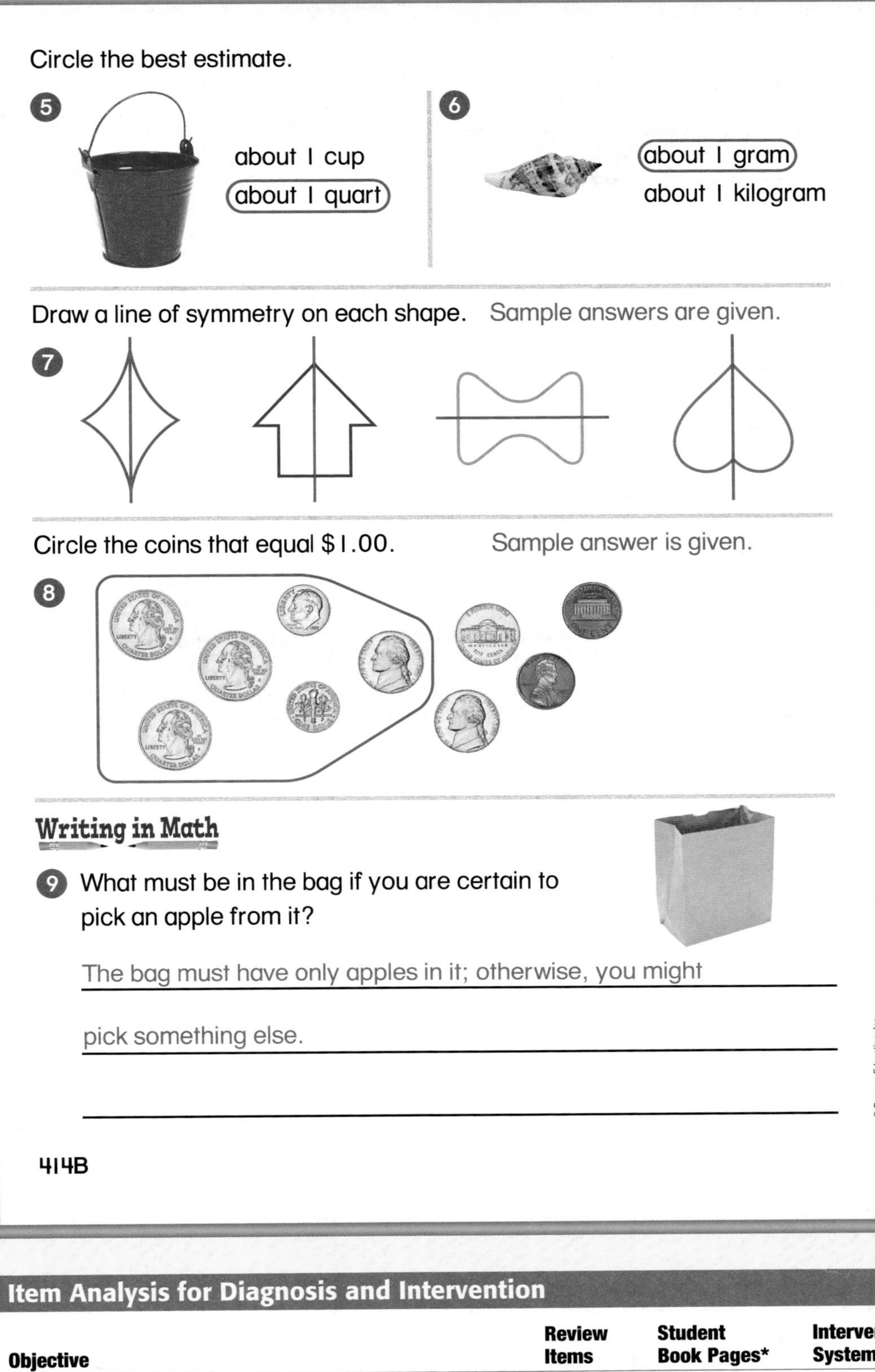

Circle the best estimate.

5. about 1 cup / **(about 1 quart)**

6. **(about 1 gram)** / about 1 kilogram

Draw a line of symmetry on each shape. Sample answers are given.

7.

Circle the coins that equal $1.00. Sample answer is given.

8.

Writing in Math

9. What must be in the bag if you are certain to pick an apple from it?

The bag must have only apples in it; otherwise, you might pick something else.

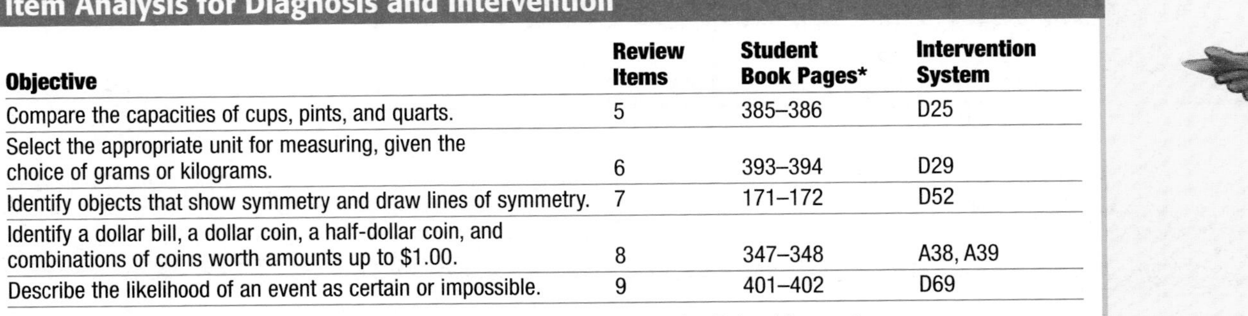

Item Analysis for Diagnosis and Intervention

Objective	Review Items	Student Book Pages*	Intervention System
Compare the capacities of cups, pints, and quarts.	5	385–386	D25
Select the appropriate unit for measuring, given the choice of grams or kilograms.	6	393–394	D29
Identify objects that show symmetry and draw lines of symmetry.	7	171–172	D52
Identify a dollar bill, a dollar coin, a half-dollar coin, and combinations of coins worth amounts up to $1.00.	8	347–348	A38, A39
Describe the likelihood of an event as certain or impossible.	9	401–402	D69

*For each lesson, there is a *Reteaching* activity in *Reaching All Learners* and a *Reteaching* master.

CHAPTER 11

Lesson Planner

Addition and Subtraction Facts to 18

Suggested Pacing: 15 days

Section A Addition Fact Strategies

11-1 pp. 417–418	11-2 pp. 419–420	11-3 pp. 421–422	11-4 pp. 423–424	11-5 pp. 425–426
Doubles **Objective** Recognize doubles as a strategy for remembering sums to 18. **Math Understanding** Doubles facts are easy to remember. **Vocabulary** Double	**Doubles Plus 1 and Doubles Minus 1** **Objective** Use doubles facts to learn doubles-plus-1 facts and doubles-minus-1 facts. **Math Understanding** If you know a doubles fact, it can help you figure out a doubles-plus-1 fact or a doubles-minus-1 fact.	**Algebra Adding 10** **Objective** Use a pattern to add numbers 1 to 8 to the number 10. **Math Understanding** There is a place-value pattern that can be used to add 10 to a single-digit number mentally.	**Making 10 to Add** **Objective** Find sums by making a 10 when adding to 8 or 9. **Math Understanding** Making a group of 10 can change a difficult addition fact to one that is easier to add mentally. **Materials for Student Pages** Single Ten-Frame (Workmat 2); 17 two-color counters	**Applying Addition Fact Strategies** **Objective** Select and apply addition fact strategies. **Math Understanding** There are a variety of strategies to use to find addition fact sums; which one is best depends on the addends.

Math Story: *Fuzzy Wuzzy*, pp. 11A–11F Home-School Connection, p. 415
Practice Game: *Get That Honey!*, p. 416

Resources in the Student Book

Ongoing Assessment and Test Prep *Also see* pp. 415G–415H.

Instant Check System™
- **Check** before Practice
- **Think About It** after examples
- **Diagnostic Checkpoint** end of sections

Test Prep
- **Test Talk** end of chapter
- **Cumulative Review and Test Prep** end of sections

Daily Real-World Problem Solving plus ...

Problem-Solving Applications lesson on pp. 447–448 uses data from Dorling Kindersley literature.

Discover Math in Your World on p. 454 uses data from a topic in the Discovery Channel School Video Library, Segment 11.

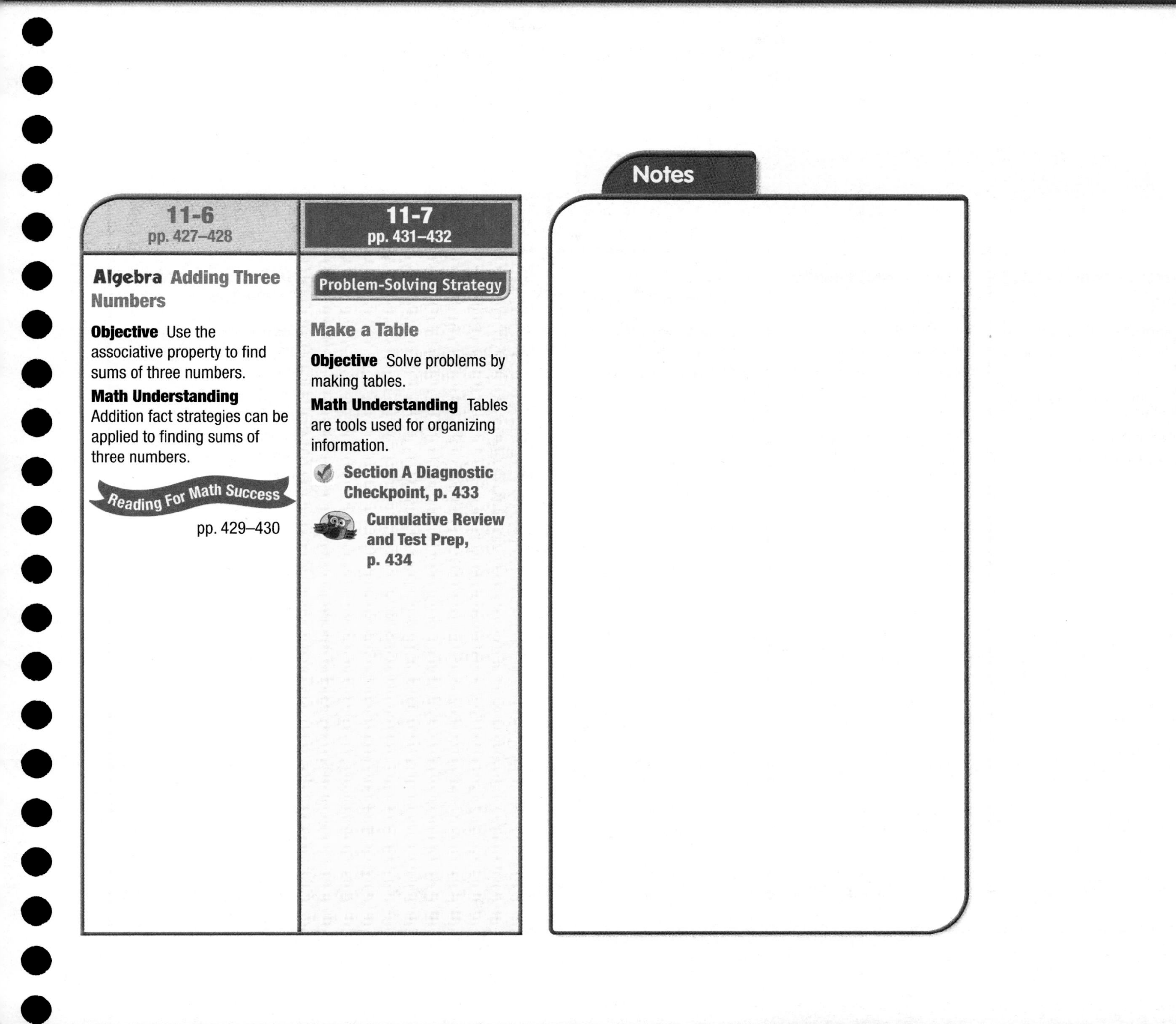

11-6 pp. 427–428	11-7 pp. 431–432
Algebra Adding Three Numbers **Objective** Use the associative property to find sums of three numbers. **Math Understanding** Addition fact strategies can be applied to finding sums of three numbers. Reading For Math Success pp. 429–430	Problem-Solving Strategy Make a Table **Objective** Solve problems by making tables. **Math Understanding** Tables are tools used for organizing information. Section A Diagnostic Checkpoint, p. 433 Cumulative Review and Test Prep, p. 434

Notes

Reading and Writing in Math *Throughout*

This feature shows how reading skills and strategies can help with problem-solving skills and strategies in math.
Also, **Reading Assists** are in the Teacher's Edition.

Writing in Math

Some lessons include **Writing in Math** exercises. Also, daily **Journal Ideas** are in the Teacher's Edition.

Technology Resources for Students *Also see* p. T20.

Take It to the NET
More Activities
www.scottforesman.com

More activities, Discovery Channel School Video Library, and Math eTools

e tools

Math eTools: electronic manipulatives online, on CD-ROM, and in the Online Student's Edition

All text pages are available online and on CD-ROM. The Online Student's Edition includes Math eTools plus glossary links for vocabulary.

Addition and Subtraction Facts to 18

(continued)

Section B Subtraction Fact Strategies

11-8 pp. 435–436	11-9 pp. 437–438	11-10 pp. 439–440	11-11 pp. 441–442	11-12 pp. 443–444
Algebra Using Related Facts **Objective** Write related addition and subtraction facts with sums through 18. **Math Understanding** Every addition fact has at least one related subtraction fact. **Vocabulary** Related facts	**Algebra Fact Families** **Objective** Write the addition and subtraction sentences that make up a fact family. **Math Understanding** Fact families use the same three numbers and can be used to show how addition and subtraction are related. **Vocabulary** Fact family	**Algebra Using Addition to Subtract** **Objective** Find differences by using known addition facts. **Math Understanding** An addition fact can be used to find the difference in a related subtraction fact.	**Using 10 to Subtract** **Objective** Find differences using a ten-frame. **Math Understanding** Making a 10 before subtracting can change a difficult subtraction fact to one that is easier to subtract mentally. **Materials for Student Pages** Single Ten-Frame (Workmat 2); two-color counters	**Applying Subtraction Fact Strategies** **Objective** Select and apply subtraction fact strategies. **Math Understanding** There are a variety of strategies to use to find subtraction fact differences; which one is best depends on the numbers involved.

Additional Resources for ...

Reaching All Learners

- **Practice** Masters/Workbook, every lesson
- **Reteaching** Masters/Workbook, every lesson
- **Enrichment** Masters/Workbook, every lesson
- **Every Student Learns** A teacher resource with daily suggestions for helping students overcome language barriers to learning math
- **Spiral Review and Test Prep** Transparencies and Masters/Workbook, every lesson
- **Math Games** Use *All Aboard* anytime after Lesson 11-12.
- **Investigation** See pp. 415I–415J.

Problem Solving

- **Problem Solving** Masters/Workbook, every lesson
- **Problem of the Day** Flipchart/Transparencies, every lesson
- **Discovery Channel School** Masters, follow-up to Segment 11 in the Discovery Channel School Video Library

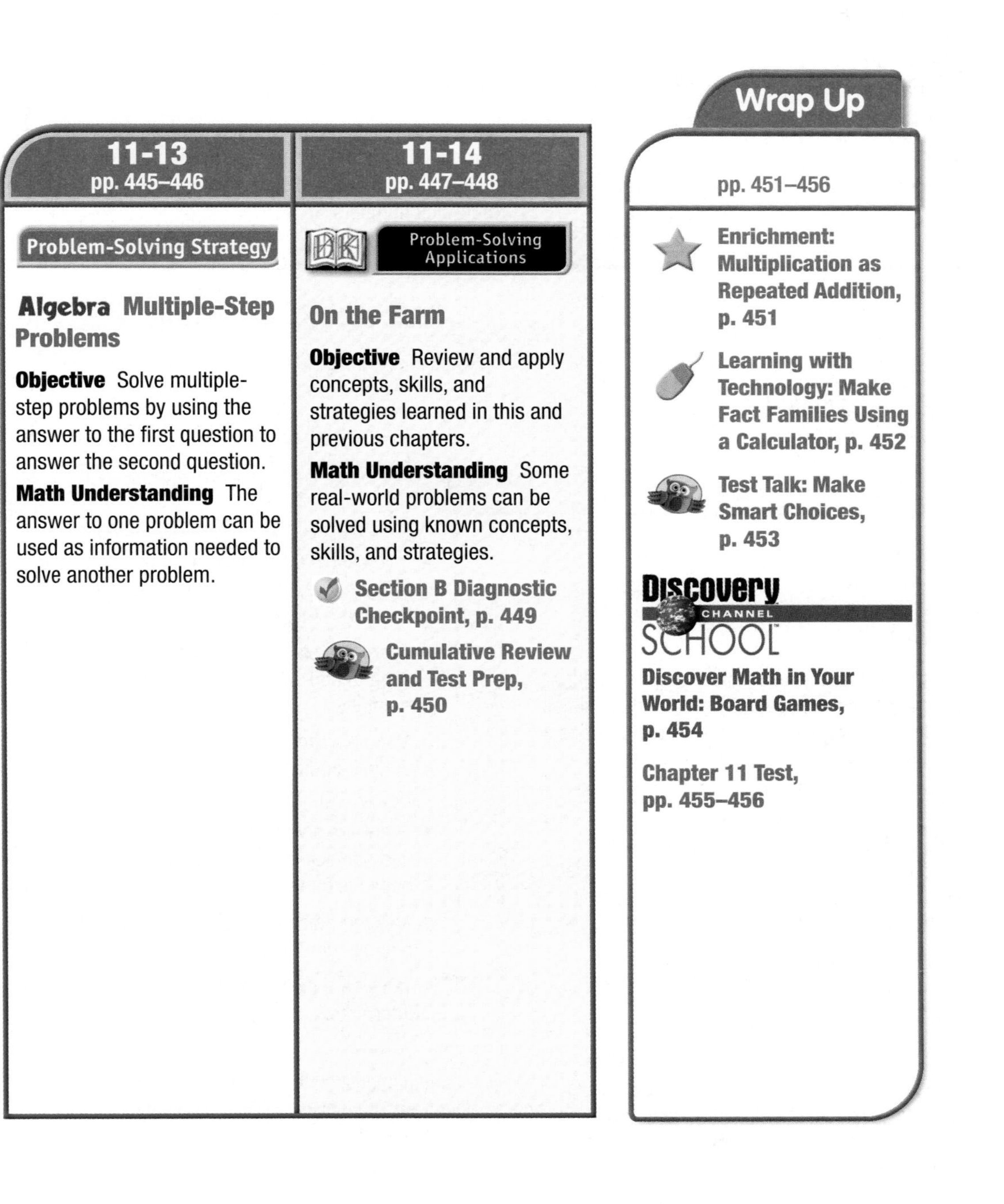

11-13
pp. 445–446

Problem-Solving Strategy

Algebra Multiple-Step Problems

Objective Solve multiple-step problems by using the answer to the first question to answer the second question.

Math Understanding The answer to one problem can be used as information needed to solve another problem.

11-14
pp. 447–448

Problem-Solving Applications

On the Farm

Objective Review and apply concepts, skills, and strategies learned in this and previous chapters.

Math Understanding Some real-world problems can be solved using known concepts, skills, and strategies.

Section B Diagnostic Checkpoint, p. 449

Cumulative Review and Test Prep, p. 450

Wrap Up
pp. 451–456

Enrichment: Multiplication as Repeated Addition, p. 451

Learning with Technology: Make Fact Families Using a Calculator, p. 452

Test Talk: Make Smart Choices, p. 453

Discovery Channel School

Discover Math in Your World: Board Games, p. 454

Chapter 11 Test, pp. 455–456

Reading in Math
- **Vocabulary Kit** Word Cards plus transparencies and activities for instructional word walls and for small groups
- **Dorling Kindersley Literature Library** Books with interesting data

Assessment, Intervention, and Test Prep
- **Assessment Sourcebook** See pp. 415G–415H.
- **Math Diagnosis and Intervention System** See pp. 415G–415H.
- **Test-Taking Practice** Transparencies, every lesson
- **SAT 9, SAT 10, TerraNova Practice and Test Prep** Includes practice tests, correlations, and more

Teacher Support
- **Teaching Tools** Masters: paper manipulatives and more
- **Home-School Connection** Masters, use Chapter 11 Family Letter at the start of the chapter. Use Study Buddies 21 and 22 after Lessons 11-4 and 11-11.
- **Professional Development Resources** See p. T18.
- **Technology Resources** See p. T20.

CHAPTER 11

Professional Development

Skills Trace - Addition and Subtraction Facts to 18

BEFORE Chapter 11	DURING Chapter 11	AFTER Chapter 11
Grade K introduced addition and subtraction strategies by expressing a number as two parts and the relationship between two numbers as 1 or 2 more or fewer. **Chapters 3 and 4 in Grade 1** developed mental math strategies for learning basic addition and subtraction facts to 12.	**Chapter 11** develops mental math strategies for learning basic addition and subtraction facts to 18.	**Chapter 12 in Grade 1** applies basic facts to add and subtract two-digit numbers. **Grade 2** develops mental math strategies for learning basic addition and subtraction facts and applies them to add and subtract two-digit and three-digit numbers.

Math Background and Teaching Tips

Section A

Addition Fact Strategies

pp. 417–434

The work related to both addition and subtraction in this chapter is a continuation of basic fact strategies first introduced in Chapters 3 and 4. Some of the addition doubles were introduced earlier. Doubles facts through the sum of 18, doubles plus 1, and doubles minus 1 are included in this section.

Breaking apart numbers underlies the informal thinking that children use naturally when they apply the doubles-plus-1 strategy. The process works because of the Associative Property of Addition. For example:

$7 + 8 = 7 + (7 + 1)$ Break apart the 8.
$= (7 + 7) + 1$ Associative Property
$= 14 + 1$
$= 15$

TIP! Make Connections *To reinforce the usefulness of this strategy, have children solve a series of addition problems in which successive problems are doubles and the doubles plus one.*

$7 + 7 =$
$7 + 8 =$

$3 + 3 =$
$3 + 4 =$

The remaining addition facts in this section are derived from the strategy "Making 10." The justification for this process is the Associate Property of Addition.

$9 + 6 = 9 + (1 + 5)$ Break apart the 6.
$= (9 + 1) + 5$ Associative Property
$= 10 + 5$
$= 15$

The ten-frame connects children to their counting work in Kindergarten where they learned quantities as related to 5s and 10s. The ten-frame provides a visual pattern to help establish the numerical pattern of adding on to 10.

TIP! For Visual Learners *Point out the pattern in the sums when one addend is a 9. Help children notice that the ones digit in the sum is 1 less than the addend that is added to 9.*

$9 + 5 = 14$ (where 4 is 1 less than 5)
$9 + 6 = 15$
$9 + 7 = 16$

Adding three numbers in any order is possible because of the grouping property, or Associative Property of Addition. Because the order of the addends does not matter, children can choose two addends at a time, applying any strategy most convenient for them.

$4 + 4 + 6 = (4 + 6) + 4$ Make a 10.
$4 + 4 + 6 = 10 + 4$
$4 + 4 + 6 = 14$

$4 + 4 + 6 = (4 + 4) + 6$ Add doubles.
$4 + 4 + 6 = 8 + 6$
$4 + 4 + 6 = 14$

The problem-solving strategy "Make a Table" provides an organized way to keep track of combinations. Listing possible combinations is featured in later work with probability experiment outcomes.

Math Understandings

- Doubles facts are easy to remember.
- If you know a doubles fact, it can help you to figure out a doubles-plus-1 fact or a doubles-minus-1 fact.
- There is a place-value pattern that can be used to add 10 to a single-digit number mentally.
- Making a group of 10 can change a difficult addition fact to one that is easier to add mentally.
- There are a variety of strategies to use to find addition fact sums; which one is best depends on the addends.
- Addition fact strategies can be applied to finding sums of three numbers.
- Tables are tools used for organizing information.

Section B

Subtraction Fact Strategies

pp. 435–450

The subtraction strategies in this section focus on the relationship between addition and subtraction. For example, to find $15 - 7$ children can think:

"7 plus what number equals 15?"
Since $7 + 8 = 15$,
then $15 - 7 = 8$.

This process works because of the inverse relationship of addition and subtraction.

If $a + b = c$,
then $c - b = a$
and $c - a = b$.

Fact families are used to emphasize the inverse relationship between addition and subtraction. Fact families are built from the Commutative Property of Addition.

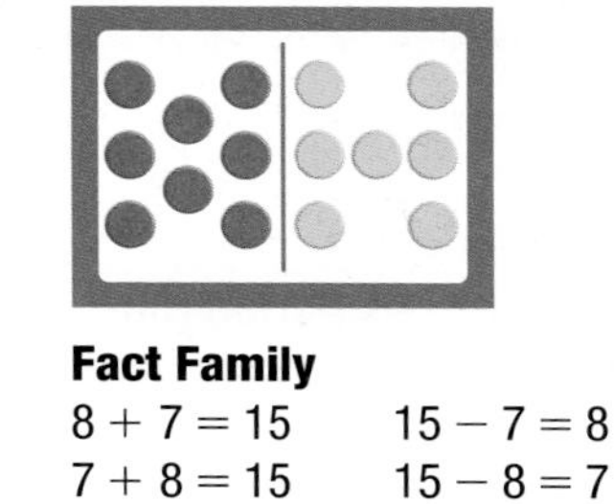

Fact Family

$8 + 7 = 15$ $\quad$ $15 - 7 = 8$
$7 + 8 = 15$ $\quad$ $15 - 8 = 7$

Knowledge of fact families will be used to solve for missing addends in later grades.

Find the Missing Addend
$n + 8 = 15$
Since $15 - 8 = 7$, then $7 + 8 = 15$.

TIP! Reinforce Big Ideas *This section involves both take-away and comparison subtraction situations. Be sure to emphasize the separating and comparing actions involved in these subtraction situations rather than specific words and phrases such as* left *or* more than.

TIP! Use Representations *Have children use pictures or objects to emphasize the structure of these problems.*

Take Away (Separate—Amount Left Unknown)
12 birds are on the fence.
8 birds fly away.
How many birds are still on the fence?

Here the total is known, and part of the total is taken away.

12 take away 8
$12 - 8 = 4$ left

Comparison (Compare—Amount More Unknown)
12 birds are on the fence.
8 birds are on the ground.
How many more birds are on the fence than on the ground?

Here there are two groups, and the numbers in each are being compared.

Math Understandings

- Every addition fact has at least one related subtraction fact.
- Fact families use the same three numbers and can be used to show how addition and subtraction are related.
- An addition fact can be used to find the difference in a related subtraction fact.
- Making a 10 before subtracting can change a difficult subtraction fact to one that is easier to subtract mentally.
- There are a variety of strategies to use to find subtraction fact differences; which one is better depends on the numbers involved.

12 compared to 8

$12 - 8 = 4$ more

Multiple-step problems require children to answer two questions. Each question can be answered by choosing the appropriate operation. For example, to solve a multiple-step problem, a child may have to do two additions or an addition followed by a subtraction. At this level of mathematics the questions are separated so children can easily identify the steps.

CHAPTER 11 Assessment, Intervention, Test Prep

Assessment Resources

DIAGNOSING READINESS

Start of Year Diagnosing Readiness for Grade 1, Assessment Sourcebook pp. 43–46 and in Online Intervention

✓ **Start of Chapter** Diagnosing Readiness for Chapter 11, Assessment Sourcebook p. 199 and in Online Intervention

✓ **Start of Lesson** Warm Up, Teacher's Edition pp. 417, 419, 421, 423, 425, 427, 431, 435, 437, 439, 441, 443, 445, 447

✓ Instant Check System™

ONGOING ASSESSMENT

✓ **Before Independent Practice** Check and Think About It, Student Book, every lesson

✓ **After a Section** Diagnostic Checkpoint, pp. 433, 449 and in Online Intervention

Basic-Facts Timed Test 11 Assessment Sourcebook, p. 37

FORMAL EVALUATION

Chapter Tests Chapter 11 Test, Student Book pp. 455–456; Assessment Sourcebook Forms A and B Free Response pp. 201–204, Forms C and D Multiple Choice pp. 205–212, Performance Assessment p. 21; Multiple-Choice Chapter Test in Online Intervention

Cumulative Tests Chapters 1–3, 1–6, 1–9, 1–12, Assessment Sourcebook, pp. 89–92, 135–138, 181–184, 227–230; Online Intervention

Test Generator Computer-generated tests; can be customized

Correlation to Assessments, Intervention, and Standardized Tests

	Assessments		Intervention	Standardized Tests				
Lessons	Diagnostic Checkpoint	Chapter Test	Math Diagnosis and Intervention System	SAT 9/10	ITBS	CTBS	CAT	MAT
11-1 Doubles	p. 433: Ex. 1	Ex. 3	Booklet B: B30	•/•	•	•	•	•
11-2 Doubles Plus 1 and Doubles Minus 1	p. 433: Ex. 1	Ex. 3	Booklet B: B31	•/•	•	•	•	•
11-3 Adding 10	p. 433: Ex. 3	Ex. 4	Booklet B: B32	•/•	•	•	•	•
11-4 Making 10 to Add	p. 433: Ex. 2, 3	Ex. 4	Booklet B: B33	•/•	•	•	•	•
11-5 Applying Addition Fact Strategies	p. 433: Ex. 3	Ex. 1	Booklet B: B34	•/•	•	•	•	•
11-6 Adding Three Numbers	p. 433: Ex. 3	Ex. 1	Booklet B: B35	•/•	•	•	•	•
11-7 Problem-Solving Strategy: Make a Table	p. 433: Ex. 4	Ex. 8	Booklet E: E25	•/	•	•	•	
11-8 Using Related Facts	p. 449: Ex. 1	Ex. 5	Booklet B: B36	•/•	•	•	•	•
11-9 Fact Families	p. 449: Ex. 2	Ex. 7	Booklet B: B37	•/•	•	•	•	•
11-10 Using Addition to Subtract	p. 449: Ex. 3	Ex. 6	Booklet B: B38	•/•	•	•	•	•
11-11 Using 10 to Subtract	p. 449: Ex. 4		Booklet B: B39	•/•	•	•	•	•
11-12 Applying Subtraction Fact Strategies		Ex. 2	Booklet B: B40	•/•	•	•	•	•
11-13 Problem-Solving Skill: Multiple-Step Problems	p. 449: Ex. 5	Ex. 9	Booklet E: E6		•	•	•	•

KEY:
SAT 9 Stanford Achievement Test
SAT 10 Stanford Achievement Test
ITBS Iowa Test of Basic Skills
CAT California Achievement Test
CTBS Comprehensive Test of Basic Skills (TerraNova)
MAT Metropolitan Achievement Test

EC NTL 12 11 10 9 8 7 6 5

Intervention and Test Prep Resources

INTERVENTION

During Instruction Helpful "If ... then ..." suggestions in the Teacher's Edition in Ongoing Assessment and Error Intervention

Math Diagnosis and Intervention System Diagnostic tests, individual and class record forms, two-page Intervention Lessons (example, practice, test prep), and one-page Intervention Practice (multiple choice), all in cross-grade strand booklets (Booklets A–E for Grades K–3, Booklets F–M for Grades 4–6)

Online Intervention Diagnostic tests; individual, class, school, and district reports; remediation including tutorials, video, games, practice exercises

TEST PREP

Test Talk before the Chapter Test, p. 453

Cumulative Review and Test Prep end of sections, pp. 434, 450

Test-Taking Practice Transparencies for every lesson

Spiral Review and Test Prep for every lesson

SAT 9, SAT 10, TerraNova Practice and Test Prep section quizzes, practice tests

Correlation to NCTM Standards and Grades Pre-K through 2 Expectations

Number and Operations

Understand numbers, ways of representing numbers, relationships among numbers, and number systems.

Grades Pre-K through 2 Expectations

- Use multiple models to develop initial understandings of place value and the base-ten number system. *Lessons 11-3, 11-4, 11-11*
- Develop understanding of the relative position and magnitude of whole numbers and of ordinal and cardinal numbers and their connections. *Lessons 11-2, 11-3, 11-10, 11-11*
- Develop a sense of whole numbers and represent and use them in flexible ways, including relating, composing, and decomposing numbers. *Lessons 11-1, 11-2, 11-3, 11-4, 11-6, 11-7, 11-8, 11-9*

Understand meanings of operations and how they relate to one another.

Grades Pre-K through 2 Expectations

- Understand various meanings of addition and subtraction of whole numbers and the relationship between the two operations. *Lessons 11-1, 11-2, 11-3, 11-4, 11-5, 11-6, 11-7, 11-8, 11-9, 11-10, 11-11, 11-12, 11-13*
- Understand the effects of adding and subtracting whole numbers. *Lessons 11-1, 11-2, 11-3, 11-4, 11-5, 11-6, 11-7, 11-8, 11-9, 11-10, 11-11, 11-12, 11-13*

Compute fluently and make reasonable estimates.

Grades Pre-K through 2 Expectations

- Develop and use strategies for whole-number computations, with a focus on addition and subtraction. *Lessons 11-1, 11-2, 11-3, 11-4, 11-5, 11-6, 11-7, 11-8, 11-9, 11-10, 11-11, 11-12, 11-13*
- Develop fluency with basic number combinations for addition and subtraction. *Lessons 11-1, 11-2, 11-3, 11-4, 11-5, 11-6, 11-8, 11-9, 11-10, 11-11, 11-12*
- Use a variety of methods and tools to compute, including objects, mental computation, estimation, paper and pencil, and calculators. *Lessons 11-1, 11-2, 11-3, 11-4, 11-5, 11-6, 11-7, 11-8, 11-9, 11-10, 11-11, 11-12, 11-13*

Algebra

Represent and analyze mathematical situations and structures using algebraic symbols.

Grades Pre-K through 2 Expectations

- Illustrate general principles and properties of operations, such as commutativity, using specific numbers. *Lessons 11-6, 11-7, 11-8, 11-9, 11-10*
- Use concrete, pictorial, and verbal representations to develop an understanding of invented and conventional symbolic notations. *Lessons 11-8, 11-9, 11-13*

Use mathematical models to represent and understand quantitative relationships.

Grades Pre-K through 2 Expectations

- Model situations that involve the addition and subtraction of whole numbers, using objects, pictures, and symbols. *Lessons 11-1, 11-2, 11-3, 11-4, 11-7, 11-8, 11-9, 11-10, 11-11*

Data Analysis and Probability

Formulate questions that can be addressed with data and collect, organize, and display relevant data to answer them.

Grades Pre-K through 2 Expectations

- Sort and classify objects according to their attributes and organize data about the objects. *Lesson 11-7*
- Represent data using concrete objects, pictures, and graphs. *Lesson 11-7*

Select and use appropriate statistical methods to analyze data.

Grades Pre-K through 2 Expectations

- Describe parts of the data and the set of data as a whole to determine what the data show. *Lesson 11-7*

The NCTM 2000 Pre-K through Grade 12 Content Standards are Number and Operations, Algebra, Geometry, Measurement, and Data Analysis and Probability. The Process Standards (Problem Solving, Reasoning and Proof, Communication, Connections, and Representation) are incorporated throughout lessons.

CHAPTER 11 Investigation

Addition and Subtraction Facts to 18

Activity 1

Use in place of the Investigating the Concept activity in Lesson 11-6.

Finding Total Cost

Overview Children will explore the concept of finding the total amounts of money by assigning values to objects, adding the values to find the total amount, and recording their methods using pictures and numbers.

Materials *(per pair)* Pattern blocks (4 squares, 4 rectangles, 4 triangles, 4 trapezoids); crayons; drawing paper

The Task

- On the board, draw a square, a rectangle, a triangle, and a trapezoid. Label each with the amounts 1¢, 2¢, 3¢, and 4¢, respectively.
- Write 16¢ on the board. **How can you show this amount using the pattern blocks?**
- Have children record each method using pictures and numbers.
- Discuss ways to show this amount. Repeat the activity for 12¢.

Observing and Questioning

- As children represent 16¢, observe whether they are using a square to represent 1¢, a rectangle to represent 2¢, a triangle to represent 3¢, and a trapezoid to represent 4¢.
- Ask the following if children have trouble getting started:
- **What amount does the square represent? the rectangle? the triangle? the trapezoid?**
- **How can you use each shape to show an amount of money? How much do two shapes represent?**
- **How did you find the total value of your shapes?**

Sharing and Summarizing

- As children share their methods for finding the total amount of money, summarize each. For example, the first child below showed 16¢ with three trapezoids, one triangle, and one square. The second child showed the same amount using four trapezoids.
- If children do not mention the similarity between adding money and adding regular numbers, ask: **How is finding money totals like adding numbers?**
- **Key Idea** Children can find the total amount of money in the same way they find the sum of regular numbers, by adding. Money is represented using a cent sign.

Follow-Up

- Have children use at least one of each pattern block to find the least amount that can be represented and the greatest amount that can be represented.

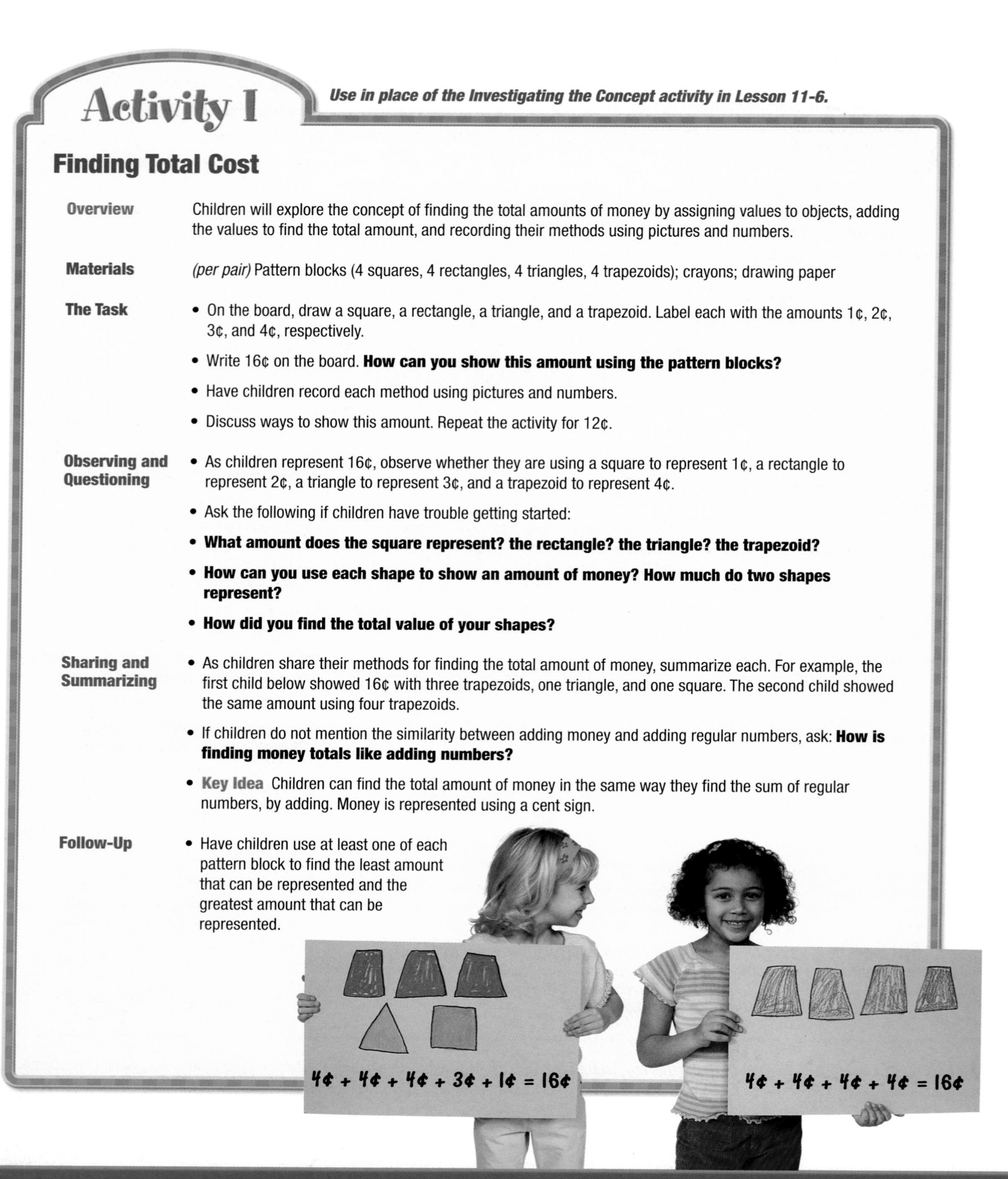

Link to *Investigations in Number, Data, and Space*® See the **Joint-Usage Plan** available from Pearson Scott Foresman.

Activity 2

Use in place of the Investigating the Concept activity in Lesson 11-9.

Finding Fact Families

Overview Children use counters to investigate and identify addition and subtraction fact families for a given number.

Materials *(per group)* 18 counters

The Task

- Display 15 counters so that all children can see them. **Can you think of a fact family that can be shown using these counters?**
- Have children work as a group to identify as many fact families as they can and record each family using pictures, numbers, and words.

Observing and Questioning

- As children work to identify fact families, observe whether they include both addition and subtraction facts in the families. Also notice whether each fact family includes the same three numbers for each fact.
- If children have difficulty finding or organizing fact families, ask the following questions:
- **How do the counters help you to find facts?**
- **How did you group your facts? Did listing them help you?**
- **Are there other fact families you can show for 15 counters?**

Sharing and Summarizing

- As children share fact families and methods, summarize each and sketch a picture on the board to represent it and write the fact in words. In the work below, a child has shown the facts $6 + 9 = 15$, $9 + 6 = 15$, $15 - 9 = 6$, and $15 - 6 = 9$ using counters.
- **Key Idea** Adding and subtracting are easier when facts are identified. There are two addition and two subtraction facts in most fact families, and each fact family uses the same three numbers.

Follow-Up

- Display 18 counters and have children identify and list as many fact families as possible.

6 + 9 = 15
9 + 6 = 15
15 - 9 = 6
15 - 6 = 9

Math Story

Fuzzy Wuzzy **(Genre: Animal fantasy)**

In this rhyme, a bear named Fuzzy Wuzzy sells honey for 5¢ a jar. When customers give him 13¢ for 2 jars of honey, Fuzzy gives them back 3¢.

Introducing the Story

Show children the cover and have them read the following rhyme:

Fuzzy Wuzzy was a bear. Fuzzy Wuzzy had no hair.
Fuzzy Wuzzy wasn't very fuzzy, was he?

Reading the Story

Have children read the story once without stopping. Then draw the table at right on the board:

1 jar	2 jars	3 jars	4 jars
5¢	10¢	15¢	20¢

Read the story again. After reading page 11C, help children read the table to find out the cost of 2 jars. *(10¢)* Tell children that they can use this reading strategy, understanding tables, whenever they listen to a story or solve math problems. (For more on *Understand Graphic Sources: Tables,* see Reading for Math Success, pp. 429–430.)

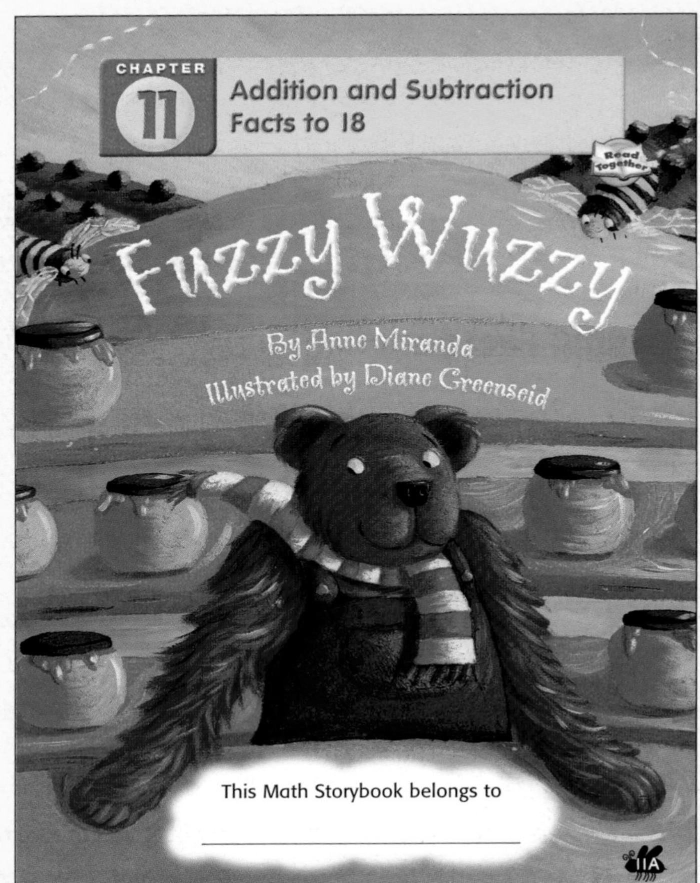

Page 11A

Page 11B

Page 11C

Page 11D **Page 11E**

Page 11F

Follow-up Activities

- **Use Picture Clues** Remind children that two jars of honey cost 10¢. Have children add 6¢ and 7¢ to find out how much Benny and Mac paid. *(13¢)* You might want to have children count the two groups of pennies shown on Fuzzy's table on page 11C. Then have them subtract 3¢ from 13¢ to find out if Benny and Mac paid the correct amount. *(Yes; 10¢)*
- **Make Predictions** Read children the following events from the story and have them put the events in the order in which they happened:
  Fuzzy Wuzzy gives Mac 3 pennies.
  Benny takes 2 jars of honey from the stand.
  Mac gives Fuzzy Wuzzy 13 pennies.
  (Benny takes 2 jars of honey from the stand. Mac gives Fuzzy Wuzzy 13 pennies. Fuzzy Wuzzy gives Mac 3 pennies.)
- **Extend the Story** Ask leading questions: **How many pennies should Benny and Mac give Fuzzy Wuzzy if they want 3 jars of honey?** *(15¢)* **4 jars of honey?** *(20¢)*

Home-School Connection

Purpose Provide families with a quick overview of the material that will be covered in Chapter 11. Included on this page: a family letter, a math activity, references to literature related to the chapter, and new math vocabulary words.

Using Student Page 415

You may wish to read and discuss the family letter with children prior to having them sign it and sending the page home.

The Home-School Connection booklet includes:

- Chapter 11 Family Letter in English and Spanish
- Study Buddies 21
- Study Buddies 22

Study Buddies pages provide reinforcement activities for children to work on with a partner. Each Study Buddy has a page for the child and a page of prompts to help the partner guide the child's learning.

Vocabulary

related facts *(pp. 435–436)*

fact family *(pp. 437–438)*

Home-School Connection

Dear Family,

Today my class started Chapter 11, **Addition and Subtraction Facts to 18.** I will learn about addition fact strategies and subtraction fact strategies. Here are some of the math words I will be learning and some things we can do to help me with my math.

Love,

____

Math Activity to Do at Home

Write 10 on a card. Then ask your child to write a doubles fact that has the sum of 10. Next, on the back of that card, together decide on a related subtraction fact to write. Continue with sums of 8, 6, and 4.

Books to Read Together

Reading math stories reinforces concepts. Look for these titles in your local library:

Mission: Addition
By Loreen Leedy
(Holiday House, 1997)

Two of Everything: A Chinese Folktale
By Lily T. Hong
(Albert Whitman, 1993)

Take It to the NET
More Activities
www.scottforesman.com

My New Math Words

related facts Addition and subtraction facts are related if they use the same numbers.

For example:

$9 + 8 = 17$
$17 - 9 = 8$

Related facts use the same numbers.

fact family A fact family is a group of related addition and subtraction facts. For example:

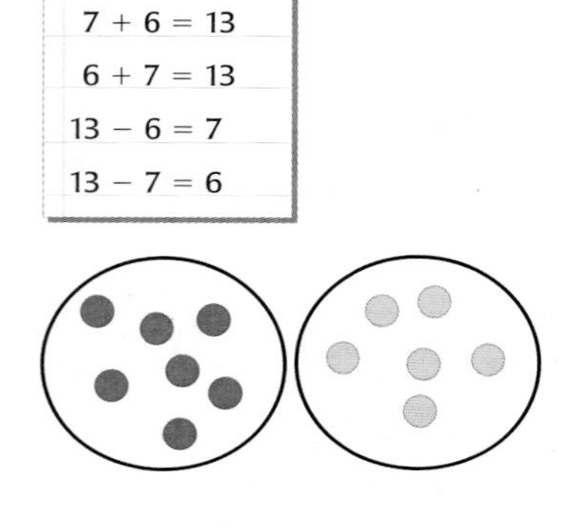

Math Vocabulary Kit

Every vocabulary word is written on a card with the definition of the word printed on the back. Vocabulary activities are provided in the *Math Vocabulary Kit Teacher's Guide.*

Add the words from the Vocabulary list at left to your Math Word Wall as they are introduced.

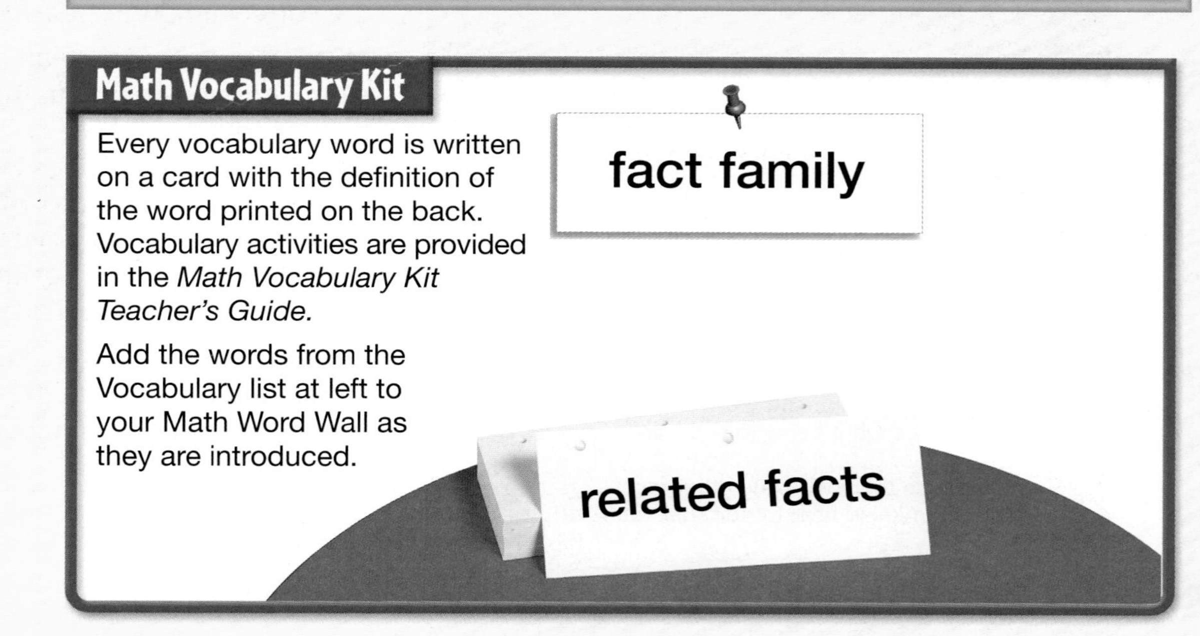

Name ______________________ Practice Game

Get That Honey!

What You Need

1 dot cube

1 marker for each player

How to Play

1. Play with a partner. Put your markers on START.
2. Take turns tossing the cube. Move that number of spaces.
3. Read what it says on the space you land on. Do what it says on the space you land on.
4. Keep playing until both of you reach Fuzzy Wuzzy and his honey!

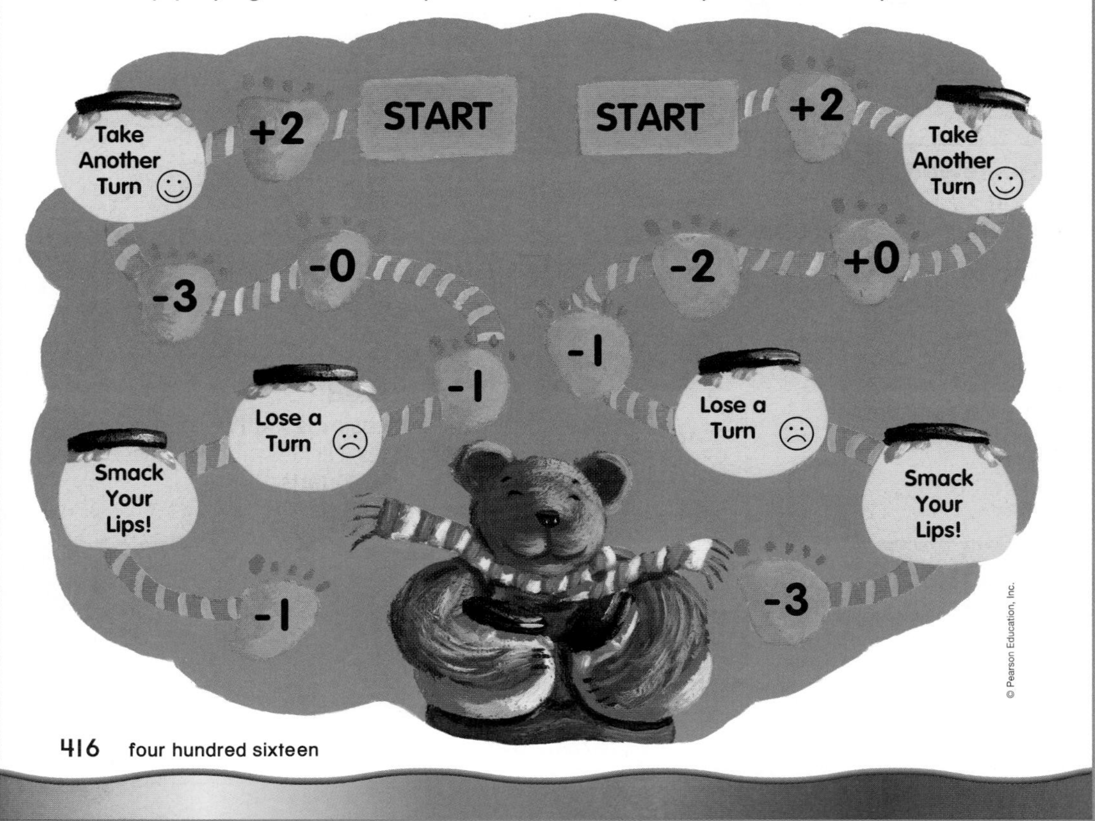

Practice Game
for School or Home

Purpose Provide children with an opportunity to practice skills they have previously learned.

Using Student Page 416

You may wish to discuss these questions with your children before they play "Get That Honey!"

- **What are some ways to add? What are some ways to subtract?**
- **What is the sum of 1 and 2? What is the difference between 5 and 1?**

Give children the materials for the game.

Describe the game and the directions. Lead children through the process of tossing the number cube, moving their markers the appropriate number of spaces, and following the directions on the space on which their markers land. Make sure children understand that they should continue playing until both players reach Fuzzy Wuzzy.

Describe another way to play: Children toss the number cube. They must move the number of spaces shown but can choose whether to move their markers forward or backward.

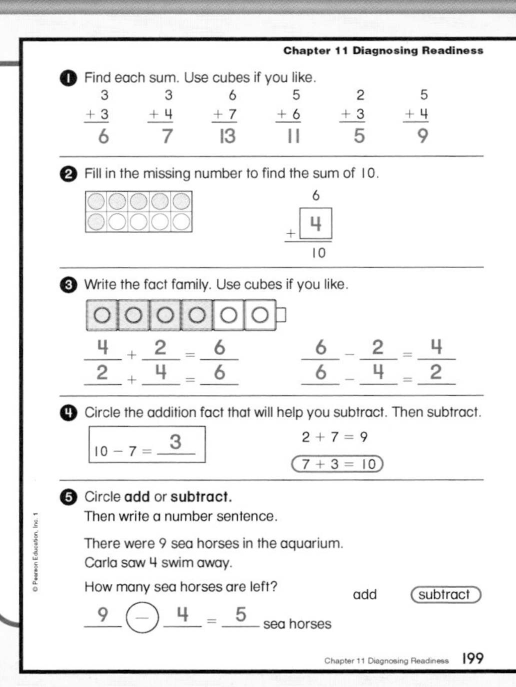

Chapter 11 Diagnosing Readiness

1. Find each sum. Use cubes if you like.

3 + 3 = 6   3 + 4 = 7   6 + 7 = 13   5 + 6 = 11   2 + 3 = 5   5 + 4 = 9

2. Fill in the missing number to find the sum of 10.

6 + 4 = 10

3. Write the fact family. Use cubes if you like.

4 + 2 = 6   6 − 2 = 4

2 + 4 = 6   6 − 4 = 2

4. Circle the addition fact that will help you subtract. Then subtract.

10 − 7 = 3   2 + 7 = 9   (7 + 3 = 10)

5. Circle **add** or **subtract**. Then write a number sentence.

There were 9 sea horses in the aquarium. Carla saw 4 swim away. How many sea horses are left?

add   (subtract)

9 − 4 = 5 sea horses

© Pearson Education, Inc. 1

Chapter 11 Diagnosing Readiness 199

Item Analysis for Diagnosis and Intervention

Objective	Items	Student Book Pages*	Intervention System
Use doubles facts to learn doubles-plus-1 facts.	1	105–106	B22
Recognize facts that have sums of 10.	2	107–108	B23
Write the addition and subtraction sentence that make up a fact family.	3	139–140	B28
Find differences by using known addition facts.	4	141–142	B29
Solve problems by choosing addition or subtraction.	5	71–72 143–144	E4

*For each lesson, there is a *Reteaching* activity in *Reaching All Learners* and a *Reteaching* master.

11-1 Doubles

Lesson Organizer

Quick Lesson Overview

Objective Recognize doubles as a strategy for remembering sums to 18.

Math Understanding Doubles facts are easy to remember.

Vocabulary Double

Math Monsters Videos Use Episode 6: *Doubles* with or anytime after Lesson 11-1.

Professional Development Note

Research Base

A focus on doubles can help children learn addition facts more easily (Rightsel & Thornton, 1985). In this lesson, children work with counters and pictures to represent double addition combinations.

NCTM Standards

- Number and Operations

(For a complete correlation to the NCTM Standards and Grades Pre-K through 2 Expectations, see Pages 415G and 415H.)

Getting Started

Spiral Review

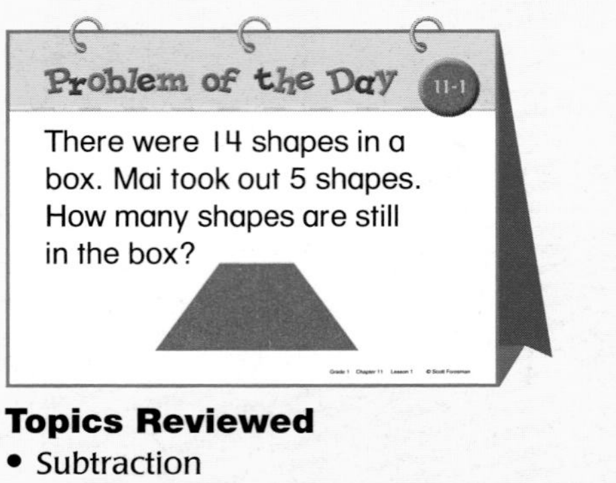

Problem of the Day 11-1

There were 14 shapes in a box. Mai took out 5 shapes. How many shapes are still in the box?

Topics Reviewed

- Subtraction
- Problem-Solving Skill: One-Step Problem

Answer There were 14 − 5, or 9 more shapes in the box.

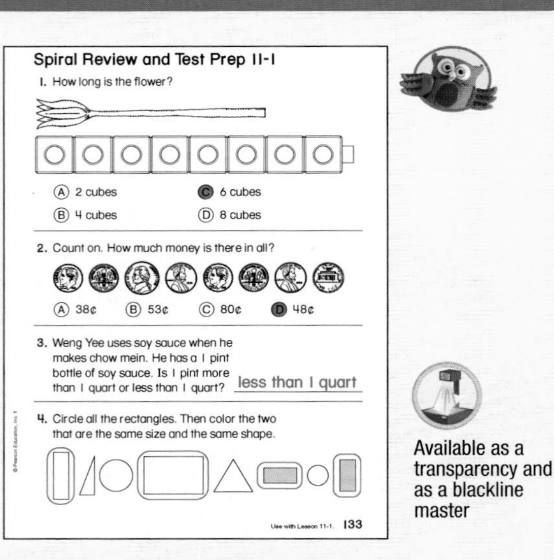

Spiral Review and Test Prep 11-1

1. How long is the flower?

Ⓐ 2 cubes Ⓒ 6 cubes
Ⓑ 4 cubes Ⓓ 8 cubes

2. Count on. How much money is there in all?

Ⓐ 38¢ Ⓑ 53¢ Ⓒ 80¢ Ⓓ 48¢

3. Weng Yee uses soy sauce when he makes chow mein. He has a 1 pint bottle of soy sauce. Is 1 pint more than 1 quart or less than 1 quart? less than 1 quart

4. Circle all the rectangles. Then color the two that are the same size and the same shape.

Use with Lesson 11-1. 133

Available as a transparency and as a blackline master

Topics Reviewed

1. Estimating, Measuring, and Comparing Length
2. Counting Dimes, Nickels, and Pennies
3. Cups, Pints, and Quarts
4. Same Size and Same Shape

Investigating the Concept

Doubles Trains

10–15 MIN **Visual/Spatial** PAIRS

Materials *(per pair)* 18 connecting cubes in one color

What to Do

- Invite one partner to secretly make two equal trains of between 5 and 9 cubes each and then to join the trains to make a double.
- The other partner counts the cubes in all, breaks the train into two equal parts, and tells a doubles fact about the trains. Have children write the fact they make.
- Have partners switch roles and repeat.

Ongoing Assessment

- **What do you notice about the sums of all of the doubles facts?** *(They are all even numbers.)*
- **Reasoning Can you make a doubles fact if you have 17 cubes?** *(No; 17 is not an even number, so it cannot be broken into two equal parts.)*

Reaching All Learners

Math Vocabulary

Make Doubles

5–10 MIN **Visual/Spatial**

Materials *(per child)* 9 two-color counters

- On the board, write $8 + 8 =$ ___, $3 + 4 =$ ___, $6 + 6 =$ ___, and $2 + 5 =$ ___. Invite a volunteer to circle the doubles facts.
- Lay out 5 counters and ask children to display 5 counters to match yours. Have a child write the doubles fact on the board.
- Use counters to make several more doubles facts.

Access Content

English Language Learners

Say the Doubles

5–10 MIN **Auditory/Linguistic**

- Write the numbers 1 through 9 on the board. Read them aloud as children read with you. Encourage individual children to read the numbers aloud.
- Point to the 4: **4 plus 4 equals 8 is a doubles fact.** Write $4 + 4 = 8$ on the board.
- Point to the other numbers in random order. Have volunteers follow the pattern and tell both the double and the sum as they write them on the board.

4 plus 4 equals 8 is a doubles fact.

$4 + 4 = 8$

Reteaching

Fair Share

10–15 MIN **Visual/Spatial**

Materials *(per group)* 18 raisins or counters

- **Ann and Fran always get the same number of treats.** Display 1 raisin (or 1 counter). **Ann gets 1 raisin, so Fran gets 1 raisin.** Put a second raisin below the first.
- Write $1 + 1 = 2$.
- **Now Ann gets 2 raisins. How many does Fran get?** Children select 2 raisins and tell how many in all. *(4)* Write the doubles fact.
- Continue through 9 raisins for Ann. **What do you notice about these doubles facts?** *(The totals are even numbers and increase by 2s.)*

Advanced Learners

Doubles Subtraction

10–15 MIN **Logical/Mathematical**

Materials Counters

- Write doubles facts $1 + 1 = 2$ through $9 + 9 = 18$ on the board.
- Have children write subtraction facts to match the addition facts, starting with $2 - 1 = 1$ through $18 - 9 = 9$. They might want to use counters to help.
- Have children discuss the patterns they observe in the two sets of facts. Challenge children to describe the relationship between the addition and subtraction doubles facts.

$1 + 1 = 2$	$2 - 1 = 1$
$2 + 2 = 4$	$4 - 2 = 2$
$3 + 3 = 6$	$6 - 3 = 3$
$4 + 4 = 8$	$8 - 4 = 4$
$5 + 5 = 10$	$10 - 5 = 5$

Objective Recognize doubles as a strategy for remembering sums to 18.

1 Warm Up

Activate Prior Knowledge Review doubles facts to 12. Write the numbers 0 through 6 in each of two columns on the board. Have volunteers draw lines to match the doubles and then say the doubles fact. Ask the class to repeat each doubles fact.

2 Teach

Learn!

Have children read aloud the doubles as they follow down the student page. Remind children that doubles facts have two addends that are the same. Have children count by 2s as they trace the pattern down the student page.

Ongoing Assessment

Talk About It

- **If there are two trains with 9 in each train, which doubles fact do they show?** *(9 + 9 = 18)*
- **What pattern do you see in the sums of the facts shown?** *(The sums are even numbers, and each is 2 more than the previous sum.)*

If children have difficulty finding sums,

then have them count the cubes.

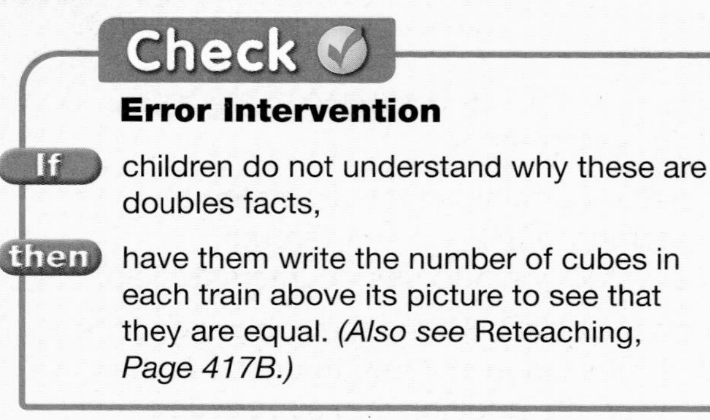

Check

Error Intervention

If children do not understand why these are doubles facts,

then have them write the number of cubes in each train above its picture to see that they are equal. *(Also see* Reteaching, *Page 417B.)*

Think About It Have children use 15 cubes to prove that they cannot make two addends that are the same.

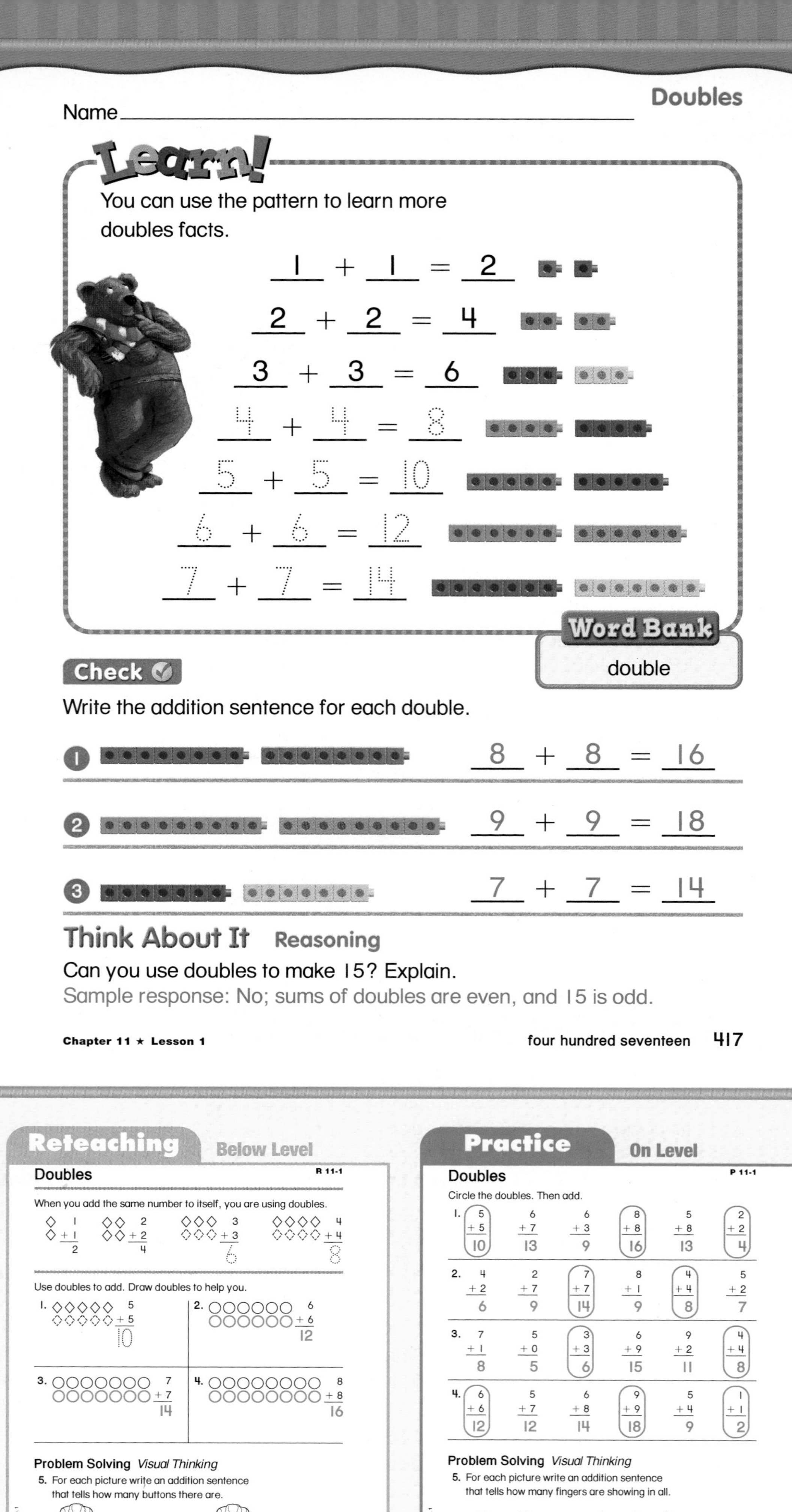

Name ________________ **Doubles**

Learn!

You can use the pattern to learn more doubles facts.

1 + 1 = 2
2 + 2 = 4
3 + 3 = 6
4 + 4 = 8
5 + 5 = 10
6 + 6 = 12
7 + 7 = 14

Word Bank
double

Check

Write the addition sentence for each double.

1. 8 + 8 = 16
2. 9 + 9 = 18
3. 7 + 7 = 14

Think About It Reasoning

Can you use doubles to make 15? Explain.
Sample response: No; sums of doubles are even, and 15 is odd.

Chapter 11 ★ Lesson 1 four hundred seventeen 417

Reteaching Below Level

Doubles R 11-1

When you add the same number to itself, you are using doubles.

1 + 1 = 2; 2 + 2 = 4; 3 + 3 = 6; 4 + 4 = 8

Use doubles to add. Draw doubles to help you.

1. 5 + 5 = 10
2. 6 + 6 = 12
3. 7 + 7 = 14
4. 8 + 8 = 16

Problem Solving *Visual Thinking*

5. For each picture write an addition sentence that tells how many buttons there are.

2 + 2 = 4 3 + 3 = 6

Use with Lesson 11-1. 133

Practice On Level

Doubles P 11-1

Circle the doubles. Then add.

1. 5 + 5 = 10; 6 + 7 = 13; 6 + 3 = 9; 8 + 8 = 16; 5 + 8 = 13; 2 + 2 = 4
2. 4 + 2 = 6; 2 + 7 = 9; 7 + 7 = 14; 8 + 1 = 9; 4 + 4 = 8; 5 + 2 = 7
3. 7 + 1 = 8; 5 + 0 = 5; 3 + 3 = 6; 6 + 9 = 15; 9 + 2 = 11; 4 + 4 = 8
4. 6 + 6 = 12; 5 + 7 = 12; 6 + 8 = 14; 9 + 9 = 18; 5 + 4 = 9; 1 + 1 = 2

Problem Solving *Visual Thinking*

5. For each picture write an addition sentence that tells how many fingers are showing in all.

5 + 5 = 10 3 + 3 = 6

Use with Lesson Lesson 11-1 133

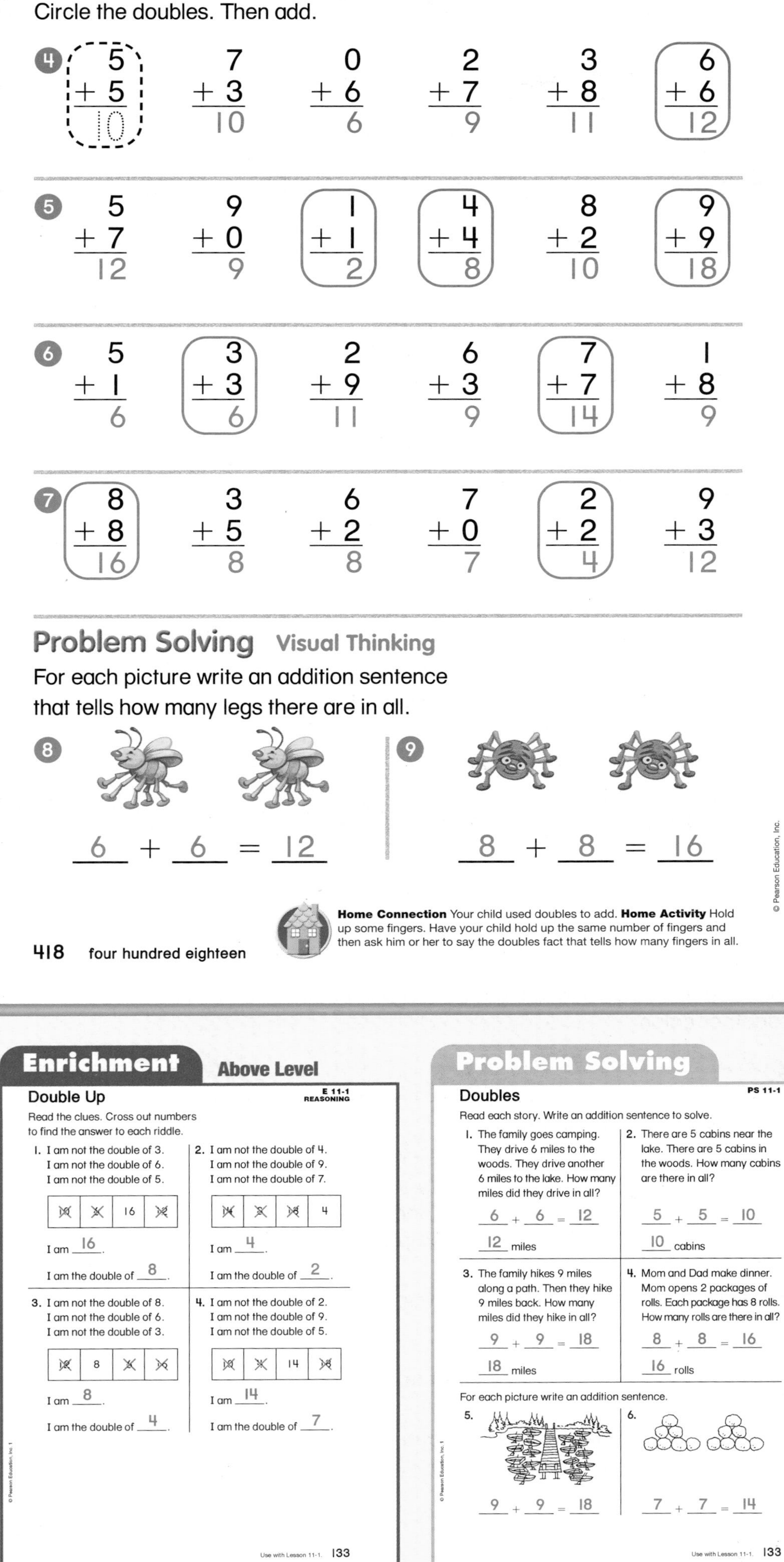

Practice

Circle the doubles. Then add.

4. 5 + 5 = 10 (circled) | 7 + 3 = 10 | 0 + 6 = 6 | 2 + 7 = 9 | 3 + 8 = 11 | 6 + 6 = 12 (circled)

5. 5 + 7 = 12 | 9 + 0 = 9 | 1 + 1 = 2 (circled) | 4 + 4 = 8 (circled) | 8 + 2 = 10 | 9 + 9 = 18 (circled)

6. 5 + 1 = 6 | 3 + 3 = 6 (circled) | 2 + 9 = 11 | 6 + 3 = 9 | 7 + 7 = 14 (circled) | 1 + 8 = 9

7. 8 + 8 = 16 (circled) | 3 + 5 = 8 | 6 + 2 = 8 | 7 + 0 = 7 | 2 + 2 = 4 (circled) | 9 + 3 = 12

Problem Solving Visual Thinking

For each picture write an addition sentence that tells how many legs there are in all.

8. 6 + 6 = 12

9. 8 + 8 = 16

Home Connection Your child used doubles to add. **Home Activity** Hold up some fingers. Have your child hold up the same number of fingers and then ask him or her to say the doubles fact that tells how many fingers in all.

Enrichment Above Level

Double Up E 11-1 REASONING

Read the clues. Cross out numbers to find the answer to each riddle.

1. I am not the double of 3. I am not the double of 6. I am not the double of 5.
   ~~10~~ ~~12~~ 16 ~~6~~
   I am 16. I am the double of 8.

2. I am not the double of 4. I am not the double of 9. I am not the double of 7.
   ~~14~~ ~~18~~ ~~8~~ 4
   I am 4. I am the double of 2.

3. I am not the double of 8. I am not the double of 6. I am not the double of 3.
   ~~16~~ 8 ~~12~~ ~~6~~
   I am 8. I am the double of 4.

4. I am not the double of 2. I am not the double of 9. I am not the double of 5.
   ~~10~~ ~~4~~ 14 ~~18~~
   I am 14. I am the double of 7.

Use with Lesson 11-1. 133

Problem Solving

Doubles PS 11-1

Read each story. Write an addition sentence to solve.

1. The family goes camping. They drive 6 miles to the woods. They drive another 6 miles to the lake. How many miles did they drive in all?
   6 + 6 = 12
   12 miles

2. There are 5 cabins near the lake. There are 5 cabins in the woods. How many cabins are there in all?
   5 + 5 = 10
   10 cabins

3. The family hikes 9 miles along a path. Then they hike 9 miles back. How many miles did they hike in all?
   9 + 9 = 18
   18 miles

4. Mom and Dad make dinner. Mom opens 2 packages of rolls. Each package has 8 rolls. How many rolls are there in all?
   8 + 8 = 16
   16 rolls

For each picture write an addition sentence.

5. 9 + 9 = 18

6. 7 + 7 = 14

Use with Lesson 11-1. 133

3 Practice

For Exercises 4–7, have children find the sums of all of the doubles they circle before they find the remaining sums.

Reading Assist: Vocabulary Review the meaning of a double. Write words with double letters, such as *butter, funny,* and *bubble.* Point out that doubles are two things that are exactly alike. Invite children to suggest other words with double letters and list them on the board.

Leveled Practice

Below Level Use cubes for all exercises.

On Level Use cubes if needed.

Above Level Do all exercises without cubes.

Early Finishers Have children make a chart with a column labeled "Addends" and a column labeled "Sum" to show doubles facts for the numbers 1 to 9.

4 Assess

Journal Idea Have children draw a picture to show 8 + 8 and then write the sum.

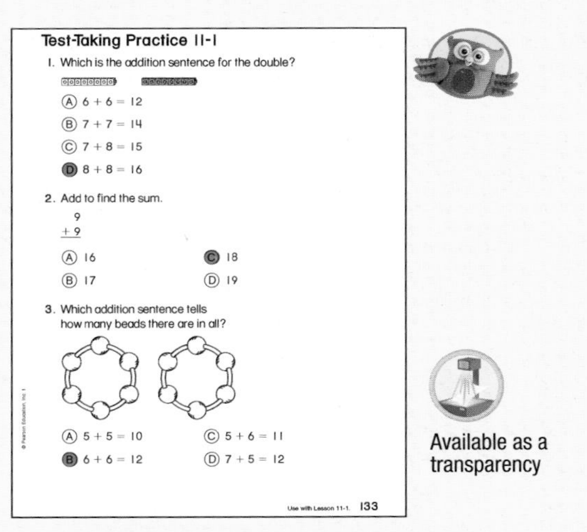

Test-Taking Practice 11-1

1. Which is the addition sentence for the double?
   (A) 6 + 6 = 12
   (B) 7 + 7 = 14
   (C) 7 + 8 = 15
   (D) 8 + 8 = 16

2. Add to find the sum.
   9 + 9
   (A) 16 (C) 18
   (B) 17 (D) 19

3. Which addition sentence tells how many beads there are in all?
   (A) 5 + 5 = 10 (C) 5 + 6 = 11
   (B) 6 + 6 = 12 (D) 7 + 5 = 12

Use with Lesson 11-1. 133

Available as a transparency

11-2 Doubles Plus 1 and Doubles Minus 1

Lesson Organizer

Quick Lesson Overview

Objective Use doubles facts to learn doubles-plus-1 facts and doubles-minus-1 facts.

Math Understanding If you know a doubles fact, it can help you to figure out a doubles-plus-1 fact or a doubles-minus-1 fact.

Professional Development Note

Effective Questioning Techniques Ask structured questions to help children understand the strategy of using a doubles fact to find the sum of a doubles-plus-1 fact or a doubles-minus-1 fact. Ask questions that focus on whether children should add 1 or subtract 1 from the sum of the doubles fact.

NCTM Standards

- Number and Operations

(For a complete correlation to the NCTM Standards and Grades Pre-K through 2 Expectations, see Pages 415G and 415H.)

Getting Started

Spiral Review

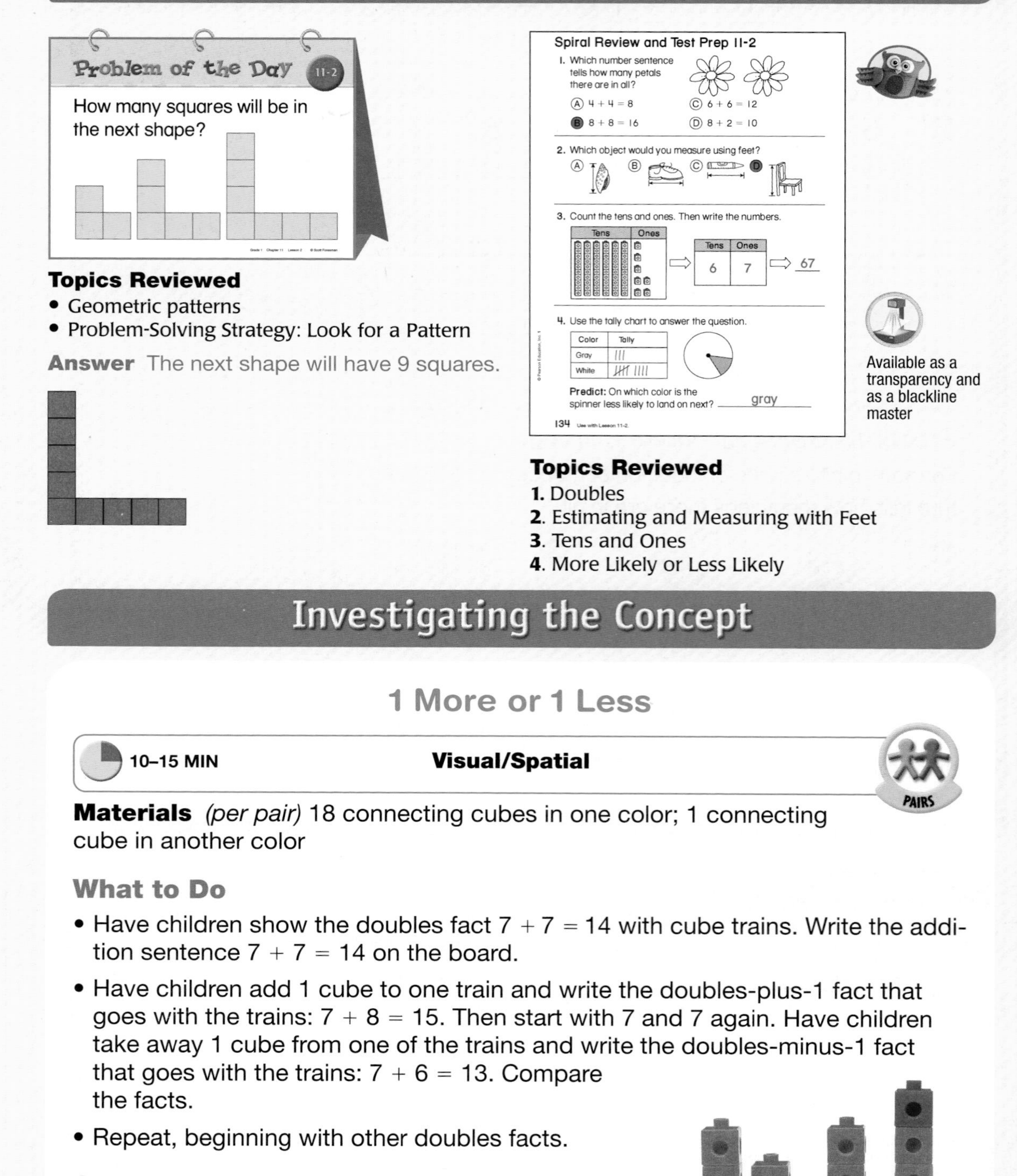

Problem of the Day 11-2

How many squares will be in the next shape?

Topics Reviewed
- Geometric patterns
- Problem-Solving Strategy: Look for a Pattern

Answer The next shape will have 9 squares.

Spiral Review and Test Prep 11-2

1. Which number sentence tells how many petals there are in all?
   - Ⓐ 4 + 4 = 8
   - Ⓑ 8 + 8 = 16
   - Ⓒ 6 + 6 = 12
   - Ⓓ 8 + 2 = 10
2. Which object would you measure using feet?
3. Count the tens and ones. Then write the numbers.

Tens	Ones
6	7

67

4. Use the tally chart to answer the question.

Color	Tally
Gray	III
White	~~IIII~~ IIII

Predict: On which color is the spinner less likely to land on next? gray

134

Available as a transparency and as a blackline master

Topics Reviewed
1. Doubles
2. Estimating and Measuring with Feet
3. Tens and Ones
4. More Likely or Less Likely

Investigating the Concept

1 More or 1 Less

10–15 MIN **Visual/Spatial** PAIRS

Materials *(per pair)* 18 connecting cubes in one color; 1 connecting cube in another color

What to Do

- Have children show the doubles fact 7 + 7 = 14 with cube trains. Write the addition sentence 7 + 7 = 14 on the board.
- Have children add 1 cube to one train and write the doubles-plus-1 fact that goes with the trains: 7 + 8 = 15. Then start with 7 and 7 again. Have children take away 1 cube from one of the trains and write the doubles-minus-1 fact that goes with the trains: 7 + 6 = 13. Compare the facts.
- Repeat, beginning with other doubles facts.

Ongoing Assessment

- **If you know that 8 + 8 = 16, then what is 8 + 9?** *(17)*
- **Number Sense Which doubles fact can you use to find the sums of 6 + 5 and 6 + 7?** *(6 + 6)*

Reaching All Learners

Reading in Math

Compare and Contrast Cubes

10–15 MIN **Visual/Spatial/Linguistic**

Materials 24 connecting cubes of the same color

- Display a group of connecting cubes with two rows of 4 cubes and another group with one row of 4 cubes and one row of 5 cubes.
- Review the terms *comparing* and *contrasting*. Have children compare and contrast the two groups of cubes. *(The second group has 1 more cube.)*
- Display two rows of 4 cubes each and another group with one row of 4 cubes and one row of 3 cubes. Have children contrast these groups. *(The second group has 1 fewer cube.)*

Access Content

English Language Learners

1 More and 1 Less

5–10 MIN **Auditory/Linguistic**

Materials *(per group)* 10 small toys

- Write "more" and "less" on the board. Pronounce the words and have children repeat them. **Let's add and subtract one toy.**
- Count out 2 toys. **2 toys. 1 more is 3.** Place a third toy next to the others. Ask children to follow this pattern with other numbers of toys.
- Then count 5 toys. **5 toys. 1 less is 4.** Take away a toy. Have children repeat with other numbers of toys.

Reteaching

Finger Count

5–10 MIN **Kinesthetic**

SMALL GROUP

- Show 4 fingers on each hand. **How many fingers are showing on each hand? How many fingers are there altogether?** Write the doubles fact $4 + 4 = 8$ on the board.
- Have children show 4 fingers on each hand. Ask them to raise the thumb on one hand. **How many fingers are there now?** Write the doubles-plus-1 fact $4 + 5 = 9$ on the board.
- Repeat the activity with other numbers to show a doubles-minus-1 fact.

Advanced Learners

How Many Does Deshawn Have?

15–20 MIN **Logical/Mathematical**

SMALL GROUP

- Write the following on the board as you read aloud: **Shawn has 5 CDs, 4 apples, 2 drums, and 8 hats. Whichever item Shawn has, Deshawn has that number, plus 2 more.**
- Ask children to work together to use doubles-plus-2 facts to figure out how many CDs, apples, drums, and hats Shawn and Deshawn have together.
- After children have solved each problem, have a representative explain how the group used doubles plus 2 to solve.

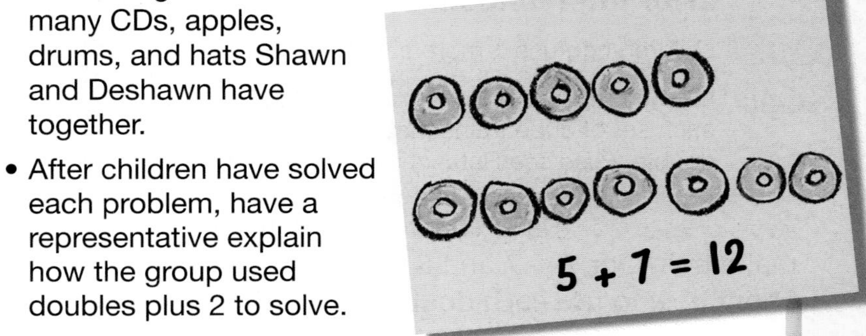

Objective Use doubles facts to learn doubles-plus-1 facts and doubles-minus-1 facts.

1 Warm Up

Activate Prior Knowledge Review doubles facts to 18. Have children take turns showing the doubles facts with sums from 2 to 18 using small objects or cubes. Invite children to name each doubles fact that they demonstrate.

2 Teach

Learn!

Discuss the first pair of cube trains at the top of the student page. **Which fact do the first trains show?** *(3 + 3 = 6)* Point out that in the next pair, 1 cube is added to show 3 + 4. In the last pair 1 cube is crossed out to show 3 + 2. Have children find the sums.

Ongoing Assessment

Talk About It

- **How can knowing a double help you learn a doubles-plus-1 fact and a doubles-minus-1 fact?** *(One of the addends has a difference of 1 from the double.)*
- **How does knowing 5 + 5 = 10 help you find 5 + 6?** *(You can add 1 to 10 to find that 5 + 6 = 11.)*

If children do not understand the doubles-plus-1 and the doubles-minus-1 processes,

then have them use cubes to illustrate each fact.

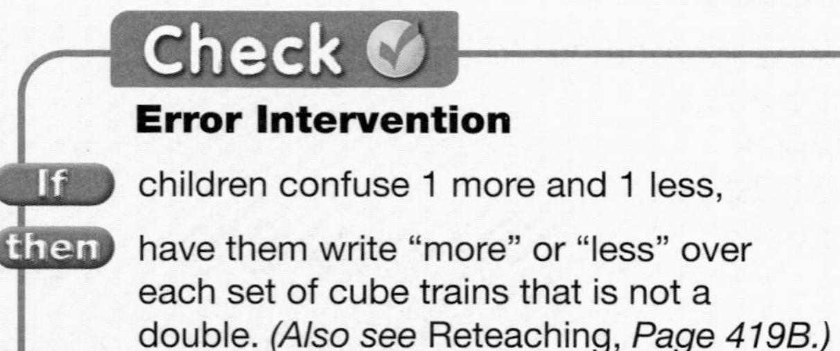

Check

Error Intervention

If children confuse 1 more and 1 less,

then have them write "more" or "less" over each set of cube trains that is not a double. *(Also see* Reteaching, *Page 419B.)*

Think About It Have children use cubes to make trains for 7 + 7 and 8 + 8. Then talk about how to use each double to find the sum of 8 + 7.

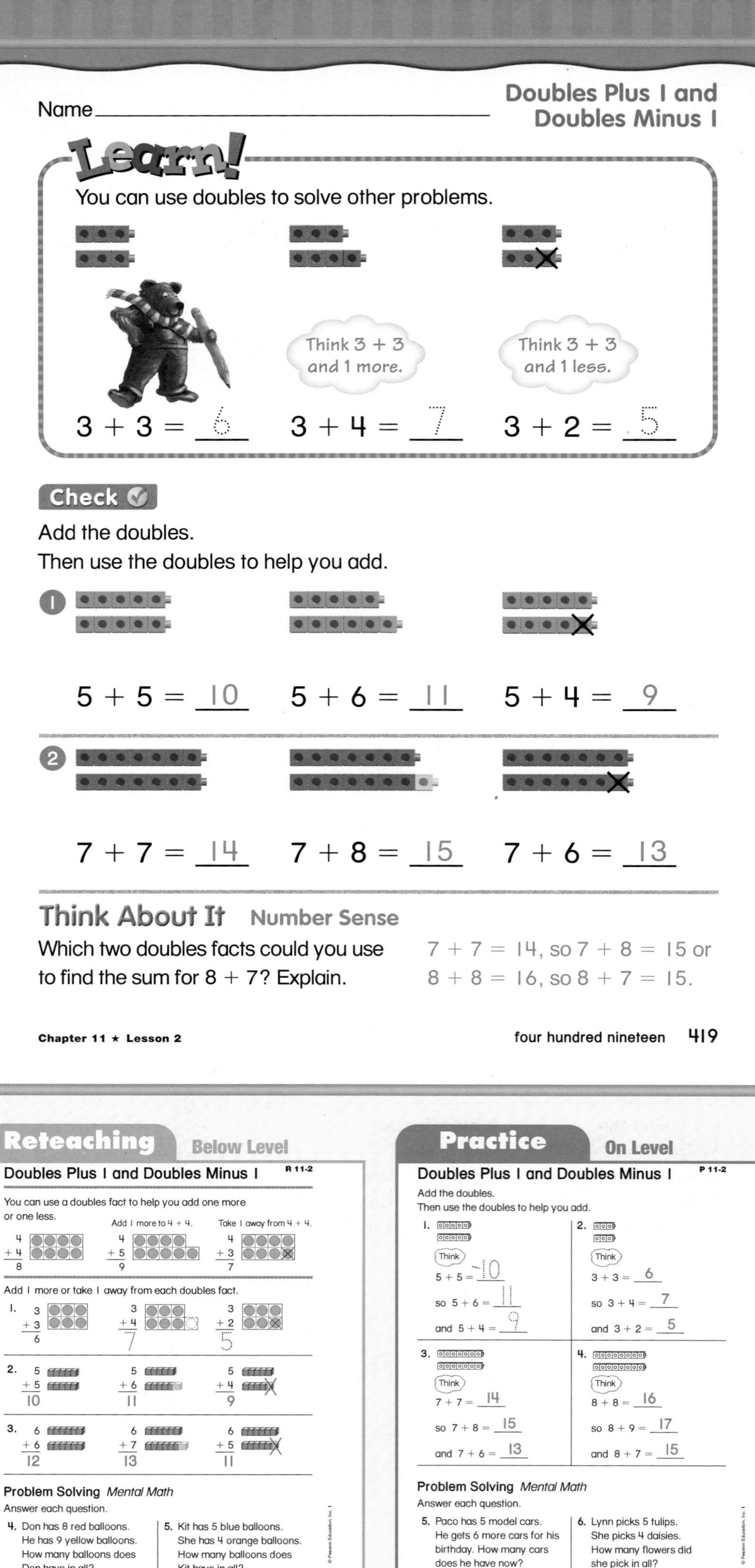

Name ____________________

Doubles Plus 1 and Doubles Minus 1

Learn!

You can use doubles to solve other problems.

Think 3 + 3 and 1 more.

Think 3 + 3 and 1 less.

3 + 3 = 6 3 + 4 = 7 3 + 2 = 5

Check

Add the doubles.
Then use the doubles to help you add.

1. 5 + 5 = 10 5 + 6 = 11 5 + 4 = 9

2. 7 + 7 = 14 7 + 8 = 15 7 + 6 = 13

Think About It Number Sense

Which two doubles facts could you use to find the sum for 8 + 7? Explain.

7 + 7 = 14, so 7 + 8 = 15 or 8 + 8 = 16, so 8 + 7 = 15.

Chapter 11 ★ Lesson 2 four hundred nineteen 419

Reteaching Below Level

Doubles Plus 1 and Doubles Minus 1 R 11-2

You can use a doubles fact to help you add one more or one less.

4 + 4 = 8; Add 1 more to 4 + 4: 4 + 5 = 9; Take 1 away from 4 + 4: 4 + 3 = 7

Add 1 more or take 1 away from each doubles fact.

1. 3 + 3 = 6; 3 + 4 = 7; 3 + 2 = 5

2. 5 + 5 = 10; 5 + 6 = 11; 5 + 4 = 9

3. 6 + 6 = 12; 6 + 7 = 13; 6 + 5 = 11

Problem Solving *Mental Math*

Answer each question.

4. Don has 8 red balloons. He has 9 yellow balloons. How many balloons does Don have in all? 17 balloons

5. Kit has 5 blue balloons. She has 4 orange balloons. How many balloons does Kit have in all? 9 balloons

134 Use with Lesson 11-2

Practice On Level

Doubles Plus 1 and Doubles Minus 1 P 11-2

Add the doubles.
Then use the doubles to help you add.

1. Think 5 + 5 = 10 so 5 + 6 = 11 and 5 + 4 = 9

2. Think 3 + 3 = 6 so 3 + 4 = 7 and 3 + 2 = 5

3. Think 7 + 7 = 14 so 7 + 8 = 15 and 7 + 6 = 13

4. Think 8 + 8 = 16 so 8 + 9 = 17 and 8 + 7 = 15

Problem Solving *Mental Math*

Answer each question.

5. Paco has 5 model cars. He gets 6 more cars for his birthday. How many cars does he have now? 11 model cars

6. Lynn picks 5 tulips. She picks 4 daisies. How many flowers did she pick in all? 9 flowers

134 Use with Lesson 11-2

Practice

Add the doubles.
Then use the doubles to help you add.

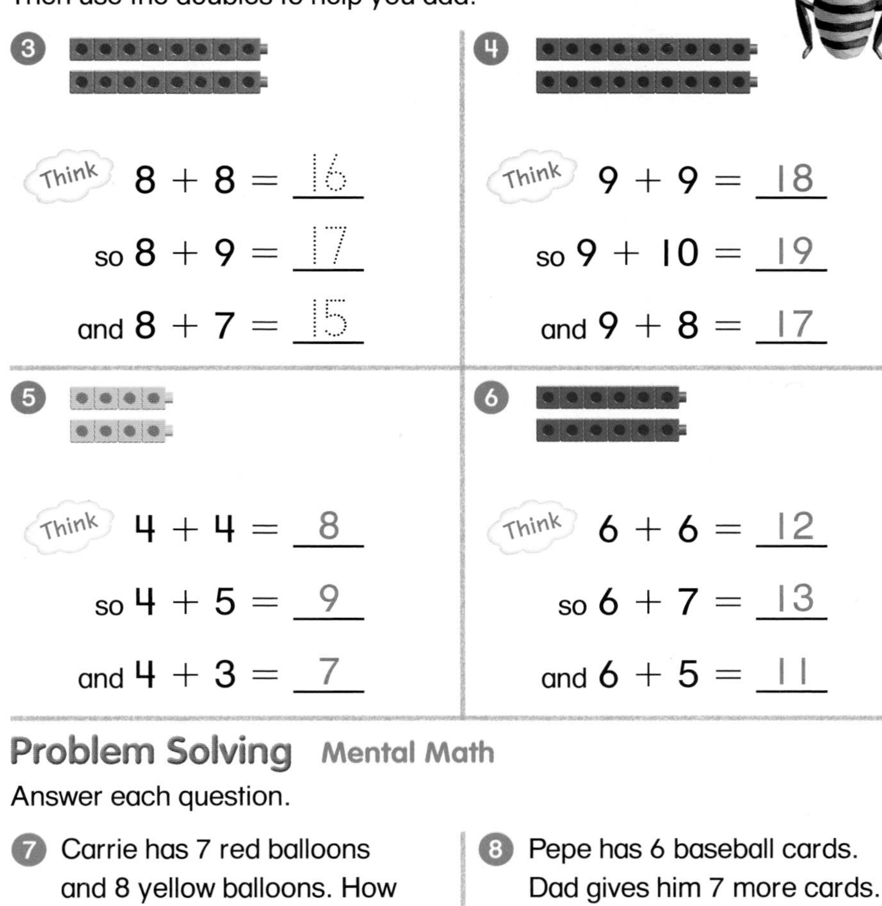

3. Think $8 + 8 = $ 16
so $8 + 9 = $ 17
and $8 + 7 = $ 15

4. Think $9 + 9 = $ 18
so $9 + 10 = $ 19
and $9 + 8 = $ 17

5. Think $4 + 4 = $ 8
so $4 + 5 = $ 9
and $4 + 3 = $ 7

6. Think $6 + 6 = $ 12
so $6 + 7 = $ 13
and $6 + 5 = $ 11

Problem Solving Mental Math

Answer each question.

7. Carrie has 7 red balloons and 8 yellow balloons. How many balloons does Carrie have in all?

15 balloons

8. Pepe has 6 baseball cards. Dad gives him 7 more cards. How many cards does Pepe have in all?

13 baseball cards

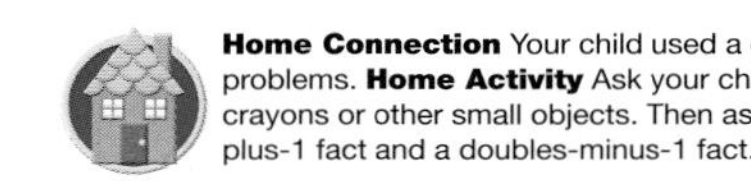

Home Connection Your child used a doubles fact to solve other addition problems. **Home Activity** Ask your child to show a doubles fact using crayons or other small objects. Then ask him or her to show you a doubles-plus-1 fact and a doubles-minus-1 fact.

Enrichment Above Level

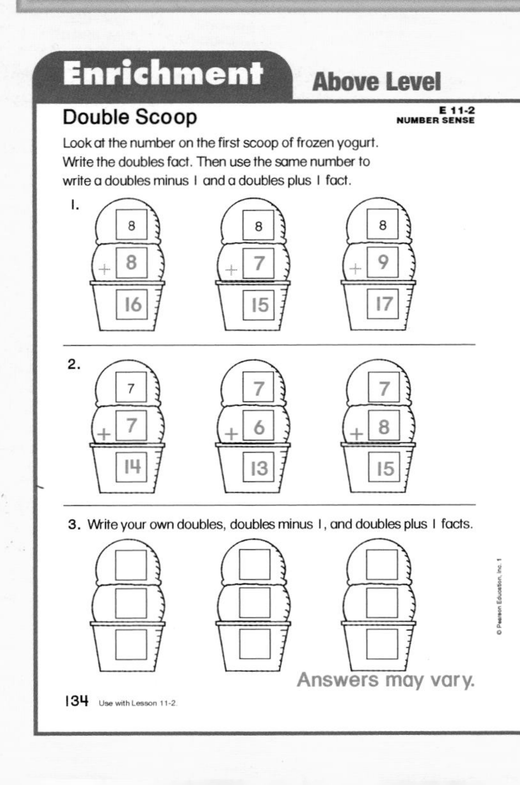

Double Scoop E 11-2 NUMBER SENSE

Look at the number on the first scoop of frozen yogurt. Write the doubles fact. Then use the same number to write a doubles minus 1 and a doubles plus 1 fact.

1. 8 + 8 = 16; 8 + 7 = 15; 8 + 9 = 17
2. 7 + 7 = 14; 7 + 6 = 13; 7 + 8 = 15
3. Write your own doubles, doubles minus 1, and doubles plus 1 facts.

Answers may vary.

134 Use with Lesson 11-2.

Problem Solving

Doubles Plus 1 and Doubles Minus 1 PS 11-2

Answer each question. Write the doubles fact you used to help you add. Doubles facts may vary.

1. At the circus, 6 dogs ride a bicycle and 5 dogs ride in a wagon. How many dogs are there in all?
11 dogs
5 + 5 = 10

2. The clown juggles 6 balls. Then the clown adds 7 more balls to juggle. How many balls does the clown juggle altogether?
13 balls
6 + 6 = 12

3. 8 clowns get out of a little car. Then 7 more clowns get out. How many clowns get out of the car altogether?
15 clowns
8 + 8 = 16

4. The animal trainer has 7 lions and 6 tigers. How many animals does he have in all?
13 animals
7 + 7 = 14

5. Cindy likes the elephants best. There are 4 baby elephants and 5 big elephants. How many elephants are there in all?
9 elephants
4 + 4 = 8

6. Cindy and Kevin want balloons. There are 8 red balloons and 9 blue balloons. How many balloons are there in all?
17 balloons
8 + 8 = 16

134 Use with Lesson 11-2.

3 Practice

Point out that there are three problems to solve in each of Exercises 3–6.

Reading Assist: Classifying Have children classify each problem in Exercise 4 by telling whether it is a doubles fact, a doubles-plus-1 fact, or a double-minus-1 fact.

Leveled Practice

Below Level Use cubes for Exercises 3–6.

On Level Use cubes as needed.

Above Level Do all exercises without cubes.

Early Finishers On the board, write $3 + 3 =$ ___; $5 + 5 =$ ___; and $7 + 7 =$___. Have children find the sums and write a doubles-plus-1 and a doubles-minus-1 fact to go with each.

4 Assess

Journal Idea Give children paper folded into three columns. Have children write the doubles facts from $5 + 5 = 10$ through $9 + 9 = 18$ in the center. In the left column, ask children to write the doubles-minus-1 facts. In the right column, have them write the doubles-plus-1 facts.

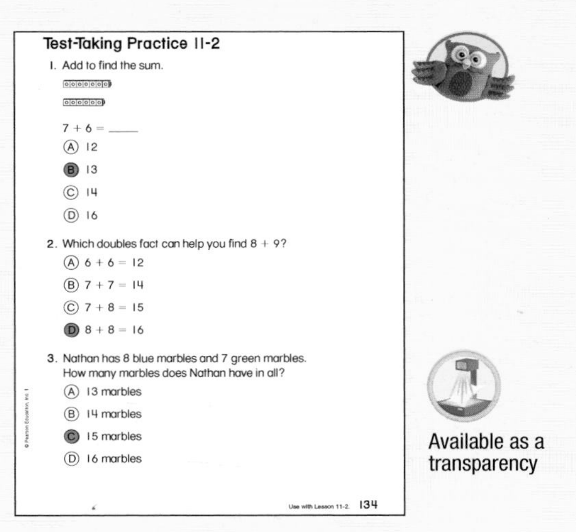

Test-Taking Practice 11-2

1. Add to find the sum.
7 + 6 = ___
Ⓐ 12
Ⓑ 13
Ⓒ 14
Ⓓ 16

2. Which doubles fact can help you find 8 + 9?
Ⓐ 6 + 6 = 12
Ⓑ 7 + 7 = 14
Ⓒ 7 + 8 = 15
Ⓓ 8 + 8 = 16

3. Nathan has 8 blue marbles and 7 green marbles. How many marbles does Nathan have in all?
Ⓐ 13 marbles
Ⓑ 14 marbles
Ⓒ 15 marbles
Ⓓ 16 marbles

Use with Lesson 11-2. 134

Available as a transparency

11-3 Adding 10

Lesson Organizer

Quick Lesson Overview

Objective Use a pattern to add numbers from 1 to 8 to the number 10.

Math Understanding There is a place-value pattern that can be used to add 10 and a single-digit number mentally.

Professional Development Note

How Children Learn Math The addition facts in this lesson are not basic facts and do not need to be committed to memory. Our place-value system creates a useful pattern for finding sums when adding to 10. Children will find the ability to add to 10 useful when doing the intermediate steps in addition and subtraction algorithms.

NCTM Standards

- Number and Operations
- Algebra

(For a complete correlation to the NCTM Standards and Grades Pre-K through 2 Expectations, see Pages 415G and 415H.)

Getting Started

Spiral Review

Problem of the Day 11-3

Marta has an even number of marbles. Sam has an odd number of marbles. Together they have 7 marbles. How many marbles could each child have?

Topics Reviewed
- Addition
- Odd and even numbers
- Problem-Solving Strategy: Make an Organized List

Answer Samples:

Marta 2, Sam 5
Marta 4, Sam 3
Marta 6, Sam 1

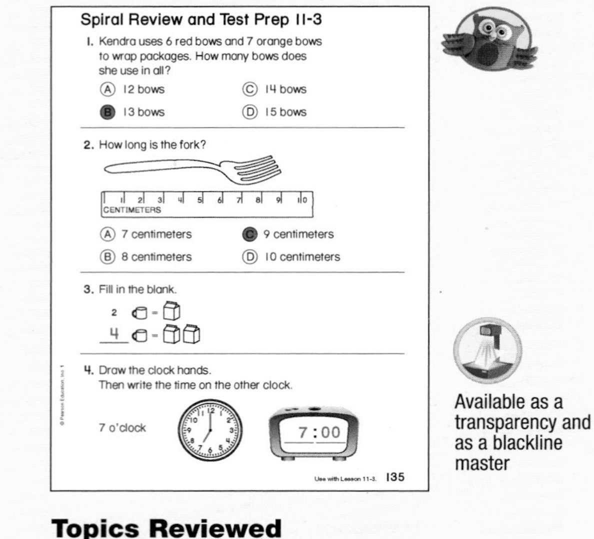

Spiral Review and Test Prep 11-3

1. Kendra uses 6 red bows and 7 orange bows to wrap packages. How many bows does she use in all?
   - (A) 12 bows
   - (B) 13 bows
   - (C) 14 bows
   - (D) 15 bows

2. How long is the fork?
   - (A) 7 centimeters
   - (B) 8 centimeters
   - (C) 9 centimeters
   - (D) 10 centimeters

3. Fill in the blank.
   2 = 1
   4 = 2

4. Draw the clock hands. Then write the time on the other clock.
   7 o'clock 7:00

Use with Lesson 11-3. 135

Available as a transparency and as a blackline master

Topics Reviewed
1. Doubles Plus 1 and Doubles Minus 1
2. Estimating and Measuring with Centimeters
3. Cups, Pints, and Quarts
4. Telling and Writing Time to the Hour

Investigating the Concept

Put in 10

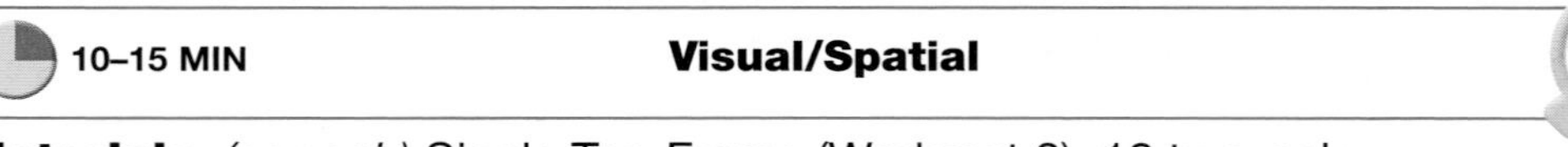

Materials *(per pair)* Single Ten-Frame (Workmat 2); 18 two-color counters

What to Do

- Have one partner fill the ten-frame with yellow counters and the other partner set out a number of red counters between 1 and 8 below the frame. Each partner writes an addition sentence to go with the counters, such as $10 + 3 = 13$. Then have partners compare their number sentences.
- Have partners trade roles and repeat. After several examples, compare the sentences and help children understand the pattern.

Ongoing Assessment

- **Which addition sentence would you write if there were 10 counters on the ten-frame and 5 counters below it?** *($10 + 5 = 15$)*
- **Reasoning What pattern do you see when you add to 10?** *(There is always a 1 in the tens place, and the number in the ones place is the number you added.)*

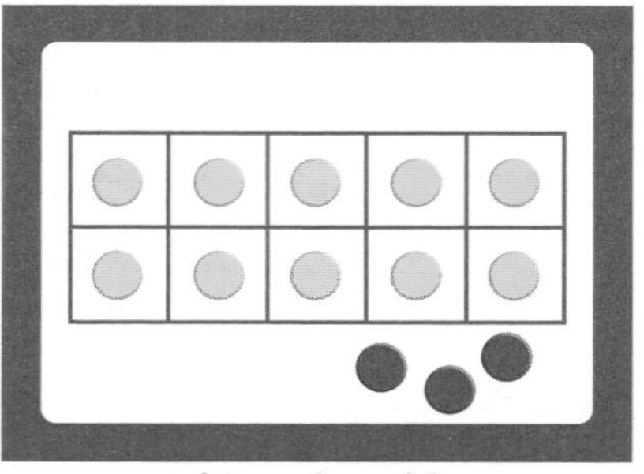

$10 + 3 = 13$

Reaching All Learners

Math Vocabulary

What Is the Sum?

5–10 MIN **Visual/Spatial/Linguistic**

Materials *(per child)* Single Ten-Frame (Workmat 2); 19 two-color counters

- Review that the sum tells how many in all. Write 10 + 2 = 12 on the board. Point to 12 and explain that 12 is the sum of 10 and 2. **12 tells how many in all.**
- Give children several problems involving adding 10 to a single digit. Have children use Workmat 2 and counters to solve the problems.
- Have volunteers tell you the sum of the numbers in each problem.

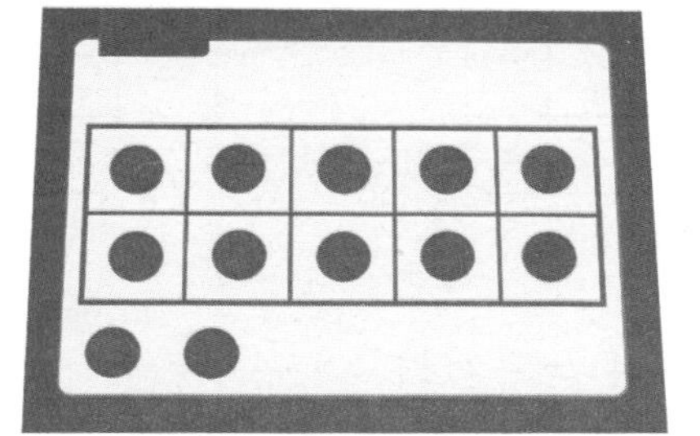

Extend Language

English Language Learners

Say How Many

10–15 MIN **Visual/Spatial/Linguistic** PAIRS

Materials *(per pair)* Single Ten-Frame (Workmat 2); 19 two-color counters; magazines

- Play a counting game. Have one child select a picture from a magazine. Have a second child choose a number greater than 10 and use counters to show the number on the ten-frame.
- The first child describes the picture, using the chosen number. For example, the child might say, "14 dogs" or "19 sandwiches."

14 dogs

Reteaching

Tens and Ones with Partners

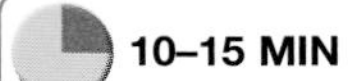

Visual/Spatial PAIRS

Materials *(per pair)* Single Ten-Frame (Workmat 2); 19 two-color counters

- Write the number sentence 10 + 4 = ___ on the board. Have one partner use counters to fill the ten-frame to show 10 and place 4 counters beneath it to show 4 more. Have the other partner fill in the sum on the board.
- Write more number sentences with sums between 11 and 19 on the board. Have one partner fill the ten-frame, while the other partner uses the counters to find and write the sums on the board.

Math and Physical Education

Make the Number

10–15 MIN **Auditory/Kinesthetic**

Materials Chalk

- Use chalk to draw a ten-frame large enough for children to stand in the squares. Draw a line below the frame for additional children to stand on.
- Have children play Make the Number. When they hear a number, they run onto or below the ten-frame to represent it.
- Continue playing until each child has had a chance to make a number.

Objective Use a pattern to add number from 1 to 8 to the number 10.

1 Warm Up

Activate Prior Knowledge Review numbers 11 to 19. Have children work in pairs with a Single Ten-Frame (Workmat 2) and counters. Call out a number between 11 and 19 and have children show it with ten-frames and counters.

2 Teach

Discuss the addition pattern illustrated by the ten-frames shown at the top of the student page. Guide children to see that the first number in the sum always stands for 1 ten and the second number always stands for the number of ones that are added.

Ongoing Assessment

Talk About It

- **How does the ten-frame look when adding to 10?** *(The ten-frame is full.)*
- **What pattern do you see when adding to 10?** *(There is a 1 in the tens place, and the number in the ones place is the number added.)*

If children have difficulty seeing the pattern,

then have them make lists showing the addends and the sums in order.

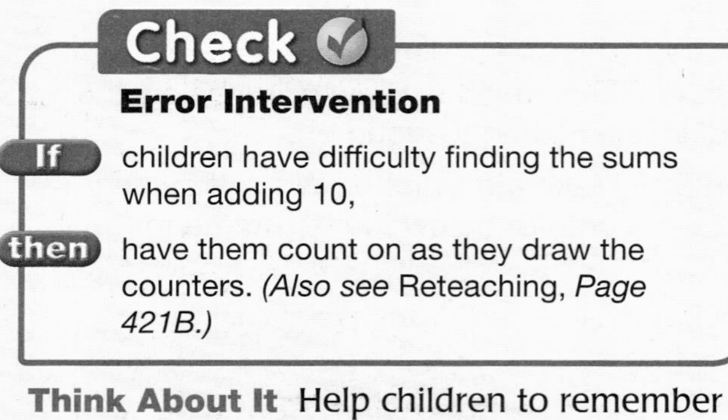

Check

Error Intervention

If children have difficulty finding the sums when adding 10,

then have them count on as they draw the counters. *(Also see Reteaching, Page 421B.)*

Think About It Help children to remember that they can add in any order, so a helpful addition fact is 10 + 4.

Adding 10

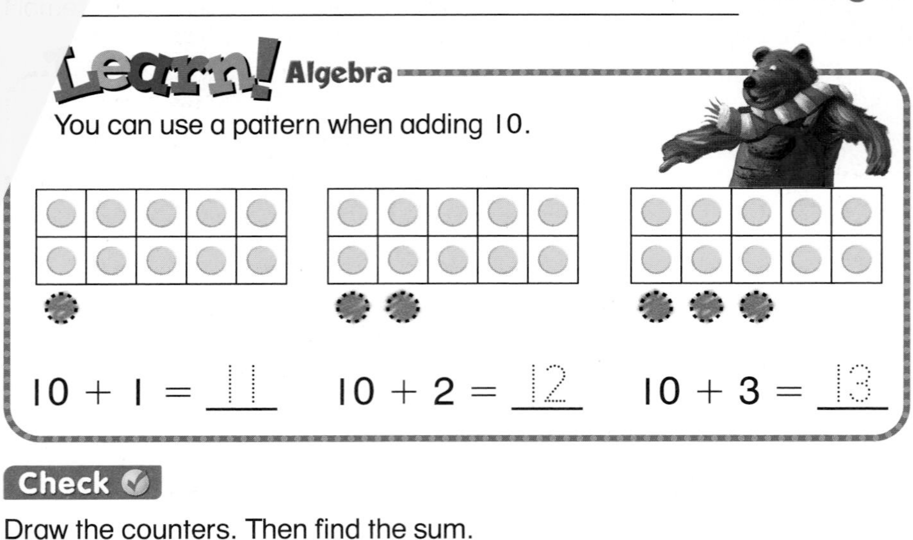

Learn! Algebra

You can use a pattern when adding 10.

10 + 1 = 11 10 + 2 = 12 10 + 3 = 13

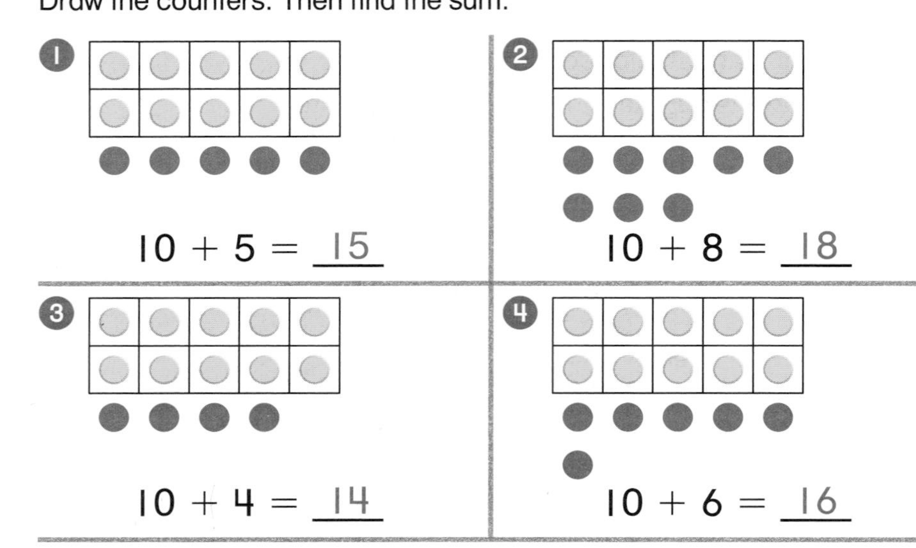

Check

Draw the counters. Then find the sum.

1. 10 + 5 = 15
2. 10 + 8 = 18
3. 10 + 4 = 14
4. 10 + 6 = 16

Think About It Reasoning

Which addition fact can help you find the sum for 4 + 10? 10 + 4

How can you show the addition fact with a ten-frame? Fill the 10 frame and then add 4 counters.

Reteaching Below Level

Adding 10 R 11-3

You can use tens to add.

This is one group of 10. This is 10 and 1 more. This is 10 and 3 more.

10 10 + 1 = 11 10 + 3 = 13

Draw counters. Then find the sum.

1. 10 + 5 = 15
2. 10 + 6 = 16
3. 10 + 7 = 17
4. 10 + 4 = 14
5. 10 + 9 = 19
6. 10 + 8 = 18

Use with Lesson 11-3. 135

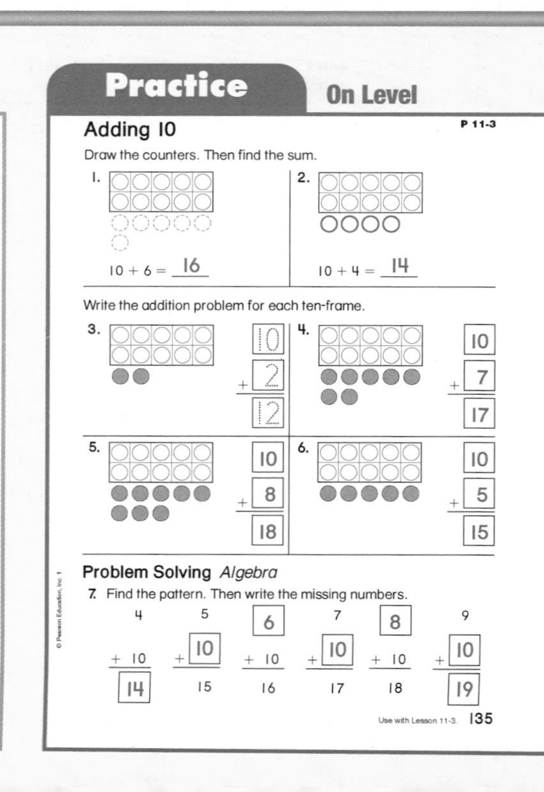

Practice On Level

Adding 10 P 11-3

Draw the counters. Then find the sum.

1. 10 + 6 = 16
2. 10 + 4 = 14

Write the addition problem for each ten-frame.

3. 10 + 2 = 12
4. 10 + 7 = 17
5. 10 + 8 = 18
6. 10 + 5 = 15

Problem Solving *Algebra*

7. Find the pattern. Then write the missing numbers.

4	5	6	7	8	9
+ 10	+ 10	+ 10	+ 10	+ 10	+ 10
14	15	16	17	18	19

Use with Lesson 11-3. 135

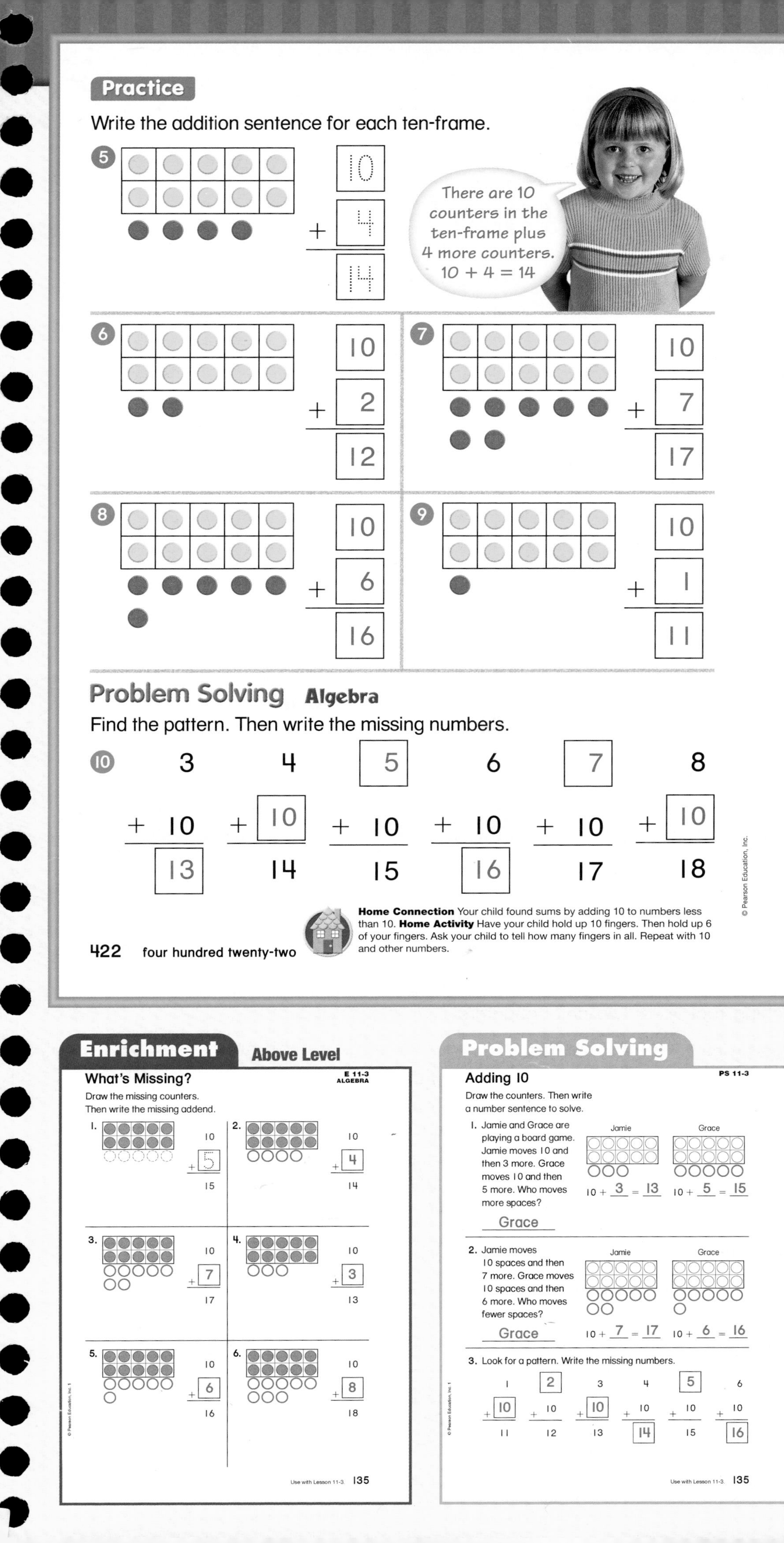

Practice

Write the addition sentence for each ten-frame.

5. $10 + 4 = 14$

6. $10 + 2 = 12$

7. $10 + 7 = 17$

8. $10 + 6 = 16$

9. $10 + 1 = 11$

Problem Solving **Algebra**

Find the pattern. Then write the missing numbers.

10.

3	4	5	6	7	8
+ 10	+ 10	+ 10	+ 10	+ 10	+ 10
13	14	15	16	17	18

Home Connection Your child found sums by adding 10 to numbers less than 10. **Home Activity** Have your child hold up 10 fingers. Then hold up 6 of your fingers. Ask your child to tell how many fingers in all. Repeat with 10 and other numbers.

Enrichment Above Level

What's Missing? E 11-3 ALGEBRA

Draw the missing counters. Then write the missing addend.

1. $10 + 5 = 15$
2. $10 + 4 = 14$
3. $10 + 7 = 17$
4. $10 + 3 = 13$
5. $10 + 6 = 16$
6. $10 + 8 = 18$

Use with Lesson 11-3. 135

Problem Solving

Adding 10 PS 11-3

Draw the counters. Then write a number sentence to solve.

1. Jamie and Grace are playing a board game. Jamie moves 10 and then 3 more. Grace moves 10 and then 5 more. Who moves more spaces?

Jamie: $10 + 3 = 13$ Grace: $10 + 5 = 15$

Grace

2. Jamie moves 10 spaces and then 7 more. Grace moves 10 spaces and then 6 more. Who moves fewer spaces?

Jamie: $10 + 7 = 17$ Grace: $10 + 6 = 16$

Grace

3. Look for a pattern. Write the missing numbers.

1	2	3	4	5	6
+ 10	+ 10	+ 10	+ 10	+ 10	+ 10
11	12	13	14	15	16

Use with Lesson 11-3. 135

3 Practice

For Exercise 10, point out that one part of each addition fact needs to be completed.

Reading Assist: Compare and Contrast How are the pictures in Exercises 6 and 7 alike? *(They both show a full ten-frame.)* **How are they different?** *(Exercise 6 has 2 counters left over. Exercise 7 has 7 counters left over.)*

Leveled Practice

Below Level Use counters and a ten-frame.

On Level Do all exercises mentally.

Above Level After completing Exercises 5–9, write the facts found after changing the order of the addends.

Early Finishers Have children use calculators to explore adding 10 to the numbers 11 through 19 to see which new pattern they can discern.

4 Assess

Journal Idea Write 10 + 3 = ___ and 10 + 4 = ___ on the board. Have children continue the pattern and write the facts that come next.

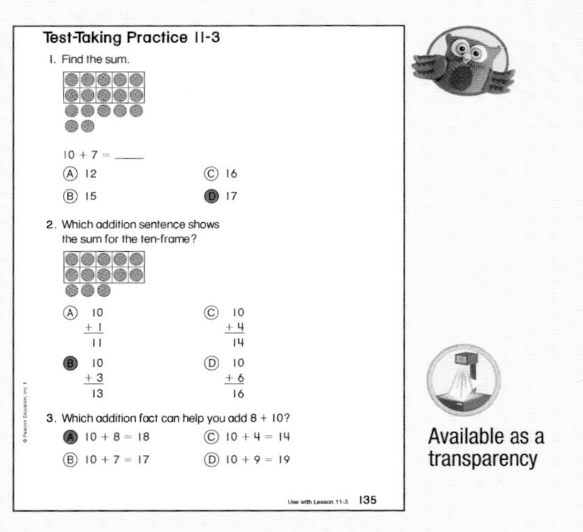

Test-Taking Practice 11-3

1. Find the sum.

10 + 7 = ___

Ⓐ 12 Ⓑ 15 Ⓒ 16 Ⓓ 17

2. Which addition sentence shows the sum for the ten-frame?

Ⓐ 10 + 1 = 11 Ⓑ 10 + 3 = 13 Ⓒ 10 + 4 = 14 Ⓓ 10 + 6 = 16

3. Which addition fact can help you add 8 + 10?

Ⓐ 10 + 8 = 18 Ⓑ 10 + 7 = 17 Ⓒ 10 + 4 = 14 Ⓓ 10 + 9 = 19

Use with Lesson 11-3. 135

Available as a transparency

11-4 Making 10 to Add

Lesson Organizer

Quick Lesson Overview

Objective Find sums by making a 10 when adding to 8 or 9.

Math Understanding Making a group of 10 can change a difficult addition fact to one that is easier to add mentally.

Materials for Student Pages
Single Ten-Frame (Workmat 2); 17 two-color counters

Professional Development Note

How Children Learn Math Being able to decompose and recompose addends to maintain a constant sum is an important strategy. For example, to add 9 + 5, children take 1 from the 5 and add it to 9 to make 10 and then add 10 + 4. So 9 + 5 = 10 + 4 = 14.

NCTM Standards

- Number and Operations

(For a complete correlation to the NCTM Standards and Grades Pre-K through 2 Expectations, see Pages 415G and 415H.)

Getting Started

Spiral Review

Problem of the Day 11-4

Solve. Then tell the information you did not need to solve the problem.
Seven cats are sleeping. Six cats are eating. Four birds are flying. How many cats are there in all?

Topics Reviewed
- Addition
- Problem-Solving Skill: Missing or Extra Information

Answer There are 7 + 6, or 13 cats. The extra information is that 4 birds are flying.

Spiral Review and Test Prep 11-4

1. How many cubes will cover the shape?
   A 4 B 3 C 1 D 2
2. Which bank has the most money?
   A B C D
3. Will it take more cubes or more paper clips to measure the bear? Circle your prediction. Then measure.
   more / more
   about ___ about ___
   Answers will vary.
4. Write the addition sentence for the ten-frame.
   10 + 8 = 18

136 Use with Lesson 11-4.

Available as a transparency and as a blackline master

Topics Reviewed
1. Look Back and Check
2. Dime
3. Use Logical Reasoning
4. Adding 10

Investigating the Concept

Make 10 First

10–15 MIN Visual/Spatial PAIRS

Materials *(per pair)* Single Ten-Frame (Workmat 2); Number Cards 0–11 (Teaching Tool 9); 18 two-color counters

What to Do

- Have one child put 9 yellow counters in the ten-frame and turn over a card between 2 and 9. The partner then puts that number of red counters under the ten-frame and names the addition problem shown.
- The first child moves 1 of the red counters into the empty spot on the ten-frame and restates the addition. Discuss what children did, pointing out that making a 10 is sometimes helpful when adding. For example: **9 + 3 is the same as 10 + 2; the sum is 12.**

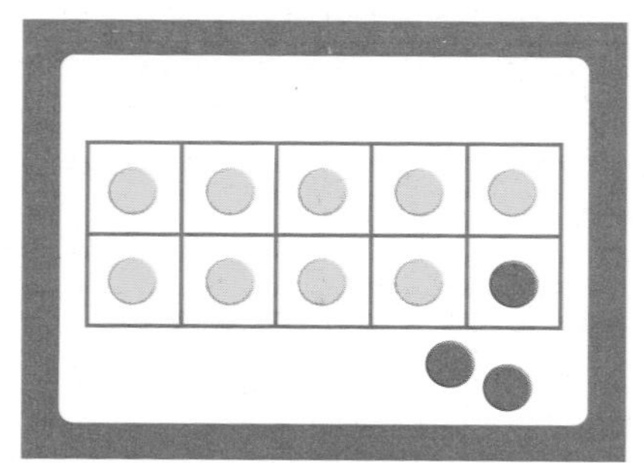

9 + 3 = 10 + 2 = 12

Ongoing Assessment

- **What do you do when adding 8 and another number?** *(Move 2 counters onto the ten-frame to fill the empty spaces.)*
- **Reasoning How do you know how many to move to the ten-frame to make a 10?** *(By looking at how many empty spots there are)*

Reaching All Learners

Reading in Math

Draw Conclusions About Addition Problems

10–15 MIN **Logical/Mathematical**

- Write 10 + 5 horizontally and vertically on the board. **What can you conclude about these addition facts?** *(They are written in different ways, but the sums are the same.)*
- Write 9 + 6 = ___ and 10 + 5 = ___ on the board. Help children conclude that different combinations of numbers can add up to the same sum.
- You might also lead children to conclude that it is easier to add 10 + 5 than to add 9 + 6 when using mental math.

Access Content

English Language Learners

Same or Different?

10–15 MIN **Auditory/Linguistic**

- Write the following pairs of problems vertically on the board: 8 + 5 and 10 + 3; 9 + 7 and 10 + 5. Point to the first pair. **Are the sums the same or different?** *(The same)* Have a volunteer prove whether the sums are the same or different.
- Point to the second pair and ask the same question. Have another volunteer write the sums to prove the answer.
- Continue with other pairs of addition problems.

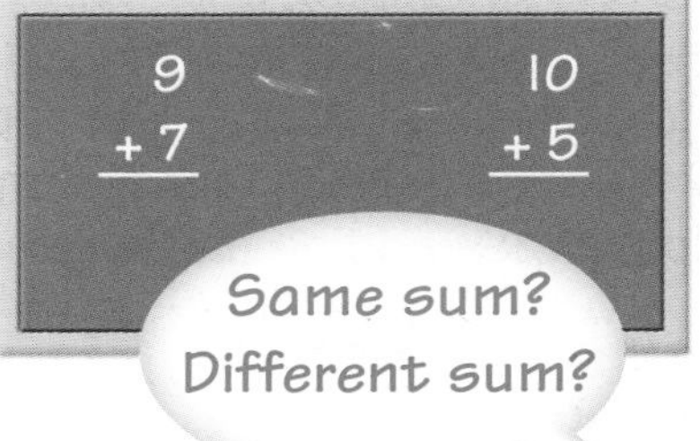

Reteaching

Making a Dime

10–15 MIN **Logical/Mathematical**

Materials *(per child)* Single Ten-Frame (Workmat 2); 1 dime; 19 pennies

- Write 9 + 2 on the board. Have children put 9 pennies on the ten-frame.
- Demonstrate adding 2 by first placing 1 penny to complete the ten-frame. Then exchange the ten-frame for 1 dime. Demonstrate how the additional penny is added to the dime to make 11.
- Continue by presenting other addition problems in which children will make a 10 and then add additional ones.

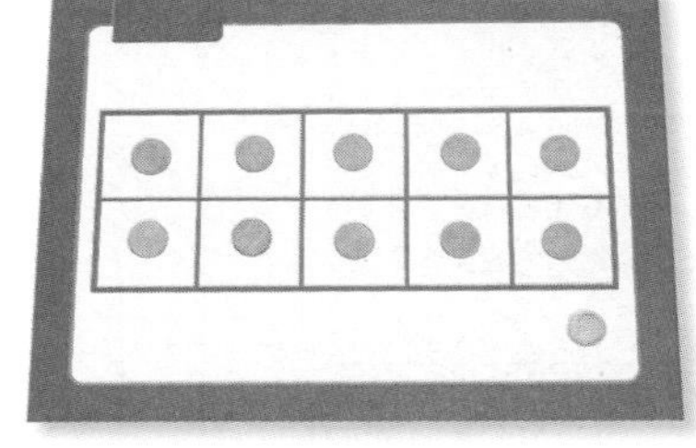

Math and Social Studies

How Many Family Members for Our Class?

15–20 MIN **Visual/Spatial**

- **Let's estimate the total number of family members for children in our class.** Record children's estimates using such language as *about, near, closer to,* and *between.*
- Poll the class and record actual numbers of family members by making tally marks. Group the tally marks by tens. Count the marks. **How many tens? How many left over?**
- Compare the estimate with the actual number of family members.

Family Members

Objective Find sums by making a 10 when adding to 8 or 9.

1 Warm Up

Activate Prior Knowledge Review how to use a ten-frame. Draw a ten-frame with 9 counters. Ask a volunteer to draw 1 counter to complete the ten-frame. **Now we have 10.** Repeat, beginning with 8 counters.

2 Teach

Learn!

Have children show the addition with their workmats and counters. Discuss the addition facts at the top of the student page. Explain the process of making a 10. **What happened to the 8?** *(2 were taken from the 5 and added to the 8 to make a 10.)* **What is the addition fact now?** *(10 + 3 = 13)* Explain that making a 10 is helpful when adding 9 as well.

Ongoing Assessment

Talk About It

- **How do you know how many counters you need to move to make a 10?** *(You should move as many counters as it takes to fill the ten-frame.)*
- **Why is it helpful to make a 10?** *(Because there is an easy pattern for adding to 10)*

If children have difficulty finding the sums,

then have them count on from 10.

Check

Error Intervention

If children have difficulty drawing counters,

then have them use counters and a ten-frame to act out the addition before writing the sums. *(Also see Reteaching, Page 423B.)*

Think About It Remind children that they can add in any order. Children should then realize that they can change the order and add 9 + 4, making a 10 first.

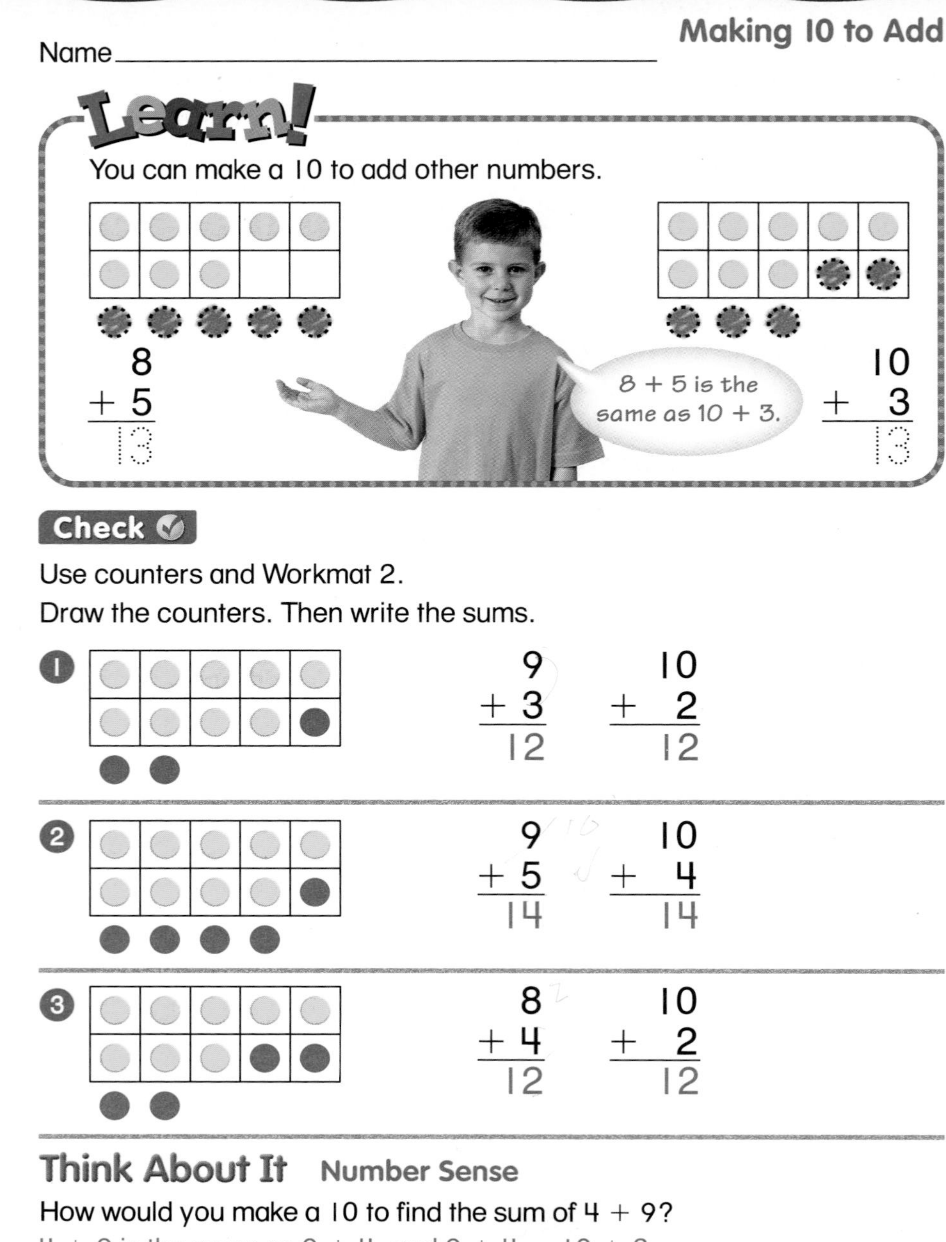

Name__________________ **Making 10 to Add**

Learn!

You can make a 10 to add other numbers.

$8 + 5 = 13$ $10 + 3 = 13$

Check

Use counters and Workmat 2.
Draw the counters. Then write the sums.

1. $9 + 3 = 12$ $10 + 2 = 12$
2. $9 + 5 = 14$ $10 + 4 = 14$
3. $8 + 4 = 12$ $10 + 2 = 12$

Think About It Number Sense

How would you make a 10 to find the sum of 4 + 9?
4 + 9 is the same as 9 + 4, and 9 + 4 = 10 + 3.

Chapter 11 ★ Lesson 4 four hundred twenty-three 423

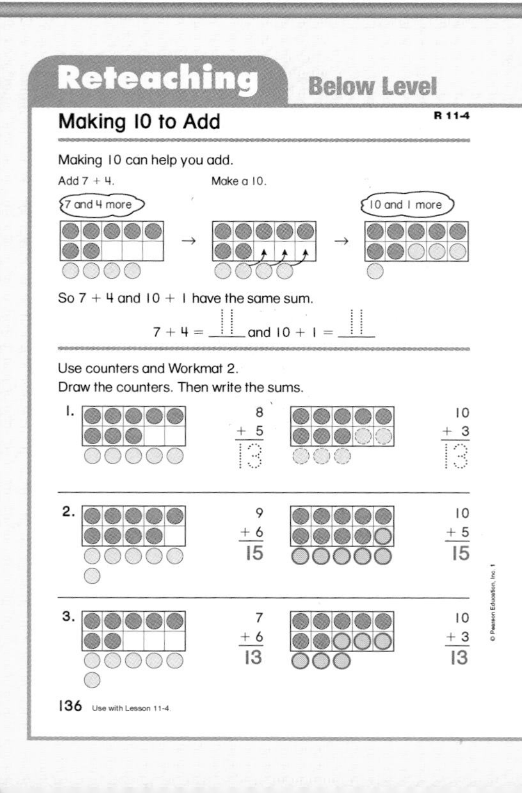

Reteaching Below Level

Making 10 to Add R 11-4

Making 10 can help you add.
Add 7 + 4. Make a 10.

7 and 4 more → 10 and 1 more

So 7 + 4 and 10 + 1 have the same sum.

7 + 4 = 11 and 10 + 1 = 11

Use counters and Workmat 2.
Draw the counters. Then write the sums.

1. $8 + 5 = 13$ $10 + 3 = 13$
2. $9 + 6 = 15$ $10 + 5 = 15$
3. $7 + 6 = 13$ $10 + 3 = 13$

136 Use with Lesson 11-4.

Practice On Level

Making 10 to Add P 11-4

Draw the counters. Then write the sums.
Use counters and Workmat 2 if you like.

1. $6 + 7 = 13$ $10 + 3 = 13$
2. $9 + 5 = 14$ $10 + 4 = 14$
3. $8 + 3 = 11$ $10 + 1 = 11$
4. $7 + 5 = 12$ $10 + 2 = 12$

Problem Solving *Algebra*

Complete each number sentence.

5. 7 + 6 = 10 + 3 = 13
6. 8 + 7 = 10 + 5 = 15
7. 9 + 9 = 10 + 8 = 18

136 Use with Lesson 11-4.

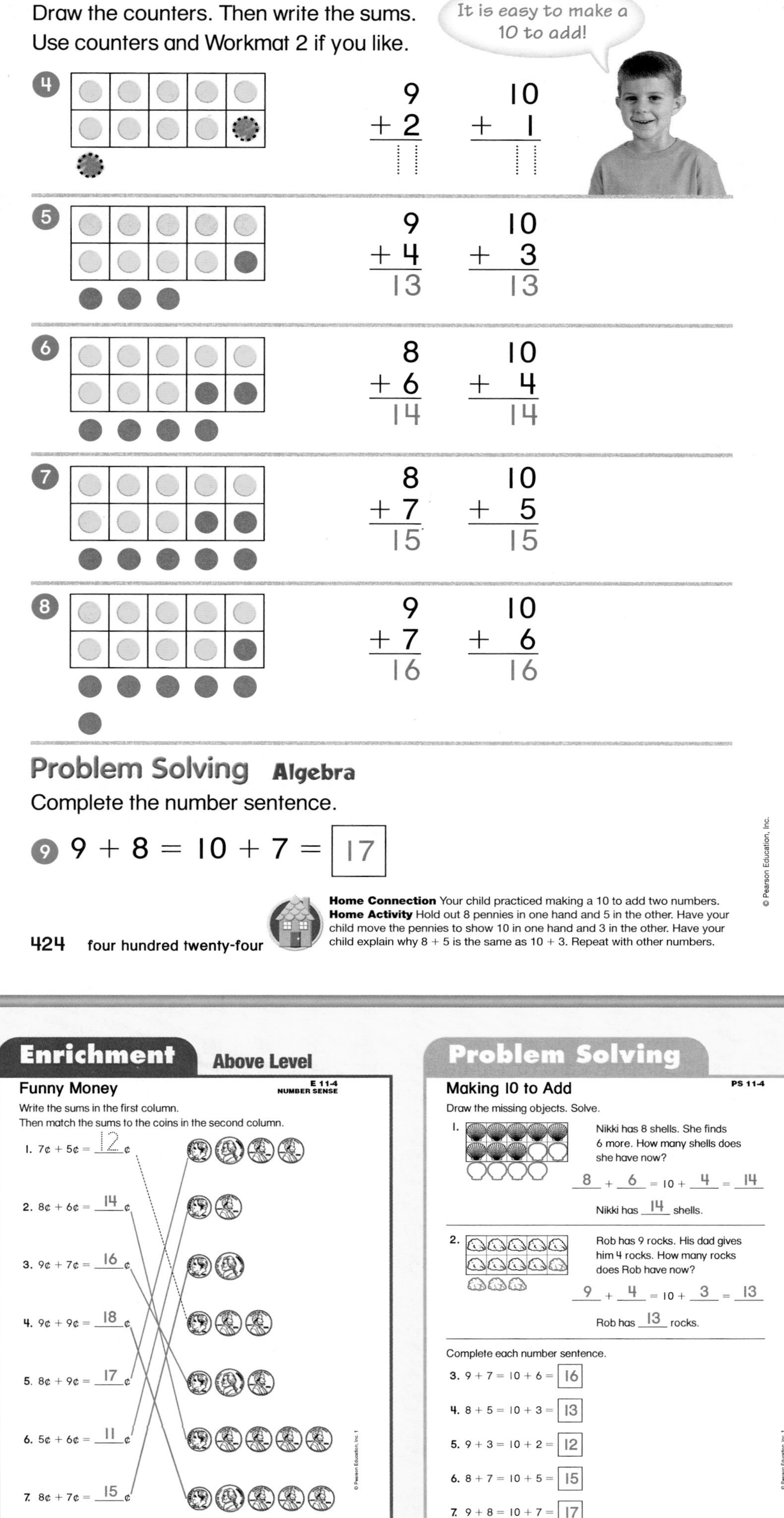

Practice

Draw the counters. Then write the sums.
Use counters and Workmat 2 if you like.

It is easy to make a 10 to add!

4. $9 + 2 = 11$; $10 + 1 = 11$

5. $9 + 4 = 13$; $10 + 3 = 13$

6. $8 + 6 = 14$; $10 + 4 = 14$

7. $8 + 7 = 15$; $10 + 5 = 15$

8. $9 + 7 = 16$; $10 + 6 = 16$

Problem Solving Algebra

Complete the number sentence.

9. $9 + 8 = 10 + 7 = 17$

Home Connection Your child practiced making a 10 to add two numbers. **Home Activity** Hold out 8 pennies in one hand and 5 in the other. Have your child move the pennies to show 10 in one hand and 3 in the other. Have your child explain why 8 + 5 is the same as 10 + 3. Repeat with other numbers.

Enrichment Above Level

Funny Money — E 11-4 NUMBER SENSE

Write the sums in the first column.
Then match the sums to the coins in the second column.

1. 7¢ + 5¢ = 12¢
2. 8¢ + 6¢ = 14¢
3. 9¢ + 7¢ = 16¢
4. 9¢ + 9¢ = 18¢
5. 8¢ + 9¢ = 17¢
6. 5¢ + 6¢ = 11¢
7. 8¢ + 7¢ = 15¢

136 Use with Lesson 11-4.

Problem Solving

Making 10 to Add — PS 11-4

Draw the missing objects. Solve.

1. Nikki has 8 shells. She finds 6 more. How many shells does she have now?
8 + 6 = 10 + 4 = 14
Nikki has 14 shells.

2. Rob has 9 rocks. His dad gives him 4 rocks. How many rocks does Rob have now?
9 + 4 = 10 + 3 = 13
Rob has 13 rocks.

Complete each number sentence.

3. 9 + 7 = 10 + 6 = 16
4. 8 + 5 = 10 + 3 = 13
5. 9 + 3 = 10 + 2 = 12
6. 8 + 7 = 10 + 5 = 15
7. 9 + 8 = 10 + 7 = 17

136 Use with Lesson 11-4.

3 Practice

Remind children to draw the counters on the ten-frame first when adding 8 or 9.

Reading Assist: Summarize Ask children to summarize the procedure they followed to complete Exercise 4.

Leveled Practice

Below Level Use counters and a ten-frame for Exercises 4–8.

On Level Use counters and a ten-frame if needed.

Above Level Do all exercises without counters or a ten-frame.

Early Finishers Have children work in pairs with fact cards showing problems that include 8 or 9 as an addend. Ask children to name the fact made by making a 10 and to tell the sum.

4 Assess

Journal Idea Have children choose a number between 11 and 18. Tell them to use that number as the sum for a fact with 9 as an addend. Then repeat with 8 as an addend.

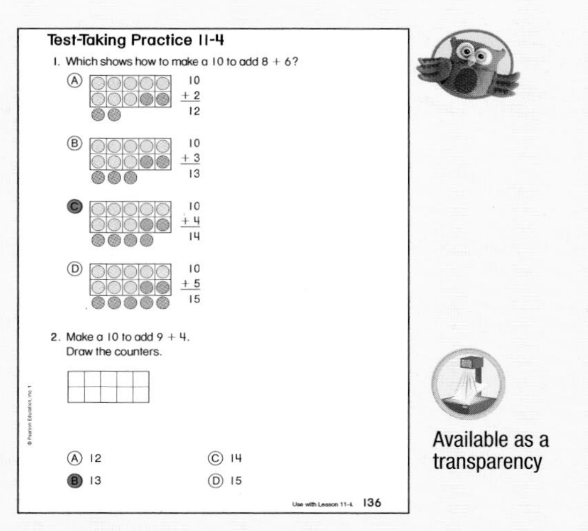

Test-Taking Practice 11-4

1. Which shows how to make a 10 to add 8 + 6?
Ⓐ 10 + 2 = 12
Ⓑ 10 + 3 = 13
Ⓒ 10 + 4 = 14
Ⓓ 10 + 5 = 15

2. Make a 10 to add 9 + 4. Draw the counters.
Ⓐ 12 Ⓑ 13 Ⓒ 14 Ⓓ 15

136 Use with Lesson 11-4

Available as a transparency

11-5 Applying Addition Fact Strategies

Lesson Organizer

Quick Lesson Overview

Objective Select and apply addition fact strategies.

Math Understanding There are a variety of strategies to use to find addition fact sums; which one is best depends on the addends.

Professional Development Note

Effective Questioning Techniques When solving a problem, children most often begin without thinking about the choices they have for finding a solution. To focus on the mathematical processes that might be used to solve a given problem, ask questions like these: **In what way will you solve this addition problem? Can you use a doubles fact? Will making a 10 help you?**

NCTM Standards

- Number and Operations

(For a complete correlation to the NCTM Standards and Grades Pre-K through 2 Expectations, see Pages 415G and 415H.)

Getting Started

Spiral Review

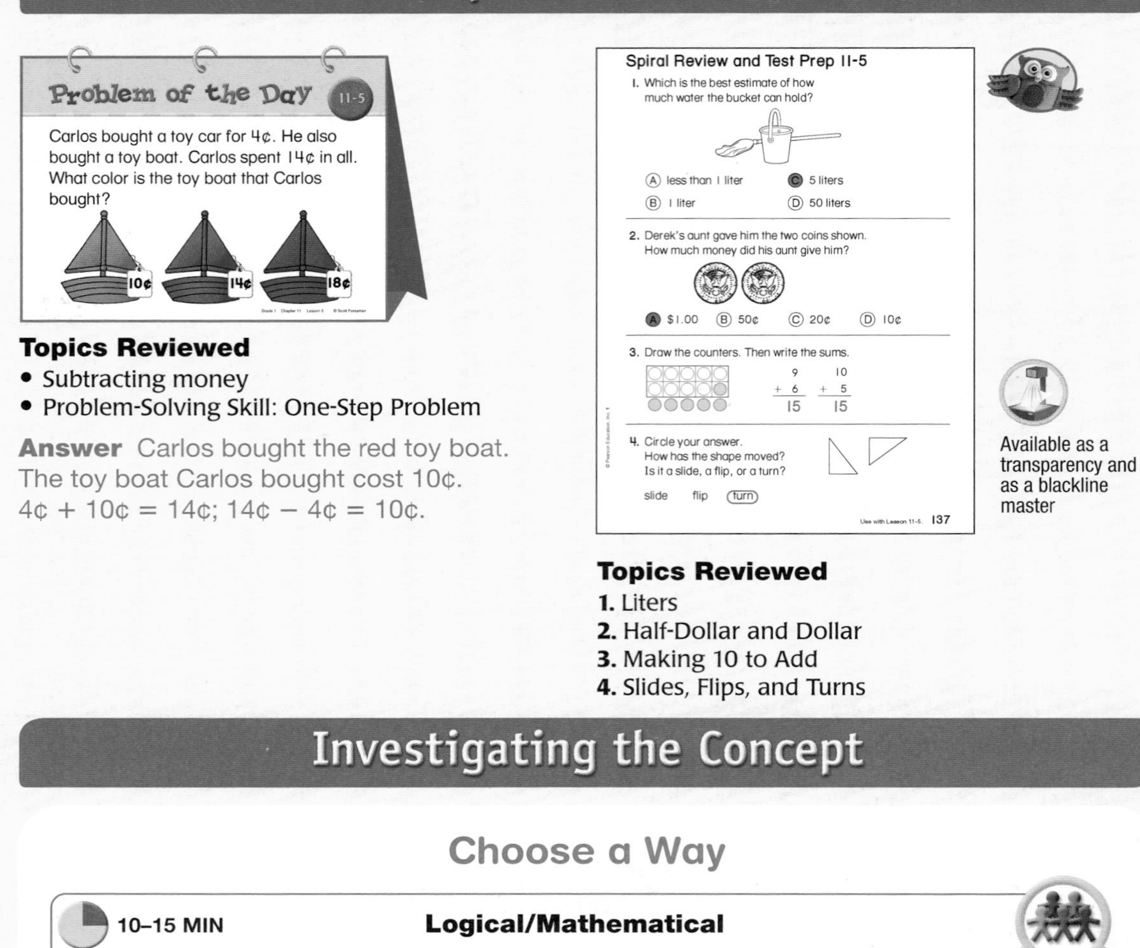

Problem of the Day 11-5

Carlos bought a toy car for 4¢. He also bought a toy boat. Carlos spent 14¢ in all. What color is the toy boat that Carlos bought?

Topics Reviewed
- Subtracting money
- Problem-Solving Skill: One-Step Problem

Answer Carlos bought the red toy boat. The toy boat Carlos bought cost 10¢. 4¢ + 10¢ = 14¢; 14¢ − 4¢ = 10¢.

Spiral Review and Test Prep 11-5

1. Which is the best estimate of how much water the bucket can hold?

Ⓐ less than 1 liter Ⓒ 5 liters
Ⓑ 1 liter Ⓓ 50 liters

2. Derek's aunt gave him the two coins shown. How much money did his aunt give him?

Ⓐ $1.00 Ⓑ 50¢ Ⓒ 20¢ Ⓓ 10¢

3. Draw the counters. Then write the sums.

9 + 6 = 15; 10 + 5 = 15

4. Circle your answer. How has the shape moved? Is it a slide, a flip, or a turn?

slide flip turn

Use with Lesson 11-5. 137

Available as a transparency and as a blackline master

Topics Reviewed
1. Liters
2. Half-Dollar and Dollar
3. Making 10 to Add
4. Slides, Flips, and Turns

Investigating the Concept

Choose a Way

10–15 MIN **Logical/Mathematical** WHOLE CLASS

Materials Addition fact cards

What to Do

- Display an addition fact card to initiate a "number talk" in which children explain the strategy they would use to find the sum. Focus on using a doubles fact or on making a 10.
- Ask a child to explain how to find the sum of 8 + 9 using a doubles fact. *(8 + 8 = 16, so the doubles-plus-1 fact is 8 + 9 = 17.)* Then ask another child to explain how to find the same sum by making a 10. *(Take 1 from 8 and add it to 9 to make 10; then add 10 + 7. 8 + 9 = 10 + 7 = 17.)*
- Repeat several times with different addition fact cards.

Ongoing Assessment

- **Reasoning** **How do you decide which strategy to use to find a sum?** *(By seeing how the numbers in the addition problem are related)*
- **Which strategy would you use to find the sum of 8 + 6?** *(Answers will vary.)*

Reaching All Learners

Math Vocabulary

Same and Different

10–15 MIN **Logical/Mathematical/Linguistic**

Materials Single Ten-Frame (Workmat 2); 19 two-color counters

- Write 9 + 8 on the board. Ask a volunteer to use the ten-frame and counters to solve the problem by making a 10.
- Write 6 + 8 on the board. Have another child solve this problem in the same way. Then challenge children to solve the problems in a different way. If necessary, show the class how to use doubles to arrive at the sum.
- Continue by having children solve other addition problems.

Activate Prior Knowledge/Build Background

English Language Learners

Review Math Vocabulary

10–15 MIN **Logical/Mathematical**

Materials Addition fact cards

- Write the following phrases on the board, review them, and have children pronounce them: "doubles, doubles plus 1, doubles minus 1, make a 10."
- Have each child choose a fact card. Then have the child tell the strategy he or she would use to solve the problem. Then let the child demonstrate how to use that strategy to solve the problem.
- Continue by having children choose cards and describe the strategies they would use to solve the problems.

doubles
doubles plus 1
doubles minus 1
make a 10

Reteaching

Different Ways to Solve a Problem

10–15 MIN **Logical/Mathematical**

Materials *(per child)* Single Ten-Frame (Workmat 2); 19 two-color counters; 19 connecting cubes

- Write 8 + 9 on the board.
- Place the ten-frames, counters, cubes, paper, and pencils on a table. Tell children that they can solve the problem in any way they wish. Allow each child to explain his or her strategy for solving the problem. Record children's strategies.
- If not mentioned, write "doubles plus 1" and "make a 10" on the board and invite a volunteer to explain each.

Ways We Can Solve 8 + 9

Count 8 and count 9 with counters

Make a 10 with the ten-frame and add 7 more

Use doubles plus 1

Math and Technology

Use a Calculator to Explore Patterns

15–20 MIN **Logical/Mathematical**

Materials *(per pair)* Chart paper; markers; calculator

- Review a doubles chart for the numbers 1 through 6, focusing on the pattern made by the sums. Have pairs of children use a calculator to continue the chart to a specified number, such as 20 + 20.
- Have children write the additional sums on chart paper. Discuss the continuing pattern of the sums.

Double	Sum
7 + 7	14
8 + 8	16
9 + 9	18
10 + 10	20
11 + 11	22

Objective Select and apply addition fact strategies.

1 Warm Up

Activate Prior Knowledge Review how to use doubles. On the board, write a list of doubles facts. Have children name the doubles-minus-1 fact and the doubles-plus-1 fact for each.

2 Teach

Learn!

Discuss the addition problem shown at the top of the student page and the two ways shown to solve it. Note that using a doubles fact and making a 10 are helpful ways to solve a problem. Help children conclude that there are different ways to find the sum in addition problems and that they can choose one that they think will be most helpful.

Ongoing Assessment

Talk About It

- **For the problem at the top of the page, is either way better for finding the sum?** *(No; both work equally well.)*
- **How would you find the sum for 8 + 7?** *(Answers will vary.)*

If children do not understand the different strategies,

then review each strategy by showing children an example of how to use each one.

Check

Error Intervention

If children have difficulty finding the sums,

then have them use cubes or a ten-frame to model the way they choose to find each sum. *(Also see* Reteaching, *Page 425B.)*

Think About It For each exercise, allow a few children to explain their strategies.

Name ____________________

Applying Addition Fact Strategies

Check

Add.

Then circle the strategy that you used. Strategies may vary.

1. 4 + 8 = 12 — make a 10 / use doubles
2. 8 + 8 = 16 — make a 10 / use doubles
3. 9 + 5 = 14 — make a 10 / use doubles
4. 9 + 8 = 17 — make a 10 / use doubles
5. 8 + 6 = 14 — make a 10 / use doubles
6. 7 + 5 = 12 — make a 10 / use doubles

Think About It Reasoning

Does it matter which strategy you use to add? Explain.

Sample response: No; the sum is the same with either strategy.

Reteaching Below Level

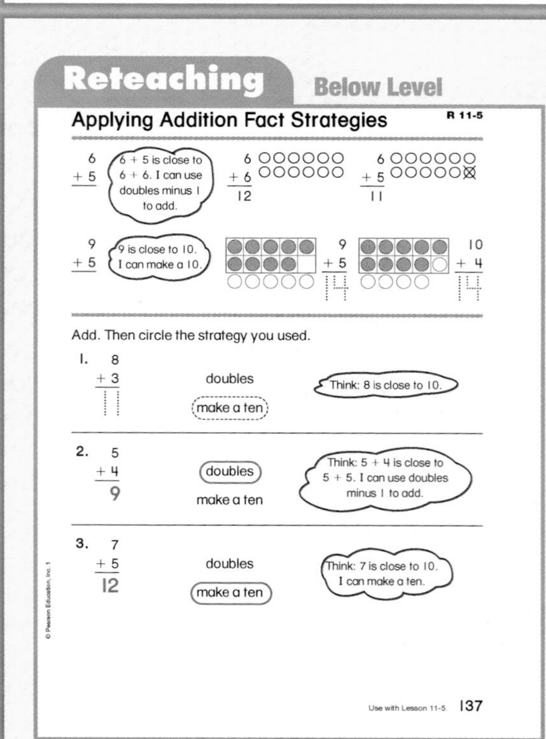

Applying Addition Fact Strategies R 11-5

6 + 5 — 6 + 5 is close to 6 + 6. I can use doubles minus 1 to add. — 6 + 6 = 12 — 6 + 5 = 11

9 + 5 — 9 is close to 10. I can make a 10. — 9 + 5 = 14 — 10 + 4 = 14

Add. Then circle the strategy you used.

1. 8 + 3 = 11 — doubles / make a ten — Think: 8 is close to 10.
2. 5 + 4 = 9 — doubles / make a ten — Think: 5 + 4 is close to 5 + 5. I can use doubles minus 1 to add.
3. 7 + 5 = 12 — doubles / make a ten — Think: 7 is close to 10. I can make a ten.

© Pearson Education, Inc. 1

Use with Lesson 11-5 137

Practice On Level

Applying Addition Fact Strategies P 11-5

Add.

1.	5 + 9 = 14	6 + 7 = 13	5 + 6 = 11	6 + 8 = 14	4 + 8 = 12	9 + 7 = 16
2.	9 + 2 = 11	5 + 7 = 12	7 + 7 = 14	8 + 7 = 15	9 + 3 = 12	5 + 8 = 13
3.	7 + 6 = 13	8 + 5 = 13	3 + 7 = 10	6 + 9 = 15	9 + 4 = 13	4 + 7 = 11
4.	9 + 5 = 14	8 + 9 = 17	6 + 6 = 12	8 + 3 = 11	4 + 9 = 13	7 + 5 = 12

Problem Solving *Writing in Math*

5. Write a story problem that can be solved by making ten to add. Then explain how to solve the problem.

Answers will vary.

Use with Lesson 11-5 137

Practice

Add.

7. $9 + 8 = 17$ | $8 + 7 = 15$ | $7 + 7 = 14$ | $9 + 4 = 13$ | $5 + 8 = 13$ | $6 + 7 = 13$

8. $6 + 9 = 15$ | $8 + 0 = 8$ | $7 + 6 = 13$ | $3 + 9 = 12$ | $8 + 5 = 13$ | $9 + 7 = 16$

9. $9 + 5 = 14$ | $6 + 8 = 14$ | $8 + 8 = 16$ | $5 + 9 = 14$ | $2 + 5 = 7$ | $9 + 6 = 15$

10. $8 + 6 = 14$ | $7 + 9 = 16$ | $4 + 9 = 13$ | $9 + 9 = 18$ | $5 + 7 = 12$ | $8 + 9 = 17$

Problem Solving Writing in Math

11. Write a story problem that can be solved using doubles. Then explain how to solve the problem.

Answers will vary.

Home Connection Your child chose a strategy and then used it to add two numbers. **Home Activity** Have your child explain how he or she solved the problems in Exercise 7.

Enrichment Above Level

What's the Point? E 11-5 DECISION MAKING

Each child earns points to use at the second-hand toy sale.

Find 2 toys each child can buy that equals the number of points earned. Use the same color to shade the child and the toys. Answers will vary.

Bobby 14 Points; Maria 17 Points; Karen 15 Points; Rudolpho 16 Points

Toys: 8 points; 8 points; 6 points; 9 points; 6 points; 8 points; 7 points; 9 points; 8 points; 9 points; 7 points

Problem Solving

Applying Addition Fact Strategies PS 11-5

Add. Circle the strategy you used. Strategies may vary.

1. Dana puts 8 stamps on each page of her stamp book. How many stamps are there on 2 pages?
   $8 + 8 = 16$ make a ten / use doubles
2. Eric has 7 trading cards. He gets 8 more cards. How many does he have now?
   $7 + 8 = 15$ make a ten / use doubles
3. Ellie has 8 dolls on one shelf and 4 on another shelf. How many dolls does Ellie have?
   $8 + 4 = 12$ make a ten / use doubles
4. Frank has 6 coins from France. He has 6 coins from Mexico. How many coins does he have in all?
   $6 + 6 = 12$ make a ten / use doubles

Writing in Math

5. Write a story problem that can be solved by using doubles or making a ten. Answers will vary.

3 Practice

For Exercise 11, remind children not only to write a problem, but also to explain their solutions.

Leveled Practice

Below Level Work with a partner using counters and a ten-frame or cubes.

On Level Use counters and a ten-frame or cubes if needed.

Above Level Do all exercises mentally.

Early Finishers Invite children to write a story problem using one of the facts from Exercise 7.

4 Assess

Journal Idea Write 9 + 5 on the board. Have children copy the problem and draw a ten-frame to show how to solve it by making a 10. Then write 6 + 7 on the board. Have children copy it and write a doubles fact they can use to solve the problem.

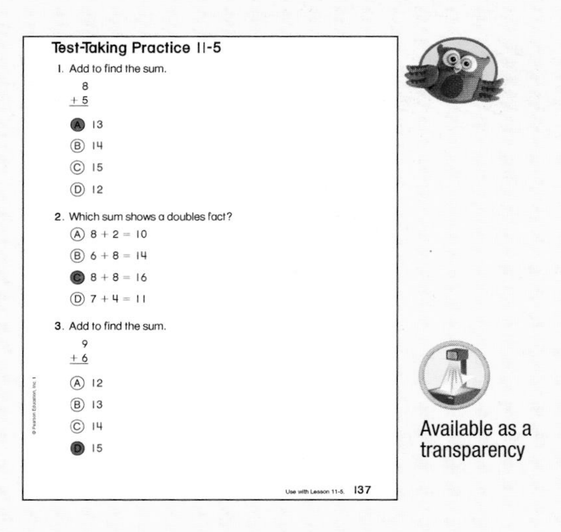

Test-Taking Practice 11-5

1. Add to find the sum. $8 + 5$
   (A) 13 (B) 14 (C) 15 (D) 12
2. Which sum shows a doubles fact?
   (A) 8 + 2 = 10 (B) 6 + 8 = 14 (C) 8 + 8 = 16 (D) 7 + 4 = 11
3. Add to find the sum. $9 + 6$
   (A) 12 (B) 13 (C) 14 (D) 15

Use with Lesson 11-5. 137

Available as a transparency

11-6 Adding Three Numbers

Lesson Organizer

Quick Lesson Overview

Objective Use the associative property to find sums of three numbers.

Math Understanding Addition fact strategies can be applied to finding sums of three numbers.

Professional Development Note

Math Background Addition is a binary process, meaning that only two numbers can be added at one time. The sum of three numbers can be found by applying addition fact strategies to two of the addends and then applying the strategies to add the sum of those two addends to the third addend. That numbers can be added in any order reflects the associative property of addition.

NCTM Standards

- Number and Operations
- Algebra

(For a complete correlation to the NCTM Standards and Grades Pre-K through 2 Expectations, see Pages 415G and 415H.)

Getting Started

Spiral Review

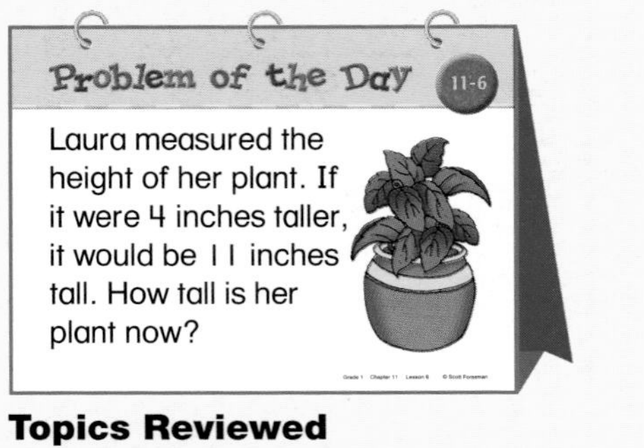
Problem of the Day 11-6

Laura measured the height of her plant. If it were 4 inches taller, it would be 11 inches tall. How tall is her plant now?

Topics Reviewed

- Measurement
- Subtraction
- Problem-Solving Skill: One-Step Problem

Answer The plant is 7 inches tall now; 11 − 4 = 7.

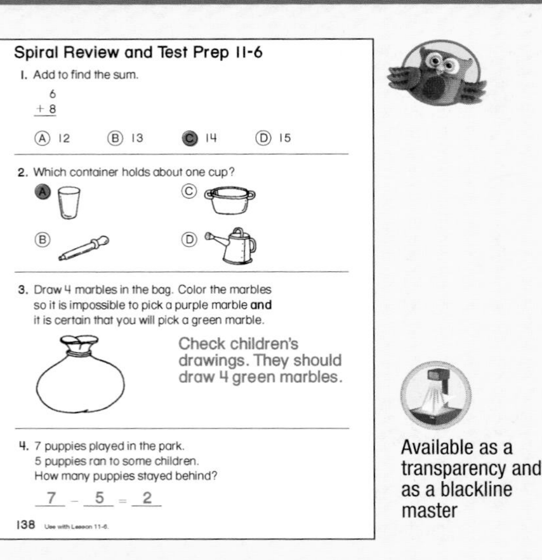
Spiral Review and Test Prep 11-6

1. Add to find the sum.

 6
 + 8

 Ⓐ 12 Ⓑ 13 ● 14 Ⓓ 15

2. Which container holds about one cup?

 ● Ⓑ Ⓒ Ⓓ

3. Draw 4 marbles in the bag. Color the marbles so it is impossible to pick a purple marble **and** it is certain that you will pick a green marble.

 Check children's drawings. They should draw 4 green marbles.

4. 7 puppies played in the park. 5 puppies ran to some children. How many puppies stayed behind?

 7 − 5 = 2

138 Use with Lesson 11-6.

Available as a transparency and as a blackline master

Topics Reviewed

1. Applying Addition Fact Strategies
2. Estimating, Measuring, and Comparing Capacity
3. Certain or Impossible
4. Write a Number Sentence

Investigating the Concept

Which Two First?

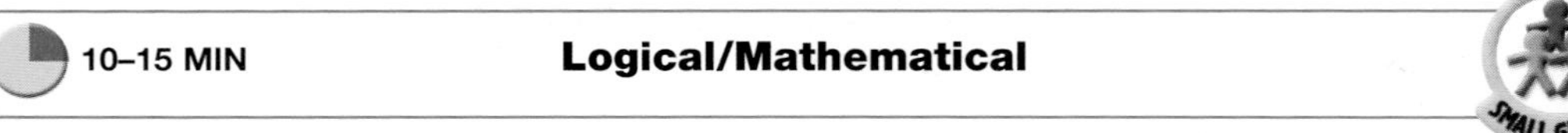

Materials *(per group)* Number Cards 0–11 (Teaching Tool 9)

What to Do

- Assign children to three groups. Choose three number cards between 0 and 9 whose sum is less than 18. For example, use 4, 5, and 6.
- Tell the first group to add 4 and 5 first and then to add 6. Have the second group add 5 and 6 first and then add 4. Have the third group add 4 and 6 first and then add 5.
- Invite the groups to explain their strategies and report their results.

Ongoing Assessment

- **Why is the sum the same for all of the groups?** *(Because all of the groups contain the same numbers, which can be added in any order to find the same sum)*
- **Reasoning** **Why might different groups use different strategies to find their sums?** *(The way you add depends on the numbers you are adding.)*

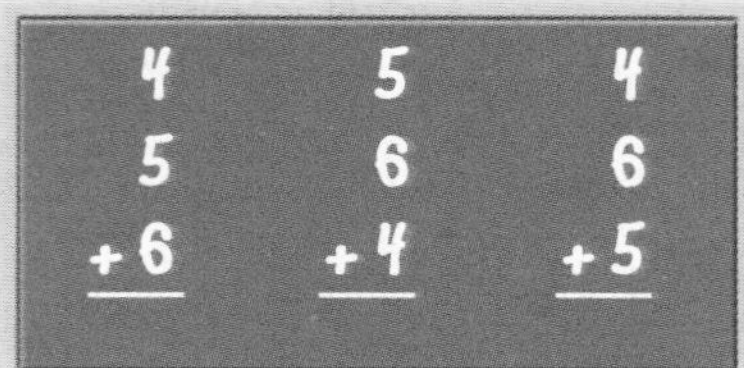

Reaching All Learners

Reading in Math

Story Problems with Three Numbers

15–20 MIN **Linguistic/Logical/Mathematical**

- Tell addition story problems, such as:
  When it began to get dark, Julia saw 2 stars twinkling in the sky. Then she saw 8 more stars. When it was very dark, Julia counted 3 more stars. How many stars did Julia see in all?
- Help children realize that addends can be added in any order, regardless of the order in which they are introduced.
- Invite children to write addition story problems with three addends and to illustrate their stories.

Access Content

English Language Learners

Understanding *First, Then, Last*

10–15 MIN **Auditory/Kinesthetic**

- Demonstrate these actions as you say the following: ***First,* I sit down. *Then,* I get out a pencil and paper. *Last,* I write.**
- Tell children to do the following: ***First,* stand up. *Then,* raise your arms. *Last,* clap your hands.** Repeat this activity several times, varying the actions. Then write sentences with the words *first, then,* and *last* that children dictate to you.

- Have the group perform the actions described in children's sentences.

Reteaching

Get in Order

15–20 MIN **Logical/Mathematical**

Materials *(per group)* Construction paper; marker; tape

- On separate sheets of paper, write 8, 7, and 2. Choose volunteers and attach a number to each child's back. Have volunteers stand in a row with their backs to the group.
- Have the volunteers change order several times. Add the sum each time.
- Have children tell what they noticed about the sums.

Students with Special Needs

Table Tennis Addition

15–20 MIN **Logical/Mathematical**

Materials *(per group)* 15 table-tennis balls; marker; paper bag

- Write the numbers 1 through 5 on three sets of table-tennis balls. Put the balls in a bag and have each child take three.
- Have children place the balls, number-side up, on the work surface. Invite children to move the balls into the order in which they will add the numbers.
- Have children switch the balls around and add again. **Does the order make a difference?** *(No)*

Objective Use the associative property to find sums of three numbers.

1 Warm Up

Activate Prior Knowledge Review adding in any order. Draw cubes on the board to show an addition fact. Have children take turns writing the number sentence and then writing the fact found by changing the order of the addends.

2 Teach

Learn!

Focus on the two ways shown on the student page for adding the three numbers. Help children notice that three numbers can be added in any order and the sum will remain the same.

Ongoing Assessment

Talk About It

- **Why might it be easier to add 6 + 4 first than to add 6 + 3 first?** *(It is easier to make a 10 first.)*
- **Why might it be better to add one pair of numbers first, rather than another pair?** *(Some pairs may be easier to add.)*

If children do not understand that the numbers can be added in any order,

then have them separate a group of cubes into three groups and move the groups around to see that the total does not change.

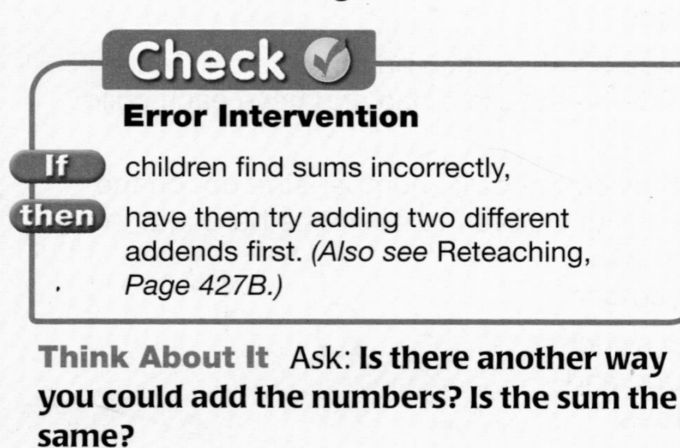

Check

Error Intervention

If children find sums incorrectly,

then have them try adding two different addends first. *(Also see* Reteaching, *Page 427B.)*

Think About It Ask: **Is there another way you could add the numbers? Is the sum the same?**

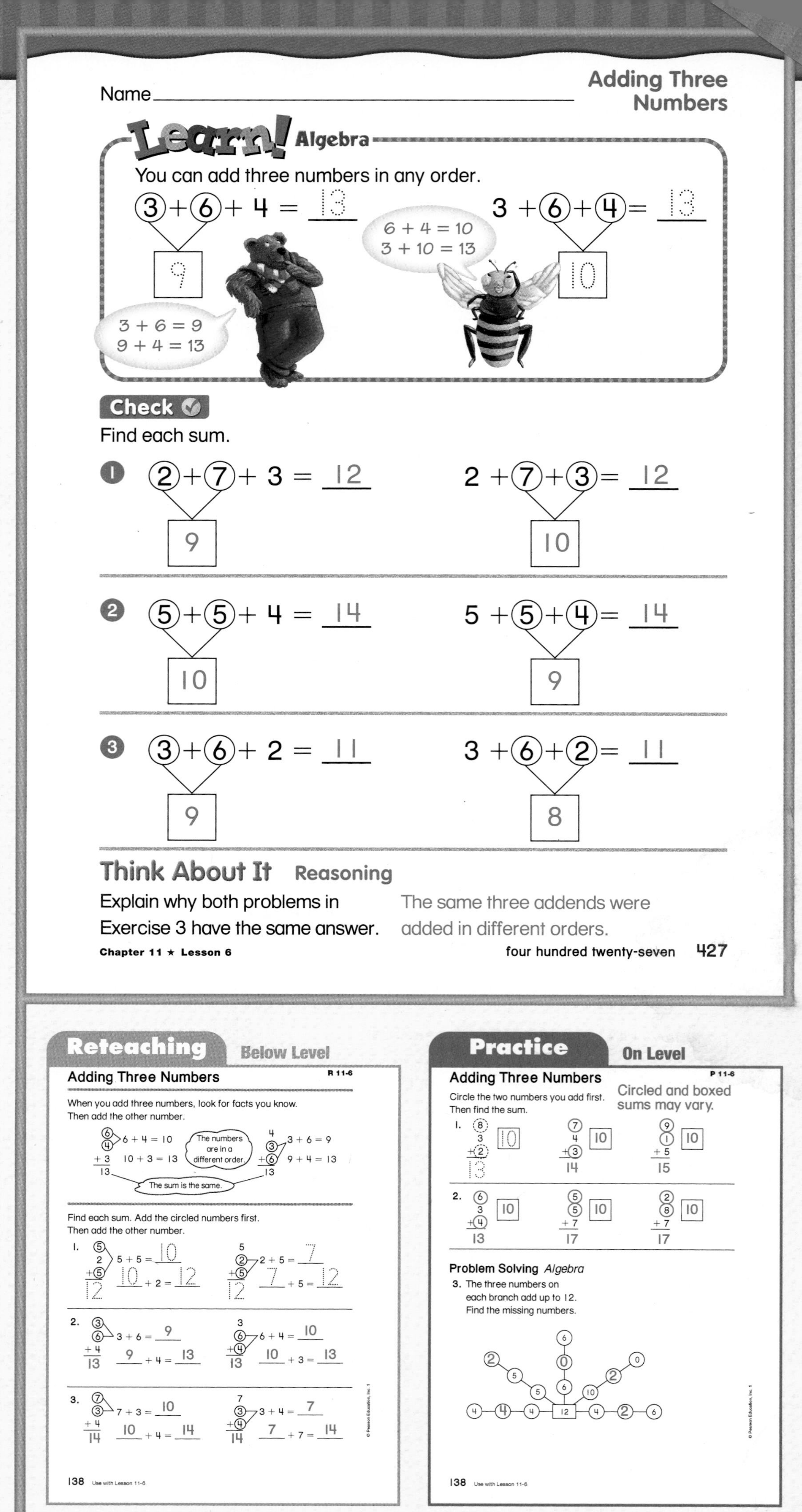

Name________________________

Adding Three Numbers

Learn! Algebra

You can add three numbers in any order.

(3)+(6)+ 4 = 13 (box: 9)

3 +(6)+(4)= 13 (box: 10)

Check

Find each sum.

1. (2)+(7)+ 3 = 12 (box: 9) 2 +(7)+(3)= 12 (box: 10)
2. (5)+(5)+ 4 = 14 (box: 10) 5 +(5)+(4)= 14 (box: 9)
3. (3)+(6)+ 2 = 11 (box: 9) 3 +(6)+(2)= 11 (box: 8)

Think About It Reasoning

Explain why both problems in Exercise 3 have the same answer. *The same three addends were added in different orders.*

Chapter 11 ★ Lesson 6 — four hundred twenty-seven 427

Reteaching Below Level

Adding Three Numbers — R 11-6

When you add three numbers, look for facts you know. Then add the other number.

6 + 4 + 3: 6 + 4 = 10, 10 + 3 = 13. 4 + 3 + 6: 3 + 6 = 9, 9 + 4 = 13. The numbers are in a different order. The sum is the same.

Find each sum. Add the circled numbers first. Then add the other number.

1. (5) 2 +(5): 5 + 5 = 10, 10 + 2 = 12; 12 — 5 (2) +(5): 2 + 5 = 7, 7 + 5 = 12; 12
2. (3)(6) + 4: 3 + 6 = 9, 9 + 4 = 13; 13 — 3 (6) +(4): 6 + 4 = 10, 10 + 3 = 13; 13
3. (7)(3) + 4: 7 + 3 = 10, 10 + 4 = 14; 14 — 7 (3) +(4): 3 + 4 = 7, 7 + 7 = 14; 14

138 Use with Lesson 11-6.

Practice On Level

Adding Three Numbers — P 11-6

Circle the two numbers you add first. Then find the sum. *Circled and boxed sums may vary.*

1. (8) 3 +(2) [10] 13; (7) 4 +(3) [10] 14; (9) (1) + 5 [10] 15
2. (6) 3 +(4) [10] 13; (5) (5) + 7 [10] 17; (2) (8) + 7 [10] 17

Problem Solving *Algebra*

3. The three numbers on each branch add up to 12. Find the missing numbers.

138 Use with Lesson 11-6.

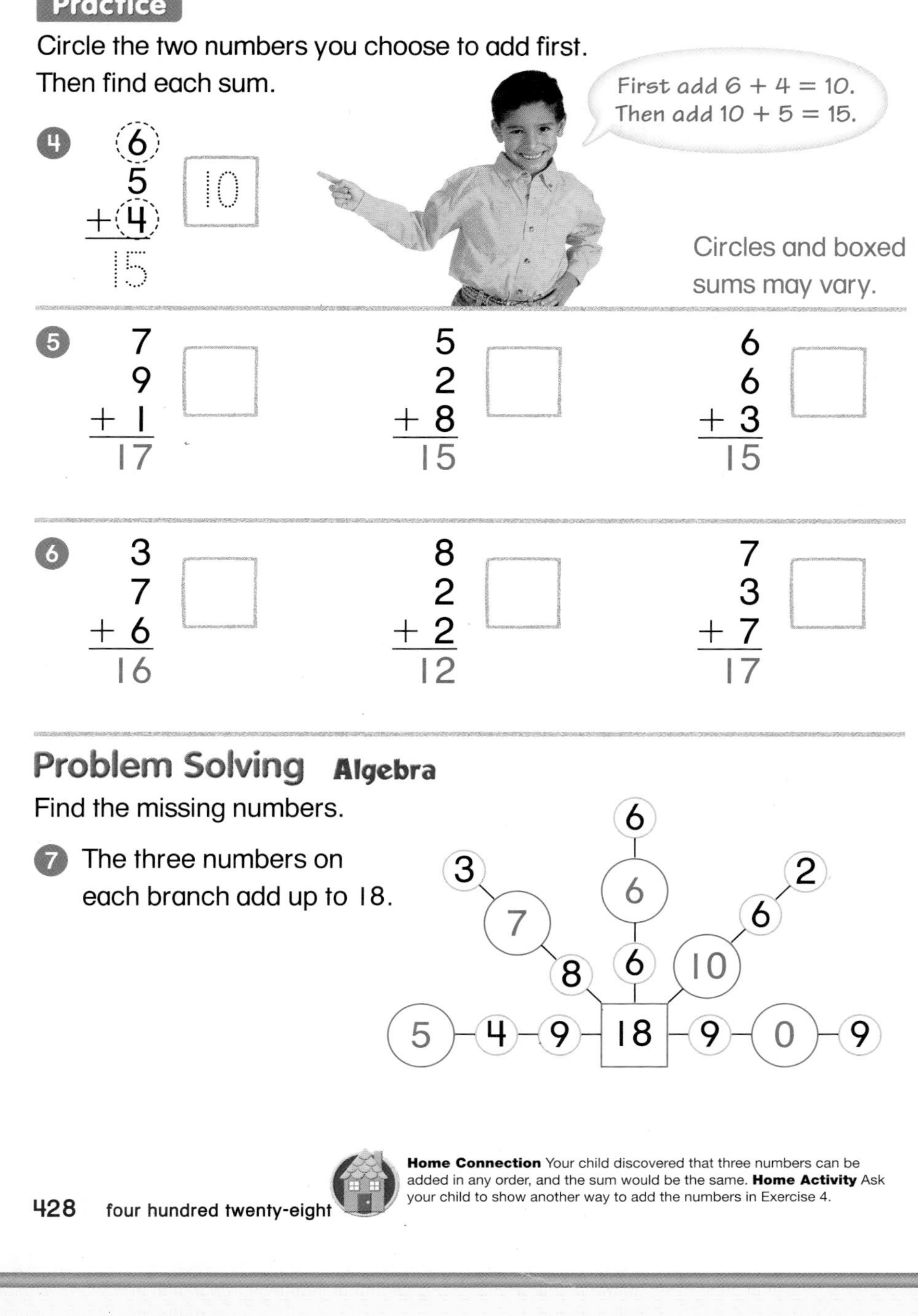

Practice

Circle the two numbers you choose to add first.
Then find each sum.

4 6 + 5 + 4 = 15 (6 and 4 circled; boxed sum 10)

Circles and boxed sums may vary.

5

7 + 9 + 1 = 17	5 + 2 + 8 = 15	6 + 6 + 3 = 15

6

3 + 7 + 6 = 16	8 + 2 + 2 = 12	7 + 3 + 7 = 17

Problem Solving **Algebra**

Find the missing numbers.

7 The three numbers on each branch add up to 18.

Home Connection Your child discovered that three numbers can be added in any order, and the sum would be the same. **Home Activity** Ask your child to show another way to add the numbers in Exercise 4.

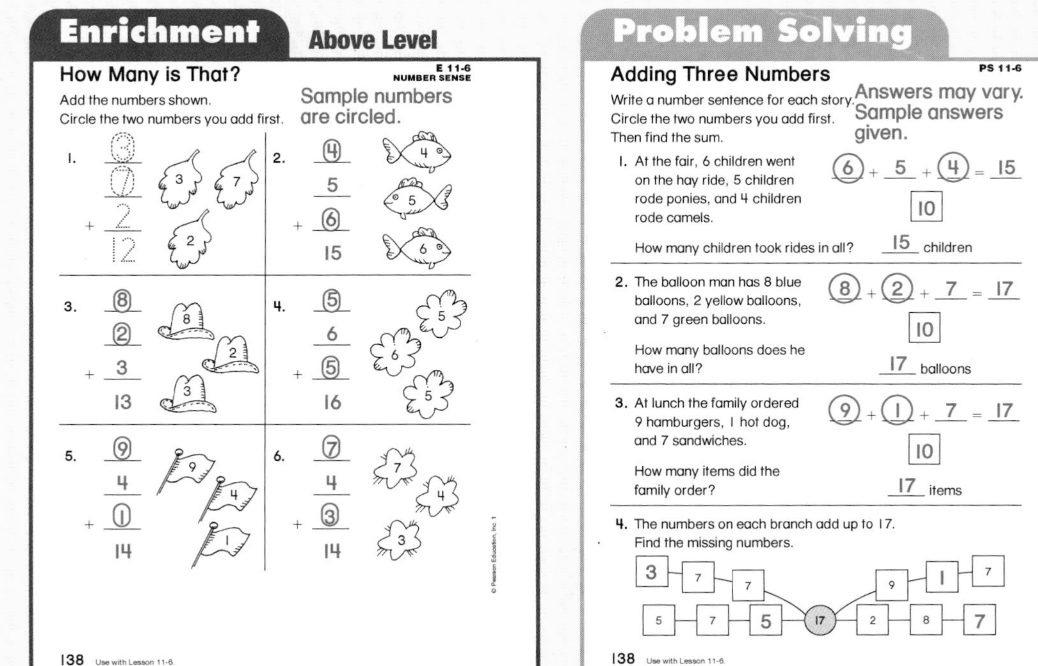

Enrichment Above Level

How Many is That? E 11-6 NUMBER SENSE

Add the numbers shown.
Circle the two numbers you add first.

Sample numbers are circled.

1. (3) + (7) + 2 = 12
2. (4) + 5 + (6) = 15
3. (8) + (2) + 3 = 13
4. (5) + 6 + (5) = 16
5. (9) + 4 + (1) = 14
6. (7) + 4 + (3) = 14

Problem Solving

Adding Three Numbers PS 11-6

Write a number sentence for each story.
Circle the two numbers you add first.
Then find the sum.

Answers may vary. Sample answers given.

1. At the fair, 6 children went on the hay ride, 5 children rode ponies, and 4 children rode camels. (6) + 5 + (4) = 15 [10]
   How many children took rides in all? 15 children
2. The balloon man has 8 blue balloons, 2 yellow balloons, and 7 green balloons. (8) + (2) + 7 = 17 [10]
   How many balloons does he have in all? 17 balloons
3. At lunch the family ordered 9 hamburgers, 1 hot dog, and 7 sandwiches. (9) + (1) + 7 = 17 [10]
   How many items did the family order? 17 items
4. The numbers on each branch add up to 17.
   Find the missing numbers.

3 Practice

Remind children that since they can add in any order, they can choose any two of the numbers to add first.

Leveled Practice

Below Level Use cubes or counters if needed.

On Level Complete all exercises as written.

Above Level Do all exercises without writing a sum in each box.

Early Finishers Encourage children to make up and solve a number puzzle similar to the one in Exercise 7.

4 Assess

Journal Idea Have children toss three number cubes and then write and solve vertical addition problems with the three numbers.

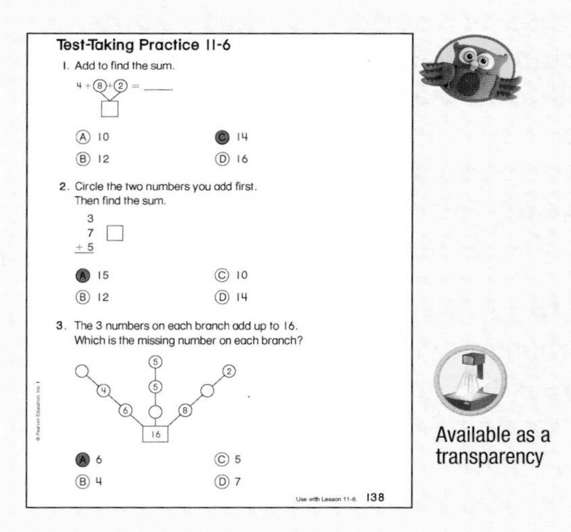

Test-Taking Practice 11-6

1. Add to find the sum.
   4 + (8) + (2) = ____
   Ⓐ 10 Ⓑ 12 ● 14 Ⓓ 16
2. Circle the two numbers you add first. Then find the sum.
   3 + 7 + 5
   ● 15 Ⓑ 12 Ⓒ 10 Ⓓ 14
3. The 3 numbers on each branch add up to 16. Which is the missing number on each branch?
   ● 6 Ⓑ 4 Ⓒ 5 Ⓓ 7

Available as a transparency

Reading for Math Success

Purpose Show children how to apply the reading skill, *Understand Graphic Sources: Tables,* to their math work. Help prepare children for the problem-solving strategy lesson, *Make a Table,* which follows.

Using Student Page 429

Reading Skills and Math Understanding Children learn that graphics such as lists, charts, and tables are sources of information. In math, children learn to complete graphics such as tables to find, record, and organize all of the possible solutions to a problem.

Model the Process Tell children that often there is more than one way to solve a problem. Explain that a table is a way of organizing all of the solutions. Model how to read a table, using the table on Student Page 429: **When I read a table, I look at the words and the pictures across the top. Those words and pictures tell me what the table is about. Then I look at the first row and read each number across and look up to the words and pictures. So, the first row means 2 Dolls and 0 Teddy Bears. Then I read all the other rows in the same way.**

Guide the Activity Have children read the story problem at the top of the page. **What problem is Mia going to solve?** Children should say that Mia is going to find all of the ways to put the two different kinds of toys into a toy box. **What does Mia use to show the different ways?** *(A table)* **What do the numbers in each row of the table mean?** Help children interpret the numbers in the table as the possible combinations of toys in a toy box. Have children complete Exercises 2 and 3.

Think About It Discuss children's responses to the question. Help children understand that there is no need for another row in the table because all of the possible solutions have already been included.

Name ____________________

Reading for Math Success

Understand Graphic Sources: Tables

1. Read this story problem.

Mia has dolls and teddy bears. Each toy box will hold 2 toys. Mia thought about all the ways to put the toys in the toy boxes.

She made a table to show the different ways.

Dolls	Teddy Bears
2	0
1	1
0	2

2. Which way does the first row of the table show?

2 dolls

3. Which way does the second row show? The third row?

1 doll and 1 teddy bear   2 teddy bears

Think About It Reasoning
Should there be another row in the table? Explain. No; all of the ways are already in the table.

Chapter 11   four hundred twenty-nine 429

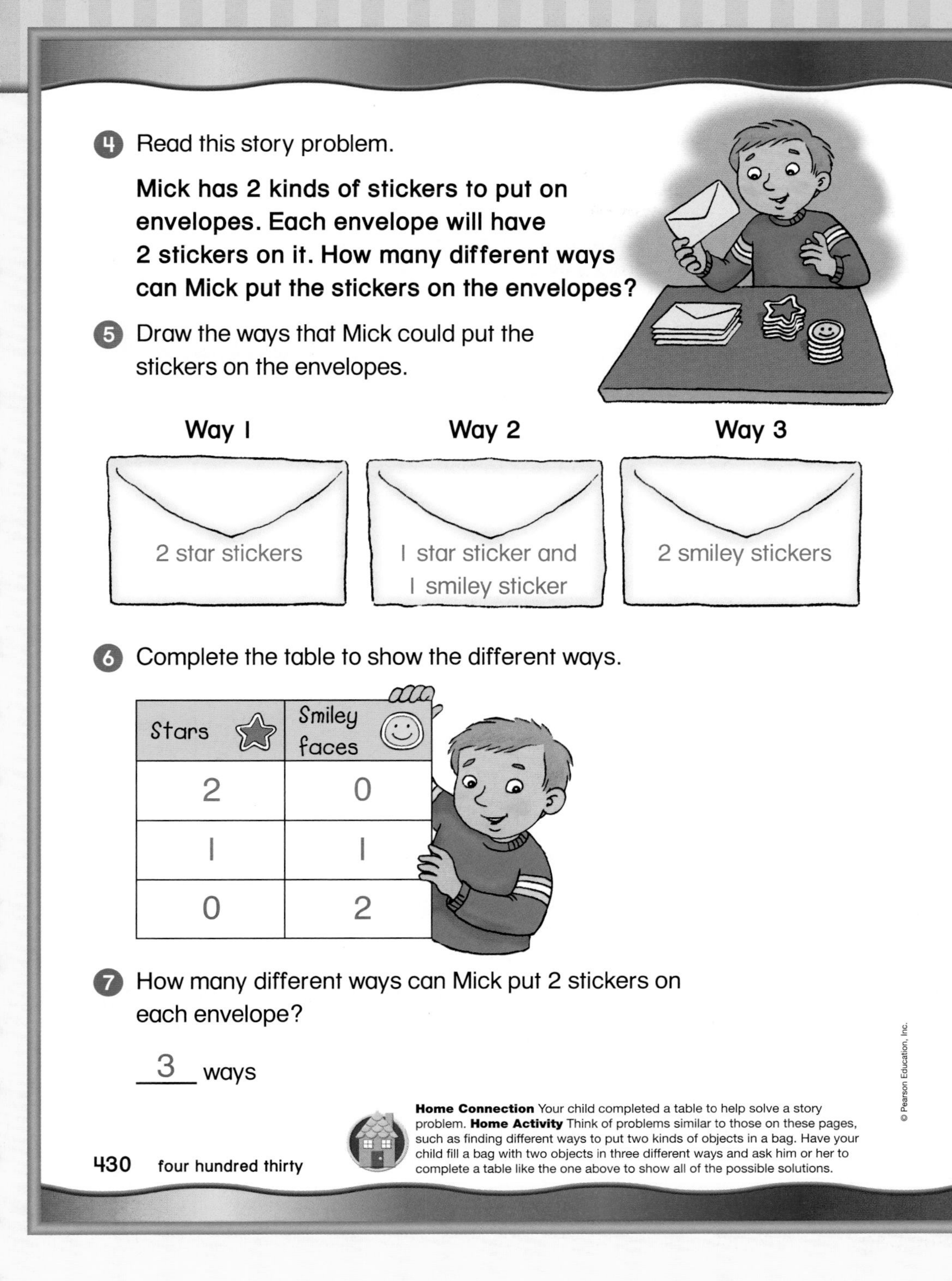

4. Read this story problem.

Mick has 2 kinds of stickers to put on envelopes. Each envelope will have 2 stickers on it. How many different ways can Mick put the stickers on the envelopes?

5. Draw the ways that Mick could put the stickers on the envelopes.

Way 1	Way 2	Way 3
2 star stickers	1 star sticker and 1 smiley sticker	2 smiley stickers

6. Complete the table to show the different ways.

Stars	Smiley faces
2	0
1	1
0	2

7. How many different ways can Mick put 2 stickers on each envelope?

3 ways

Home Connection Your child completed a table to help solve a story problem. **Home Activity** Think of problems similar to those on these pages, such as finding different ways to put two kinds of objects in a bag. Have your child fill a bag with two objects in three different ways and ask him or her to complete a table like the one above to show all of the possible solutions.

Using Student Page 430

Explain that the story problem in Exercise 4 is similar to the one at the top of page 429. Have children independently read it and complete the drawings and the table to show all of the possible solutions.

When children have finished, have them compare their drawings and tables.

Error Intervention

If children are having difficulty making connections between the story problem and the numbers in a table,

then act out the story problem. Use a clear plastic cup and two different-colored blocks to represent the envelope and the stickers in the story problem on page 430. Repeat the problem to be solved. **How many ways can we put these two different stickers in the envelope?** Draw a table on the board labeled *Stars* and *Smiley Faces.* As children suggest each way to put the blocks in the cup, have them write those numbers in the table. Repeat until children see that they have found all of the possible solutions.

Journal Idea Children can write tables in their journals to keep track of information such as scores on spelling or math tests. Explain that tables also can be used to record and organize information. Tell children that using tables to list solutions is only one way that a table can be used.

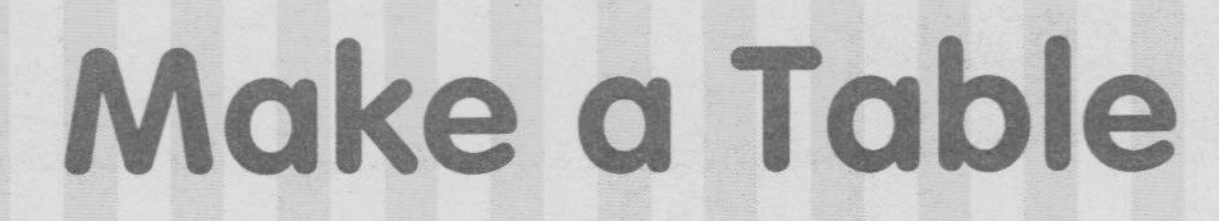

PROBLEM-SOLVING STRATEGY 11-7

Lesson Organizer

Quick Lesson Overview

Objective Solve problems by making tables.

Math Understanding Tables are tools used for organizing information.

Professional Development Note

How Children Learn Math Being able to create an organized table is an important skill used for solving many types of problems. Discerning patterns in tables is a good way to determine whether all possibilities have been listed.

NCTM Standards

- Number and Operations
- Data Analysis and Probability

(For a complete correlation to the NCTM Standards and Grades Pre-K through 2 Expectations, see Pages 415G and 415H.)

Getting Started

Spiral Review

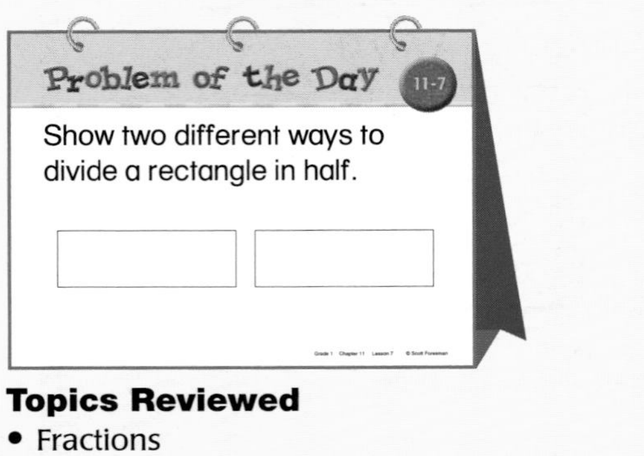

Topics Reviewed

- Fractions
- Plane shapes
- Problem-Solving Strategy: Draw a Picture

Answer Sample:

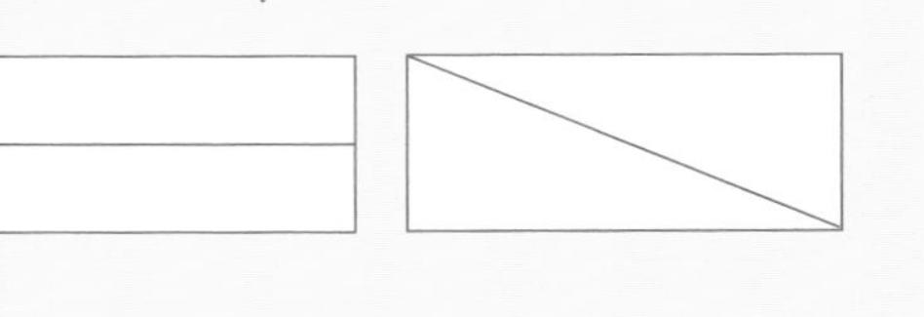

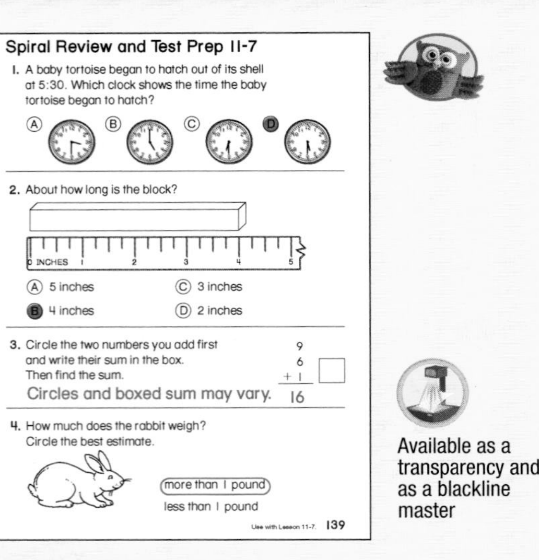

Spiral Review and Test Prep 11-7

1. A baby tortoise began to hatch out of its shell at 5:30. Which clock shows the time the baby tortoise began to hatch?
Ⓐ Ⓑ Ⓒ Ⓓ

2. About how long is the block?
Ⓐ 5 inches Ⓒ 3 inches
Ⓑ 4 inches Ⓓ 2 inches

3. Circle the two numbers you add first and write their sum in the box. Then find the sum.
9 + 6 + 1 = 16
Circles and boxed sum may vary.

4. How much does the rabbit weigh? Circle the best estimate.
more than 1 pound
less than 1 pound

139

Available as a transparency and as a blackline master

Topics Reviewed

1. Telling and Writing Time to the Half Hour
2. Estimating and Measuring with Inches
3. Adding Three Numbers
4. Pounds

Investigating the Concept

Making a Table

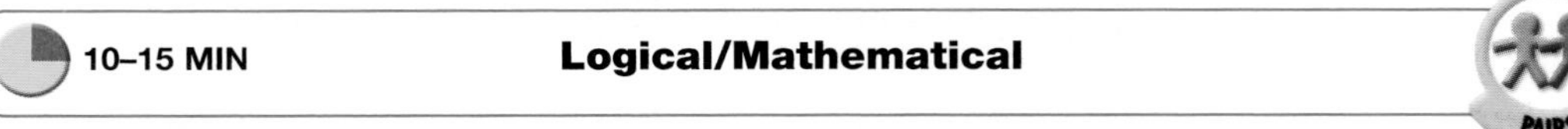

PAIRS

Materials Chart paper; *(per pair)* 3 pens; 3 pencils; 3 crayons; plastic bag

What to Do

- Have children display their groups of pens, pencils, and crayons. Tell children that you are going to fill a plastic bag with 3 items. Explain that there are many ways to do that. Ask children to work in pairs to use their items and plastic bags to help you figure out how many different ways there are.
- Keep track of the different ways in a three-column table labeled with the following heads: "Pens," "Pencils," "Crayons." Continue the table until all of the ways are found.

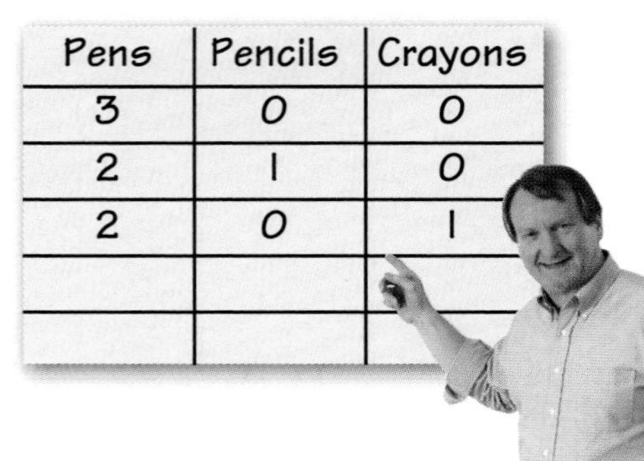

Pens	Pencils	Crayons
3	0	0
2	1	0
2	0	1

Ongoing Assessment

- **Number Sense In how many different ways can you fill the bag?** *(10 ways)*
- **How do you know you found all of the ways?** *(Sample response: Every possible way has been listed.)*

Reaching All Learners

Oral Language in Math

Toys on a Shelf

10–15 MIN **Visual/Spatial/Kinesthetic**

Materials 3 balls; 3 stuffed animals; 3 toy cars; *(per child)* three-column table

- Explain that children have to put toys on shelves but that only 3 toys will fit on each shelf.
- Ask the class to think of different ways that the toys can be placed on the shelves.
- As suggestions are made, have the three children show the different combinations on the desk. The rest of the class can record the numbers of each kind of toy in their tables.

Access Content

English Language Learners

Making a Table

10–15 MIN **Visual/Spatial**

Materials *(per pair)* Two-column table; 3 smiley-face stickers; 3 star stickers; 3 small pieces of paper

- Explain that you want to put 2 stickers on each piece of paper and that you want each piece of paper to be different. Have pairs help you by showing ways in which to put 2 stickers on each piece of paper.
- Display a two-column table, with a smiley face heading one column and a star heading the other. Review how to summarize information in the table. When children have shown three ways to apply the stickers, have them fill in the table.

Reteaching

Juice on a Table

5–10 MIN **Visual/Spatial**

PAIRS

Materials *(per pair)* Two-column table; 10 two-color counters

- Suggest that children pretend they are at a party. Tell them that every child can have 2 glasses of juice. Red counters stand for fruit punch, and yellow counters represent lemonade.
- Have pairs prepare a table such as the one below. Children place counters on the table to show the different ways in which they can pour punch and lemonade for their friends.

Math and Social Studies

Modes of Transportation

10–15 MIN **Logical/Mathematical**

WHOLE CLASS

Materials Large three-column table

- **Let's plan a 3-day trip across the country.**
- Ask children to suggest three modes of transportation for the class trip. Children might suggest an airplane, a bus, or a train. Write each vehicle name at the top of a column.
- Have children think of ways they can combine these vehicles during the 3-day trip. For example, a child might say: **We could take an airplane all 3 days.** Fill in a 3 below "Airplane" and zeros below "Bus" and "Train."
- Challenge children to think of all of the different ways they can travel.

Objective Solve problems by making tables.

1 Warm Up

Activate Prior Knowledge Review how to find information in a table. Write the following information in a table on the board: "Apples 25¢, Pears 30¢, Oranges 35¢." Ask children questions about the information.

2 Teach

Learn!

Read through the problem-solving steps together: Read and Understand, Plan and Solve, Look Back and Check. As you go through the steps, refer to the table. Discuss the different ways to fill the basket shown in the table and determine whether all of the possibilities have been listed.

Ongoing Assessment

Talk About It

- **In how many different ways can Sandra fill the basket with 3 fruits?** *(10 ways)*
- **How do you know that you found all of the ways?** *(Sample response: Every possible way has been listed.)*

If children enter wrong numbers in the table,

then help them see that the numbers in each row must add up to 3.

Check

Error Intervention

If children have difficulty interpreting the table,

then reread the problem and act it out with counters. *(Also see* Reteaching, *Page 431B.)*

Think About It Ask: **What might have happened if you had not used the table?** *(Sample response: It would have been hard to tell if all of the ways were counted.)*

Name ____________________

PROBLEM-SOLVING STRATEGY

Make a Table

Learn!

1. Sandra is making fruit baskets. She has pears, apples, and plums. Each basket holds 3 pieces of fruit. How many different baskets can Sandra make?

Pears	Apples	Plums
3	0	0
0	3	0
0	0	3
2	1	0
2	0	1
1	2	0
0	2	1
1	0	2
0	1	2
1	1	1

Read and Understand

You need to find how many different ways Sandra can fill a basket with 3 pieces of fruit.

Plan and Solve

You can make a table. Then you can count the ways.

There are __10__ different ways.

Look Back and Check

Did you find all of the ways? How do you know?

Think About It Reasoning

How did the table help you answer the question?

Sample response: I counted the number of rows in the table.

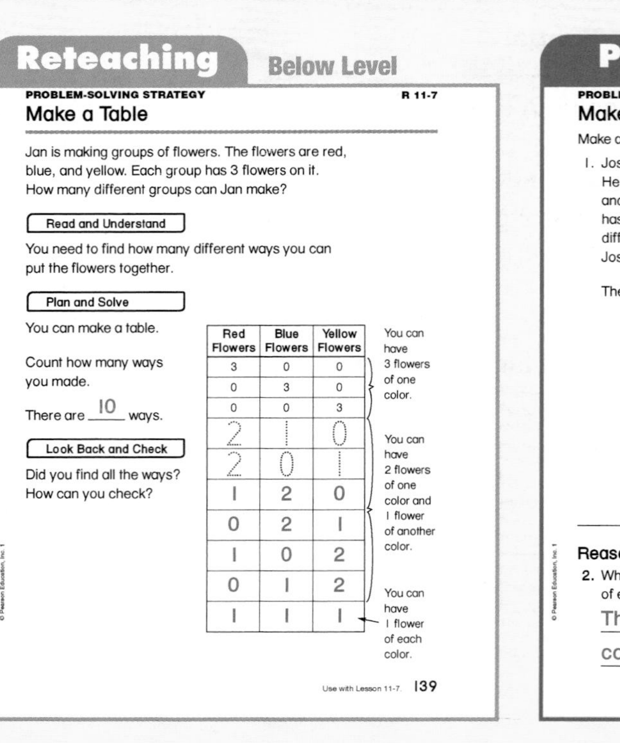

Reteaching Below Level

PROBLEM-SOLVING STRATEGY R 11-7

Make a Table

Jan is making groups of flowers. The flowers are red, blue, and yellow. Each group has 3 flowers on it. How many different groups can Jan make?

Read and Understand

You need to find how many different ways you can put the flowers together.

Plan and Solve

You can make a table.

Count how many ways you made.

There are __10__ ways.

Look Back and Check

Did you find all the ways? How can you check?

Red Flowers	Blue Flowers	Yellow Flowers
3	0	0
0	3	0
0	0	3
2	1	0
2	0	1
1	2	0
0	2	1
1	0	2
0	1	2
1	1	1

You can have 3 flowers of one color.

You can have 2 flowers of one color and 1 flower of another color.

You can have 1 flower of each color.

Practice On Level

PROBLEM-SOLVING STRATEGY P 11-7

Make a Table

Make a table to solve the problem.

Order of answers may vary.

1. José is making snack packs. He has bags of raisins, nuts, and pretzels. Each snack pack has 3 bags. How many different snack packs can José make?

There are __10__ different ways.

Raisins	Nuts	Pretzels
3	0	0
0	3	0
0	0	3
2	1	0
2	0	1
1	2	0
1	0	2
0	1	2
0	2	1
1	1	1

Reasoning

2. What do you notice about the sum of each column of the table?

The sum of the numbers in each column is 10.

Practice

Make a table to solve the problem.

2. Dad is making gift bags. He has yo-yos, kazoos, and rings. Each bag holds 3 toys. How many different bags can Dad make?

Dad can make 10 different bags.

Order of answers may vary.

Yo-Yos	Kazoos	Rings
3	0	0
0	3	0
0	0	3
2	1	0
2	0	1
1	2	0
0	2	1
1	0	2
0	1	2
1	1	1

Reasoning

3. What do you notice about each row of the table?

The sum of the numbers in each row is 3.

Home Connection Your child made tables to help solve problems. **Home Activity** Ask your child to explain how he or she filled in the table at the top of the page and to tell how the table helped solve the problem.

Enrichment Above Level

E 11-7 DECISION MAKING

Line Up the Animals

You play "Marching Animals" with 3 game pieces. You have a bird, a cat, and a dog. How many different ways can you line up these game pieces? Make a list. Draw a line after each line up.

First	Second	Third
Dog	Cat	Bird
Dog	Bird	Cat
Cat	Dog	Bird
Cat	Bird	Dog
Bird	Cat	Dog
Bird	Dog	Cat

There are 6 different ways to line up the game pieces.

Use with Lesson 11-7. 139

Problem Solving

PROBLEM-SOLVING STRATEGY PS 11-7

Make a Table

Dan has a red sock, a yellow sock, a blue sock, and a white sock. He likes to wear different colors together. How many different ways can Dan wear the 4 socks?

You can make a table.
Write: R for red
B for blue
W for white
Y for yellow

Find all the different ways. Complete the table.

Dan can wear the socks 6 different ways.

Check to make sure you found all the ways.

#1	#2
R	B
R	W
R	Y
B	W
B	Y
W	Y

1. How many different ways can Dan wear socks with just a green sock, a purple sock, and a yellow sock?

3 different ways

#1	#2
G	P
G	Y
P	Y

Using the page Help children *plan and solve* by identifying the different ways the colors can be put together and writing them on the chart.

Use with Lesson 11-7. 139

3 Practice

You may wish to discuss Exercise 2 as a class before children record their answers.

Reading Assist: Draw Conclusions Call attention to the completed table. Ask children what conclusion they can draw about the number of ways that 3 kinds of items can be grouped into sets of 3. Children should realize that there are always 10 ways.

Leveled Practice

Below Level Listen as the teacher reads Exercise 2. Use counters for all problems.

On Level Read and complete all problems, using counters if needed.

Above Level Read and complete problems without counters.

Early Finishers Have children draw pictures to illustrate each of the ways listed in Exercise 2.

4 Assess

Journal Idea Have children explain why tables are helpful in solving some problems.

Test-Taking Practice 11-7

1. Make a table to solve the problem.

Bill is putting stones in a box. He has purple stones and blue stones. The box holds 3 stones. How many different ways can he put the stones in the box?

Purple Stones	Blue Stones
3	0
2	1
1	2
0	3

There are 4 different ways.

2. Nina is making gift bags. She has whistles and balloons. Each bag holds 4 gifts. How many different ways can Nina make the gift bags?

Ⓐ There are 4 different ways.
Ⓑ There are 5 different ways.
Ⓒ There are 6 different ways.
Ⓓ There are 10 different ways.

Use with Lesson 11-7. 139

Available as a transparency

Diagnostic Checkpoint

Purpose Provide assessment of children's progress to date by checking their understanding of key content covered in the previous section.

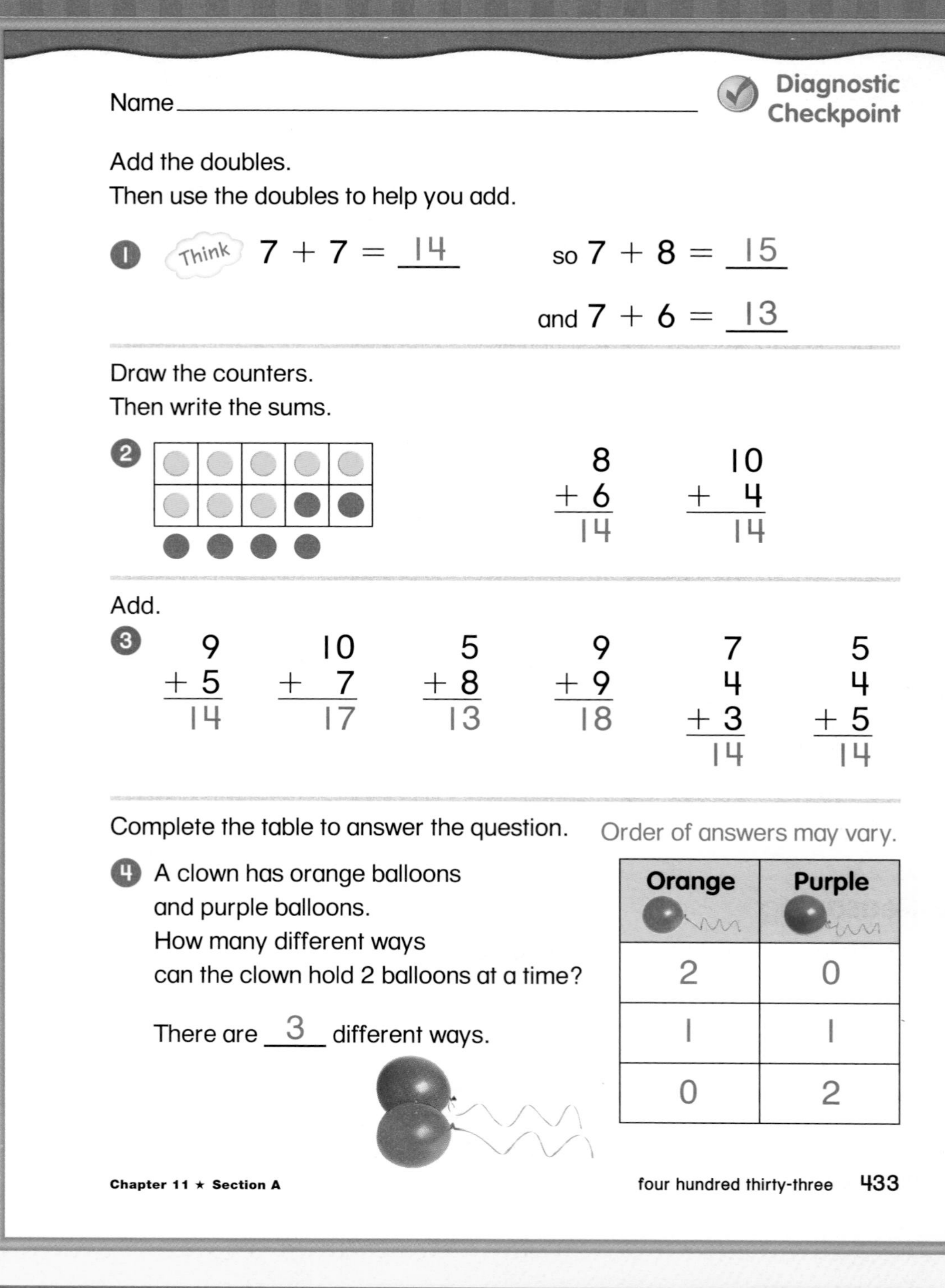

Name________________________ Diagnostic Checkpoint

Add the doubles.
Then use the doubles to help you add.

1. Think $7 + 7 =$ 14 so $7 + 8 =$ 15
and $7 + 6 =$ 13

Draw the counters.
Then write the sums.

2. $8 + 6 = 14$ $10 + 4 = 14$

Add.

3. $9 + 5 = 14$ $10 + 7 = 17$ $5 + 8 = 13$ $9 + 9 = 18$ $7 + 4 + 3 = 14$ $5 + 4 + 5 = 14$

Complete the table to answer the question. Order of answers may vary.

4. A clown has orange balloons and purple balloons.
How many different ways can the clown hold 2 balloons at a time?

There are 3 different ways.

Orange	Purple
2	0
1	1
0	2

Chapter 11 ★ Section A four hundred thirty-three 433

Item Analysis for Diagnosis and Intervention

Objective	Items	Student Book Pages*	Intervention System
Recognize doubles as a strategy for remembering sums to 18.	1	417–418	B30
Use doubles facts to learn doubles-plus-1 facts and doubles-minus-1 facts.	1	419–420	B31
Find sums by making a 10 when adding to 8 or 9.	2–3	423–424	B33
Use a pattern to add numbers 1 to 8 to the number 10.	3	421–422	B32
Use the associative property to find sums of three numbers.	3	427–428	B35
Solve problems by making tables.	4	431–432	E25

*For each lesson, there is a *Reteaching* activity in *Reaching All Learners* and a *Reteaching* master.

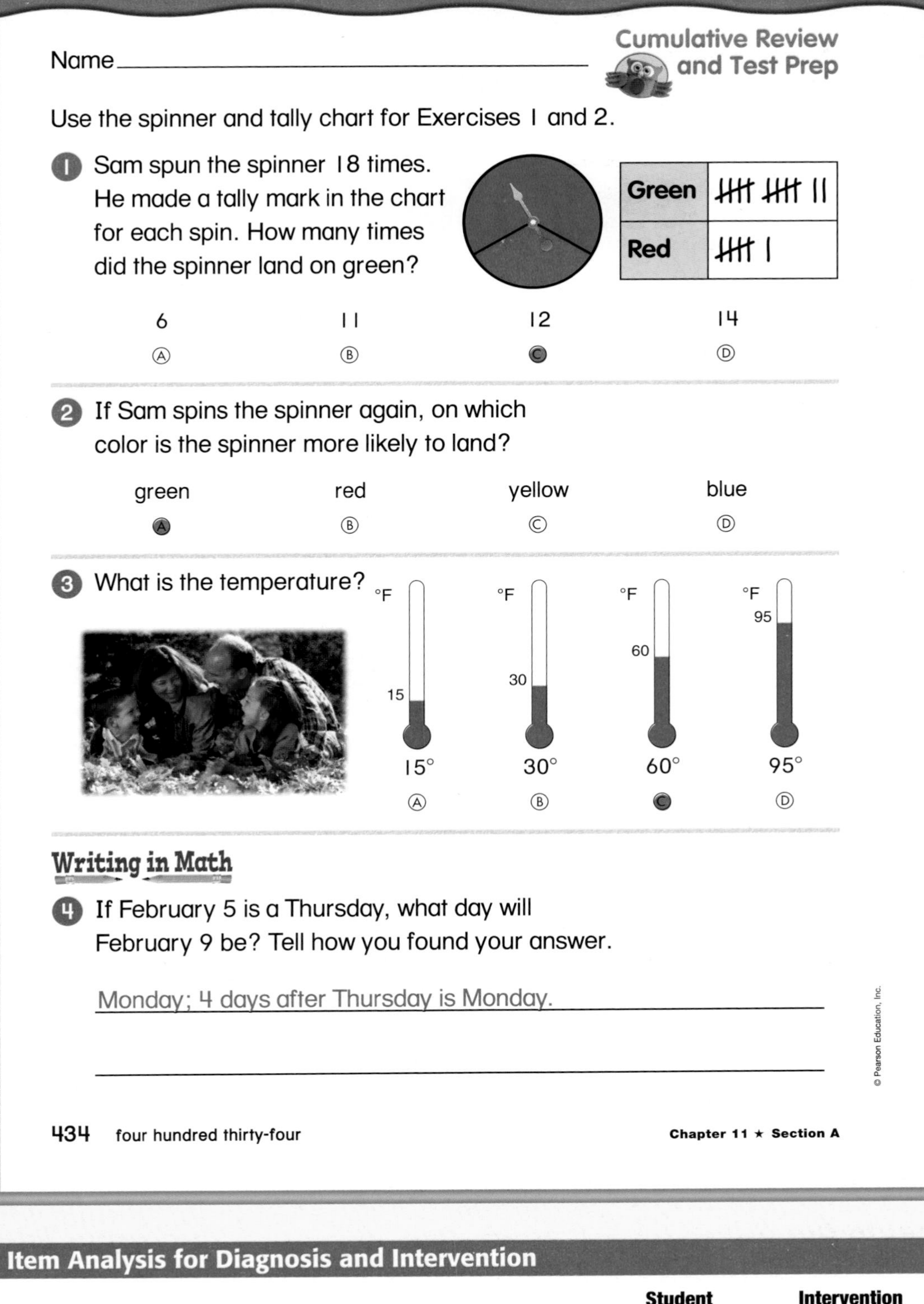
Name ____________________

Cumulative Review and Test Prep

Use the spinner and tally chart for Exercises 1 and 2.

1. Sam spun the spinner 18 times. He made a tally mark in the chart for each spin. How many times did the spinner land on green?

Green	~~IIII~~ ~~IIII~~ II
Red	~~IIII~~ I

6 Ⓐ   11 Ⓑ   12 ● (C)   14 Ⓓ

2. If Sam spins the spinner again, on which color is the spinner more likely to land?

green ● (A)   red Ⓑ   yellow Ⓒ   blue Ⓓ

3. What is the temperature?

15° Ⓐ   30° Ⓑ   60° ● (C)   95° Ⓓ

Writing in Math

4. If February 5 is a Thursday, what day will February 9 be? Tell how you found your answer.

Monday; 4 days after Thursday is Monday.

Cumulative Review and Test Prep

Purpose Provide children with a review of math concepts. Items appear as they would on a standardized test so children become familiar with that format.

Item Analysis for Diagnosis and Intervention

Objective	Items	Student Book Pages*	Intervention System
Experiment and record data using tally marks.	1	313–314	D67
Describe the likelihood of an event as more likely or less likely.	2	403–404	D69
Compare temperatures on a thermometer and match them to activities or objects.	3	395–396	D9
Read and use a calendar to name the days of the week.	4	225–226	D8

*For each lesson, there is a *Reteaching* activity in *Reaching All Learners* and a *Reteaching* master.

11-8 Using Related Facts

Lesson Organizer

Quick Lesson Overview

Objective Write related addition and subtraction facts with sums through 18.

Math Understanding Every addition fact has at least one related subtraction fact.

Vocabulary Related facts

Professional Development Note

Research Base

Using related addition facts can help children learn subtraction facts more easily (Thornton & Smith, 1988). In this lesson, children work with related addition and subtraction facts.

NCTM Standards

- Number and Operations
- Algebra

(For a complete correlation to the NCTM Standards and Grades Pre-K through 2 Expectations, see Pages 415G and 415H.)

Getting Started

Spiral Review

Problem of the Day 11-8

George made a bar graph of the favorite sports of some children. Soccer got 4 votes. Baseball and football each got 2 votes. Nobody voted for golf. Show what his graph looks like.

Topics Reviewed
- Bar graphs
- Problem-Solving Strategy: Make a Graph

Answer Sample:

Our Favorite Sports

Sport	Votes
Baseball	2
Soccer	4
Golf	0
Football	2

Scale: 0 1 2 3 4 5

Spiral Review and Test Prep 11-8

1. Count how many inches around this shape.
   - Ⓐ 5 inches
   - Ⓑ 10 inches
   - Ⓒ 8 inches
   - Ⓓ 9 inches

2. What fraction tells how much is shaded?
   - Ⓐ $\frac{1}{4}$ Ⓑ $\frac{1}{3}$ Ⓒ $\frac{3}{4}$ Ⓓ $\frac{1}{2}$

3. There are three coins in Kelsey's pocket. Some are dimes and some are pennies. What is the greatest amount of money Kelsey could have? 21 ¢

   What is the least amount of money she could have? 12 ¢

4. Complete the table.

   Elise is making bracelets. She has green beads and white beads. Each bracelet uses 3 beads. How many different ways can Elise make bracelets?

Green Beads	White Beads
3	0
2	1
1	2
0	3

There are 4 different ways.

140 Use with Lesson 11-8.

Available as a transparency and as a blackline master

Topics Reviewed
1. Understanding Perimeter
2. Thirds and Fourths
3. Counting Dimes, Nickels, and Pennies
4. Make a Table

Investigating the Concept

Related Facts

Materials *(per pair)* 18 two-color counters; index cards

What to Do

- Have one child make a group of 8 red counters and a group of 9 yellow counters and then join the groups. **Which addition fact tells what happened?** Have the child write $8 + 9 = 17$ on an index card.
- Have the partner separate the groups. **Which subtraction fact tells what happened?** Have the child record the subtraction fact $17 - 9 = 8$ (or $17 - 8 = 9$).
- Discuss related facts. Explain that every addition fact has at least one related subtraction fact. Emphasize that related facts have the same parts and the same wholes.

Ongoing Assessment

- **Which operation is joining? separating or comparing?** *(Adding; subtracting)*
- **Reasoning What is alike about the facts?** *(The parts and the wholes)*

Reaching All Learners

Math Vocabulary

How Are We Related?

5–10 MIN **Linguistic/Auditory**

- **What does it mean to be *related* to someone?** *(You are in the same family.)* **How can you tell you are in the same family?** *(Sample responses: You have the same last name. You live in the same house.)*
- Explain that in math, *related facts* have the same parts and wholes and, thus, the same numbers. Write $6 + 2 = 8$ on the board. Ask the class for a related subtraction fact. *($8 - 2 = 6$ or $8 - 6 = 2$)*
- Repeat with other addition and subtraction facts.

English Language Learners

Extend Language

Understanding Related Facts

10–15 MIN **Linguistic**

Materials *(per pair)* Number Cards 0–11 (Teaching Tool 9); Number Cards 12–20 (Teaching Tool 11)

- Demonstrate the activity by placing 5 cards on the table to make an addition fact, such as $5 + 7 = 12$.
- Show how to change the addition to subtraction by changing the + to − and by switching the 12 and the 5. **This is a related fact.**
- Have partners repeat the activity. Encourage children to use the words *same, add,* and *subtract* in conversations with their partners.

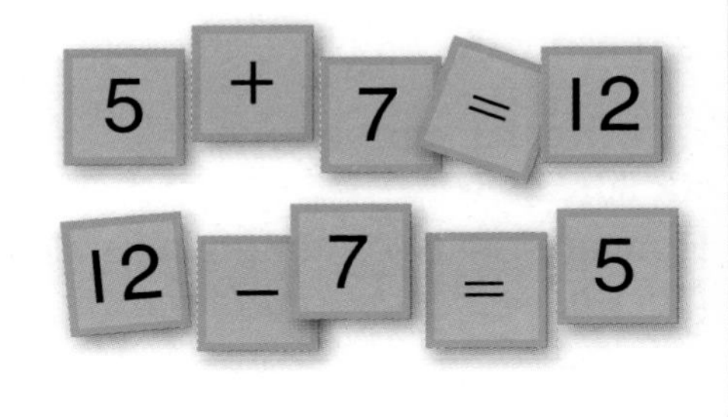

Reteaching

Looking Backward

10–15 MIN **Logical/Mathematical**

PAIRS

Materials *(per pair)* Index cards labeled with addition facts

- Show an index card, such as $3 + 4 = 7$. Then place your index fingers over the + and the =. Ask the pair to read the numbers backward. Write the numbers on the board.
- **What is a related subtraction fact?** Ask where the − and the = should be placed to make a related subtraction fact. *($7 - 4 = 3$)*

Math and Technology

Find the Missing Number

10–15 MIN **Logical/Mathematical**

PAIRS

Materials *(per pair)* Calculator; index cards labeled with addition problems

- Have one child draw a card and enter the problem into the calculator without letting the partner see.
- Have the partner take the calculator with the sum in the display and ask for one of the addends. That child then subtracts that addend from the sum to find the missing number.
- Have partners repeat the activity, alternating jobs.

Objective Write related addition and subtraction facts with sums through 18.

1 Warm Up

Activate Prior Knowledge Review addition facts. Using addition fact cards, have children work in pairs to practice their facts.

2 Teach

Learn!

Direct children's attention to the guitars at the top of the student page. Remind children that the two facts are called related facts because they represent the same parts and the same whole as those in the picture. For this reason, they include the same numbers.

Ongoing Assessment
Talk About It

- **How are the two related facts alike?** *(They have the same parts and the same wholes.)*
- **How can an addition fact help you write a subtraction fact?** *(Begin the subtraction fact with the sum of the addition fact and then subtract one of the addends.)*

If children have difficulty understanding the relationship between the facts,

then have them use counters to model the joining and separating situations.

Check
Error Intervention

If children make errors, such as relating $8 + 5 = 13$ and $8 - 5 = 3$,

then remind them that the sentences must include only the three numbers in the original fact. *(Also see* Reteaching, *Page 435B.)*

Think About It To help children answer the questions, point out that the sum of 9 and 8 is 17, which is the number that begins the subtraction sentence.

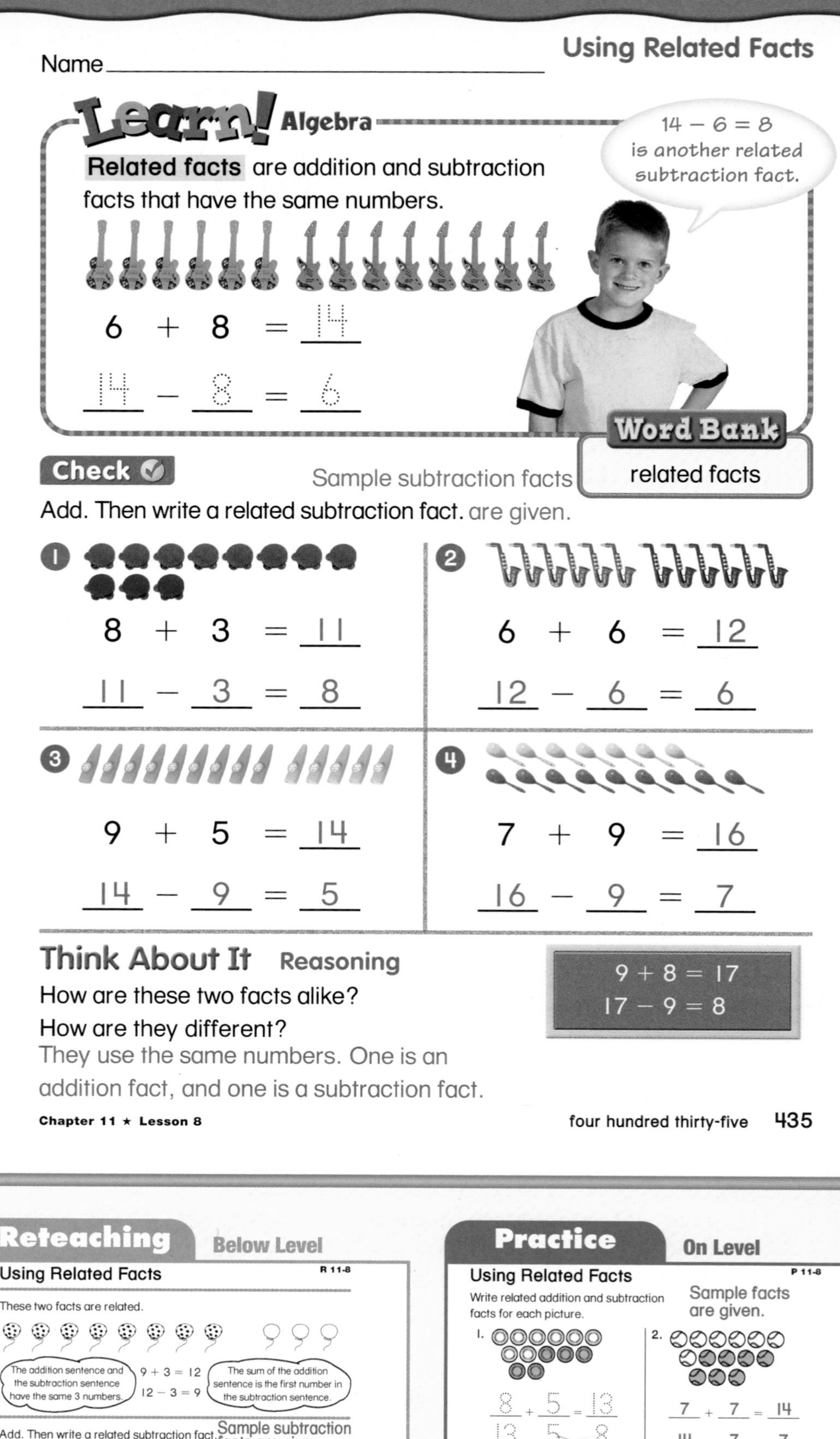

Name ____________________ **Using Related Facts**

Learn! Algebra

Related facts are addition and subtraction facts that have the same numbers.

6 + 8 = 14

14 − 8 = 6

Word Bank
related facts

Check

Add. Then write a related subtraction fact. Sample subtraction facts are given.

1. 8 + 3 = 11
   11 − 3 = 8
2. 6 + 6 = 12
   12 − 6 = 6
3. 9 + 5 = 14
   14 − 9 = 5
4. 7 + 9 = 16
   16 − 9 = 7

Think About It Reasoning

How are these two facts alike?

How are they different?

9 + 8 = 17
17 − 9 = 8

They use the same numbers. One is an addition fact, and one is a subtraction fact.

Chapter 11 ★ Lesson 8 — four hundred thirty-five 435

Reteaching Below Level

Using Related Facts R 11-8

These two facts are related.

9 + 3 = 12
12 − 3 = 9

The addition sentence and the subtraction sentence have the same 3 numbers.

The sum of the addition sentence is the first number in the subtraction sentence.

Add. Then write a related subtraction fact. Sample subtraction facts are given.

1. 8 + 4 = 12
   12 − 4 = 8
2. 7 + 6 = 13
   13 − 6 = 7
3. 9 + 2 = 11
   11 − 9 = 2
4. 8 + 5 = 13
   13 − 8 = 5
5. 9 + 7 = 16
   16 − 9 = 7
6. 8 + 7 = 15
   15 − 8 = 7

140 Use with Lesson 11-8.

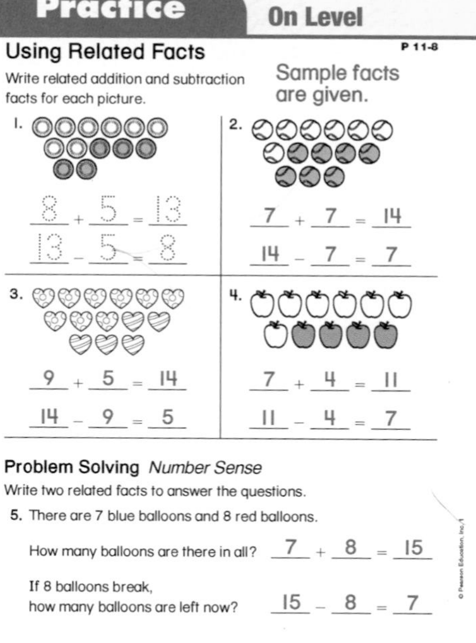

Practice On Level

Using Related Facts P 11-8

Write related addition and subtraction facts for each picture. Sample facts are given.

1. 8 + 5 = 13
   13 − 5 = 8
2. 7 + 7 = 14
   14 − 7 = 7
3. 9 + 5 = 14
   14 − 9 = 5
4. 7 + 4 = 11
   11 − 4 = 7

Problem Solving *Number Sense*

Write two related facts to answer the questions.

5. There are 7 blue balloons and 8 red balloons.

How many balloons are there in all? 7 + 8 = 15

If 8 balloons break, how many balloons are left now? 15 − 8 = 7

140 Use with Lesson 11-8.

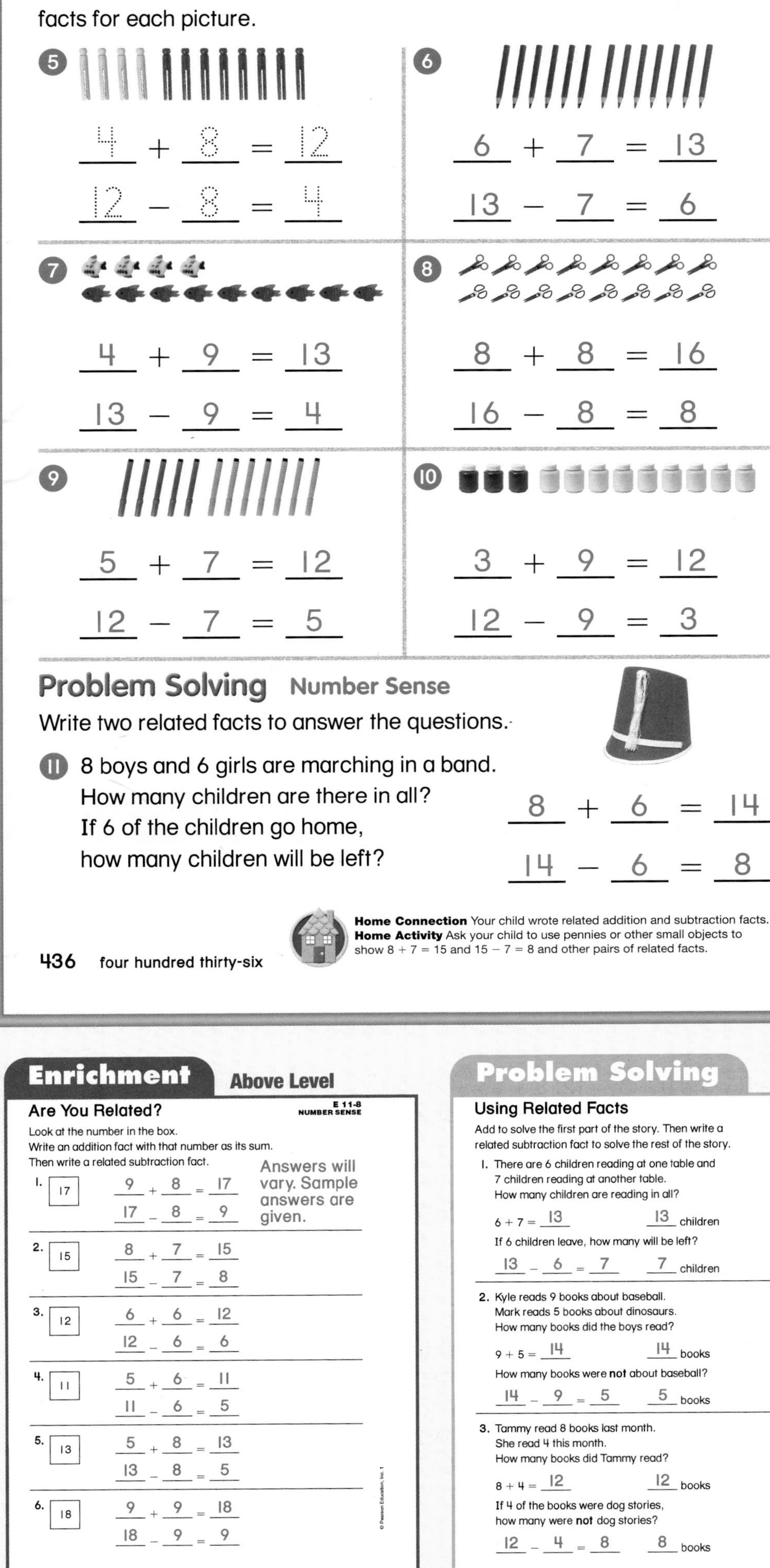

Practice

Write related addition and subtraction facts for each picture. Sample answers are given.

5. 4 + 8 = 12; 12 − 8 = 4

6. 6 + 7 = 13; 13 − 7 = 6

7. 4 + 9 = 13; 13 − 9 = 4

8. 8 + 8 = 16; 16 − 8 = 8

9. 5 + 7 = 12; 12 − 7 = 5

10. 3 + 9 = 12; 12 − 9 = 3

Problem Solving Number Sense

Write two related facts to answer the questions.

11. 8 boys and 6 girls are marching in a band. How many children are there in all? If 6 of the children go home, how many children will be left?

8 + 6 = 14

14 − 6 = 8

Home Connection Your child wrote related addition and subtraction facts. **Home Activity** Ask your child to use pennies or other small objects to show 8 + 7 = 15 and 15 − 7 = 8 and other pairs of related facts.

© Pearson Education, Inc.

436 four hundred thirty-six

Enrichment Above Level

E 11-8 NUMBER SENSE

Are You Related?

Look at the number in the box. Write an addition fact with that number as its sum. Then write a related subtraction fact.

Answers will vary. Sample answers are given.

1. 17: 9 + 8 = 17; 17 − 8 = 9
2. 15: 8 + 7 = 15; 15 − 7 = 8
3. 12: 6 + 6 = 12; 12 − 6 = 6
4. 11: 5 + 6 = 11; 11 − 6 = 5
5. 13: 5 + 8 = 13; 13 − 8 = 5
6. 18: 9 + 9 = 18; 18 − 9 = 9

140 Use with Lesson 11-8.

Problem Solving

PS 11-8

Using Related Facts

Add to solve the first part of the story. Then write a related subtraction fact to solve the rest of the story.

1. There are 6 children reading at one table and 7 children reading at another table. How many children are reading in all?

   6 + 7 = 13 — 13 children

   If 6 children leave, how many will be left?

   13 − 6 = 7 — 7 children

2. Kyle reads 9 books about baseball. Mark reads 5 books about dinosaurs. How many books did the boys read?

   9 + 5 = 14 — 14 books

   How many books were **not** about baseball?

   14 − 9 = 5 — 5 books

3. Tammy read 8 books last month. She read 4 this month. How many books did Tammy read?

   8 + 4 = 12 — 12 books

   If 4 of the books were dog stories, how many were **not** dog stories?

   12 − 4 = 8 — 8 books

140 Use with Lesson 11-8.

3 Practice

Suggest that children check their responses by making sure that the same three numbers in the addition sentence are also in the subtraction sentence.

Reading Assist: Compare and Contrast Have children compare and contrast the processes of addition and subtraction.

Leveled Practice

Below Level Use counters for all exercises.

On Level Use counters if needed.

Above Level Write a third number sentence for Exercise 11 that uses the same numbers.

Early Finishers Have each child make a set of fact cards with an addition sentence on the front and a related subtraction sentence on the back. A child can show an addition fact to a partner, who should then name a related subtraction fact.

4 Assess

Journal Idea Have each child write and illustrate a set of related addition and subtraction number sentences.

Test-Taking Practice 11-8

1. Which related addition and subtraction sentences match the picture?

   (A) 4 + 7 = 11; 11 − 7 = 4
   (B) 3 + 7 = 10; 10 − 7 = 3
   (C) 4 + 4 = 8; 8 − 4 = 4
   (D) 4 + 8 = 12; 12 − 8 = 4

2. Add to find the sum. Which shows a related subtraction fact?

   9 + 5 = ___

   (A) 9 − 5 = 4
   (B) 12 − 9 = 3
   (C) 14 − 5 = 9
   (D) 15 − 5 = 10

Use with Lesson 11-8 140

Available as a transparency

11-9 Fact Families

Lesson Organizer

Quick Lesson Overview

Objective Write the addition and subtraction sentences that make up a fact family.

Math Understanding Fact families use the same three numbers and can be used to show how addition and subtraction are related.

Vocabulary Fact family

Professional Development Note

Effective Questioning Techniques As you work through the lesson, there will be many opportunities to ask children to tell how the number sentences in a fact family are alike and different. Encourage their thinking with questions, such as: **Which number is the sum in the addition sentence? Which number do you use to begin the subtraction sentence? Which numbers are used in related facts?**

NCTM Standards

- Number and Operations
- Algebra

(For a complete correlation to the NCTM Standards and Grades Pre-K through 2 Expectations, see Pages 415G and 415H.)

Getting Started

Spiral Review

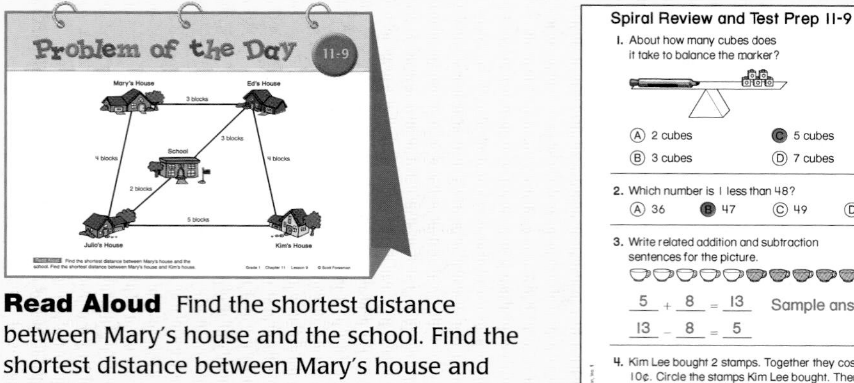

Spiral Review and Test Prep 11-9

1. About how many cubes does it take to balance the marker?
   Ⓐ 2 cubes ● 5 cubes
   Ⓑ 3 cubes Ⓓ 7 cubes
2. Which number is 1 less than 48?
   Ⓐ 36 ● 47 Ⓒ 49 Ⓓ 58
3. Write related addition and subtraction sentences for the picture.
   5 + 8 = 13 Sample answer given.
   13 − 8 = 5
4. Kim Lee bought 2 stamps. Together they cost 10¢. Circle the stamps Kim Lee bought. Then write an addition sentence to check your work.
   6¢ 3¢ 4¢ 8¢
   6 ¢ + 4 ¢ = 10 ¢

Use with Lesson 11-9. 141

Read Aloud Find the shortest distance between Mary's house and the school. Find the shortest distance between Mary's house and Kim's house.

Topics Reviewed

- Length
- Addition
- Problem-Solving Skill: Use Data from a Map

Answer Both ways from Mary's house to the school are the same distance; 3 + 3 = 6 blocks or 4 + 2 = 6 blocks. The shortest distance between Mary's house and Kim's house is 3 + 4 = 7 blocks.

Available as a transparency and as a blackline master

Topics Reviewed

1. Estimating, Measuring, and Comparing Weight
2. 1 More, 1 Less; 10 More, 10 Less
3. Using Related Facts
4. Try, Check, and Revise

Investigating the Concept

Triangular Fact Cards

10–15 MIN **Logical/Mathematical**

Materials *(per pair)* 4 construction paper triangles

What to Do

- On the board write 9 + 3 = 12; 3 + 9 = 12; 12 − 3 = 9; 12 − 9 = 3. Explain that related addition and subtraction facts make up a fact family. Point out that the parts and the wholes are the same.
- Demonstrate how to use a triangle to record the numbers in a family with 12, the whole, at the top and the parts, 3 and 9, at each corner.
- Invite children to make similar triangles for facts with sums up to 18. Then have partners write the facts for each fact family they show.

Ongoing Assessment

- **Which number in 6 + 7 = 13 will be first in the related subtraction facts in the fact family? Why?** *(13; because it is the greatest number)*
- **Number Sense How do you know which of the three numbers stands for the sum?** *(The sum is the number that represents the whole.)*

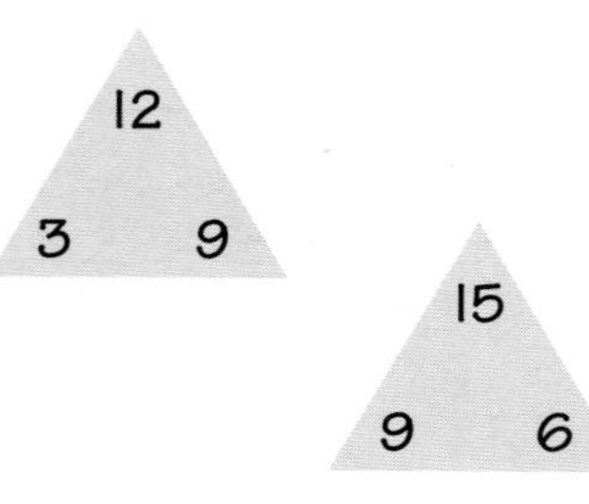

Reaching All Learners

Math Vocabulary

Who Is in a Fact Family?

10–15 MIN **Logical/Mathematical** WHOLE CLASS

Materials Bag containing Number Cards 0–11 (Teaching Tool 9)

- Remind children what *related* means. **What do we call people who are related?** *(A family)* Tell children that a *fact family* has addition and subtraction facts that are related. The facts are alike and different.
- Have one child draw two number cards from the bag and explain how to write one addition fact using these members of the fact family. Have children use the same numbers to write the related facts in this family.

Extend Language

English Language Learners

Understanding Fact Families

10–15 MIN **Linguistic** SMALL GROUP

Materials Index cards labeled with addition and subtraction facts

- Review the definition of *fact family*.
- Show one card, such as 6 + 3 = 9. **This is an addition fact.** Then show the three related cards: 3 + 6 = 9; 9 − 6 = 3; and 9 − 3 = 6. **This is a fact family.**
- Have groups sort the cards, identifying *facts* and grouping the cards to make *fact families.*

fact family

3 + 6 = 9

9 − 6 = 3

an addition fact

6 + 3 = 9

9 − 3 = 6

Reteaching

Tossing Facts!

10–15 MIN **Logical/Mathematical** PAIRS

Materials *(per pair)* 2 number cubes

- Have one child toss the number cubes to get the two addends for the first fact in a fact family. Have the child write an addition fact using those numbers and have the second child write the related addition fact.
- Have the first child write one related subtraction fact and the second child write the other related subtraction fact.
- Have the second child toss the number cubes and repeat the activity.

3 + 4 = 7
4 + 3 = 7
7 − 3 = 4
7 − 4 = 3

Math and Social Studies

Communication in a Family

10–15 MIN **Social/Cooperative** WHOLE CLASS

Materials Cards with facts that make fact families; tape

- Tell children that they will need to communicate to find their fact families. Tape number facts on children's backs and explain that they will help each other make fact families by looking at each other's facts and helping related facts get together.
- Advise children to hold hands with the "relatives" they find until they have four people.

Objective Write the addition and subtraction sentences that make up a fact family.

1 Warm Up

Activate Prior Knowledge Review related facts. Invite a group of 5 children to stand. Then invite 6 more. **5 + 6 = 11.** Then have 6 children sit. **Which subtraction sentence tells what happened?** *(11 − 6 = 5)* Write the related facts on the board. Continue with other related facts.

2 Teach

Learn!

Together, look at the numbers on the hat. Explain that those numbers can be used to create a fact family. Explain that related addition and subtraction facts make up a fact family. Identify the four addition and subtraction facts that make up this fact family.

Ongoing Assessment

Talk About It

- **Which two numbers represent the parts, and which number represents the whole?** *(9 and 7 are the parts; 16 is the whole.)*
- **Which fact family can you make with the numbers 2, 9, and 11?** *(2 + 9 = 11; 9 + 2 = 11; 11 − 9 = 2; 11 − 2 = 9)*

If children have trouble seeing the part-part-whole relationship,

then have them identify the parts and the whole in each number sentence.

Check

Error Intervention

If children write the sums or differences incorrectly,

then have them use counters. *(Also see Reteaching, Page 437B.)*

Think About It Ask: **What is the related addition fact for 6 + 6 = 12? for 7 + 7 = 14?**

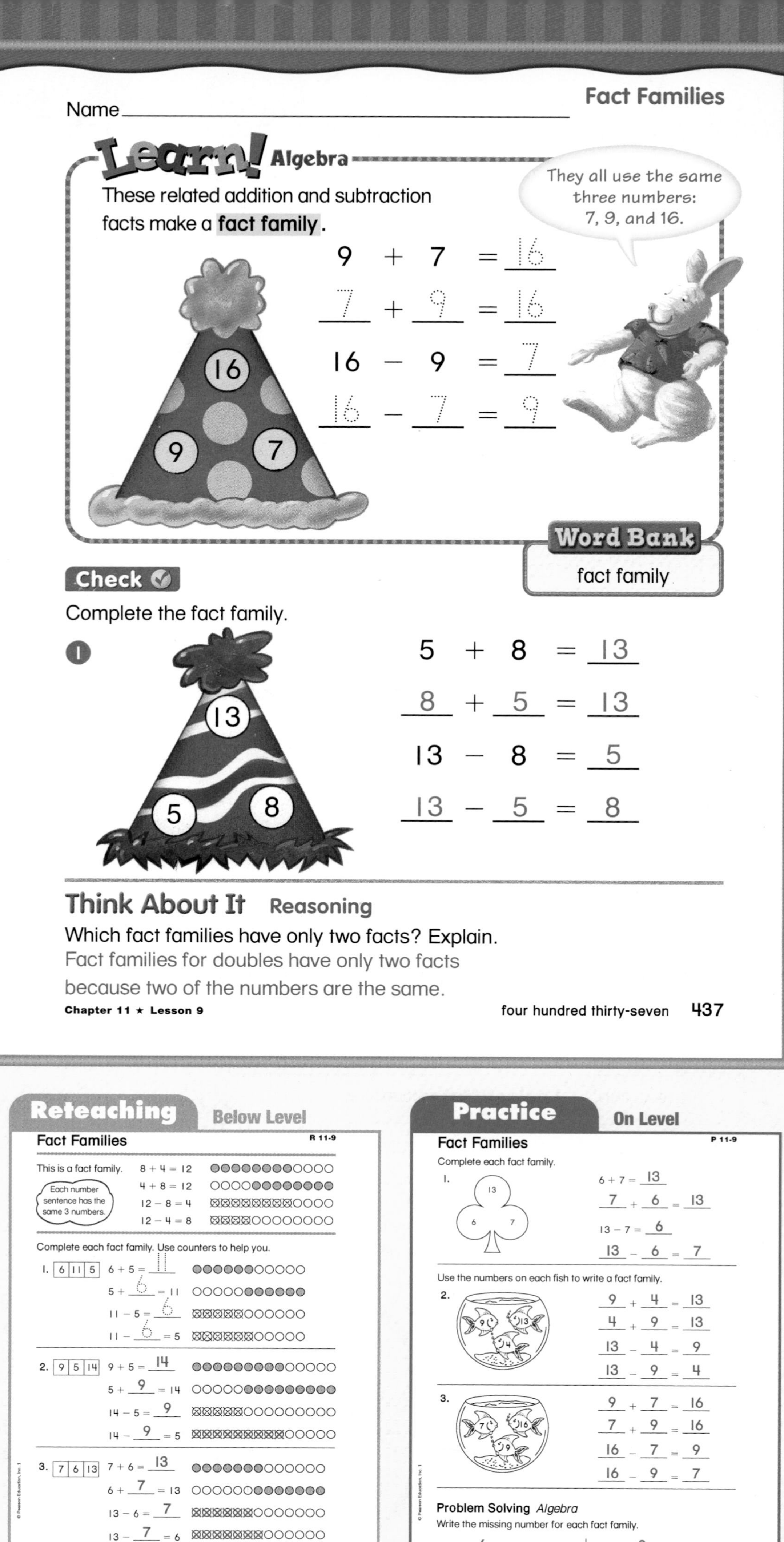

Name______________________ **Fact Families**

Learn! Algebra

These related addition and subtraction facts make a **fact family**.

9 + 7 = 16
7 + 9 = 16
16 − 9 = 7
16 − 7 = 9

They all use the same three numbers: 7, 9, and 16.

Word Bank
fact family

Check

Complete the fact family.

1. 5 + 8 = 13
8 + 5 = 13
13 − 8 = 5
13 − 5 = 8

Think About It Reasoning

Which fact families have only two facts? Explain.
Fact families for doubles have only two facts because two of the numbers are the same.

Chapter 11 ★ Lesson 9 four hundred thirty-seven 437

Reteaching Below Level

Fact Families R 11-9

This is a fact family. Each number sentence has the same 3 numbers.
8 + 4 = 12
4 + 8 = 12
12 − 8 = 4
12 − 4 = 8

Complete each fact family. Use counters to help you.

1. 6 11 5: 6 + 5 = 11; 5 + 6 = 11; 11 − 5 = 6; 11 − 6 = 5
2. 9 5 14: 9 + 5 = 14; 5 + 9 = 14; 14 − 5 = 9; 14 − 9 = 5
3. 7 6 13: 7 + 6 = 13; 6 + 7 = 13; 13 − 6 = 7; 13 − 7 = 6

Use with Lesson 11-9. 141

Practice On Level

Fact Families P 11-9

Complete each fact family.

1. 6 + 7 = 13; 7 + 6 = 13; 13 − 7 = 6; 13 − 6 = 7

Use the numbers on each fish to write a fact family.

2. 9 + 4 = 13; 4 + 9 = 13; 13 − 4 = 9; 13 − 9 = 4
3. 9 + 7 = 16; 7 + 9 = 16; 16 − 7 = 9; 16 − 9 = 7

Problem Solving *Algebra*
Write the missing number for each fact family.

4. 15 6 9
5. 5 13 8

Use with Lesson 11-9. 141

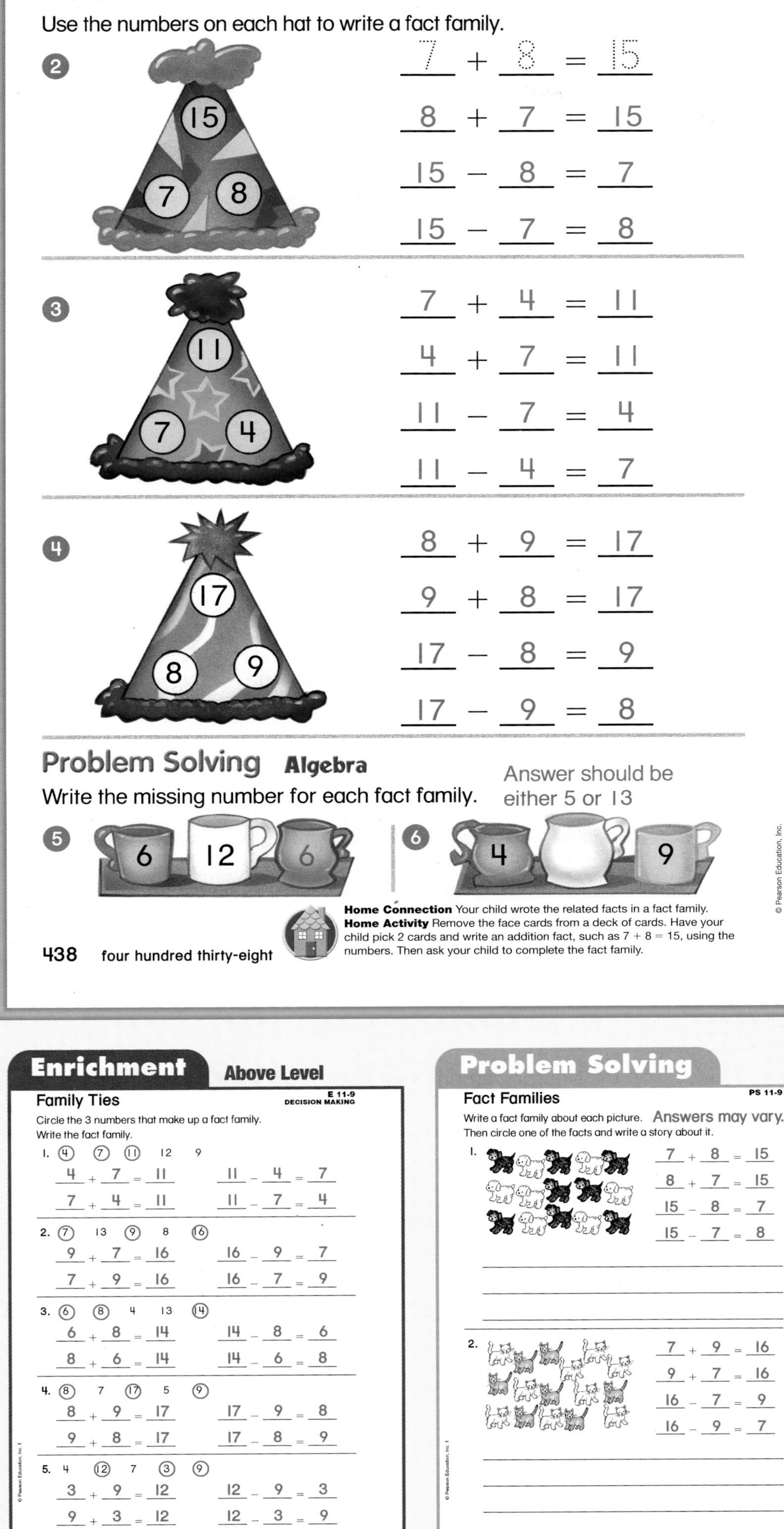

Practice

Use the numbers on each hat to write a fact family.

2. (15, 7, 8)
7 + 8 = 15
8 + 7 = 15
15 − 8 = 7
15 − 7 = 8

3. (11, 7, 4)
7 + 4 = 11
4 + 7 = 11
11 − 7 = 4
11 − 4 = 7

4. (17, 8, 9)
8 + 9 = 17
9 + 8 = 17
17 − 8 = 9
17 − 9 = 8

Problem Solving **Algebra**

Write the missing number for each fact family.

Answer should be either 5 or 13

5. 6 12 6

6. 4 9

© Pearson Education, Inc.

Home Connection Your child wrote the related facts in a fact family.
Home Activity Remove the face cards from a deck of cards. Have your child pick 2 cards and write an addition fact, such as 7 + 8 = 15, using the numbers. Then ask your child to complete the fact family.

438 four hundred thirty-eight

Enrichment Above Level

Family Ties — E 11-9 DECISION MAKING

Circle the 3 numbers that make up a fact family. Write the fact family.

1. (4) (7) (11) 12 9
4 + 7 = 11 11 − 4 = 7
7 + 4 = 11 11 − 7 = 4

2. (7) 13 (9) 8 (16)
9 + 7 = 16 16 − 9 = 7
7 + 9 = 16 16 − 7 = 9

3. (6) (8) 4 13 (14)
6 + 8 = 14 14 − 8 = 6
8 + 6 = 14 14 − 6 = 8

4. (8) 7 (17) 5 (9)
8 + 9 = 17 17 − 9 = 8
9 + 8 = 17 17 − 8 = 9

5. 4 (12) 7 (3) (9)
3 + 9 = 12 12 − 9 = 3
9 + 3 = 12 12 − 3 = 9

Use with Lesson 11-9 141

Problem Solving

Fact Families — PS 11-9

Write a fact family about each picture. Then circle one of the facts and write a story about it. Answers may vary.

1.
7 + 8 = 15
8 + 7 = 15
15 − 8 = 7
15 − 7 = 8

2.
7 + 9 = 16
9 + 7 = 16
16 − 7 = 9
16 − 9 = 7

Use with Lesson 11-9 141

3 Practice

Remind children to identify which number represents the whole and which numbers represent the parts on each hat.

Reading Assist: Draw Conclusions Ask children what conclusion they can draw about the number at the top of each hat. Children should conclude it is the greatest number and stands for the sum of the other numbers, or the whole.

Leveled Practice

Below Level Use cubes to model each exercise and to show the facts.

On Level Use cubes if needed.

Above Level Write a fact family not shown on the page.

Early Finishers Assign partners. Have one child write an addition sentence. Then have the partner write the facts that complete the family.

4 Assess

Journal Idea Have children write and illustrate their choices of fact family.

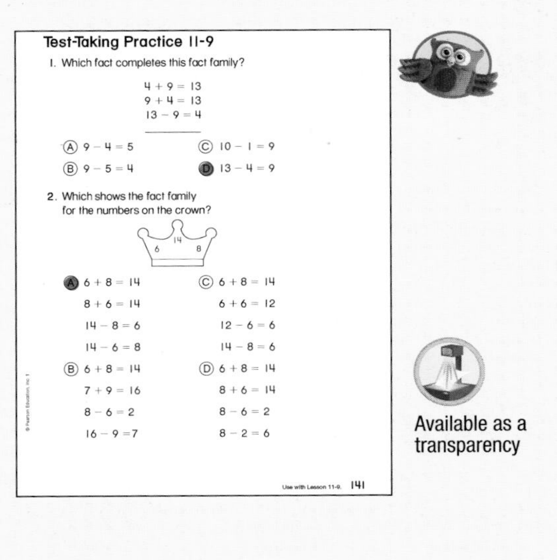

Test-Taking Practice 11-9

1. Which fact completes this fact family?
4 + 9 = 13
9 + 4 = 13
13 − 9 = 4

(A) 9 − 4 = 5 (C) 10 − 1 = 9
(B) 9 − 5 = 4 (D) 13 − 4 = 9

2. Which shows the fact family for the numbers on the crown?

(A) 6 + 8 = 14, 8 + 6 = 14, 14 − 8 = 6, 14 − 6 = 8
(C) 6 + 8 = 14, 6 + 6 = 12, 12 − 6 = 6, 14 − 8 = 6
(B) 6 + 8 = 14, 7 + 9 = 16, 8 − 6 = 2, 16 − 9 = 7
(D) 6 + 8 = 14, 8 + 6 = 14, 8 − 6 = 2, 8 − 2 = 6

Use with Lesson 11-9 141

Available as a transparency

11-10 Using Addition to Subtract

Lesson Organizer

Quick Lesson Overview

Objective Find differences by using known addition facts.

Math Understanding An addition fact can be used to find the difference in a related subtraction fact.

Professional Development Note

Managing Instruction Have children work in pairs as they complete these student pages. Pair children who understand the inverse relationship between addition and subtraction with those who still need more practice.

NCTM Standards

- Number and Operations
- Algebra

(For a complete correlation to the NCTM Standards and Grades Pre-K through 2 Expectations, see Pages 415G and 415H.)

Getting Started

Spiral Review

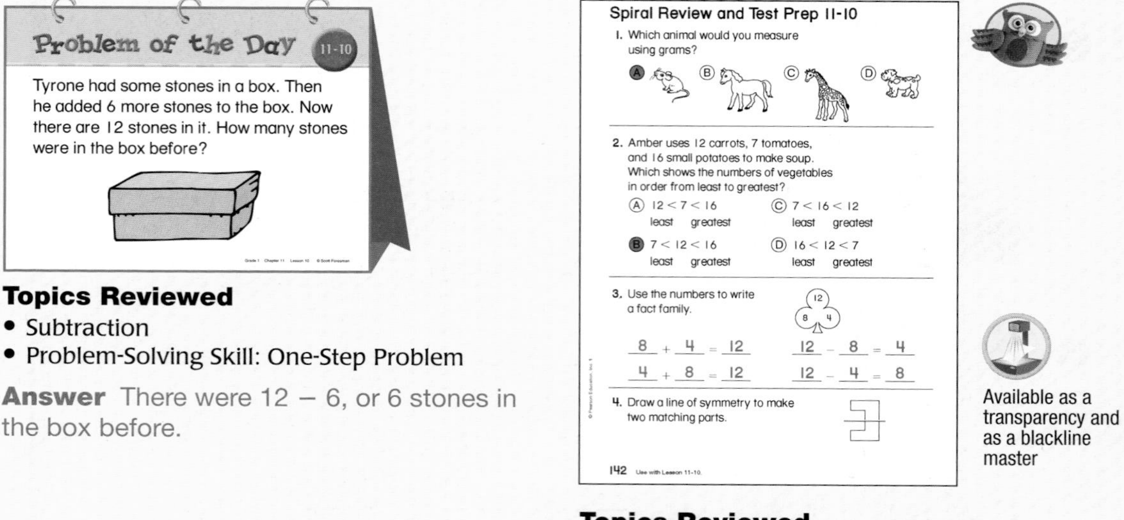

Problem of the Day 11-10

Tyrone had some stones in a box. Then he added 6 more stones to the box. Now there are 12 stones in it. How many stones were in the box before?

Spiral Review and Test Prep 11-10

1. Which animal would you measure using grams?

Ⓐ Ⓑ Ⓒ Ⓓ

2. Amber uses 12 carrots, 7 tomatoes, and 16 small potatoes to make soup. Which shows the numbers of vegetables in order from least to greatest?

Ⓐ 12 < 7 < 16 (least, greatest) Ⓒ 7 < 16 < 12 (least, greatest)

Ⓑ 7 < 12 < 16 (least, greatest) Ⓓ 16 < 12 < 7 (least, greatest)

3. Use the numbers to write a fact family.

8 + 4 = 12 12 − 8 = 4

4 + 8 = 12 12 − 4 = 8

4. Draw a line of symmetry to make two matching parts.

142 Use with Lesson 11-10.

Topics Reviewed
- Subtraction
- Problem-Solving Skill: One-Step Problem

Answer There were 12 − 6, or 6 stones in the box before.

Available as a transparency and as a blackline master

Topics Reviewed
1. Grams and Kilograms
2. Ordering Three Numbers
3. Fact Families
4. Symmetry

Investigating the Concept

Make a Match

10–15 MIN | **Logical/Mathematical** | PAIRS

Materials *(per pair)* Subtraction fact cards

What to Do

- Write 15 − 7 = ___ on the board. Demonstrate how 8 + 7 = 15 can help solve the problem.
- Have partners lay out the subtraction fact cards and take turns choosing a card and naming the addition sentence that can be used to solve the problem. Then have them solve the subtraction problem.
- Have pairs change roles until all of the cards have been taken.

Ongoing Assessment

- **Which addition fact would you use to find 14 − 8?** *(8 + 6 = 14 or 6 + 8 = 14)*
- **Reasoning How do you know which addition fact to use?** *(Use the addition fact that contains the same numbers as the subtraction fact and has a sum that is the first number in the subtraction sentence.)*

Reaching All Learners

Oral Language in Math

Backward Stories

10–15 MIN **Linguistic**

- Tell an addition story, such as: **I had 2 jump ropes. My friend gave me 3 more jump ropes. How many jump ropes did I have then?**
- As a group, rewrite the story going backward (the inverse operation). For example, the story might read: "I had 5 jump ropes. My friend took her 3 jump ropes back. How many jump ropes did I have left?"
- Have children dictate stories, write them, and solve them as a group.

I had 5 jump ropes. My friend took her 3 jump ropes back. How many jump ropes did I have left?

$5 - 3 =$

Activate Prior Knowledge/Build Background

English Language Learners

If ... Then ...

10–15 MIN **Linguistic/Logical/Mathematical**

Materials Addition fact cards

- Model the activity by showing an addition fact card and saying, for example: **If you know $5 + 3 = 8$, then you know $8 - 3 = 5$.**
- Repeat with another card, asking a child for the related subtraction fact.
- Have partners take turns in the roles. One child says, "If you know ___ + ___ = ___ , then you know ...," and the second child gives the subtraction fact.

Reteaching

Counter Flip

10–15 MIN **Visual/Spatial**

PAIRS

Materials *(per pair)* 19 two-color counters

- Have one child put a number of counters, such as 14, on the table with the yellow side up. Have another child turn over some of those counters, such as 6, to red and write the fact: $8 + 6 = 14$.
- Move away the group of red counters and show children how they can use the addition fact and counters to write the related subtraction fact: $14 - 6 = 8$.
- Have children work in pairs to repeat the activity.

$14 - 6 = 8$

$8 + 6 = 14$

Advanced Learners

Folded Corner Mystery

10–15 MIN **Logical/Mathematical**

PAIRS

Materials Construction paper triangles labeled with numbers from a fact family

- Ask one child to choose a triangle and determine which numbers are addends. He or she folds one addend back so that it cannot be seen.
- Have the second child write the addition fact using the remaining two numbers and the missing addend and then write the related subtraction fact.
- Repeat the activity with new triangles, alternating roles.

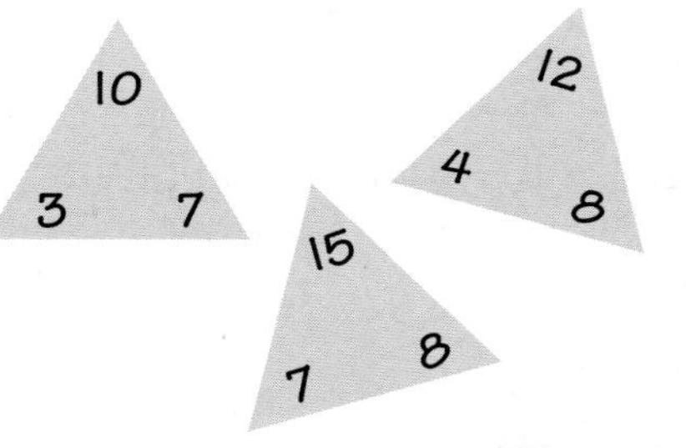

Objective Find differences by using known addition facts.

1 Warm Up

Activate Prior Knowledge Review related facts. Place a set of related fact cards facedown. Have children take turns choosing two facts and saying whether they are related.

2 Teach

Learn!

Have children explain how knowing $5 + 8 = 13$ helps you do the subtraction $13 - 8$. Complete the related facts. Discuss how the two facts are alike. Point out that the facts are part of a fact family. Elicit from children the other facts in the family.
(8 + 5 = 13, 13 − 5 = 8)

Ongoing Assessment

Talk About It

- **Which numbers are the same in the two number sentences?** *(5, 8, 13)*
- **How can a related addition fact help you subtract?** *(The addition and the subtraction use the same numbers.)*

If children have trouble seeing the relationship between the addition and subtraction sentences,

then have them use counters.

Check

Error Intervention

If children have trouble completing a number sentence,

then have them identify which numbers represent the parts and which number represents the whole. *(Also see Reteaching, Page 439B.)*

Think About It Encourage children to replace the shapes with numbers from a fact family in order to see the pattern of the related addition and subtraction sentences.

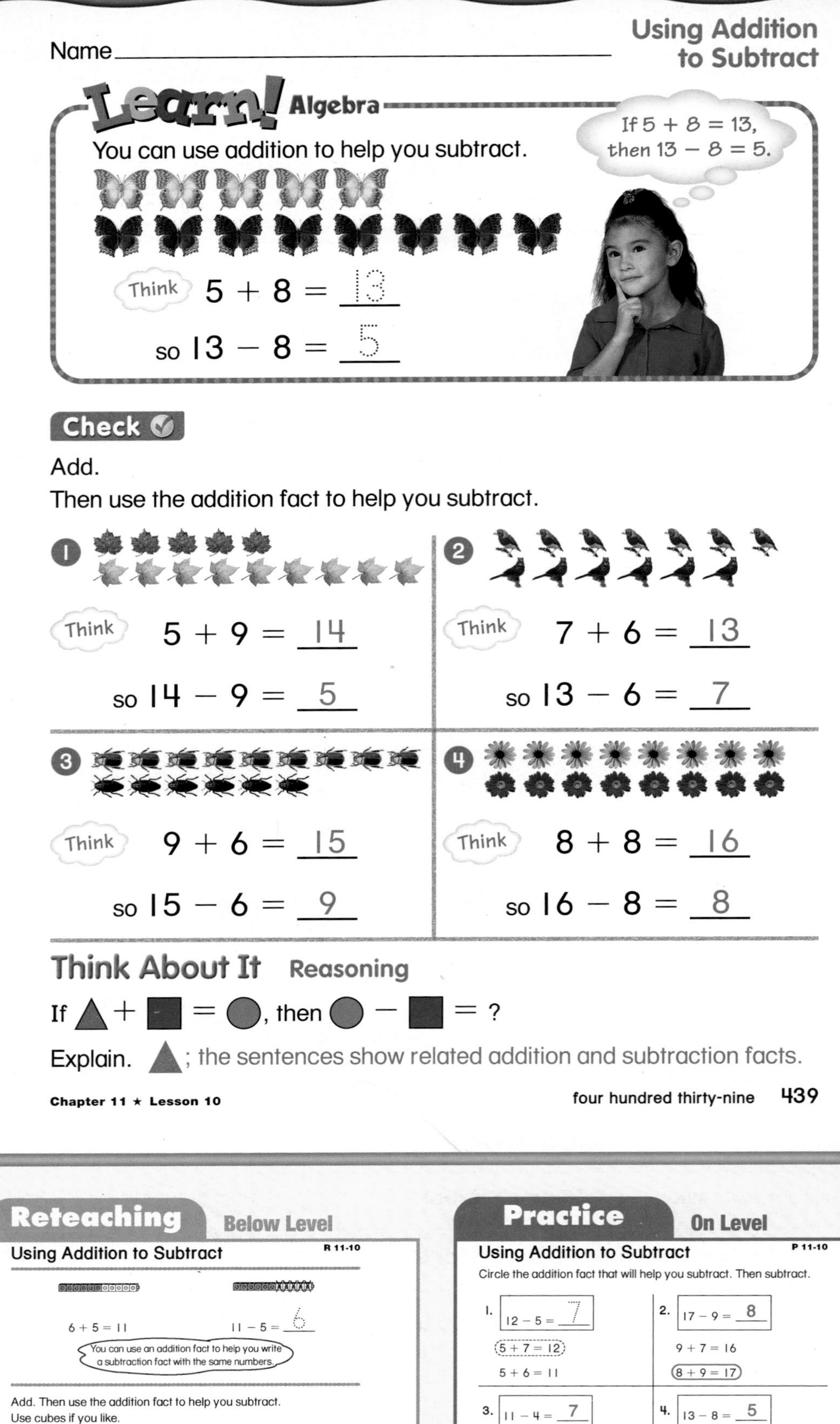

Name ____________________

Using Addition to Subtract

Learn! Algebra

You can use addition to help you subtract.

Think $5 + 8 = \underline{13}$

so $13 - 8 = \underline{5}$

Check

Add.
Then use the addition fact to help you subtract.

1. Think $5 + 9 = \underline{14}$ so $14 - 9 = \underline{5}$
2. Think $7 + 6 = \underline{13}$ so $13 - 6 = \underline{7}$
3. Think $9 + 6 = \underline{15}$ so $15 - 6 = \underline{9}$
4. Think $8 + 8 = \underline{16}$ so $16 - 8 = \underline{8}$

Think About It Reasoning

If ▲ + ■ = ●, then ● − ■ = ?

Explain. ▲; the sentences show related addition and subtraction facts.

Chapter 11 ★ Lesson 10 four hundred thirty-nine 439

Reteaching Below Level

Using Addition to Subtract R 11-10

$6 + 5 = 11$ $11 - 5 = \underline{6}$

You can use an addition fact to help you write a subtraction fact with the same numbers.

Add. Then use the addition fact to help you subtract. Use cubes if you like.

1. $4 + 9 = \underline{13}$ $13 - 9 = \underline{4}$
2. $8 + 7 = \underline{15}$ $15 - 7 = \underline{8}$
3. $7 + 4 = \underline{11}$ $11 - 4 = \underline{7}$
4. $6 + 7 = \underline{13}$ $13 - 7 = \underline{6}$

142 Use with Lesson 11-10.

Practice On Level

Using Addition to Subtract P 11-10

Circle the addition fact that will help you subtract. Then subtract.

1. $12 - 5 = \underline{7}$ (5 + 7 = 12) 5 + 6 = 11
2. $17 - 9 = \underline{8}$ 9 + 7 = 16 (8 + 9 = 17)
3. $11 - 4 = \underline{7}$ 4 + 6 = 10 (4 + 7 = 11)
4. $13 - 8 = \underline{5}$ 5 + 9 = 14 (8 + 5 = 13)
5. $16 - 8 = \underline{8}$ (8 + 8 = 16) 8 + 9 = 17
6. $15 - 6 = \underline{9}$ 6 + 10 = 16 (9 + 6 = 15)

Problem Solving *Mental Math*

Solve.

7. Roger does 8 of his 15 math problems. How many problems does Roger still need to do?
$\underline{7}$ problems

142 Use with Lesson 11-10.

Practice

Circle the addition fact that will help you subtract.
Then subtract.

5. $14 - 8 = $ 6
   - (circled) $6 + 8 = 14$
   - $9 + 6 = 15$

6. $12 - 3 = $ 9
   - $9 + 7 = 16$
   - (circled) $9 + 3 = 12$

7. $13 - 6 = $ 7
   - (circled) $7 + 6 = 13$
   - $9 + 4 = 13$

8. $15 - 8 = $ 7
   - (circled) $8 + 7 = 15$
   - $5 + 8 = 13$

9. $11 - 9 = $ 2
   - $9 + 5 = 14$
   - (circled) $2 + 9 = 11$

10. $16 - 7 = $ 9
    - $7 + 7 = 14$
    - (circled) $9 + 7 = 16$

11. $17 - 8 = $ 9
    - (circled) $9 + 8 = 17$
    - $8 + 3 = 11$

12. $18 - 9 = $ 9
    - (circled) $9 + 9 = 18$
    - $9 + 7 = 16$

Problem Solving Mental Math

Solve.

13. The chipmunk stored 9 of its 17 acorns.
    How many acorns does it still need to store? 8 acorns

Home Connection Your child used addition facts to help with subtraction. **Home Activity** Write 15 − 6 on a piece of paper. Ask your child to write a related addition fact and then solve the subtraction problem. Continue with other subtraction problems.

3 Practice

Remind children to solve each subtraction problem after circling its related addition fact.

Reading Assist: Make Judgments Ask children to make a judgment about what is essential for each addition sentence they choose in Exercises 5–12.

Leveled Practice

Below Level Use counters.

On Level Use counters if necessary.

Above Level After doing Exercise 13, write two related facts with the numbers.

Early Finishers Have children use a calculator to test related addition and subtraction number sentences using larger numbers, to see if the pattern holds.

4 Assess

Journal Idea Have children copy and complete the following sentence frame:
___ − ___ = ___ because ___ + ___ = ___.

Test-Taking Practice 11-10

1. Which related addition fact will help you subtract 15 − 7?
   - Ⓐ $9 + 5 = 14$
   - Ⓑ $7 + 8 = 15$ (marked)
   - Ⓒ $9 + 9 = 18$
   - Ⓓ $10 + 5 = 15$
2. Use the related addition fact to help you subtract.
   $4 + 7 = 11$
   So, $11 - 4 =$ ____.
   - Ⓐ $11 - 4 = 4$
   - Ⓑ $11 - 4 = 8$
   - Ⓒ $11 - 4 = 7$ (marked)
   - Ⓓ $11 - 4 = 6$
3. Macey pasted 6 beads on a frame. She had 15 beads when she started. How many beads does she have left to paste?
   - Ⓐ 9 beads (marked)
   - Ⓑ 8 beads
   - Ⓒ 6 beads
   - Ⓓ 7 beads

Use with Lesson 11-10. 142

Available as a transparency

Enrichment Above Level

Jed's New Pet E 11-10 NUMBER SENSE

What pet does Jed get?
Complete the addition and subtraction sentences.
Draw a line to connect Jed to the related addition and subtraction facts to find his new pet.

Start — Jed — Start

$9 + 7 =$ 16	$5 + 7 =$ 12			
$17 - 9 =$ 8	$16 - 9 =$ 7	$12 - 7 =$ 5		
$8 + 9 =$ 17	$16 - 7 =$ 9	$16 - 8 =$ 8	$12 - 5 =$ 7	
$9 + 6 =$ 15 Turtle	$17 - 8 =$ 9 Parrot	$7 + 9 =$ 16 Hamster	$8 + 7 =$ 15 Dog	$15 - 8 =$ 7 Cat

Jed got a hamster.

142 Use with Lesson 11-10.

Problem Solving

Using Addition to Subtract PS 11-10

Circle the addition fact that will help you subtract.
Then write a subtraction sentence to solve.

1. Mike had 14 peanuts. He fed 9 peanuts to the monkeys. How many peanuts does Mike have left?
   - (circled) $9 + 5 = 14$
   - $9 + 6 = 15$

   5 peanuts — 14 − 9 = 5
2. There are 15 children at the zoo. If 8 children want to see lions and the others want to see zebras, how many children want to see zebras?
   - $8 + 6 = 14$
   - (circled) $8 + 7 = 15$

   7 children — 15 − 8 = 7
3. Rick has 16¢. He buys a zoo pin for 9¢. How much does he have left?
   - $9 + 8 = 17$
   - (circled) $9 + 7 = 16$

   7¢ — 16¢ − 9¢ = 7¢
4. Mark gave 9 animal stickers to Jody. Mark had 15 animal stickers in all. How many animal stickers does Mark have left? 6 animal stickers

142 Use with Lesson 11-10.

11-11 Using 10 to Subtract

Lesson Organizer

Quick Lesson Overview

Objective Find differences using a ten-frame.

Math Understanding Making a 10 before subtracting can change a difficult subtraction fact to one easier to subtract mentally.

Materials for Student Pages
Single Ten-Frame (Workmat 2);
18 two-color counters

Professional Development Note

How Children Learn Math One strategy to use when subtracting 8 or 9 is to use a 10. Children subtract 10 in place of 8 (or 9) and then add back 2 (or 1) to find the difference. This idea can be more clearly shown by using the ten-frame. For example, children see that 12 − 9 is the same as 12 − 10 = 2 plus the 1 in the ten-frame. So 12 − 9 = 3. They see that 12 − 8 is the same as 12 − 10 = 2 plus the 2 in the ten-frame. So 12 − 8 = 4.

NCTM Standards

- Number and Operations

(For a complete correlation to the NCTM Standards and Grades Pre-K through 2 Expectations, see Pages 415G and 415H.)

Getting Started

Spiral Review

Problem of the Day 11-11

Carla has a basket of 17 shells. Five of them are spotted. The rest are not. How many shells are not spotted?

Topics Reviewed
- Addition and subtraction
- Problem-Solving Skill: One-Step Problem

Answer Twelve shells are not spotted; 17 − 5 = 12 and 12 + 5 = 17.

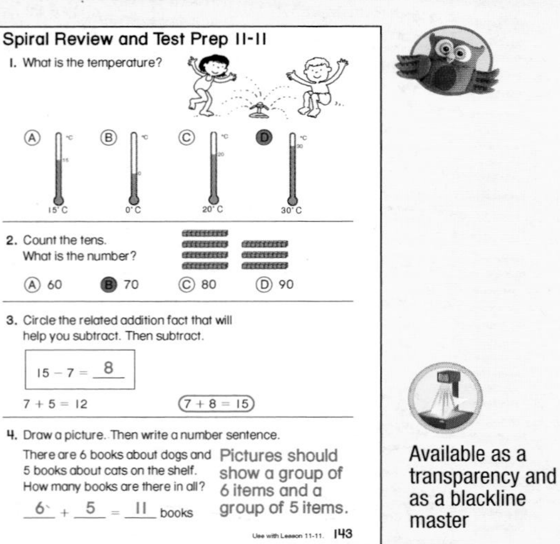
Spiral Review and Test Prep 11-11

1. What is the temperature?

Ⓐ 15°C Ⓑ 0°C Ⓒ 20°C Ⓓ 30°C

2. Count the tens. What is the number?

Ⓐ 60 Ⓑ 70 Ⓒ 80 Ⓓ 90

3. Circle the related addition fact that will help you subtract. Then subtract.

15 − 7 = 8

7 + 5 = 12 7 + 8 = 15

4. Draw a picture. Then write a number sentence.
There are 6 books about dogs and 5 books about cats on the shelf. How many books are there in all?

6 + 5 = 11 books

Pictures should show a group of 6 items and a group of 5 items.

143

Available as a transparency and as a blackline master

Topics Reviewed
1. Temperature
2. Numbers Made with Tens
3. Using Addition to Subtract
4. Draw a Picture

Investigating the Concept

Subtracting 10

Materials *(per child)* Single Ten-Frame (Workmat 2); 15 two-color counters

What to Do
- Explain that sometimes it is helpful to use a 10 when subtracting. Have children fill the ten-frame with 10 counters and place the remaining 5 counters below the ten-frame, keeping all of the counters with the red side showing.
- Write 15 − 9 = ___ on the board. Starting with the counters in the ten-frame, have children turn over 9 of the counters. **1 counter left in the ten-frame plus 5 counters below the ten-frame makes 6 in all. 15 − 9 = 6.** Repeat with 15 − 8.

Ongoing Assessment
- **How many counters in the ten-frame are still red when you do the subtraction 15 − 8?** *(2)*
- **Number Sense How can you use 10 to help you do the subtraction 13 − 9?** *(3 counters outside the ten-frame plus 1 inside equals 4. 13 − 9 = 4)*

Reaching All Learners

Oral Language in Math

What Is the Problem?

10–15 MIN **Visual/Spatial/Linguistic**

Materials *(per group)* Single Ten-Frame (Workmat 2); two-color counters; paper bag with index cards labeled with subtraction facts

- A child draws a card, hides it from the group, and illustrates the subtraction fact using a ten-frame and counters.
- The group guesses the subtraction fact by explaining the steps: "There were 15 counters, 5 were taken away, and 1 in the ten-frame leaves 9 counters."
- Repeat with other facts.

Access Content

English Language Learners

Taking Away from 10

10–15 MIN **Visual/Spatial**

PAIRS

Materials *(per pair)* Single Ten-Frame (Workmat 2); 18 two-color counters

- Review how to use the ten-frame to solve a subtraction problem by taking away from 10 first.
- Write the number 16 on the board. Have pairs work together to show 16 counters (10 on a ten-frame and 6 below). Next to the 16, write − 9 = ___ and read the problem aloud: **16 minus 9 equals ___.**
- Have children use counters to solve the problem. Ask for their answers in the format you provided, 16 − 9 = 7.

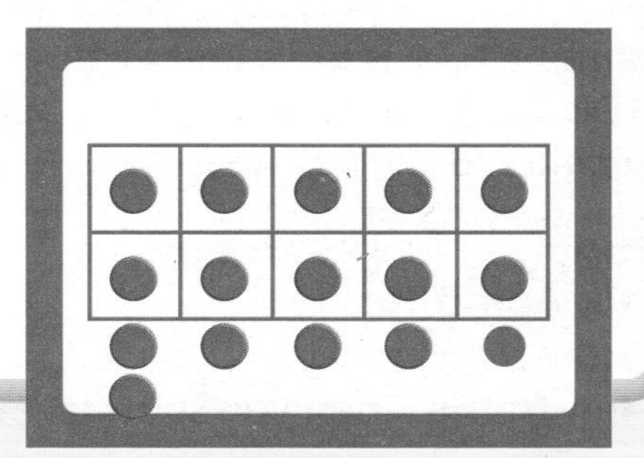

Reteaching

Turning Red

10–15 MIN **Visual/Spatial/Linguistic**

PAIRS

Materials *(per pair)* Single Ten-Frame (Workmat 2); 18 two-color counters

- **You are going to solve 14 − 8.** Have a child place 10 yellow counters on a ten-frame and put 4 extra yellow counters to the side.
- The partner turns over 8 counters to red and says, "Subtract 8 yellow." The first child tells how many yellow counters remain on the ten-frame *(2)* and how many are to the side *(4)*. **How many yellow counters are left altogether?** *(6)*
- Repeat, alternating roles.

Students with Special Needs

10 and More

10–15 MIN **Visual/Spatial**

INDIVIDUAL

Materials *(per child)* Single Ten-Frame (Workmat 2); 19 two-color counters

- Each child places 10 counters red side up on a ten-frame. **Now subtract (turn over) 1 counter. How many are left?** *(9)*
- Help children visualize taking away from 10 by subtracting numbers 2 through 9. Then turn all counters to red. Give each child 1 more to put below the ten-frame.
- Repeat the activity with 11 counters, subtracting 1 at a time. Remind children to include the extra counter in their calculations.
- Repeat with additional counters.

Objective Find differences using a ten-frame.

1 Warm Up

Activate Prior Knowledge Review how to use a ten-frame. Show 11 with a filled ten-frame and 1 counter left over. Write "11 is 10 and 1 left over" on the board. Continue establishing the same pattern for the numbers 12 to 19.

2 Teach

Learn!

Explain that it can be helpful to use a ten-frame when subtracting 9. Point out that just by looking, children can see that 12 − 9 is 12 − 10 = 2 plus the 1 still in the ten-frame. **12 − 9 is the same as 12 − 10 = 2 plus 1.** Discuss what happens when subtracting 8. *(Subtract 10 and add back 2.)*

Ongoing Assessment

Talk About It

- **How many will you have left in the ten-frame when you subtract 9? 8?** *(1; 2)*
- **Why is it helpful to think about subtracting 10 when you have to subtract 9 or 8?** *(It is easy to see 10 on a ten-frame.)*

If children have difficulty seeing that 12 − 9 is 1 more than 12 − 10,

then have them move the 1 counter still on the ten-frame down with the 2 counters not on the ten-frame.

Check

Error Intervention

If children make errors when finding the difference,

then check to be sure they crossed out the correct number of counters. *(Also see* Reteaching, *Page 441B.)*

Think About It Explain that the greater the number that you take away, the less will be left as the difference.

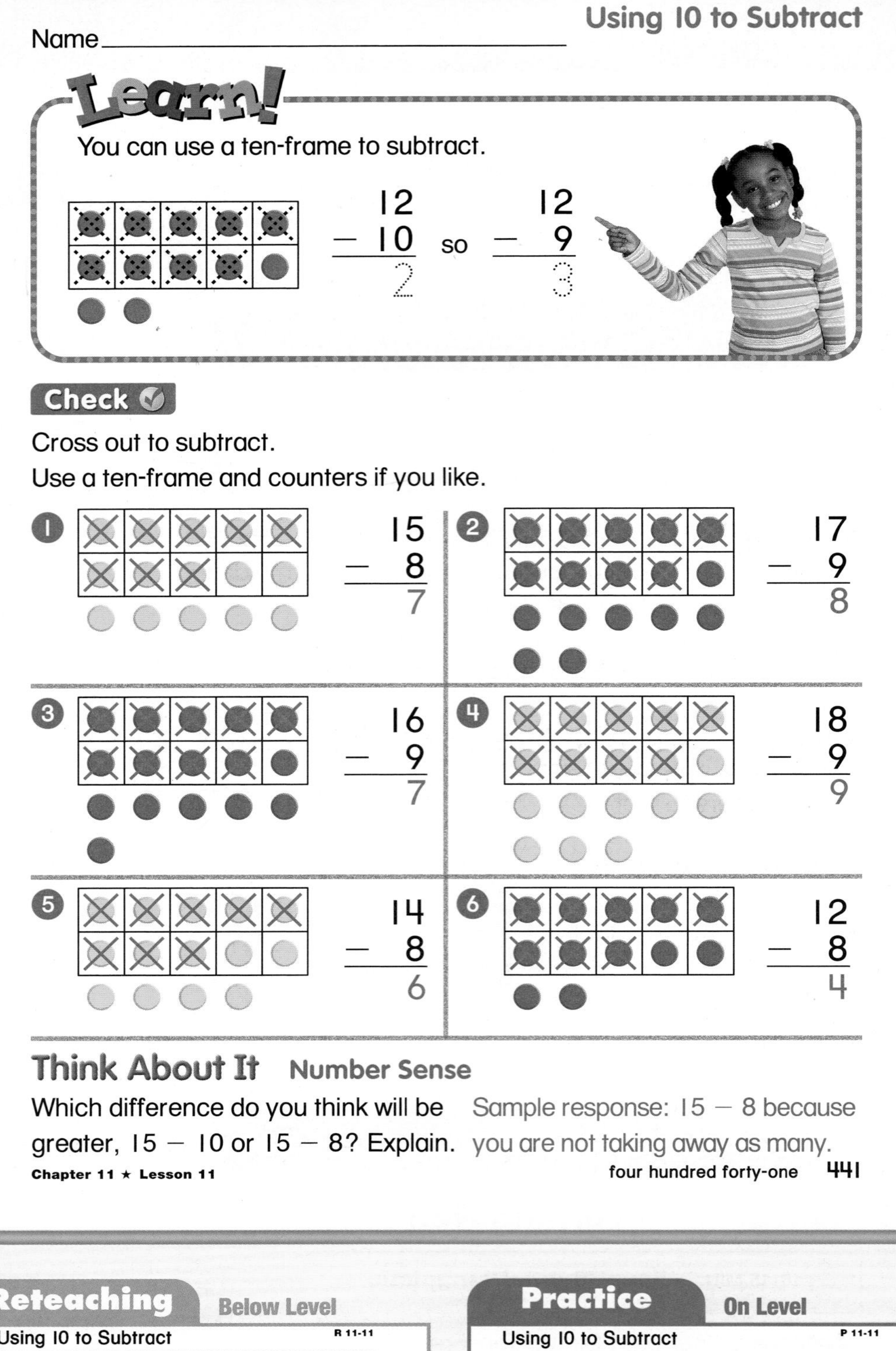

Name ______________________

Using 10 to Subtract

Learn!

You can use a ten-frame to subtract.

12 − 10 = 2 so 12 − 9 = 3

Check

Cross out to subtract.
Use a ten-frame and counters if you like.

1. 15 − 8 = 7
2. 17 − 9 = 8
3. 16 − 9 = 7
4. 18 − 9 = 9
5. 14 − 8 = 6
6. 12 − 8 = 4

Think About It Number Sense

Which difference do you think will be greater, 15 − 10 or 15 − 8? Explain. Sample response: 15 − 8 because you are not taking away as many.

Chapter 11 ★ Lesson 11 four hundred forty-one 441

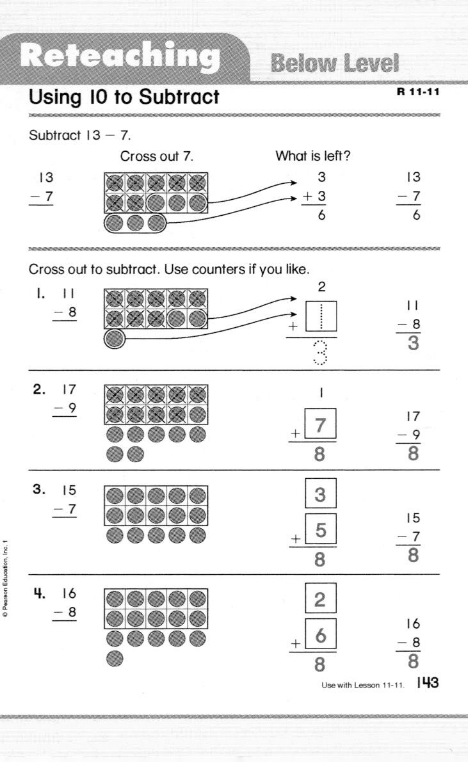

Reteaching Below Level

Using 10 to Subtract R 11-11

Subtract 13 − 7.

Cross out 7. What is left?

13 − 7: 3 + 3 = 6; 13 − 7 = 6

Cross out to subtract. Use counters if you like.

1. 11 − 8: 2 + 1 = 3; 11 − 8 = 3
2. 17 − 9: 1 + 7 = 8; 17 − 9 = 8
3. 15 − 7: 3 + 5 = 8; 15 − 7 = 8
4. 16 − 8: 2 + 6 = 8; 16 − 8 = 8

© Pearson Education, Inc. 1

Use with Lesson 11-11. 143

Practice On Level

Using 10 to Subtract P 11-11

Cross out to subtract.
Use a ten-frame and counters if you like.

1. 12 − 7 = 5
2. 16 − 9 = 7
3. 15 − 6 = 9
4. 14 − 7 = 7
5. 18 − 9 = 9
6. 15 − 7 = 8
7. 17 − 9 = 8
8. 17 − 8 = 9

Problem Solving *Estimation*

Circle your answer.

9. You bought some juice. You gave the clerk a dime and a few nickels. How much did the juice probably cost?

12¢ 14¢ 25¢

Use with Lesson 11-11. 143

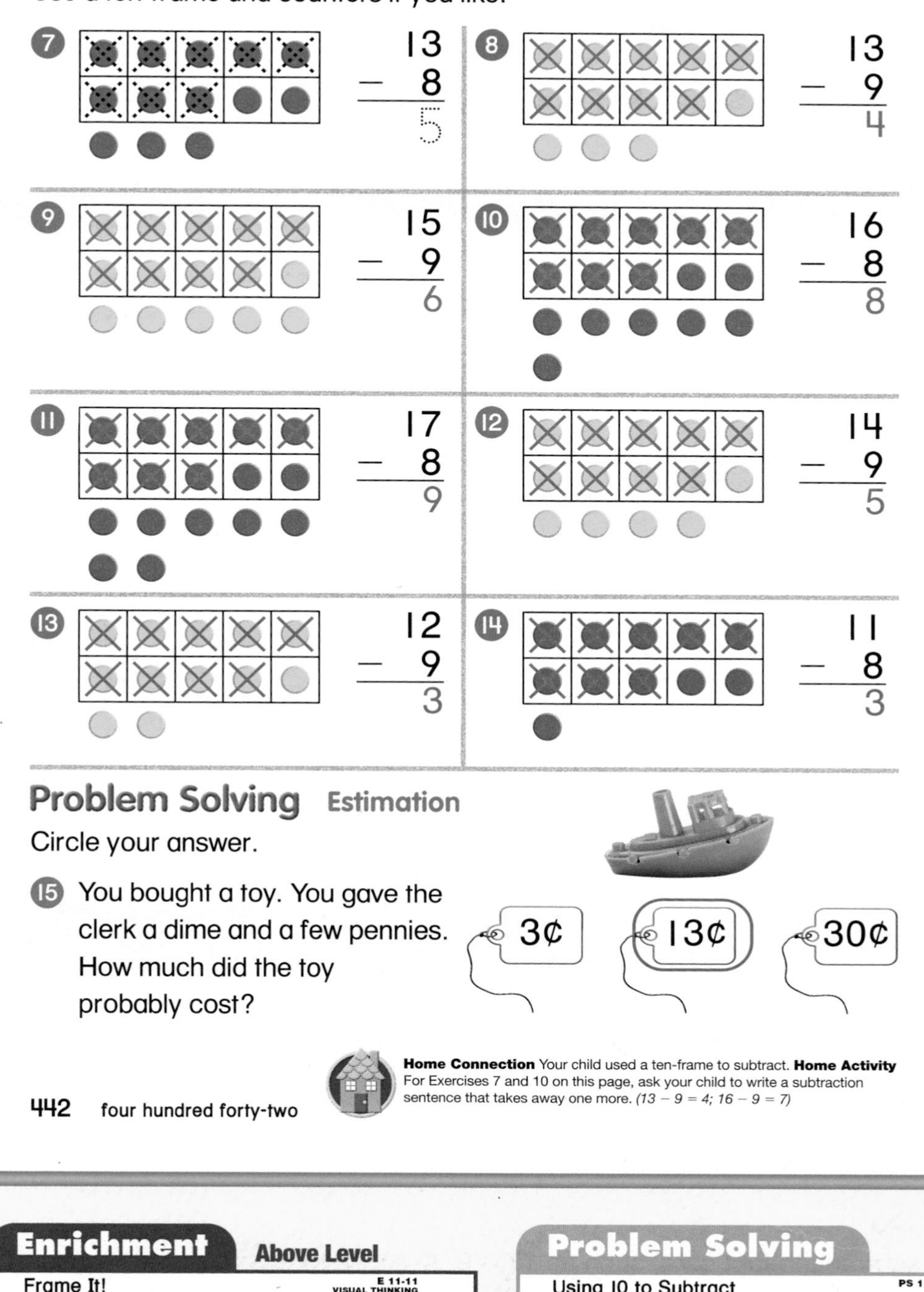

Practice

Cross out to subtract.
Use a ten-frame and counters if you like.

7. $13 - 8 = 5$
8. $13 - 9 = 4$
9. $15 - 9 = 6$
10. $16 - 8 = 8$
11. $17 - 8 = 9$
12. $14 - 9 = 5$
13. $12 - 9 = 3$
14. $11 - 8 = 3$

Problem Solving Estimation

Circle your answer.

15. You bought a toy. You gave the clerk a dime and a few pennies. How much did the toy probably cost?

3¢ 13¢ 30¢

Home Connection Your child used a ten-frame to subtract. **Home Activity** For Exercises 7 and 10 on this page, ask your child to write a subtraction sentence that takes away one more. *(13 − 9 = 4; 16 − 9 = 7)*

442 four hundred forty-two

Enrichment Above Level

Frame It! E 11-11 VISUAL THINKING

Write the number shown for each ten-frame. Use that number to write a subtraction fact. Cross out to complete your fact.

Answers may vary. Sample answers are given.

1. $15 - 6 = 9$
2. $17 - 8 = 9$
3. $13 - 5 = 8$
4. $18 - 9 = 9$
5. $14 - 7 = 7$
6. $16 - 9 = 7$
7. $11 - 5 = 6$
8. $12 - 8 = 4$

Use with Lesson 11-11. 143

Problem Solving

Using 10 to Subtract PS 11-11

Cross out to subtract. Use a ten frame and counters if you like.

1. Carmen has 12 grapes. She eats 7. How many grapes are left? 5 grapes
2. Sam picks 14 apples. He puts 9 in a basket. He puts the rest in a bag. How many apples are in the bag? 5 apples
3. William picks 17 flowers. 8 are daisies. The rest are roses. How many roses did William pick? 9 roses

Circle your answer.

4. Hector buys an apple. He gives the clerk a nickel and a few pennies. How much did the apple probably cost? 4¢ 8¢ 15¢

Use with Lesson 11-11. 143

3 Practice

For Exercise 15, remind children that an estimate does not have to be exact.

Reading Assist: Make Predictions Show fact cards for 14 − 9 and 14 − 8. Have children predict which will have the greater difference. Continue with other similar pairs of fact cards.

Leveled Practice

Below Level Use counters and a ten-frame for all exercises.

On Level Use counters and a ten-frame if needed.

Above Level Do all exercises mentally.

Early Finishers Have children choose a number between 11 and 18 and write three number sentences that show subtracting 10, 9, and 8 from the number.

4 Assess

Journal Idea Have children subtract 9 from each of the numbers between 11 and 18. Ask them to write each fact and to discuss the pattern they see.

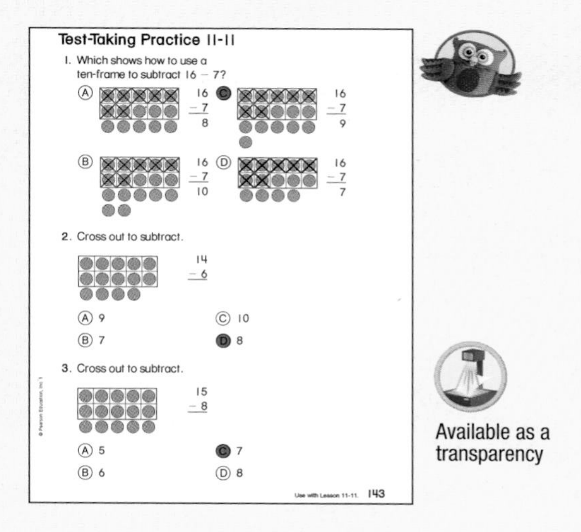

Test-Taking Practice 11-11

1. Which shows how to use a ten-frame to subtract 16 − 7?
 A. 16 − 7 = 8 B. 16 − 7 = 10 C. 16 − 7 = 9 D. 16 − 7 = 7
2. Cross out to subtract. 14 − 6
 A. 9 B. 7 C. 10 D. 8
3. Cross out to subtract. 15 − 8
 A. 5 B. 6 C. 7 D. 8

Use with Lesson 11-11. 143

Available as a transparency

Applying Subtraction Fact Strategies

Lesson Organizer

Quick Lesson Overview 

Objective Select and apply subtraction fact strategies.

Math Understanding There are a variety of strategies to use to find subtraction fact differences; which one is best depends on the numbers involved.

Professional Development Note

Math Background It is important for children to be able to recognize the various mathematical properties of a subtraction fact in order to select the appropriate strategy for remembering it. Children can apply their knowledge of addition strategies to help them choose appropriate subtraction strategies.

NCTM Standards

- Number and Operations

(For a complete correlation to the NCTM Standards and Grades Pre-K through 2 Expectations, see Pages 415G and 415H.)

Getting Started

Spiral Review

Problem of the Day 11-12

Pat has 2 cubes and 2 rectangular prisms. He will build towers using any two of these solids. How many different towers can he build?

Cubes	Rectangular Prisms

Topics Reviewed
- Geometric solids
- Problem-Solving Strategy: Make a Table

Answer Sample:

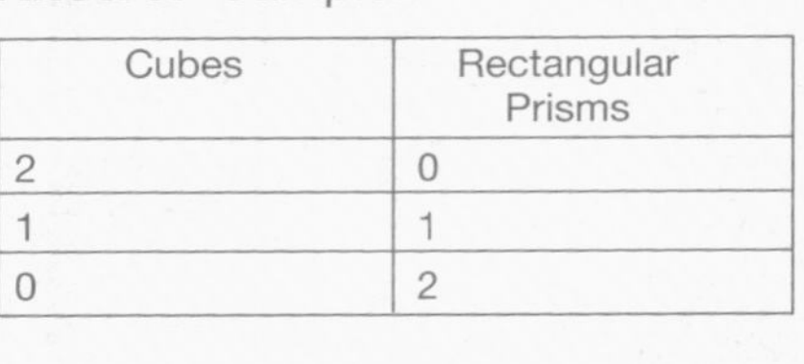

Cubes	Rectangular Prisms
2	0
1	1
0	2

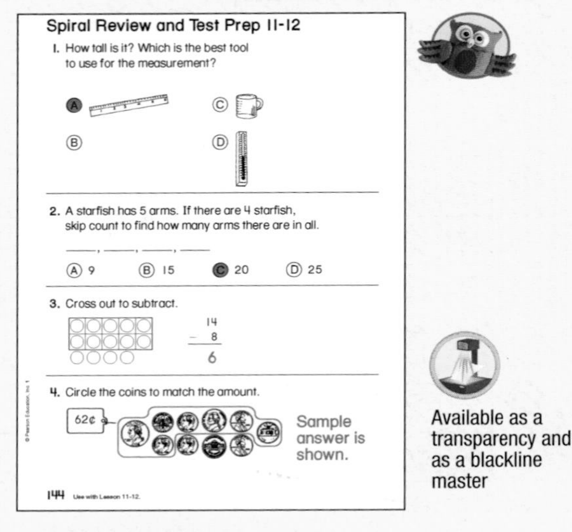

Spiral Review and Test Prep 11-12

1. How tall is it? Which is the best tool to use for the measurement?

Ⓐ Ⓑ Ⓒ Ⓓ

2. A starfish has 5 arms. If there are 4 starfish, skip count to find how many arms there are in all.

Ⓐ 9 Ⓑ 15 Ⓒ 20 Ⓓ 25

3. Cross out to subtract.

$14 - 8 = 6$

4. Circle the coins to match the amount.

62¢

Sample answer is shown.

144

Available as a transparency and as a blackline master

Topics Reviewed
1. Choosing a Measurement Tool
2. Using Skip Counting
3. Using 10 to Subtract
4. Counting Sets of Coins

Investigating the Concept

What Is the Difference?

10–15 MIN **Logical/Mathematical**

Materials Subtraction fact cards

What to Do

- Show a subtraction fact card, such as 13 − 9. Ask a child to explain how to find the difference using a related addition fact. *(To find 13 − 9 using a related fact, remember that 4 + 9 = 13. So 13 − 9 = 4.)*
- Then ask a child to explain how to find the difference by using a 10. *(Think 13 − 10 = 3 and then add 1. So 13 − 9 = 4.)*
- Repeat with other facts. Emphasize that using a 10 is a useful strategy when subtracting 8 or 9.

Ongoing Assessment

- **How did you decide which way to find the difference?** *(By seeing how the numbers are related to each other)*
- **Reasoning Do you always have to choose a way to find the difference?** *(Sample response: No; sometimes the answer has been memorized.)*

Reaching All Learners

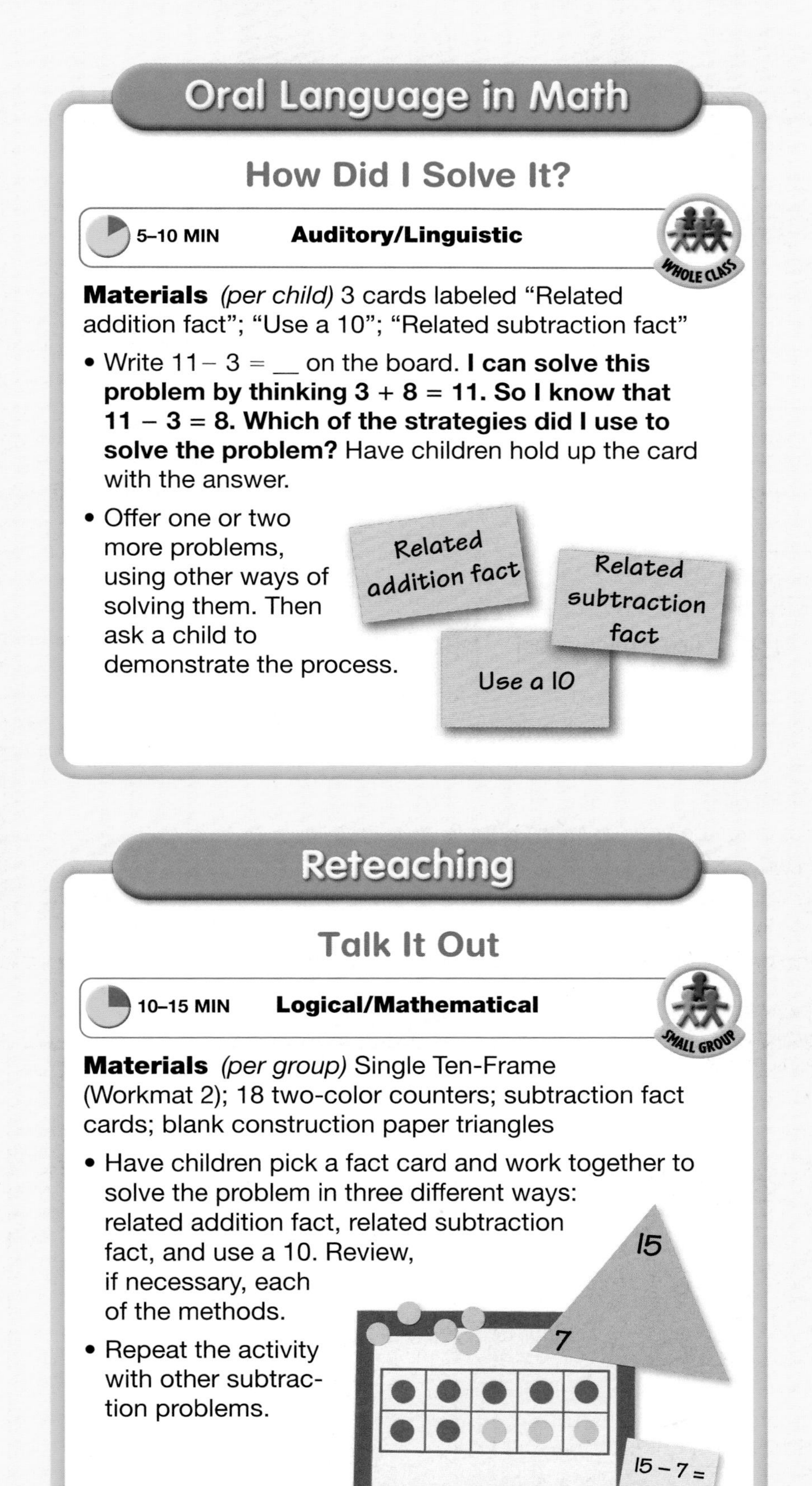

Oral Language in Math

How Did I Solve It?

5–10 MIN **Auditory/Linguistic** WHOLE CLASS

Materials *(per child)* 3 cards labeled "Related addition fact"; "Use a 10"; "Related subtraction fact"

- Write 11 – 3 = __ on the board. **I can solve this problem by thinking 3 + 8 = 11. So I know that 11 – 3 = 8. Which of the strategies did I use to solve the problem?** Have children hold up the card with the answer.
- Offer one or two more problems, using other ways of solving them. Then ask a child to demonstrate the process.

Reteaching

Talk It Out

10–15 MIN **Logical/Mathematical** SMALL GROUP

Materials *(per group)* Single Ten-Frame (Workmat 2); 18 two-color counters; subtraction fact cards; blank construction paper triangles

- Have children pick a fact card and work together to solve the problem in three different ways: related addition fact, related subtraction fact, and use a 10. Review, if necessary, each of the methods.
- Repeat the activity with other subtraction problems.

Activate Prior Knowledge/Build Background

English Language Learners

Use What You Know

10–15 MIN **Logical/Mathematical**

Materials Index cards labeled with subtraction problems

- Remind children that *related facts* are facts that are part of the same *fact family* and that you can use the *related facts* to solve subtraction problems.
- Give each pair an index card with a subtraction problem.
- Have children work together to write an addition fact and a subtraction fact that can help them solve the problem.

9 + 5 = 14
14 – 5 = 9
14 – 9 = __

Students with Special Needs

Solution Match Game

15–20 MIN **Visual/Spatial** SMALL GROUP

Materials *(per child)* Subtraction fact cards; cards with help for solving each problem (for example, for 12 – 5 = __, "helping cards" should read: 5 + 7 = 12 and 12 – 7 = 5)

- Give each child a subtraction problem card. Put all of the related cards in the center of the workspace, facedown.
- Have children take turns picking a card. If the problem on the card is related to their subtraction problem, that is, if it uses a strategy that can help them solve their problem, they keep it; if not, they put it back.
- Continue until all "helping cards" have been chosen and children have solved their subtraction problems.

Objective Select and apply subtraction fact strategies.

1 Warm Up

Activate Prior Knowledge Review how to use 10 to subtract. Write 14 − 8 on the board and illustrate it with a ten-frame. Discuss the subtraction strategy as follows: **14 − 8 is the same as 14 − 10 = 4 plus 2. So 14 − 8 = 6.**

2 Teach

Learn!

Have children discuss the two subtraction strategies shown at the top of the student page. Remind children that they can use a related addition fact to help them subtract or they can use a 10. Have volunteers take turns telling how to use each strategy to find the difference for 14 − 8.

Ongoing Assessment

Talk About It

- **Is one way better than the other for finding the difference?** *(No; they both work equally well.)*
- **Would you use a 10 when subtracting to find 13 − 2?** *(No; it is better to use a 10 when subtracting 8 or 9.)*

If children do not understand the strategies,

then have them review each strategy by working through a problem together.

Check

Error Intervention

If children have difficulty selecting a strategy,

then have them use connecting cubes or a ten-frame to model the way to find each difference. *(Also see* Reteaching, *Page 443B.)*

Think About It Have children count how many times they used each strategy and ask them to share their results with the class.

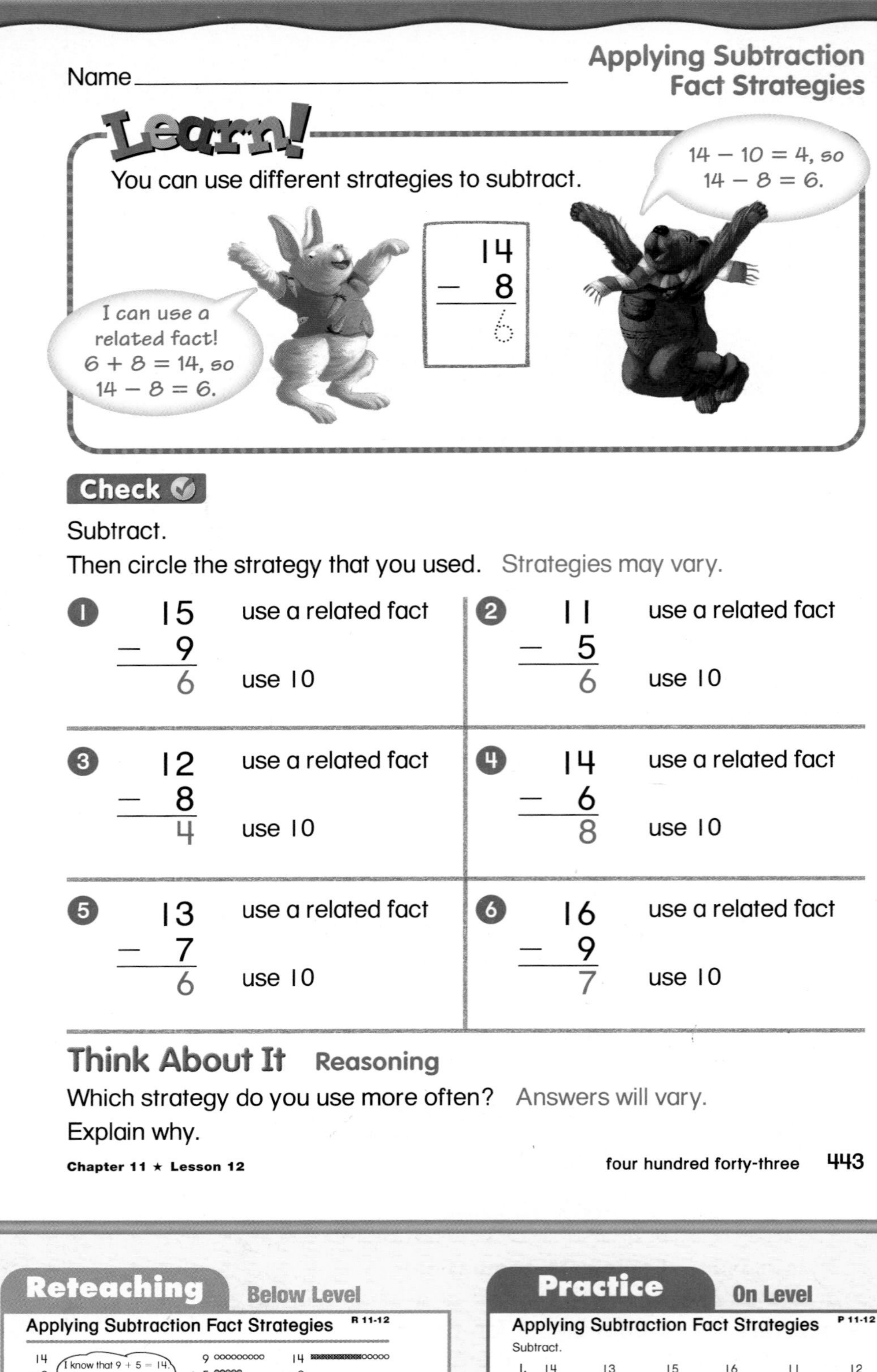

Name ____________________

Applying Subtraction Fact Strategies

Learn!

You can use different strategies to subtract.

Check

Subtract.

Then circle the strategy that you used. Strategies may vary.

1. 15 − 9 = 6 — use a related fact / use 10
2. 11 − 5 = 6 — use a related fact / use 10
3. 12 − 8 = 4 — use a related fact / use 10
4. 14 − 6 = 8 — use a related fact / use 10
5. 13 − 7 = 6 — use a related fact / use 10
6. 16 − 9 = 7 — use a related fact / use 10

Think About It Reasoning

Which strategy do you use more often? Answers will vary.

Explain why.

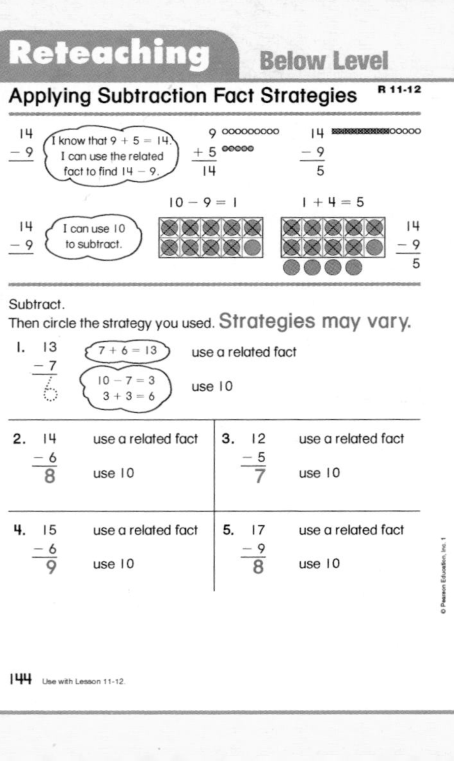

Reteaching Below Level

Applying Subtraction Fact Strategies R 11-12

14 − 9 — I know that 9 + 5 = 14. I can use the related fact to find 14 − 9. 9 + 5 = 14; 14 − 9 = 5

14 − 9 — I can use 10 to subtract. 10 − 9 = 1; 1 + 4 = 5; 14 − 9 = 5

Subtract.

Then circle the strategy you used. Strategies may vary.

1. 13 − 7 = 6 — use a related fact (7 + 6 = 13) / use 10 (10 − 7 = 3, 3 + 3 = 6)
2. 14 − 6 = 8 — use a related fact / use 10
3. 12 − 5 = 7 — use a related fact / use 10
4. 15 − 6 = 9 — use a related fact / use 10
5. 17 − 9 = 8 — use a related fact / use 10

144 Use with Lesson 11-12.

Practice On Level

Applying Subtraction Fact Strategies P 11-12

Subtract.

1.	14 − 9 = 5	13 − 5 = 8	15 − 7 = 8	16 − 8 = 8	11 − 8 = 3	12 − 7 = 5
2.	18 − 9 = 9	15 − 6 = 9	14 − 5 = 9	16 − 9 = 7	11 − 3 = 8	15 − 8 = 7
3.	17 − 8 = 9	12 − 5 = 7	13 − 7 = 6	16 − 7 = 9	12 − 4 = 8	14 − 7 = 7
4.	10 − 5 = 5	13 − 9 = 4	14 − 6 = 8	17 − 9 = 8	14 − 8 = 6	11 − 5 = 6

Problem Solving *Reasonableness*

Circle your answer.

5. If Mary has 13 − 8 pennies and Terry has 13 − 6 pennies, then which sentence is true?

Mary has more pennies than Terry.

(Terry has more pennies than Mary.)

144 Use with Lesson 11-12.

Practice

Subtract.

7.

13	14	17	15
− 9	− 7	− 8	− 6
4	7	9	9

8.

16	13	14	17	9	15
− 8	− 8	− 8	− 9	− 9	− 9
8	5	6	8	0	6

9.

13	15	12	16	14	13
− 4	− 8	− 3	− 9	− 6	− 7
9	7	9	7	8	6

10.

15	14	13	10	18	14
− 7	− 9	− 6	− 7	− 9	− 5
8	5	7	3	9	9

11.

12	7	11	8	10	12
− 4	− 0	− 5	− 8	− 4	− 6
8	7	6	0	6	6

Problem Solving Reasonableness

Circle your answer.

12. If Jay has 12 − 8 ribbons and May has 12 − 5 ribbons, then which sentence is true?

Jay has more ribbons than May.

(May has more ribbons than Jay.)

Home Connection Your child chose a strategy and used it to subtract. **Home Activity** Have your child explain how he or she solved the problems in Exercise 7.

3 Practice

Remind children that there are many strategies that can be used to solve the problems on the student page.

Leveled Practice

Below Level Work in pairs to complete all exercises, using counters and a ten-frame.

On Level Use counters and a ten-frame if needed.

Above Level Complete all exercises without using counters or a ten-frame.

Early Finishers Have each child write the related addition fact used to solve each subtraction problem.

4 Assess

Journal Idea Ask children to write five addition facts and their related subtraction facts.

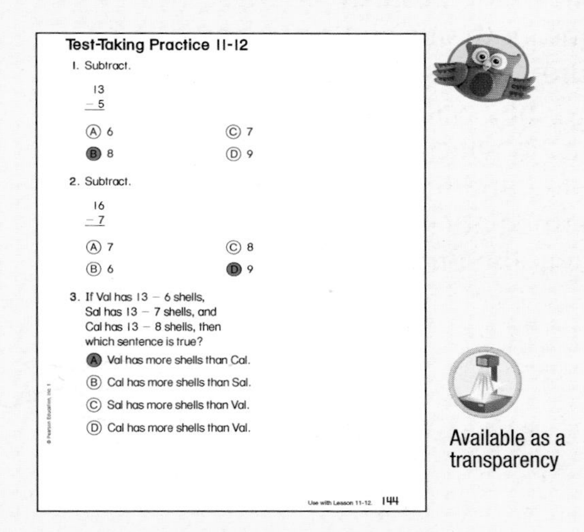

Test-Taking Practice 11-12

1. Subtract.

13
− 5

Ⓐ 6 Ⓒ 7
● 8 Ⓓ 9

2. Subtract.

16
− 7

Ⓐ 7 Ⓒ 8
Ⓑ 6 ● 9

3. If Val has 13 − 6 shells, Sal has 13 − 7 shells, and Cal has 13 − 8 shells, then which sentence is true?

● Val has more shells than Cal.
Ⓑ Cal has more shells than Sal.
Ⓒ Sal has more shells than Val.
Ⓓ Cal has more shells than Val.

Use with Lesson 11-12. 144

Available as a transparency

Enrichment Above Level

You Name It! E 11-12 DECISION MAKING

For each addition fact write a related subtraction fact. Then complete the story problems using the subtraction facts you wrote. Sample answers are given.

1. 8 + 4 = 12 — 12 − 4 = 8
2. 6 + 7 = 13 — 13 − 7 = 6
3. 9 + 6 = 15 — 15 − 6 = 9
4. 5 + 6 = 11 — 11 − 6 = 5
5. Ann Marie found 15 shells. She gave 6 shells to Amy. Ann Marie has 9 shells left.
6. Peter makes 13 muffins. He eats 7 of them. There are 6 muffins left.
7. Dan has 12 model cars. He wants to keep 8 of them. The rest he gives away. Dan gives 4 cars away.
8. Rita reads 11 books. 6 of the books are about dogs. How many books are not about dogs? 5 books

144 Use with Lesson 11-12.

Problem Solving

Applying Subtraction Fact Strategies PS 11-12

Write a subtraction sentence to solve. Then circle the strategy you used. Strategies may vary.

1. Pat has 14 beads. She uses 8 beads to make a bracelet. How many beads does she have left?
   14 − 8 = 6
   6 beads
   use a related fact use 10
2. Mike has 16 stamps. He uses 9 of them to mail letters. How many stamps does he have left?
   16 − 9 = 7
   7 stamps
   use a related fact use 10
3. Meg has 11 stuffed animals. She gives 6 to a friend. How many does she have left?
   11 − 6 = 5
   5 stuffed animals
   use a related fact use 10
4. Tom has 12 action figures. He brings 4 action figures to a friend's house. How many does he leave at home?
   12 − 4 = 8
   8 action figures
   use a related fact use 10

Circle your answer.

5. If Lenny has 11 − 5 apples and Laura has 11 − 3 apples, then which sentence is true?
   (Laura has more apples than Lenny.)
   Lenny has more apples than Laura.

144 Use with Lesson 11-12.

Multiple-Step Problems

Lesson Organizer

Quick Lesson Overview

Objective Solve multiple-step problems by using the answer to the first question to answer the second question.

Math Understanding The answer to one problem can be used as information needed to solve another problem.

Professional Development Note

Math Background In this lesson, children are asked to solve multiple-step problems in which the answer to one part is needed to solve the next part of the problem. In these problems, both questions are stated. As children's problem-solving skills improve, they will be asked to solve problems in which the first question is unstated and the child must elicit the intermediate information needed for solving the problem.

NCTM Standards

- Number and Operations
- Algebra

(For a complete correlation to the NCTM Standards and Grades Pre-K through 2 Expectations, see Pages 415G and 415H.)

Getting Started

Spiral Review

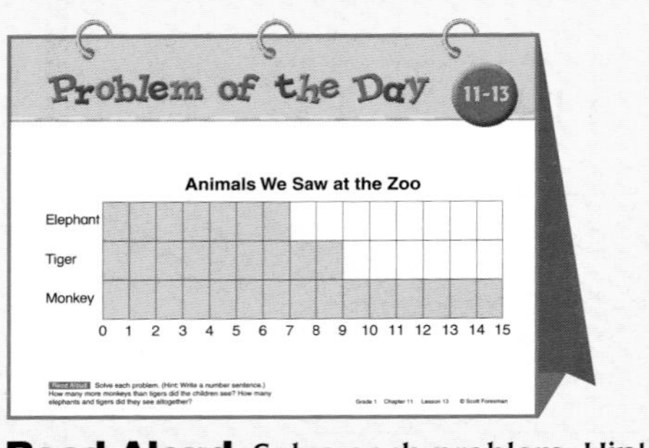

Read Aloud Solve each problem. Hint: Write a number sentence. How many more monkeys than tigers did the children see? How many elephants and tigers did they see altogether?

Topics Reviewed

- Addition and subtraction
- Problem-Solving Strategy: Write a Number Sentence

Answer They saw 6 more monkeys than tigers; $15 - 9 = 6$. They saw 16 elephants and tigers; $7 + 9 = 16$.

Spiral Review and Test Prep 11-13

1. Subtract to find the difference.
   16
   − 9
   Ⓐ 6 Ⓑ 9 Ⓒ 8 Ⓓ 7
2. Jade spun this spinner 12 times. She landed on gray 9 times. How many times did she land on white?
   Ⓐ 9 Ⓑ 5 Ⓒ 4 Ⓓ 3
3. Sun Kam bought some celery to make chow mein. The celery cost 23¢. If she gave the clerk 3 dimes, did she get change? Explain.
   Yes. Sample answer: 3 dimes are 30¢ and 23¢ is less money than 30¢.
4. Write how many hundreds, tens, and ones there are. Then write the number.
   2 hundreds 5 tens 7 ones = 257

Use with Lesson 11-13. 145

Available as a transparency and as a blackline master

Topics Reviewed

1. Applying Subtraction Fact Strategies
2. More Likely or Less Likely
3. Use Data from a Table
4. Hundreds

Investigating the Concept

Story Chains

10–15 MIN **Linguistic/Logical/Mathematical**

What to Do

- Begin a story as follows: **I had 6 apples. Then my mother gave me 6 more apples. How many apples do I have in all?** *(6 + 6 = 12)*
- Then continue the story, noting that the answer to the first part must be used to answer the question in the second part. **If I eat 3 of the apples, how many will I have left?** *(12 − 3 = 9)* Have volunteers continue the chain, noting the addition or subtraction.
- Next, begin a new chain of stories.

Ongoing Assessment

- **How are the stories connected?** *(The answer to the first story problem is needed to answer the question in the next story problem.)*
- **Reasoning How can you remember the information you need?** *(Write down the number sentences and the answers.)*

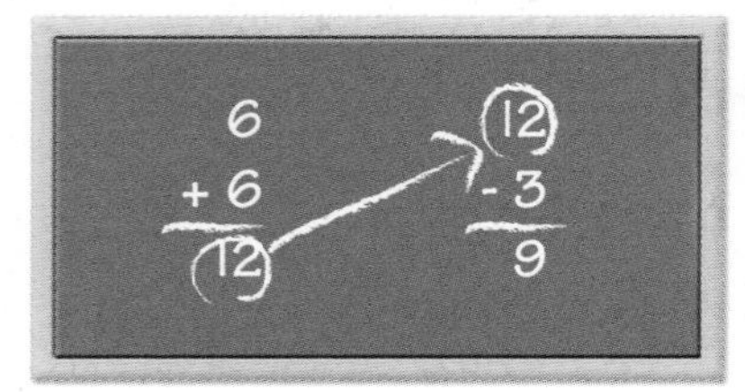

Reaching All Learners

Writing in Math

Keep the Problem Going

10–15 MIN **Linguistic**

- Invite a child to think of a one-step word problem and to say it aloud.
- Have a volunteer solve it and then write a related problem based on the solution to the first problem. Have another volunteer solve this second problem.
- Have children work in pairs to write two-part problems to share with the whole class. Invite the other children to solve the problems.

I had 4 granola bars.
My friend gave me 3 more.
How many did I have?
$4 + 3 = 7$

I ate 2 of the granola bars.
How many do I have left?
$7 - 2 = 5$

Access Content

English Language Learners

Listen and Follow

10–15 MIN **Auditory/Kinesthetic**

Materials Pennies or other manipulatives

- Explain that you will say story problems that take a few steps to solve. Children will listen carefully and follow along.
- Give some pennies to each child to use to solve the problem. **I had 8 pennies.** (Children take 8 pennies.) **I lost 2.** (Children put 2 back.) **My friend gave me 4 more.** (Children take 4 pennies.) **How many pennies do I have now?** *(10)*

- Give children the opportunity to make up problems.

Reteaching

Acting Out the Problem

5–10 MIN **Kinesthetic**

- Invite 3 children to the front of the class. **I had 3 balls.** (Ask children to hop up and down like bouncing balls.) **2 of them bounced away.** (Cue 2 children to hop back to their seats.) **Which number sentence tells what happened?** *($3 - 2 = 1$)* **Then my friend threw his ball to me.** (Invite another child to hop up.) **Which number sentence tells how many balls I have now?** *($1 + 1 = 2$)*
- Repeat with other children and other word problems, telling the whole story before asking for the number sentences.

Advanced Learners

What Do You See?

10–15 MIN **Logical/Mathematical**

Materials Connecting cubes of different colors

- Invite children to watch carefully and write the problems as they see them.
- Place 5 blue connecting cubes in a row, add 4 red cubes, take away 3 red cubes, and, finally, add 2 yellow cubes. Ask children which number problems they saw. *($5 + 4 = 9$, $9 - 3 = 6$, $6 + 2 = 8$)*
- Repeat with other problems.

Objective Solve multiple-step problems by using the answer to the first question to answer the second question.

1 Warm Up

Activate Prior Knowledge Review how to choose an operation. Tell simple joining and separating stories. Ask children to decide whether to use addition or subtraction to solve them.

2 Teach

Learn!

Read aloud the problem at the top of the student page. Solve the first problem. Help children see that the answer to the first problem will be used in the next part of the problem. Then solve the second problem.

Ongoing Assessment

Talk About It

- **How do you know which operation to use?** *(To find a whole or to join groups, use addition. To take away, separate groups, or compare, use subtraction.)*
- **Why is it important to answer the first question correctly?** *(If you answer incorrectly, then the answer to the second question might also be incorrect.)*

If children do not see that the answer to the first question is used to answer the second question,

then have them circle the 12 in both problems.

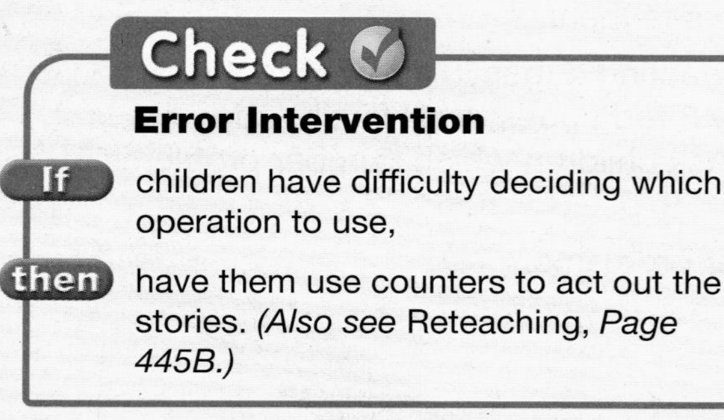

Check

Error Intervention

If children have difficulty deciding which operation to use,

then have them use counters to act out the stories. *(Also see* Reteaching, *Page 445B.)*

Think About It Ask: **In Exercise 1, where did the 7 in the second addition sentence come from?**

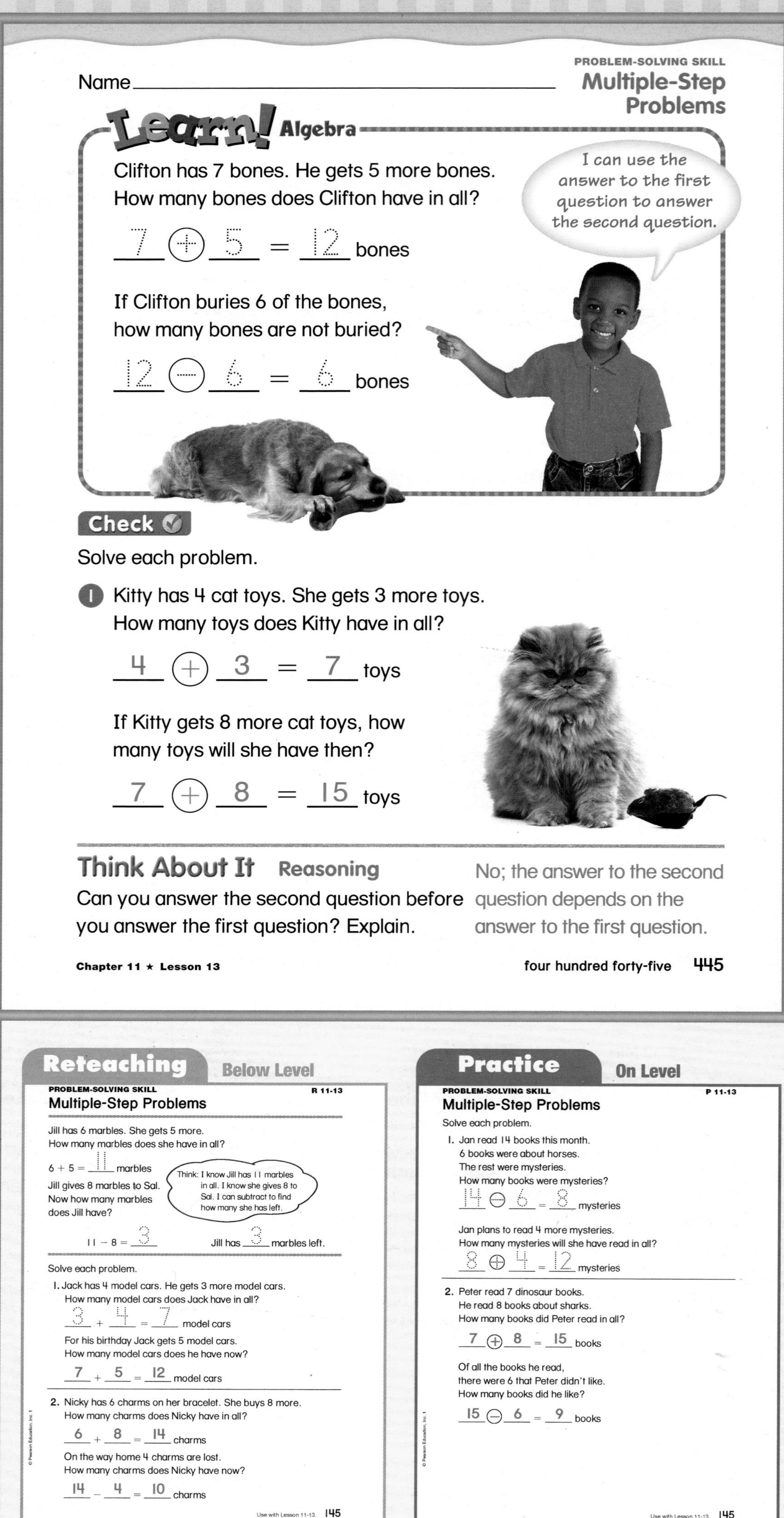

Name ______________________

PROBLEM-SOLVING SKILL
Multiple-Step Problems

Learn! Algebra

Clifton has 7 bones. He gets 5 more bones. How many bones does Clifton have in all?

7 (+) 5 = 12 bones

If Clifton buries 6 of the bones, how many bones are not buried?

12 (−) 6 = 6 bones

Check

Solve each problem.

1. Kitty has 4 cat toys. She gets 3 more toys. How many toys does Kitty have in all?

   4 (+) 3 = 7 toys

   If Kitty gets 8 more cat toys, how many toys will she have then?

   7 (+) 8 = 15 toys

Think About It Reasoning
Can you answer the second question before you answer the first question? Explain.
No; the answer to the second question depends on the answer to the first question.

Chapter 11 ★ Lesson 13 — four hundred forty-five 445

Reteaching Below Level

PROBLEM-SOLVING SKILL R 11-13
Multiple-Step Problems

Jill has 6 marbles. She gets 5 more.
How many marbles does she have in all?

6 + 5 = 11 marbles

Jill gives 8 marbles to Sal.
Now how many marbles does Jill have?

Think: I know Jill has 11 marbles in all. I know she gives 8 to Sal. I can subtract to find how many she has left.

11 − 8 = 3 Jill has 3 marbles left.

Solve each problem.

1. Jack has 4 model cars. He gets 3 more model cars.
   How many model cars does Jack have in all?
   3 + 4 = 7 model cars
   For his birthday Jack gets 5 model cars.
   How many model cars does he have now?
   7 + 5 = 12 model cars
2. Nicky has 6 charms on her bracelet. She buys 8 more.
   How many charms does Nicky have in all?
   6 + 8 = 14 charms
   On the way home 4 charms are lost.
   How many charms does Nicky have now?
   14 − 4 = 10 charms

Use with Lesson 11-13. 145

Practice On Level

PROBLEM-SOLVING SKILL P 11-13
Multiple-Step Problems

Solve each problem.

1. Jan read 14 books this month.
   6 books were about horses.
   The rest were mysteries.
   How many books were mysteries?
   14 (−) 6 = 8 mysteries
   Jan plans to read 4 more mysteries.
   How many mysteries will she have read in all?
   8 (+) 4 = 12 mysteries
2. Peter read 7 dinosaur books.
   He read 8 books about sharks.
   How many books did Peter read in all?
   7 (+) 8 = 15 books
   Of all the books he read, there were 6 that Peter didn't like.
   How many books did he like?
   15 (−) 6 = 9 books

Use with Lesson 11-13. 145

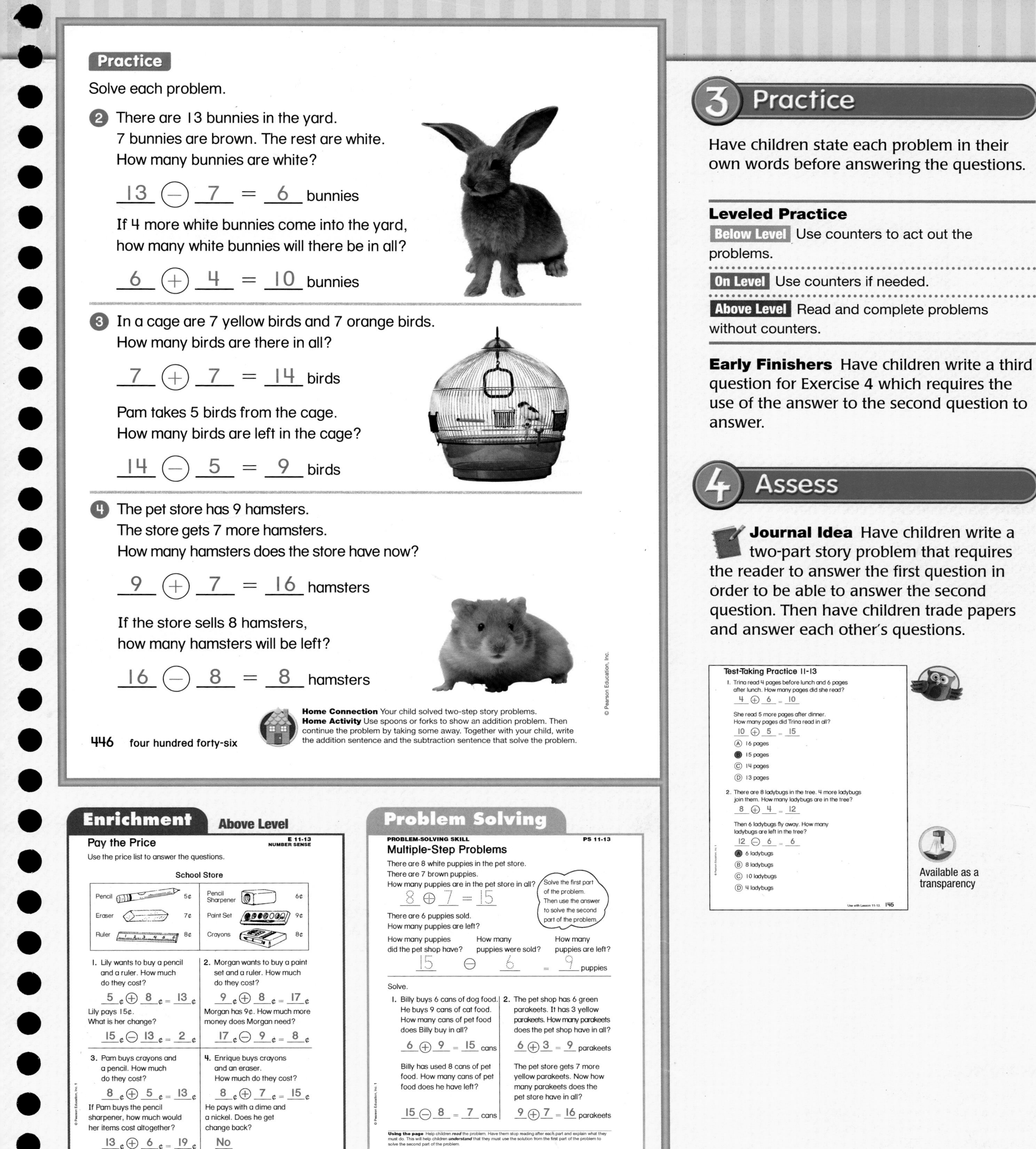

Practice

Solve each problem.

2 There are 13 bunnies in the yard.
7 bunnies are brown. The rest are white.
How many bunnies are white?

13 ⊖ 7 = 6 bunnies

If 4 more white bunnies come into the yard, how many white bunnies will there be in all?

6 ⊕ 4 = 10 bunnies

3 In a cage are 7 yellow birds and 7 orange birds.
How many birds are there in all?

7 ⊕ 7 = 14 birds

Pam takes 5 birds from the cage.
How many birds are left in the cage?

14 ⊖ 5 = 9 birds

4 The pet store has 9 hamsters.
The store gets 7 more hamsters.
How many hamsters does the store have now?

9 ⊕ 7 = 16 hamsters

If the store sells 8 hamsters, how many hamsters will be left?

16 ⊖ 8 = 8 hamsters

Home Connection Your child solved two-step story problems. **Home Activity** Use spoons or forks to show an addition problem. Then continue the problem by taking some away. Together with your child, write the addition sentence and the subtraction sentence that solve the problem.

Enrichment — Above Level

Pay the Price

E 11-13 NUMBER SENSE

Use the price list to answer the questions.

School Store

Pencil	5¢	Pencil Sharpener	6¢
Eraser	7¢	Paint Set	9¢
Ruler	8¢	Crayons	8¢

1. Lily wants to buy a pencil and a ruler. How much do they cost?
5¢ ⊕ 8¢ = 13¢
Lily pays 15¢. What is her change?
15¢ ⊖ 13¢ = 2¢

2. Morgan wants to buy a paint set and a ruler. How much do they cost?
9¢ ⊕ 8¢ = 17¢
Morgan has 9¢. How much more money does Morgan need?
17¢ ⊖ 9¢ = 8¢

3. Pam buys crayons and a pencil. How much do they cost?
8¢ ⊕ 5¢ = 13¢
If Pam buys the pencil sharpener, how much would her items cost altogether?
13¢ ⊕ 6¢ = 19¢

4. Enrique buys crayons and an eraser. How much do they cost?
8¢ ⊕ 7¢ = 15¢
He pays with a dime and a nickel. Does he get change back?
No

Use with Lesson 11-13. 145

Problem Solving

PROBLEM-SOLVING SKILL — PS 11-13

Multiple-Step Problems

There are 8 white puppies in the pet store.
There are 7 brown puppies.
How many puppies are in the pet store in all?

8 ⊕ 7 = 15

Solve the first part of the problem. Then use the answer to solve the second part of the problem.

There are 6 puppies sold.
How many puppies are left?

How many puppies did the pet shop have?		How many puppies were sold?		How many puppies are left?
15	⊖	6	=	9 puppies

Solve.

1. Billy buys 6 cans of dog food. He buys 9 cans of cat food. How many cans of pet food does Billy buy in all?
6 ⊕ 9 = 15 cans
Billy has used 8 cans of pet food. How many cans of pet food does he have left?
15 ⊖ 8 = 7 cans

2. The pet shop has 6 green parakeets. It has 3 yellow parakeets. How many parakeets does the pet shop have in all?
6 ⊕ 3 = 9 parakeets
The pet store gets 7 more yellow parakeets. Now how many parakeets does the pet store have in all?
9 ⊕ 7 = 16 parakeets

Using the page Help children *read* the problem. Have them stop reading after each part and explain what they must do. This will help children *understand* that they must use the solution from the first part of the problem to solve the second part of the problem.

Use with Lesson 11-13. 145

3 Practice

Have children state each problem in their own words before answering the questions.

Leveled Practice

Below Level Use counters to act out the problems.

On Level Use counters if needed.

Above Level Read and complete problems without counters.

Early Finishers Have children write a third question for Exercise 4 which requires the use of the answer to the second question to answer.

4 Assess

Journal Idea Have children write a two-part story problem that requires the reader to answer the first question in order to be able to answer the second question. Then have children trade papers and answer each other's questions.

Test-Taking Practice 11-13

1. Trina read 4 pages before lunch and 6 pages after lunch. How many pages did she read?
4 ⊕ 6 = 10
She read 5 more pages after dinner. How many pages did Trina read in all?
10 ⊕ 5 = 15
Ⓐ 16 pages
Ⓑ 15 pages
Ⓒ 14 pages
Ⓓ 13 pages

2. There are 8 ladybugs in the tree. 4 more ladybugs join them. How many ladybugs are in the tree?
8 ⊕ 4 = 12
Then 6 ladybugs fly away. How many ladybugs are left in the tree?
12 ⊖ 6 = 6
Ⓐ 6 ladybugs
Ⓑ 8 ladybugs
Ⓒ 10 ladybugs
Ⓓ 4 ladybugs

Use with Lesson 11-13. 145

Available as a transparency

On the Farm

Lesson Organizer

Quick Lesson Overview

Objective Review and apply concepts, skills, and strategies learned in this and previous chapters.

Math Understanding Some real-world problems can be solved using known concepts, skills, and strategies.

Professional Development Note

Math Background Children have had experience using doubles, doubles-plus-1, and doubles-minus-1 facts; using a 10; and using related facts to help find a sum or difference. Children can now apply what they know to solve new problems.

NCTM Standards

- Number and Operations

(For a complete correlation to the NCTM Standards and Grades Pre-K through 2 Expectations, see Pages 415G and 415H.)

Getting Started

Spiral Review

Problem of the Day 11-14

Solve. Tell how you found your answer.
Mary has V raisins. She gets X more. Then she eats I raisin. How many raisins does Mary have now?

Standard Numeral	Roman Numeral
1	I
5	V
10	X

Read Aloud The Romans used I, V, and X for the numbers 1, 5, and 10. The symbols probably came from an earlier method of writing numbers when cuts were made on a wooden stick.

Grade 1 Chapter 11 Lesson 14 © Scott Foresman

Read Aloud The Romans used I, V, and X for the numbers 1, 5, and 10. The symbols probably came from an earlier method of writing numbers when cuts were made on a wooden stick.

Topics Reviewed
- Number sense
- Addition and subtraction
- Problem-Solving Skill: Multiple-Step Problem

Answer Mary has 14 raisins.

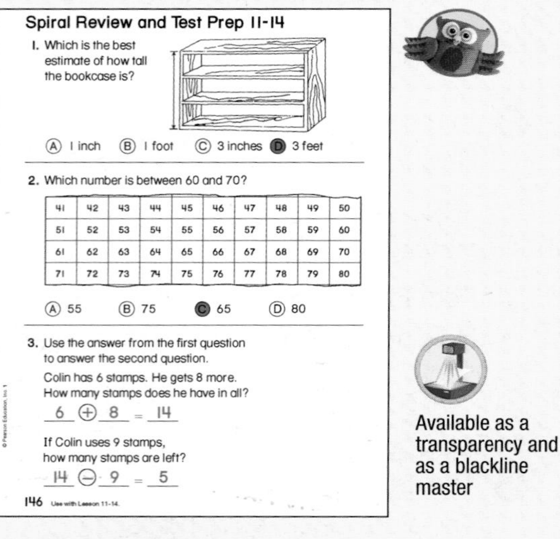

Spiral Review and Test Prep 11-14

1. Which is the best estimate of how tall the bookcase is?

Ⓐ 1 inch Ⓑ 1 foot Ⓒ 3 inches Ⓓ 3 feet

2. Which number is between 60 and 70?

41	42	43	44	45	46	47	48	49	50
51	52	53	54	55	56	57	58	59	60
61	62	63	64	65	66	67	68	69	70
71	72	73	74	75	76	77	78	79	80

Ⓐ 55 Ⓑ 75 Ⓒ 65 Ⓓ 80

3. Use the answer from the first question to answer the second question.

Colin has 6 stamps. He gets 8 more. How many stamps does he have in all?

6 ⊕ 8 = 14

If Colin uses 9 stamps, how many stamps are left?

14 ⊖ 9 = 5

146 Use with Lesson 11-14.

© Pearson Education, Inc. 1

Available as a transparency and as a blackline master

Topics Reviewed
1. Estimating and Measuring with Feet
2. Skip-Counting Patterns on the Hundred Chart
3. Multiple-Step Problems

Investigating the Concept

Reviewing Addition and Subtraction

10–15 MIN **Logical/Mathematical**

What to Do

- Write the following on the board: 6 + 7 = ___; 12 − 4 = ___; 8 + 6 = ___.
- Ask a volunteer to write the doubles fact that could be used to find the sum of 6 + 7. *(6 + 6 = 12 or 7 + 7 = 14)*
- Invite a child to write three facts to complete the fact family for 12 − 4 = 8. *(8 + 4 = 12; 12 − 8 = 4; 4 + 8 = 12)*
- Choose a volunteer to explain how to make a 10 to find the sum of 8 + 6. *(Take 2 from 6 and add it to 8 to make 10. 10 + 4 = 14, so 8 + 6 = 14.)*

Since I know 6 + 6 = 12, I also know 6 + 7 = 13.

6 + 7 = ___

Ongoing Assessment

- **Which doubles fact can help you find the difference for 18 – 9?** *(9 + 9 = 18)*
- **Reasoning When is it helpful to use a doubles fact?** *(When you are finding the sum of a doubles-minus-1 fact or a doubles-plus-1 fact)*

Reaching All Learners

Reading in Math

Math Big Book

15–20 MIN **Linguistic/Logical/Mathematical**

Materials Large sheets of paper; crayons or markers

- Write a math story with the class.
- Use this pattern to begin the book:

  "A rooster wakes up at Greenhill Farm.
  Six chickens wake up at Greenhill Farm.
  The rooster and chickens wake up 9 chicks.
  How many chickens are up at Greenhill Farm?"

- Have children illustrate the book and write number sentences to go with the illustrations. Continue with other numbers of animals and where they live.

Activate Prior Knowledge/Build Background

English Language Learners

Farmers' Market

15–20 MIN **Kinesthetic/Linguistic**

Materials Plastic fruits, vegetables, and flowers; dimes; pennies; posterboard; markers

- Invite children to set up a farmers' market by assembling the plastic produce, labeling the items, and pricing them.
- Help children write names for the items that they will sell.
- Give the customers a supply of dimes and pennies and give the sellers paper and pencils to calculate the totals of the items sold.

Reteaching

Cows in the Barn

15–20 MIN **Kinesthetic/Logical/Mathematical**

Materials 2 dot cubes; markers; posterboard; counters

- Prepare a gameboard by drawing a path from a meadow to a barn. Have children toss the dot cubes, add to find the sum of the numbers shown, and try to get their cow (counter) to the barn.
- The game can be varied by adding an additional cube with 1s and 0s for adding doubles-plus-1 facts.

Math and Science

Domestic Animal Research

15–20 MIN **Linguistic**

WHOLE CLASS

- Compile interesting statistics on farm animals to make a "Do You Know?" bulletin board.
- Begin by talking about animals that people raise on farms, such as pigs, cows, sheep, and chickens.
- Brainstorm interesting questions to research, such as: **How many eggs does a hen lay in one day? in one week? in one month? How many babies do pigs have? How many more babies do pigs have than sheep?**

Objective Review and apply concepts, skills, and strategies learned in this and previous chapters.

1 Warm Up

Activate Prior Knowledge Review related facts. Ask one child to write an addition sentence on the board. Then ask another child to write a related subtraction sentence.

2 Teach

Explain to children that they will use what they already know about addition and subtraction facts to solve the problems on the student page. Read the first problem aloud.

Ongoing Assessment

Talk About It

- **What do we need to find out?** *(How many eggs are hatching in all)*
- **What do we know?** *(One hen is hatching 7 eggs, and another hen is hatching 7 eggs.)*
- **How can we solve this problem?** *(Sample responses: Act it out, use counters, draw a picture, or use numbers.)*
- **Which doubles fact can help you solve this problem?** *(7 + 7 = 14)*

If children cannot complete the number sentence,

then have them circle the numbers in the story problem and decide whether to add or subtract.

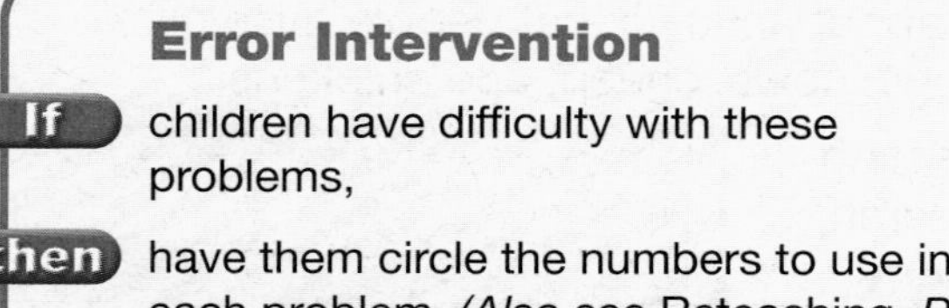

Error Intervention

If children have difficulty with these problems,

then have them circle the numbers to use in each problem. *(Also see* Reteaching, *Page 447B.)*

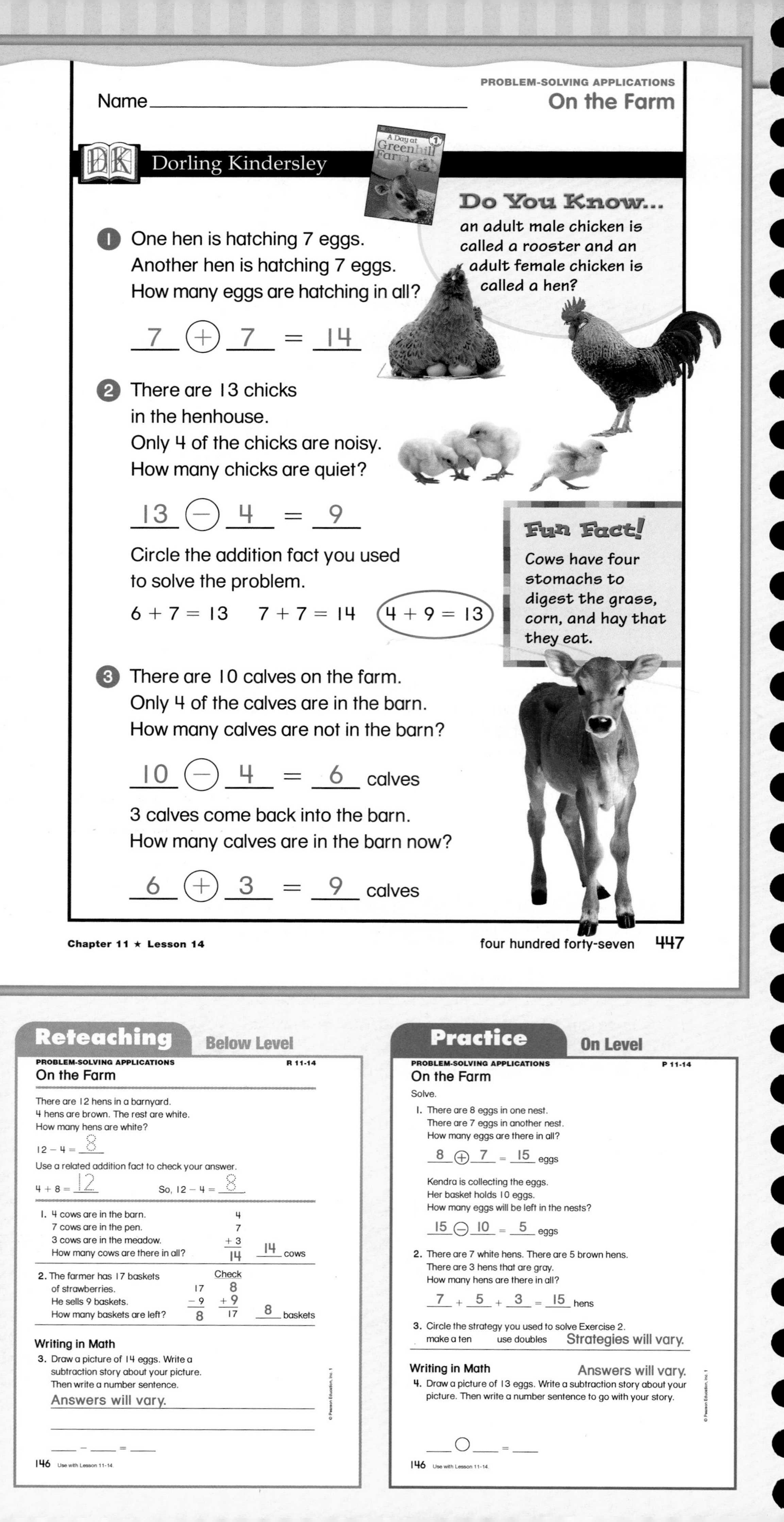

PROBLEM-SOLVING APPLICATIONS
On the Farm

Name ____________________

Dorling Kindersley

Do You Know... an adult male chicken is called a rooster and an adult female chicken is called a hen?

1. One hen is hatching 7 eggs. Another hen is hatching 7 eggs. How many eggs are hatching in all?

   7 (+) 7 = 14

2. There are 13 chicks in the henhouse. Only 4 of the chicks are noisy. How many chicks are quiet?

   13 (−) 4 = 9

   Circle the addition fact you used to solve the problem.

   6 + 7 = 13 7 + 7 = 14 (4 + 9 = 13)

Fun Fact! Cows have four stomachs to digest the grass, corn, and hay that they eat.

3. There are 10 calves on the farm. Only 4 of the calves are in the barn. How many calves are not in the barn?

   10 (−) 4 = 6 calves

   3 calves come back into the barn. How many calves are in the barn now?

   6 (+) 3 = 9 calves

Chapter 11 ★ Lesson 14 four hundred forty-seven 447

Reteaching Below Level

PROBLEM-SOLVING APPLICATIONS R 11-14
On the Farm

There are 12 hens in a barnyard.
4 hens are brown. The rest are white.
How many hens are white?

12 − 4 = 8

Use a related addition fact to check your answer.

4 + 8 = 12 So, 12 − 4 = 8

1. 4 cows are in the barn. 7 cows are in the pen. 3 cows are in the meadow. How many cows are there in all? 4 + 7 + 3 = 14; 14 cows

2. The farmer has 17 baskets of strawberries. He sells 9 baskets. How many baskets are left? 17 − 9 = 8; Check 8 + 9 = 17; 8 baskets

Writing in Math

3. Draw a picture of 14 eggs. Write a subtraction story about your picture. Then write a number sentence.
Answers will vary.
___ − ___ = ___

146 Use with Lesson 11-14.

Practice On Level

PROBLEM-SOLVING APPLICATIONS P 11-14
On the Farm

Solve.

1. There are 8 eggs in one nest. There are 7 eggs in another nest. How many eggs are there in all?
   8 (+) 7 = 15 eggs

   Kendra is collecting the eggs. Her basket holds 10 eggs. How many eggs will be left in the nests?
   15 (−) 10 = 5 eggs

2. There are 7 white hens. There are 5 brown hens. There are 3 hens that are gray. How many hens are there in all?
   7 + 5 + 3 = 15 hens

3. Circle the strategy you used to solve Exercise 2.
   make a ten use doubles Strategies will vary.

Writing in Math Answers will vary.

4. Draw a picture of 13 eggs. Write a subtraction story about your picture. Then write a number sentence to go with your story.
___ ◯ ___ = ___

146 Use with Lesson 11-14.

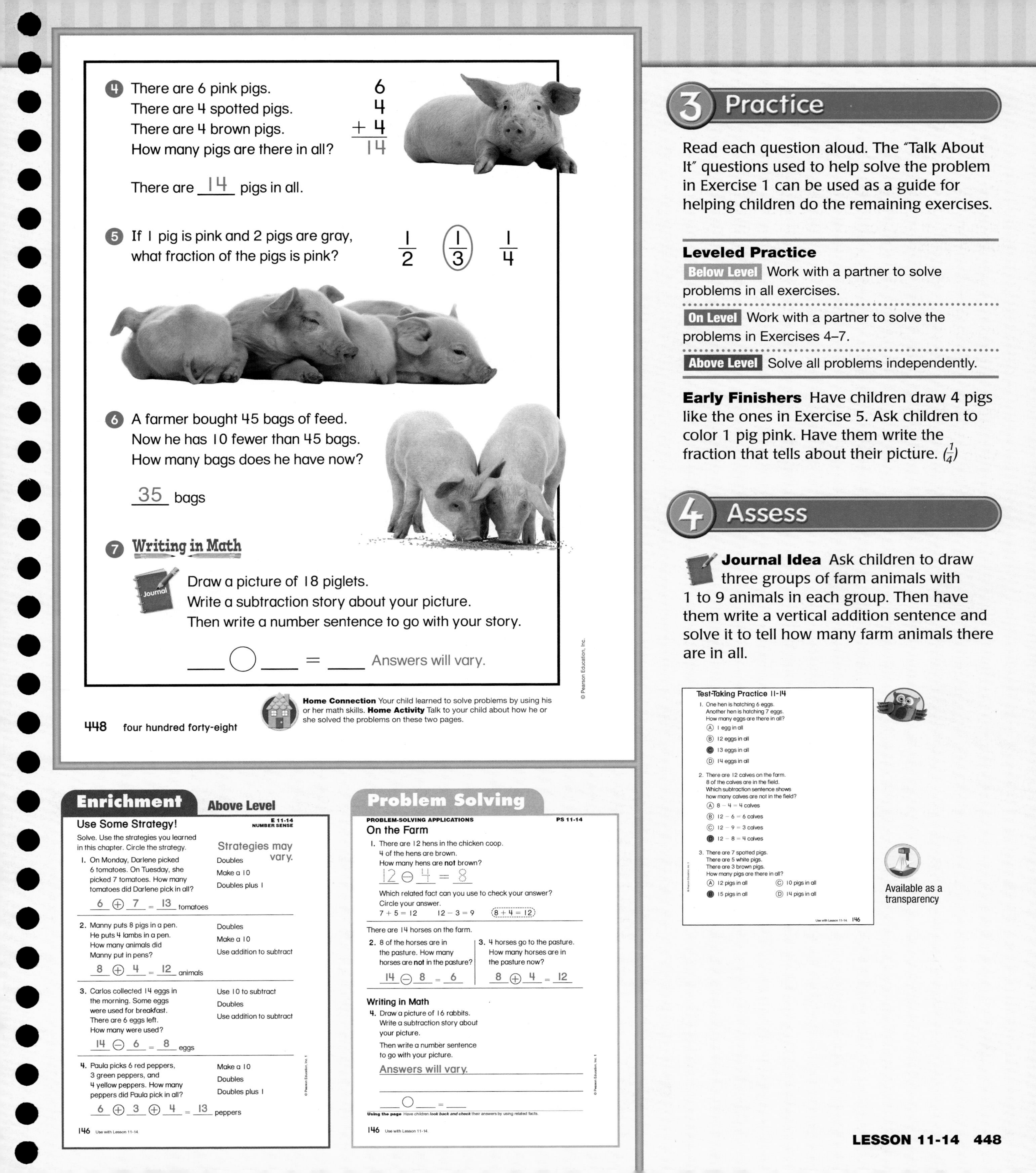

4. There are 6 pink pigs.
   There are 4 spotted pigs.
   There are 4 brown pigs.
   How many pigs are there in all?

   $6 + 4 + 4 = 14$

   There are 14 pigs in all.

5. If 1 pig is pink and 2 pigs are gray, what fraction of the pigs is pink?

   $\frac{1}{2}$ ($\frac{1}{3}$) $\frac{1}{4}$

6. A farmer bought 45 bags of feed.
   Now he has 10 fewer than 45 bags.
   How many bags does he have now?

   35 bags

7. **Writing in Math**

   Journal

   Draw a picture of 18 piglets.
   Write a subtraction story about your picture.
   Then write a number sentence to go with your story.

   ___ ◯ ___ = ___ Answers will vary.

Home Connection Your child learned to solve problems by using his or her math skills. **Home Activity** Talk to your child about how he or she solved the problems on these two pages.

3 Practice

Read each question aloud. The "Talk About It" questions used to help solve the problem in Exercise 1 can be used as a guide for helping children do the remaining exercises.

Leveled Practice

Below Level Work with a partner to solve problems in all exercises.

On Level Work with a partner to solve the problems in Exercises 4–7.

Above Level Solve all problems independently.

Early Finishers Have children draw 4 pigs like the ones in Exercise 5. Ask children to color 1 pig pink. Have them write the fraction that tells about their picture. ($\frac{1}{4}$)

4 Assess

Journal Idea Ask children to draw three groups of farm animals with 1 to 9 animals in each group. Then have them write a vertical addition sentence and solve it to tell how many farm animals there are in all.

Test-Taking Practice 11-14

1. One hen is hatching 6 eggs.
   Another hen is hatching 7 eggs.
   How many eggs are there in all?
   (A) 1 egg in all
   (B) 12 eggs in all
   (C) 13 eggs in all (filled)
   (D) 14 eggs in all

2. There are 12 calves on the farm.
   8 of the calves are in the field.
   Which subtraction sentence shows how many calves are not in the field?
   (A) $8 - 4 = 4$ calves
   (B) $12 - 6 = 6$ calves
   (C) $12 - 9 = 3$ calves
   (D) $12 - 8 = 4$ calves (filled)

3. There are 7 spotted pigs.
   There are 5 white pigs.
   There are 3 brown pigs.
   How many pigs are there in all?
   (A) 12 pigs in all
   (B) 15 pigs in all (filled)
   (C) 10 pigs in all
   (D) 14 pigs in all

Use with Lesson 11-14. 146

Available as a transparency

Enrichment — Above Level

Use Some Strategy! E 11-14 NUMBER SENSE

Solve. Use the strategies you learned in this chapter. Circle the strategy.

Strategies may vary.

1. On Monday, Darlene picked 6 tomatoes. On Tuesday, she picked 7 tomatoes. How many tomatoes did Darlene pick in all?
   Doubles / Make a 10 / Doubles plus 1
   $6 + 7 = 13$ tomatoes

2. Manny puts 8 pigs in a pen. He puts 4 lambs in a pen. How many animals did Manny put in pens?
   Doubles / Make a 10 / Use addition to subtract
   $8 + 4 = 12$ animals

3. Carlos collected 14 eggs in the morning. Some eggs were used for breakfast. There are 6 eggs left. How many were used?
   Use 10 to subtract / Doubles / Use addition to subtract
   $14 - 6 = 8$ eggs

4. Paula picks 6 red peppers, 3 green peppers, and 4 yellow peppers. How many peppers did Paula pick in all?
   Make a 10 / Doubles / Doubles plus 1
   $6 + 3 + 4 = 13$ peppers

146 Use with Lesson 11-14.

Problem Solving

PROBLEM-SOLVING APPLICATIONS PS 11-14

On the Farm

1. There are 12 hens in the chicken coop. 4 of the hens are brown. How many hens are **not** brown?
   $12 - 4 = 8$
   Which related fact can you use to check your answer? Circle your answer.
   $7 + 5 = 12$ $12 - 3 = 9$ ($8 + 4 = 12$)

There are 14 horses on the farm.

2. 8 of the horses are in the pasture. How many horses are **not** in the pasture?
   $14 - 8 = 6$

3. 4 horses go to the pasture. How many horses are in the pasture now?
   $8 + 4 = 12$

Writing in Math

4. Draw a picture of 16 rabbits. Write a subtraction story about your picture. Then write a number sentence to go with your picture.
   Answers will vary.
   ___ ◯ ___ = ___

Using the page Have children *look back and check* their answers by using related facts.

146 Use with Lesson 11-14.

Diagnostic Checkpoint

Purpose Provide assessment of children's progress to date by checking their understanding of key content covered in the previous section.

Vocabulary Review

You may wish to review these terms before assigning the page:

fact family A group of related facts using the same set of numbers *(pp. 437–438)*

related facts An addition fact and a subtraction fact that use the same numbers *(pp. 435–436)*

Activities for this section are available in the Math Vocabulary Kit.

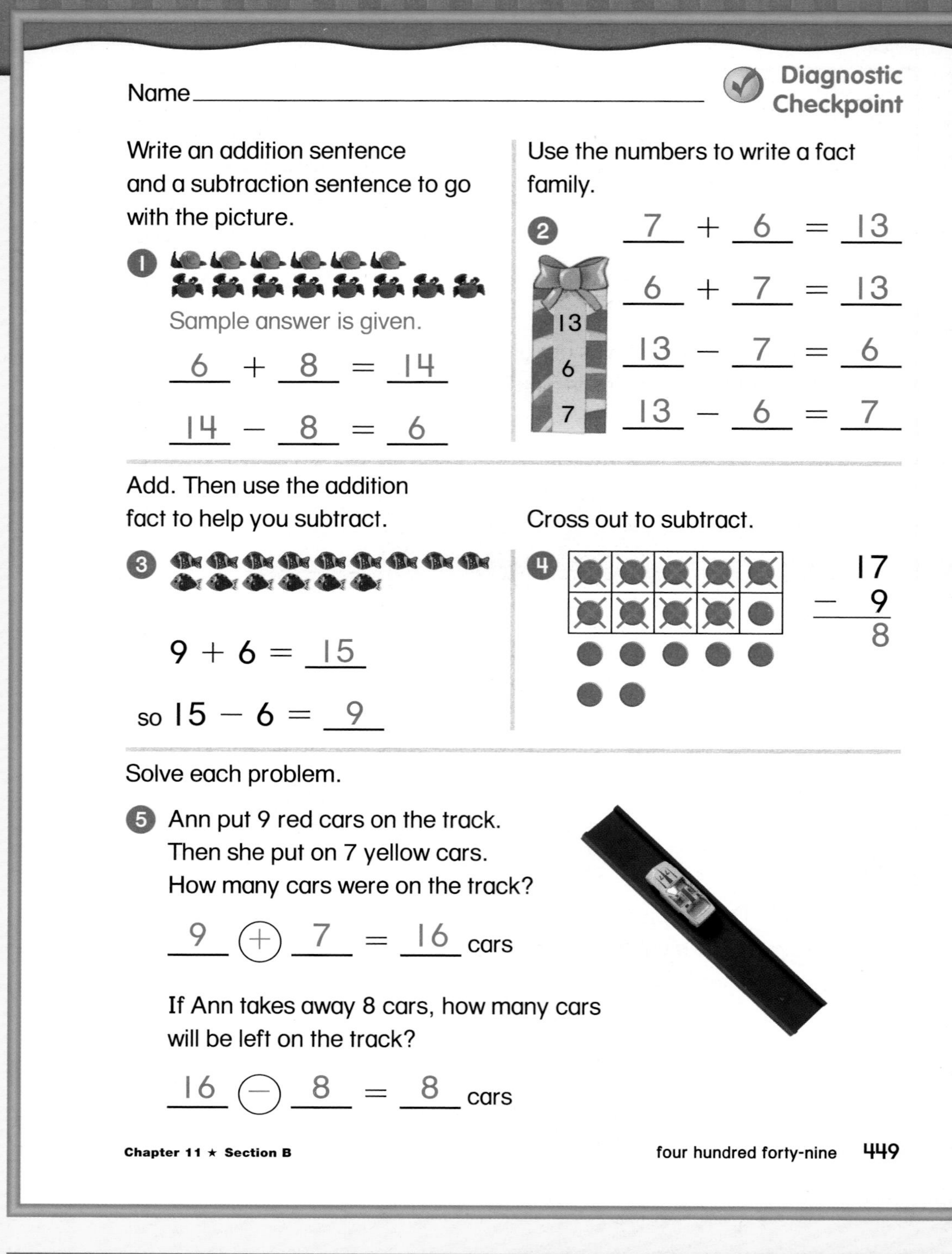

Name ____________________

Diagnostic Checkpoint

Write an addition sentence and a subtraction sentence to go with the picture.

1. Sample answer is given.

6 + 8 = 14

14 − 8 = 6

Use the numbers to write a fact family.

2. 13, 6, 7

7 + 6 = 13

6 + 7 = 13

13 − 7 = 6

13 − 6 = 7

Add. Then use the addition fact to help you subtract.

3. 9 + 6 = 15

so 15 − 6 = 9

Cross out to subtract.

4. 17 − 9 = 8

Solve each problem.

5. Ann put 9 red cars on the track. Then she put on 7 yellow cars. How many cars were on the track?

9 (+) 7 = 16 cars

If Ann takes away 8 cars, how many cars will be left on the track?

16 (−) 8 = 8 cars

Item Analysis for Diagnosis and Intervention

Objective	Items	Student Book Pages*	Intervention System
Write related addition and subtraction facts with sums through 18.	1	435–436	B36
Write the addition and subtraction sentences that make up a fact family.	2	437–438	B37
Find differences by using known addition facts.	3	439–440	B38
Find differences using a ten-frame.	4	441–442	B39
Solve multiple-step problems by using the answer to the first question to answer the second question.	5	445–446	E6

*For each lesson, there is a *Reteaching* activity in *Reaching All Learners* and a *Reteaching* master.

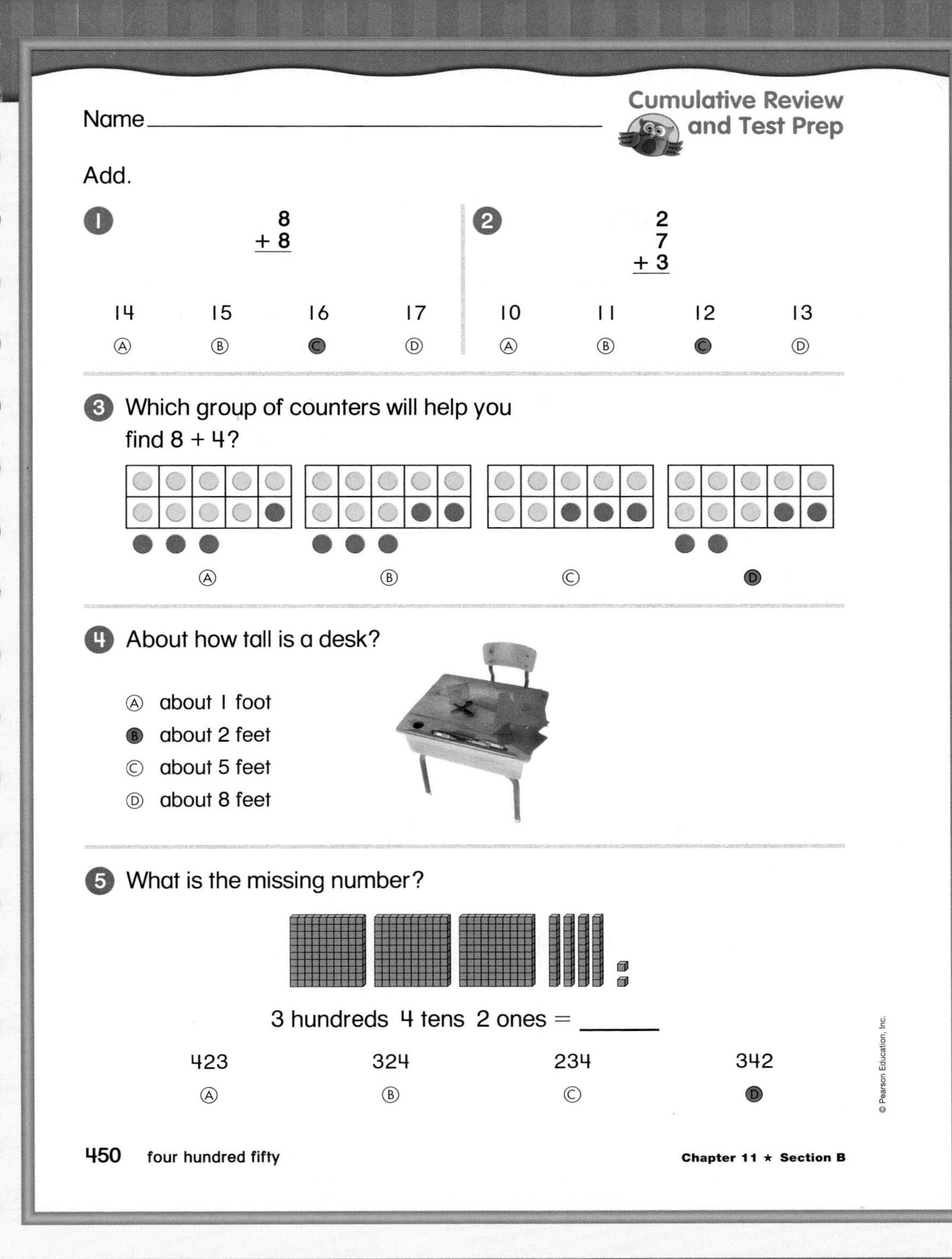

Name ________________________

Cumulative Review and Test Prep

Add.

1. $\begin{array}{r} 8 \\ +\ 8 \\ \hline \end{array}$

14 Ⓐ 15 Ⓑ 16 Ⓒ 17 Ⓓ

2. $\begin{array}{r} 2 \\ 7 \\ +\ 3 \\ \hline \end{array}$

10 Ⓐ 11 Ⓑ 12 Ⓒ 13 Ⓓ

3. Which group of counters will help you find 8 + 4?

Ⓐ Ⓑ Ⓒ Ⓓ

4. About how tall is a desk?

Ⓐ about 1 foot
Ⓑ about 2 feet
Ⓒ about 5 feet
Ⓓ about 8 feet

5. What is the missing number?

3 hundreds 4 tens 2 ones = ______

423 Ⓐ 324 Ⓑ 234 Ⓒ 342 Ⓓ

Cumulative Review and Test Prep

Purpose Provide children with a review of math concepts. Items appear as they would on a standardized test so children become familiar with that format.

Item Analysis for Diagnosis and Intervention

Objective	Items	Student Book Pages*	Intervention System
Recognize doubles as a strategy for remembering sums to 18.	1	417–418	B30
Use the associative property to find sums of three numbers.	2	427–428	B35
Find sums by making a 10 when adding to 8 or 9.	3	423–424	B33
Estimate and measure the length or height of objects to the nearest foot using a 12-inch ruler.	4	373–374	D22
Write a three-digit number for a given model of hundreds, tens, and ones.	5	303–304	A30

*For each lesson, there is a *Reteaching* activity in *Reaching All Learners* and a *Reteaching* master.

Enrichment

Purpose Provide children with related mathematical topics and applications beyond the basic chapter content.

Using Student Page 451

Remind children that they have already learned that they can add numbers to find a sum. Tell them that this page will show how repeated addition can be used to add numbers that are equal in value.

Before having children work through the page, you may want to use counters and yarn to show how groups of the same size can be combined. Have children work in groups of three. Ask each child to show 2 counters inside a ring of yarn and have each group tell how they can find the total number of counters for their group. Guide children to discover that since there are three groups of 2, they can add 2 three times to find the total. Have each child show 4 or 5 counters and find the sums. Then repeat the process, having children work in groups of four. Emphasize that the total is the sum of all the groups of the same size.

Once children are comfortable with the process, read the directions on the page and make sure children understand how to complete the exercises.

When writing the number sentences, make sure children record a number for each sticker they count and that they include a plus sign between each number. For the Writing in Math feature, children should note that since the sum of three 5s is 15, they can find four 5s by adding 1 more 5 and finding that 15 + 5 = 20.

Name ____________________ **Enrichment**

Multiplication as Repeated Addition

Sonia made this picture with more than 50 stickers.

Can you find the three 5s?

Complete the table.

How many stickers are in each shape?	How many stickers are there in all?
1. 5	5 + 5 + 5 = 15
2. 4	4 + 4 + 4 = 12
3. 3	3 + 3 + 3 + 3 + 3 = 15
4. 2	2 + 2 + 2 + 2 = 8
5. 1	1 + 1 + 1 + 1 + 1 + 1 = 6

Writing in Math

6. If three 5s are 15, then how many are four 5s? Explain how you got your answer.

Sample response: 20; since 5 + 5 + 5 = 15, 15 + 5 = 20

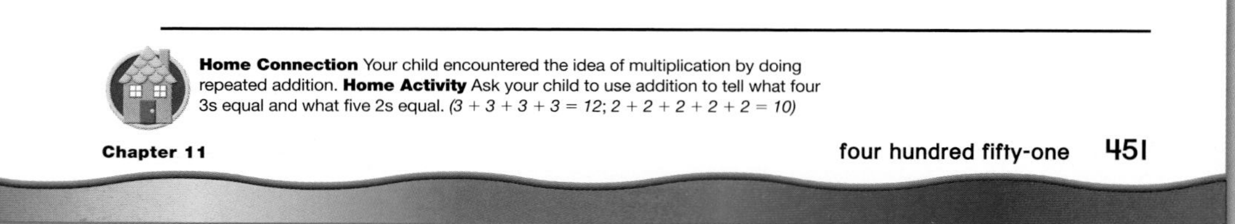

Home Connection Your child encountered the idea of multiplication by doing repeated addition. **Home Activity** Ask your child to use addition to tell what four 3s equal and what five 2s equal. *(3 + 3 + 3 + 3 = 12; 2 + 2 + 2 + 2 + 2 = 10)*

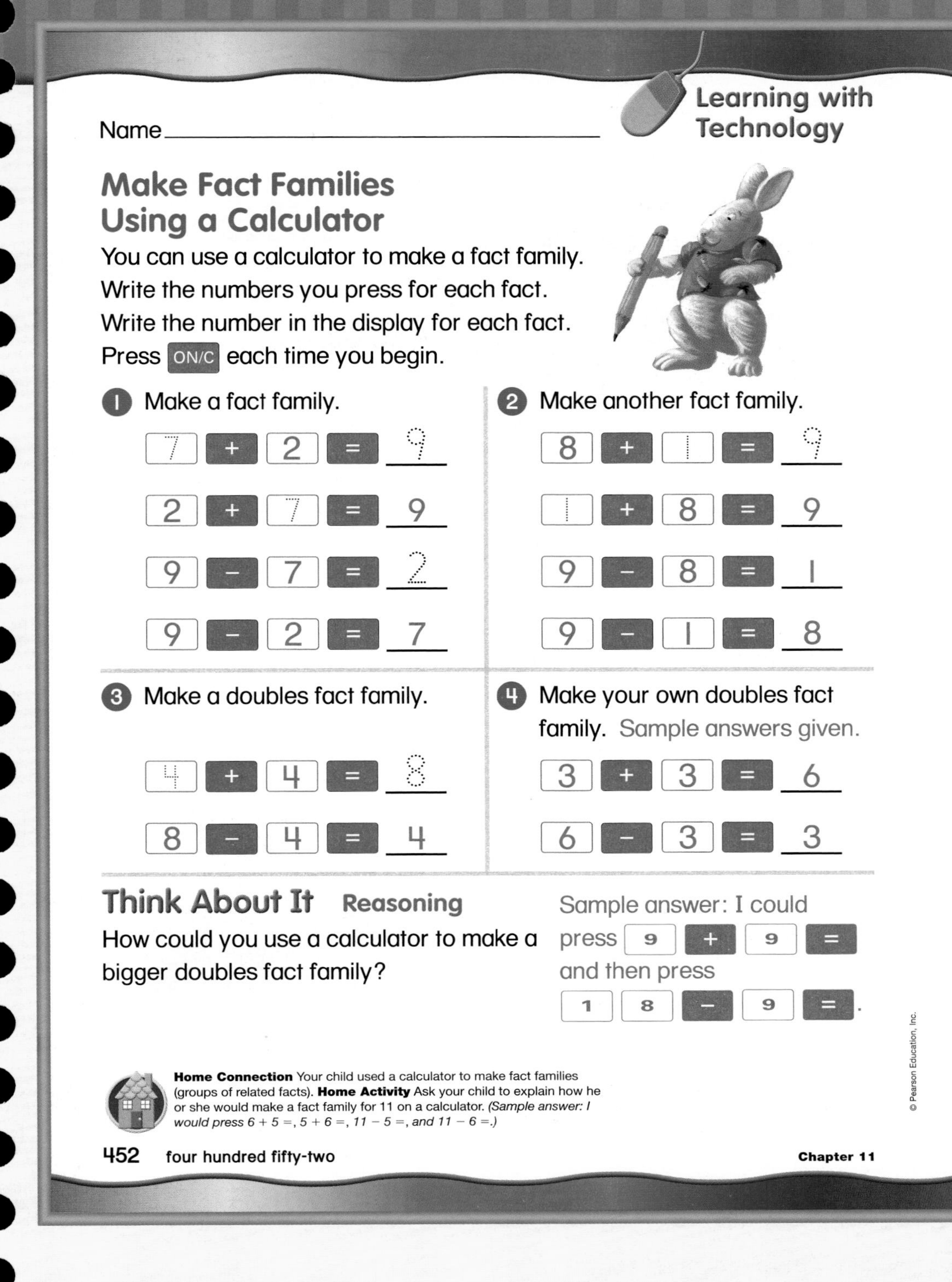

Learning with Technology

Name ______________________

Make Fact Families Using a Calculator

You can use a calculator to make a fact family.
Write the numbers you press for each fact.
Write the number in the display for each fact.
Press ON/C each time you begin.

1. Make a fact family.

7 + 2 = 9
2 + 7 = 9
9 − 7 = 2
9 − 2 = 7

2. Make another fact family.

8 + 1 = 9
1 + 8 = 9
9 − 8 = 1
9 − 1 = 8

3. Make a doubles fact family.

4 + 4 = 8
8 − 4 = 4

4. Make your own doubles fact family. Sample answers given.

3 + 3 = 6
6 − 3 = 3

Think About It Reasoning

How could you use a calculator to make a bigger doubles fact family?

Sample answer: I could press 9 + 9 = and then press 1 8 − 9 =.

Home Connection Your child used a calculator to make fact families (groups of related facts). **Home Activity** Ask your child to explain how he or she would make a fact family for 11 on a calculator. *(Sample answer: I would press 6 + 5 =, 5 + 6 =, 11 − 5 =, and 11 − 6 =.)*

Take It to the NET
Video and Activities
www.scottforesman.com

The video includes pre-viewing and post-viewing questions. A Discovery Channel Blackline Master is also provided.

Learning with Technology

Purpose Make fact families using a calculator.

Using Student Page 452

Distribute calculators to children. Briefly review what they know about the calculator, identifying specific keys: the ON/C key, the + symbol key, and the digits 0–9.

Remind children that the ON/C key clears the calculator screen so that a new number sentence can be entered. Tell children that they will use their calculators to make fact families.

Read the directions on the page and lead children through the first number sentence in Exercise 1. Invite a volunteer to tell which number must be used to complete the fact, given the numbers that already appear in the number sentence. Check to make sure that children have written and entered 7 + 2 = into the calculator. Circulate to check that the resulting screen display shows 9. Work through the remainder of Exercise 1, making sure children enter the other three number sentences correctly and get the appropriate results.

Have children complete Exercises 2–4 independently. For Exercises 3 and 4, review with children that a fact family with a doubles fact has only two facts. Invite children to recall why that makes sense. *(Sample response: There are only two facts because both of the addends in a doubles fact are the same number. Since both of the addends are the same number, there is only one possible subtraction fact.)*

Think About It Make sure that children have entered the same number into their calculators for both addends and that they subtract this number from the sum to create the subtraction fact. To extend the lesson, have children make fact families for doubles with greater numbers, such as 11 + 11 or 12 + 12.

Test Talk

Purpose Teach children a particular test-taking strategy and help them become more comfortable with the language and format used on standardized tests.

Using Student Page 453

This page is designed to give children practice in understanding test questions.

Children often have difficulty on standardized tests not because they haven't been introduced to the concept or skill being tested, but because they fail to understand what they are being asked to do or how they are being asked to do it. This page can help with both the what and the how.

Discuss the question in Exercise 1. You may wish to have children fill in a ten-frame with counters and place 4 counters below the ten-frame to help find 10 + 4. Then discuss why 14 is the correct answer.

Have children complete Exercise 2 independently. Remind them that if their answer is not one of the choices given, they should solve the problem again. When they have finished, make sure that children have added all 3 numbers and selected 17 as the correct answer choice. Explain that if they chose 10 or 14 as an answer choice, they have only added two of the three numbers.

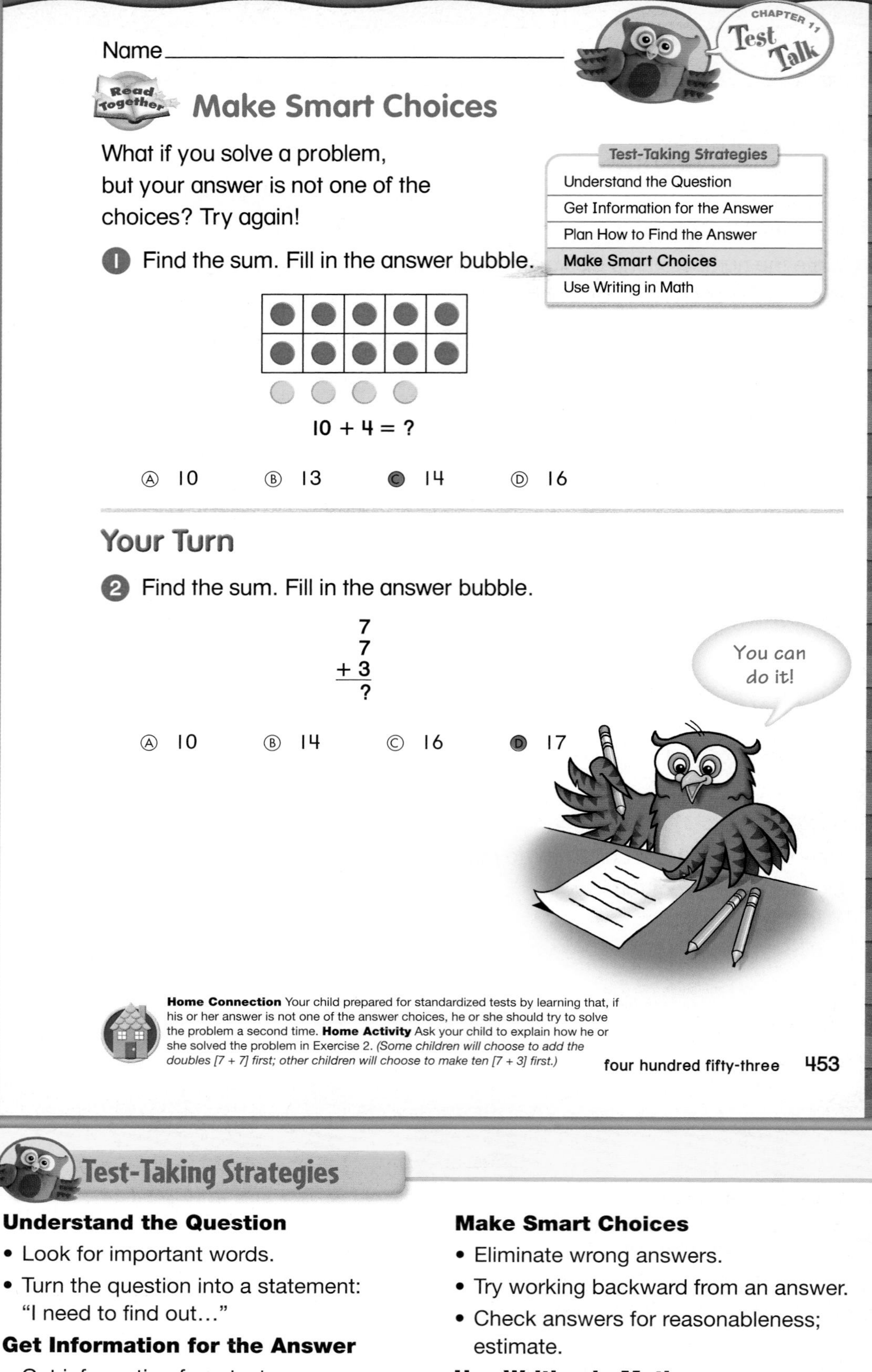

Name ________________

Chapter 11 Test Talk

Read Together

Make Smart Choices

What if you solve a problem, but your answer is not one of the choices? Try again!

Test-Taking Strategies
- Understand the Question
- Get Information for the Answer
- Plan How to Find the Answer
- **Make Smart Choices**
- Use Writing in Math

1. Find the sum. Fill in the answer bubble.

$10 + 4 = ?$

Ⓐ 10 Ⓑ 13 ● 14 Ⓓ 16

Your Turn

2. Find the sum. Fill in the answer bubble.

$$\begin{array}{r} 7 \\ 7 \\ +\ 3 \\ \hline ? \end{array}$$

Ⓐ 10 Ⓑ 14 Ⓒ 16 ● 17

Home Connection Your child prepared for standardized tests by learning that, if his or her answer is not one of the answer choices, he or she should try to solve the problem a second time. **Home Activity** Ask your child to explain how he or she solved the problem in Exercise 2. *(Some children will choose to add the doubles [7 + 7] first; other children will choose to make ten [7 + 3] first.)*

four hundred fifty-three 453

Test-Taking Strategies

Understand the Question
- Look for important words.
- Turn the question into a statement: "I need to find out…"

Get Information for the Answer
- Get information from text.
- Get information from pictures, maps, diagrams, tables, graphs.

Plan How to Find the Answer
- Think about problem-solving skills and strategies.
- Choose computation methods.

Make Smart Choices
- Eliminate wrong answers.
- Try working backward from an answer.
- Check answers for reasonableness; estimate.

Use Writing in Math
- Make your answer brief but complete.
- Use words from the problem and use math terms accurately.
- Describe steps in order.
- Draw pictures to explain your thinking.

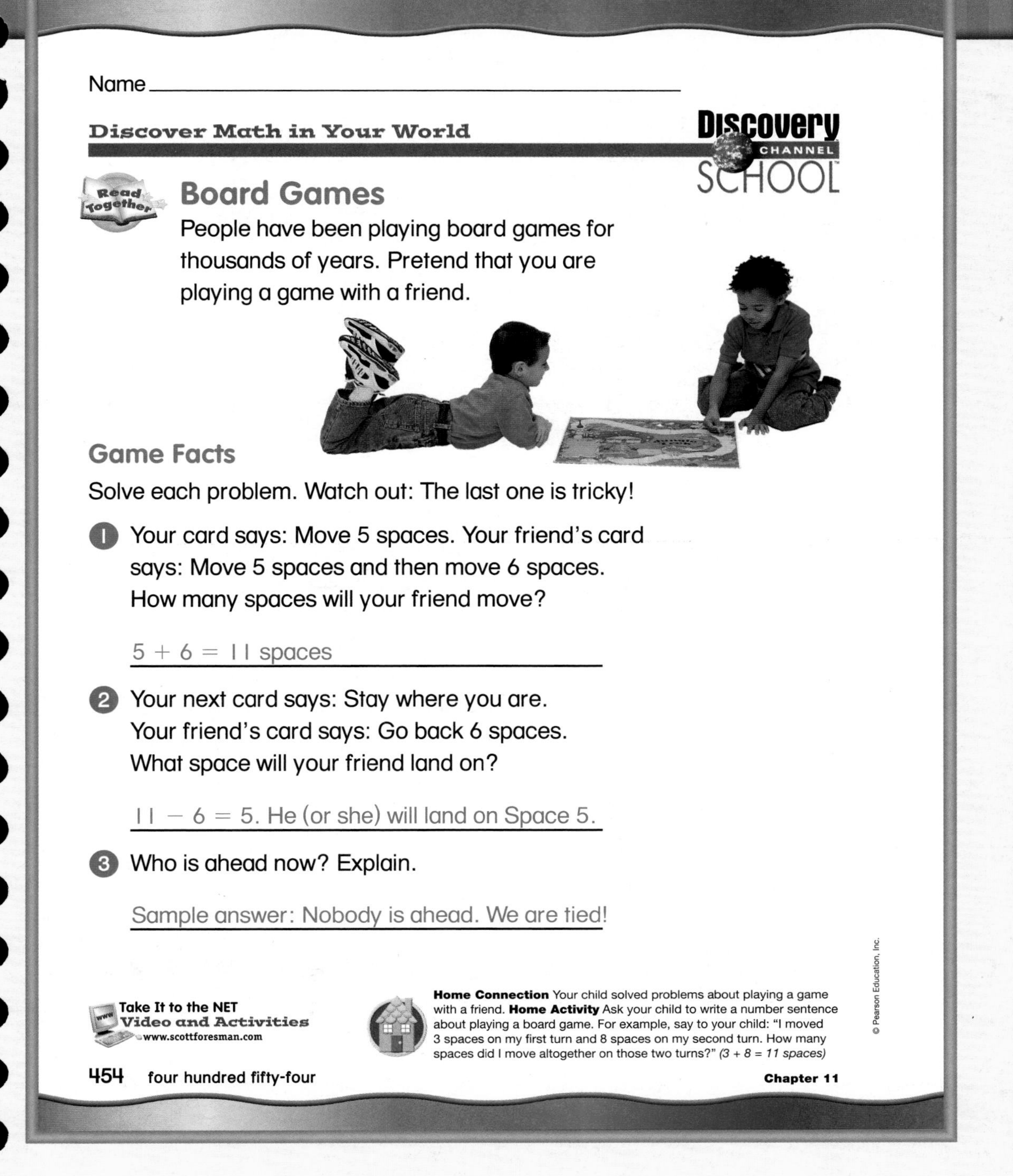

Name ____________________

Discover Math in Your World

Discovery Channel School

Read Together

Board Games

People have been playing board games for thousands of years. Pretend that you are playing a game with a friend.

Game Facts

Solve each problem. Watch out: The last one is tricky!

1. Your card says: Move 5 spaces. Your friend's card says: Move 5 spaces and then move 6 spaces. How many spaces will your friend move?

   $5 + 6 = 11$ spaces

2. Your next card says: Stay where you are. Your friend's card says: Go back 6 spaces. What space will your friend land on?

   $11 - 6 = 5$. He (or she) will land on Space 5.

3. Who is ahead now? Explain.

   Sample answer: Nobody is ahead. We are tied!

Take It to the NET
Video and Activities
www.scottforesman.com

Home Connection Your child solved problems about playing a game with a friend. **Home Activity** Ask your child to write a number sentence about playing a board game. For example, say to your child: "I moved 3 spaces on my first turn and 8 spaces on my second turn. How many spaces did I move altogether on those two turns?" *(3 + 8 = 11 spaces)*

Take It to the NET
Video and Activities
www.scottforesman.com

The video includes pre-viewing and post-viewing questions. A Discovery Channel Blackline Master is also provided.

Discover Math in Your World

Purpose Help children connect math content to everyday applications.

Using Student Page 454

In this activity, children will use fact families to help them answer questions about moves on a board game.

Discuss board games with children. Have them name some board games they have played and ask them to recall the directions for the game. Tell them that they will use math skills for many of the games that they play.

Read the paragraph at the top of the page and discuss the photo. Read through each question with children, making sure that they understand it. To help children remember where the game pieces are, you might want to let them use a gameboard and markers to make the moves. Some children may be able to answer the questions without materials by keeping a mental picture of where the pieces are on the gameboard.

Tell children that they can use what they know about fact families to answer each question. You may wish to have children write a number sentence for each exercise. *(Exercise 1: $5 + 6 = 11$; Exercise 2: $11 - 6 = 5$)* Ask children what they notice about the facts that they used to solve the problems. *(Sample response: The facts make up a fact family using the numbers 5, 6, and 11.)*

Chapter Test

Purpose Assess children's progress by checking their understanding of the concepts and skills covered in Chapter 11. Use as a review, practice test, or chapter test.

MindPoint Quiz Show CD-ROM Use *MindPoint Quiz Show* for additional practice on Chapter 11.

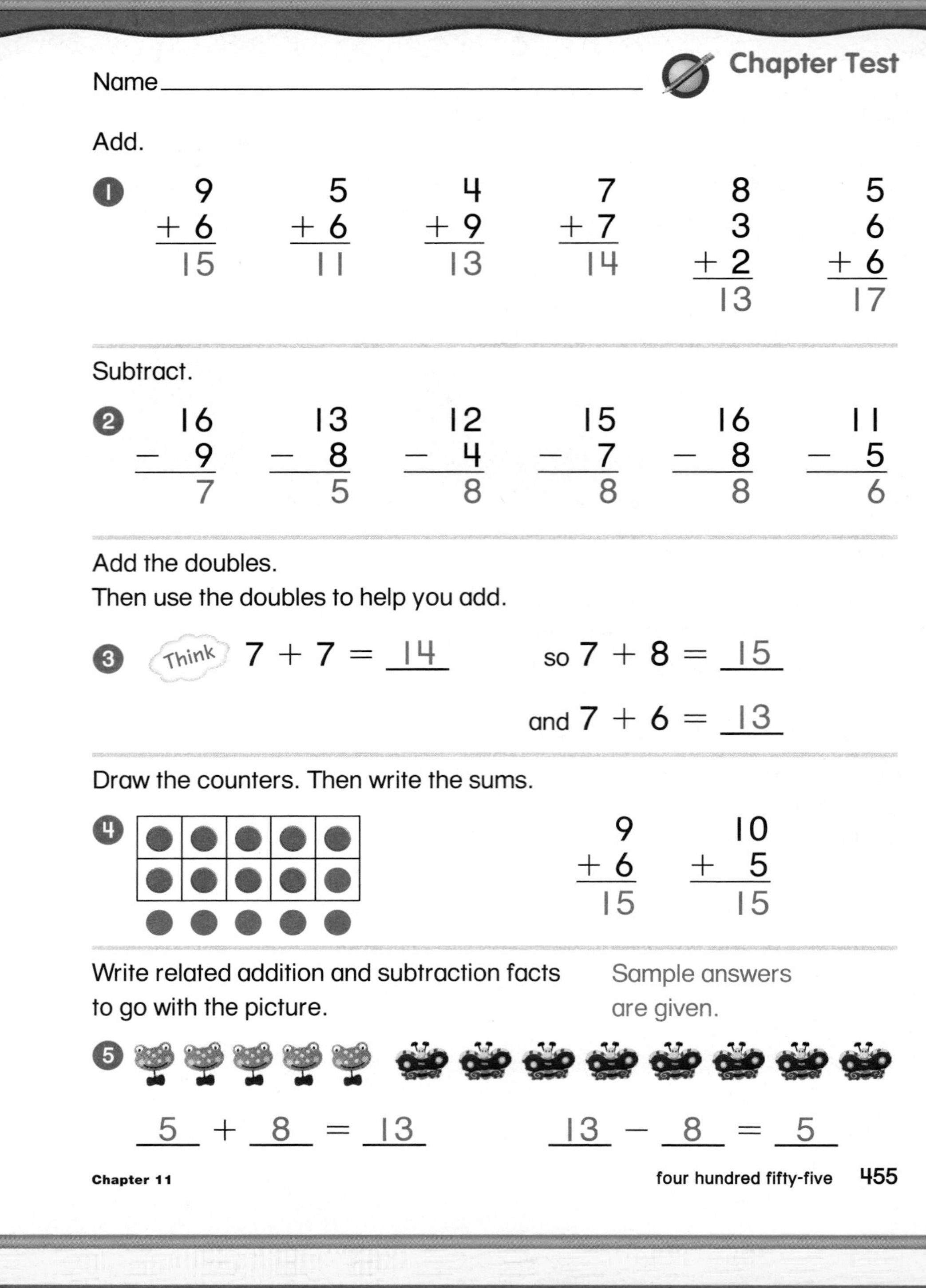

Name ______________________ Chapter Test

Add.

1. $9 + 6 = 15$ $5 + 6 = 11$ $4 + 9 = 13$ $7 + 7 = 14$ $8 + 3 + 2 = 13$ $5 + 6 + 6 = 17$

Subtract.

2. $16 - 9 = 7$ $13 - 8 = 5$ $12 - 4 = 8$ $15 - 7 = 8$ $16 - 8 = 8$ $11 - 5 = 6$

Add the doubles.
Then use the doubles to help you add.

3. Think $7 + 7 = 14$ so $7 + 8 = 15$

and $7 + 6 = 13$

Draw the counters. Then write the sums.

4. $9 + 6 = 15$ $10 + 5 = 15$

Write related addition and subtraction facts to go with the picture. Sample answers are given.

5. $5 + 8 = 13$ $13 - 8 = 5$

Chapter 11 four hundred fifty-five 455

Item Analysis for Diagnosis and Intervention

Objective	Items	Student Book Pages*	Intervention System
Select and apply addition fact strategies.	1	425–426	B34
Use the associative property to find sums of three numbers.	1	427–428	B35
Select and apply subtraction fact strategies.	2	443–444	B34
Recognize doubles as a strategy for remembering sums to 18.	3	417–418	B30
Use doubles facts to learn doubles-plus-1 facts and doubles-minus-1 facts.	3	419–420	B31
Use a pattern to add numbers 1 to 8 to the number 10.	4	421–422	B32
Find sums by making a 10 when adding to 8 or 9.	4	423–424	B33
Write related addition and subtraction facts with sums through 18.	5	435–436	B36

*For each lesson, there is a *Reteaching* activity in *Reaching All Learners* and a *Reteaching* master.

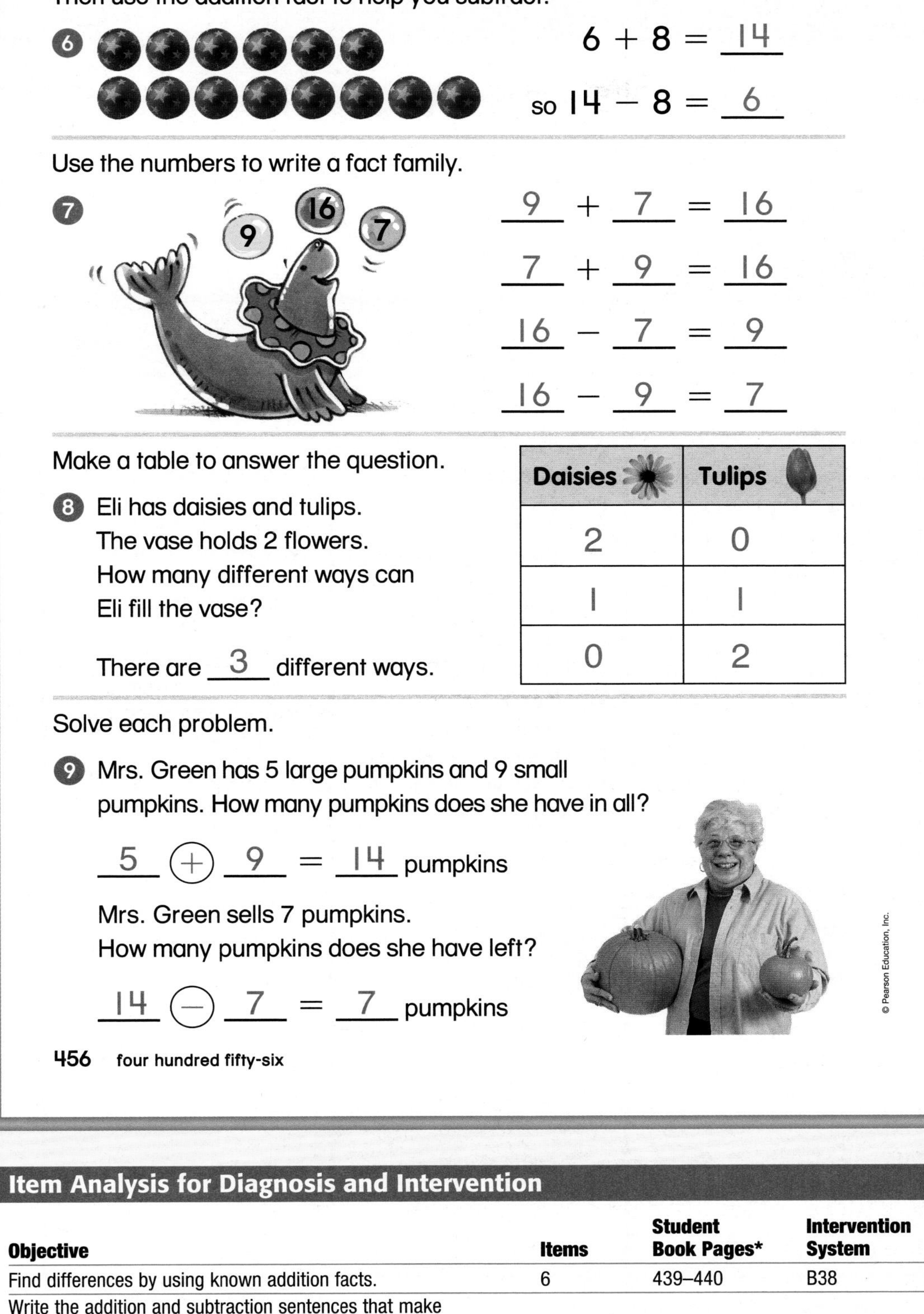

Add.
Then use the addition fact to help you subtract.

6. $6 + 8 = 14$
so $14 - 8 = 6$

Use the numbers to write a fact family.

7.

$9 + 7 = 16$
$7 + 9 = 16$
$16 - 7 = 9$
$16 - 9 = 7$

Make a table to answer the question.

8. Eli has daisies and tulips.
The vase holds 2 flowers.
How many different ways can Eli fill the vase?

There are 3 different ways.

Daisies	Tulips
2	0
1	1
0	2

Solve each problem.

9. Mrs. Green has 5 large pumpkins and 9 small pumpkins. How many pumpkins does she have in all?

5 (+) 9 = 14 pumpkins

Mrs. Green sells 7 pumpkins.
How many pumpkins does she have left?

14 (−) 7 = 7 pumpkins

Assessment Sourcebook

These additional assessment options may be found in the *Assessment Sourcebook:*

- Chapter 11 Free-Response Test (Forms A and B)
- Chapter 11 Multiple-Choice Test (Forms C and D)
- Chapter 11 Performance Assessment

Chapter 11 Test Form A

1. Add.

$7 + 5 = 12$ $9 + 8 = 17$ $8 + 8 = 16$ $6 + 7 = 13$ $6 + 4 + 3 = 13$ $3 + 7 + 7 = 17$

2. Subtract.

$14 - 8 = 6$ $15 - 9 = 6$ $11 - 7 = 4$ $13 - 5 = 8$ $14 - 7 = 7$ $16 - 9 = 7$

3. Add the doubles. Then use the doubles to help you add.

Think $6 + 6 = 12$ so $6 + 7 = 13$
and $6 + 5 = 11$

4. Draw the counters. Then write the sums.

$9 + 5 = 14$ $10 + 4 = 14$

5. Write related addition and subtraction facts to go with the picture.

Sample answers are given.

$6 + 8 = 14$ $14 - 8 = 6$

6. Add. Then use the addition fact to help you subtract.

$7 + 9 = 16$
so $16 - 9 = 7$

7. Use the numbers to write a fact family.

$5 + 8 = 13$
$8 + 5 = 13$
$13 - 8 = 5$
$13 - 5 = 8$

8. Make a table to answer the question.

Sara has pencils and pens.
The box holds 3 items.
How many different ways can Sara fill the box?

There are 4 different ways.

Pencil	Pen
3	0
2	1
1	2
0	3

9. Solve each problem.

John has 7 baseball cards and 8 football cards.
How many cards does he have in all?

7 (+) 8 = 15 cards

John gives 6 cards to his friend.
How many cards does he have left?

15 (−) 6 = 9 cards

Item Analysis for Diagnosis and Intervention

Objective	Items	Student Book Pages*	Intervention System
Find differences by using known addition facts.	6	439–440	B38
Write the addition and subtraction sentences that make up a fact family.	7	437–438	B37
Solve problems by making tables.	8	431–432	E25
Solve multiple-step problems by using the answer to the first question to answer the second question.	9	445–446	E6

*For each lesson, there is a *Reteaching* activity in *Reaching All Learners* and a *Reteaching* master.

CHAPTER 12

Lesson Planner

Two-Digit Addition and Subtraction

Suggested Pacing: 12 to 13 days

Section A Addition

12-1 pp. 459–460	12-2 pp. 461–462	12-3 pp. 463–464	12-4 pp. 465–466	12-5 pp. 467–468
Adding Groups of 10 **Objective** Add two multiples of 10 for sums to 100. **Math Understanding** Adding groups of tens is similar to adding numbers less than ten.	**Adding Tens to Two-Digit Numbers** **Objective** Add tens to a two-digit number. **Math Understanding** When adding tens to a two-digit number, only the tens digit changes.	**Adding Two-Digit Numbers** **Objective** Add 2 two-digit numbers without regrouping. **Math Understanding** When adding two-digit numbers, the ones are combined with the tens.	**Regrouping in Addition** **Objective** Use models to add a one-digit quantity to a two-digit quantity with and without regrouping. **Math Understanding** When there are 10 or more ones in a quantity, 10 of the ones can be regrouped to make a new ten without changing the quantity. **Vocabulary** Regroup **Materials for Student Pages** *(per pair)* Place-Value Mat A (Workmat 4); 85 connecting cubes	Problem-Solving Skill **Exact Answer or Estimate** **Objective** Solve problems by deciding whether an estimate is enough or whether an exact answer is needed. **Math Understanding** Sometimes a problem can be solved without finding the exact answer. **Section A Diagnostic Checkpoint, p. 469** **Cumulative Review and Test Prep, p. 470**

Math Story: ***Paco and His Flying Saucer,*** **pp. 12A–12F** **Home-School Connection, p. 457**
Practice Game: ***Money in the Bank,*** **p. 458**

Resources in the Student Book

Ongoing Assessment and Test Prep *Also see* pp. 457G–457H.

Instant Check System™
- **Check** before Practice
- **Think About It** after examples
- **Diagnostic Checkpoint** end of sections

Test Prep
- **Test Talk** end of chapter
- **Cumulative Review and Test Prep** end of sections

Daily Real-World Problem Solving plus ...

Problem-Solving Applications lesson on pp. 483–484 uses data from Dorling Kindersley literature.

Discover Math in Your World on p. 490 uses data from a topic in the Discovery Channel School Video Library, Segment 12.

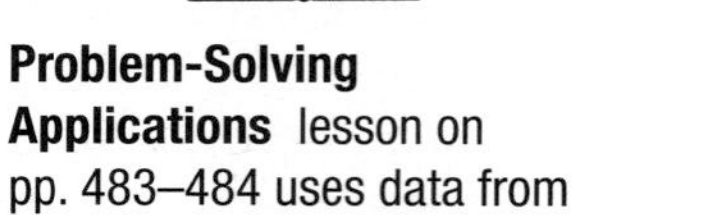

Reading and Writing in Math *Throughout*

This feature shows how reading skills and strategies can help with problem-solving skills and strategies in math.
Also, **Reading Assists** are in the Teacher's Edition.

Writing in Math

Some lessons include **Writing in Math** exercises. Also, daily **Journal Ideas** are in the Teacher's Edition.

Technology Resources for Students *Also see* p. T20.

More activities, Discovery Channel School Video Library, and Math eTools

Math eTools: electronic manipulatives online, on CD-ROM, and in the Online Student's Edition

All text pages are available online and on CD-ROM. The Online Student's Edition includes Math eTools plus glossary links for vocabulary.

Two-Digit Addition and Subtraction

(continued)

Section B Subtraction

12-6 pp. 471–472	12-7 pp. 473–474	12-8 pp. 475–476	12-9 pp. 477–478	12-10 pp. 481–482
Subtracting Groups of 10 **Objective** Subtract a multiple of 10 from a multiple of 10, 100 or less. **Math Understanding** Subtracting groups of tens is similar to subtracting numbers less than 10.	**Subtracting Tens from Two-Digit Numbers** **Objective** Subtract a multiple of 10 from a two-digit number. **Math Understanding** When subtracting tens from a two-digit number, only the tens digit changes.	**Subtracting Two-Digit Numbers** **Objective** Subtract a two-digit number from a two-digit number without regrouping. **Math Understanding** When subtracting two-digit numbers, the ones are subtracted from the ones, and the tens are subtracted from the tens.	**Regrouping in Subtraction** **Objective** Use models to subtract a one-digit quantity from a two-digit quantity with and without regrouping. **Math Understanding** When there are fewer ones to begin with than are being subtracted, a ten can be regrouped into 10 ones without changing the original quantity. **Materials for Student Pages** *(per pair)* Place-Value Mat A (Workmat 4); 95 connecting cubes Reading For Math Success pp. 479–480	Problem-Solving Strategy **Make a Graph** **Objective** Solve problems by making and interpreting bar graphs. **Math Understanding** Organizing data in a graph can make it easier to interpret and compare the data.

Additional Resources for …

Reaching All Learners

- **Practice** Masters/Workbook, every lesson
- **Reteaching** Masters/Workbook, every lesson
- **Enrichment** Masters/Workbook, every lesson
- **Every Student Learns** A teacher resource with daily suggestions for helping students overcome language barriers to learning math
- **Spiral Review and Test Prep** Transparencies and Masters/Workbook, every lesson
- **Math Games** Use *Add or Subtract* anytime after Lesson 12-3.
- **Investigation** See pp. 457I–457J.

Problem Solving

- **Problem Solving** Masters/Workbook, every lesson
- **Problem of the Day** Flipchart/Transparencies, every lesson
- **Discovery Channel School** Masters, follow-up to Segment 12 in the Discovery Channel School Video Library

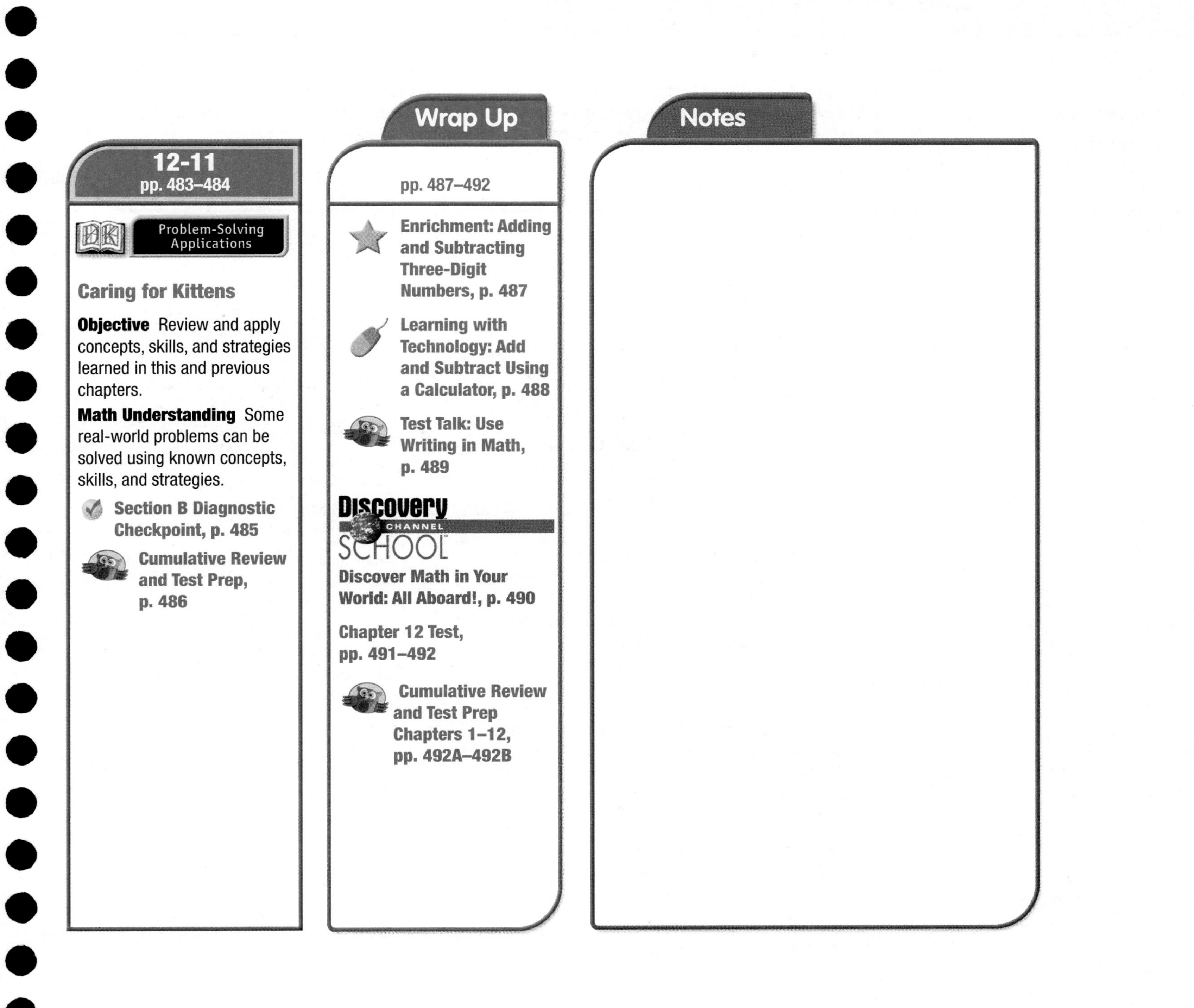

Reading in Math

- **Vocabulary Kit** Word Cards plus transparencies and activities for instructional word walls and for small groups
- **Dorling Kindersley Literature Library** Books with interesting data

Assessment, Intervention, and Test Prep

- **Assessment Sourcebook** See pp. 457G–457H.
- **Math Diagnosis and Intervention System** See pp. 457G–457H.
- **Test-Taking Practice** Transparencies, every lesson
- **SAT 9, SAT 10, TerraNova Practice and Test Prep** Includes practice tests, correlations, and more

Teacher Support

- **Teaching Tools** Masters: paper manipulatives and more
- **Home-School Connection** Masters, use Chapter 12 Family Letter at the start of the chapter. Use Study Buddies 23 and 24 after Lessons 12-5 and 12-9.
- **Professional Development Resources** See p. T18.
- **Technology Resources** See p. T20.

CHAPTER 12

Professional Development

Skills Trace - Two-Digit Addition and Subtraction

BEFORE Chapter 12	DURING Chapter 12	AFTER Chapter 12
Chapter 8 in Grade 1 developed place-value concepts for numbers up to 100. **Chapter 11 in Grade 1** developed mental math strategies for learning basic addition and subtraction facts.	**Chapter 12** introduces finding sums and differences of two-digit numbers without regrouping and two-digit and one-digit numbers with regrouping.	**Grade 2** focuses on estimating, finding, and checking sums and differences of two-digit numbers including money amounts.

Math Background and Teaching Tips

Section A

Addition

pp. 459–470

The traditional algorithm is based on breaking apart numbers by place value and adding digits with the same place value. Breaking apart and adding by place value turns the complex calculation into a set of simpler calculations where all one needs to know is place value and basic facts.

Consider the following expanded way to add two two-digit numbers.

TIP! Reinforce Big Ideas *Emphasize the place values of the digits. Break apart and add by place value to turn the calculation into a set of simpler calculations.*

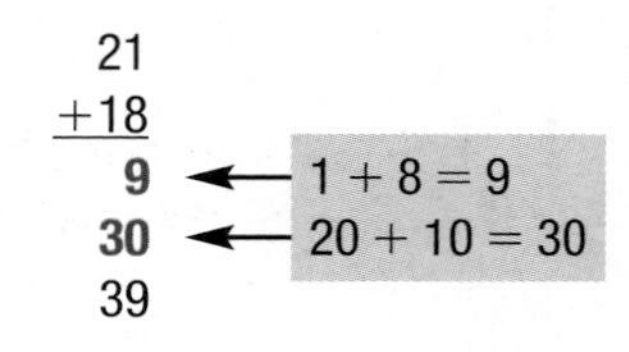

This expanded algorithm emphasizes the place values of the digits in the tens place, expressing them as 20 and 10. Notice the two "partial sums" in green. The traditional algorithm is simply a shortcut for these partial sums.

With the traditional algorithm, we still break apart the numbers using place value, but rather than recording partial sums, a single sum is recorded.

$$\begin{array}{r} 21 \\ +18 \\ \hline 39 \end{array}$$

$21 + 18 = (20 + 1) + (10 + 8)$
Breaking apart 21 + 8 by place value
$= (20 + 10) + (1 + 8)$
Using the Commutative and Associative Properties of Addition
$= 30 + 9$
$= 39$

TIP! Facilitate Reasoning *Groupable models are effective place-value models for young children. Connecting cubes or bundles of sticks work well as models that children can use to compose and decompose.*

Regrouping is possible because our numeration system is a place-value system based on groups of 10. Any quantity in any place that exceeds 10 is regrouped.

TIP! Encourage Flexibility *Children can decompose addends to make addition simpler and more meaningful. They can choose numbers to break apart that will give them basic facts with which to work.*

Math Understandings

- Adding groups of 10 is similar to adding numbers less than 10.
- When adding tens to a two-digit number, only the tens digit changes.
- When adding two-digit numbers, the ones are combined with the ones, and the tens are combined with the tens.
- When there are 10 or more ones in a quantity, 10 of the ones can be regrouped to make a new ten without changing the quantity.
- Sometimes a problem can be solved without finding the exact answer.

$38 + 4 =$

$= (30 + 8) + 4$	Break apart 38.
$= 30 + (8 + 4)$	Use the Commutative and Associative Properties of Addition. Add basic facts.
$= 30 + 12$	Find partial sums.
$= 42$	

Section B

Subtraction

pp. 471–486

Similar to addition, subtracting two-digit numbers involves breaking apart the numbers using place value and subtracting digits in corresponding place values.

Consider the following expanded way to subtract two two-digit numbers.

TIP! Reinforce Big Ideas *Emphasize the place values of the digits. Break apart and subtract by place value to turn the problem into a set of simpler calculations.*

$27 - 14 =$	$(20 + 7)$ $-(10 + 4)$	Break apart numbers using place value.
$=$	$10 + 3$	Subtract ones and tens.
$=$	13	Add the partial differences.

Whereas the overall approach to subtraction is the same as the approach for addition, the traditional algorithm for subtraction is more difficult to master for most children. Children may resort naturally to other methods for subtracting with two-digit numbers. A common method is counting up.

$27 - 14 =$

$14 + 6 = 20$
$20 + 7 = 27$
So, $6 + 7 = 13$.

$27 - 14 = 13$

Counting is a relatively efficient and accurate method for small numbers, but becomes unreliable for most children as numbers get larger.

As in addition, regrouping in subtraction is possible because our numeration system is a place-value system based on groups of 10.

TIP! Encourage Flexibility *Children can decompose the minuend or minuend and subtrahend to make their subtraction simpler and more meaningful.*

$43 - 8 =$

minuend (43) subtrahend (8)

$= (40 + 3) - 8$	Break apart 40.
$= (30 + 13) - 8$	Regroup 40 as 30 + 10.
$= 30 + (13 - 8)$	Create a basic fact.
$= 30 + 5$	Add.
$= 35$	

Or

$= 43 - (3 + 5)$	Break apart 8.
$= (43 - 3) - 5$	Associative property to group 43 and 3, subtract.
$= 40 - 5$	Subtract.
$= 35$	

Children may find counting up a relatively effective method for finding a difference when a subtraction exercise "bridges a 10."

Math Understandings

- Subtracting groups of 10 is similar to subtracting numbers less than 10.
- When subtracting tens from a two-digit number, only the tens digit changes.
- When subtracting two-digit numbers, the ones are subtracted from the ones, and the tens are subtracted from the tens.
- When there are fewer ones to begin with than are being subtracted, a ten can be regrouped into 10 ones without changing the original quantity.
- Organizing data in a graph can make it easier to interpret and compare the data.

$43 - 8 =$

$8 + 2 = 10$	Add 2 more to 8 to reach 10.
$10 + 30 = 40$	Add 30 more to reach 40.
$40 + 3 = 43$	Add 3 more to reach 43.

So, $2 + 30 + 3 = 35$.

$43 - 8 = 35$

Making a graph is a problem-solving strategy that visually displays answers to questions. Children receive the most benefit from this type of activity when it is connected to their own experiences.

Assessment, Intervention, Test Prep

Assessment Resources

DIAGNOSING READINESS

Start of Year Diagnosing Readiness for Grade 1, Assessment Sourcebook pp. 43–46 and in Online Intervention

Start of Chapter Diagnosing Readiness for Chapter 12, Assessment Sourcebook p. 213 and in Online Intervention

Start of Lesson Warm Up, Teacher's Edition pp. 459, 461, 463, 465, 467, 471, 473, 475, 477, 481, 483

Instant Check System™

ONGOING ASSESSMENT

Before Independent Practice Check and Think About It, Student Book, every lesson

After a Section Diagnostic Checkpoint, pp. 469, 485 and in Online Intervention

Basic-Facts Timed Test 12 Assessment Sourcebook, p. 38

FORMAL EVALUATION

Chapter Tests Chapter 12 Test Student Book pp. 491–492; Assessment Sourcebook Forms A and B Free Response pp. 215–218, Forms C and D Multiple Choice pp. 219–226, Performance Assessment p. 23; Multiple-Choice Chapter Test in Online Intervention

Cumulative Tests Chapters 1–3, 1–6, 1–9, 1–12 Assessment Sourcebook, pp. 89–92, 135–138, 181–184, 227–230; Online Intervention

Test Generator Computer-generated tests; can be customized

Correlation to Assessments, Intervention, and Standardized Tests

	Assessments		Intervention	Standardized Tests				
Lessons	Diagnostic Checkpoint	Chapter Test	Math Diagnosis and Intervention System	SAT 9/10	ITBS	CTBS	CAT	MAT
12-1 Adding Groups of 10	p. 469: Ex. 1	Ex. 1	Booklet C: C1	•/•	•	•	•	•
12-2 Adding Tens to Two-Digit Numbers	p. 469: Ex. 2	Ex. 3, 5	Booklet C: C2	•/•	•	•	•	•
12-3 Adding Two-Digit Numbers	p. 469: Ex. 3	Ex. 7	Booklet C: C4	•/•	•	•	•	•
12-4 Regrouping in Addition	p. 469: Ex. 4, 5	Ex. 9, 10, 11	Booklet C: C3	•/•	•	•	•	•
12-5 Problem-Solving Skill: Exact Answer or Estimate?	p. 469: Ex. 6	Ex. 15	Booklet E: E10			•		
12-6 Subtracting Groups of 10	p. 485: Ex. 1, 2	Ex. 2	Booklet C: C5	•/•	•	•	•	•
12-7 Subtracting Tens from Two-Digit Numbers	p. 485: Ex. 3, 4	Ex. 4, 6	Booklet C: C6	•/•	•	•	•	•
12-8 Subtracting Two-Digit Numbers	p. 485: Ex. 5	Ex. 8	Booklet C: C8	•/•	•	•	•	•
12-9 Regrouping in Subtraction	p. 485: Ex. 6, 7	Ex. 12, 13, 14	Booklet C: C7	•/•	•	•	•	•
12-10 Problem-Solving Strategy: Make a Graph			Booklet E: E27	/•	•	•	•	

KEY: **SAT 9** Stanford Achievement Test; **SAT 10** Stanford Achievement Test; **ITBS** Iowa Test of Basic Skills; **CAT** California Achievement Test; **CTBS** Comprehensive Test of Basic Skills (TerraNova); **MAT** Metropolitan Achievement Test

Intervention and Test Prep Resources

INTERVENTION

During Instruction Helpful "If ... then ..." suggestions in the Teacher's Edition in Ongoing Assessment and Error Intervention

Math Diagnosis and Intervention System Diagnostic tests, individual and class record forms, two-page Intervention Lessons (example, practice, test prep), and one-page Intervention Practice (multiple choice), all in cross-grade strand booklets (Booklets A–E for Grades K–3, Booklets F–M for Grades 4–6)

Online Intervention Diagnostic tests; individual, class, school, and district reports; remediation including tutorials, video, games, practice exercises

TEST PREP

Test Talk before the Chapter Test, p. 489

Cumulative Review and Test Prep end of sections, pp. 470, 486 and end of Chapter 12, pp. 492A–492B

Test-Taking Practice Transparencies for every lesson

Spiral Review and Test Prep for every lesson

SAT 9, SAT 10, TerraNova Practice and Test Prep section quizzes, practice tests

Correlation to NCTM Standards and Grades Pre-K through 2 Expectations

Number and Operations

Understand numbers, ways of representing numbers, relationships among numbers, and number systems.

Grades Pre-K through 2 Expectations

- Count with understanding and recognize "how many" in sets of objects. *Lessons 12-1, 12-2, 12-4, 12-6, 12-7, 12-9*
- Use multiple models to develop initial understandings of place value and the base-ten number system. *Lessons 12-1, 12-2, 12-3, 12-4, 12-6, 12-7, 12-8, 12-9*
- Develop a sense of whole numbers and represent and use them in flexible ways, including relating, composing, and decomposing numbers. *Lessons 12-1, 12-2, 12-5, 12-6, 12-7*
- Connect number words and numerals to the quantities they represent, using various physical models and representations. *Lessons 12-1, 12-2, 12-4, 12-6, 12-7, 12-9*

Understand meanings of operations and how they relate to one another.

Grades Pre-K through 2 Expectations

- Understand various meanings of addition and subtraction of whole numbers and the relationship between the two operations. *Lessons 12-1, 12-2, 12-3, 12-4, 12-5, 12-6, 12-7, 12-8, 12-9*
- Understand the effects of adding and subtracting whole numbers. *Lessons 12-1, 12-2, 12-3, 12-4, 12-5, 12-6, 12-7, 12-8, 12-9*

Compute fluently and make reasonable estimates.

Grades Pre-K through 2 Expectations

- Develop and use strategies for whole-number computations, with a focus on addition and subtraction. *Lessons 12-1, 12-2, 12-3, 12-4, 12-5, 12-6, 12-7, 12-8, 12-9*
- Use a variety of methods and tools to compute, including objects, mental computation, estimation, paper and pencil, and calculators. *Lessons 12-1, 12-2, 12-3, 12-4, 12-5, 12-6, 12-7, 12-8, 12-9*

Algebra

Represent and analyze mathematical situations and structures using algebraic symbols.

Grades Pre-K through 2 Expectations

- Use concrete, pictorial, and verbal representations to develop an understanding of invented and conventional symbolic notations. *Lessons 12-1, 12-2, 12-3, 12-6, 12-7, 12-8*

Use mathematical models to represent and understand quantitative relationships.

Grades Pre-K through 2 Expectations

- Model situations that involve the addition and subtraction of whole numbers, using objects, pictures, and symbols. *Lessons 12-1, 12-2, 12-4, 12-6, 12-7, 12-9*

Data Analysis and Probability

Formulate questions that can be addressed with data and collect, organize, and display relevant data to answer them.

Grades Pre-K through 2 Expectations

- Represent data using concrete objects, pictures, and graphs. *Lesson 12-10*

Select and use appropriate statistical methods to analyze data.

Grades Pre-K through 2 Expectations

- Describe parts of the data and the set of data as a whole to determine what the data show. *Lesson 12-10*

The NCTM 2000 Pre-K through Grade 12 Content Standards are Number and Operations, Algebra, Geometry, Measurement, and Data Analysis and Probability. The Process Standards (Problem Solving, Reasoning and Proof, Communication, Connections, and Representation) are incorporated throughout lessons.

Investigation

Two-Digit Addition and Subtraction

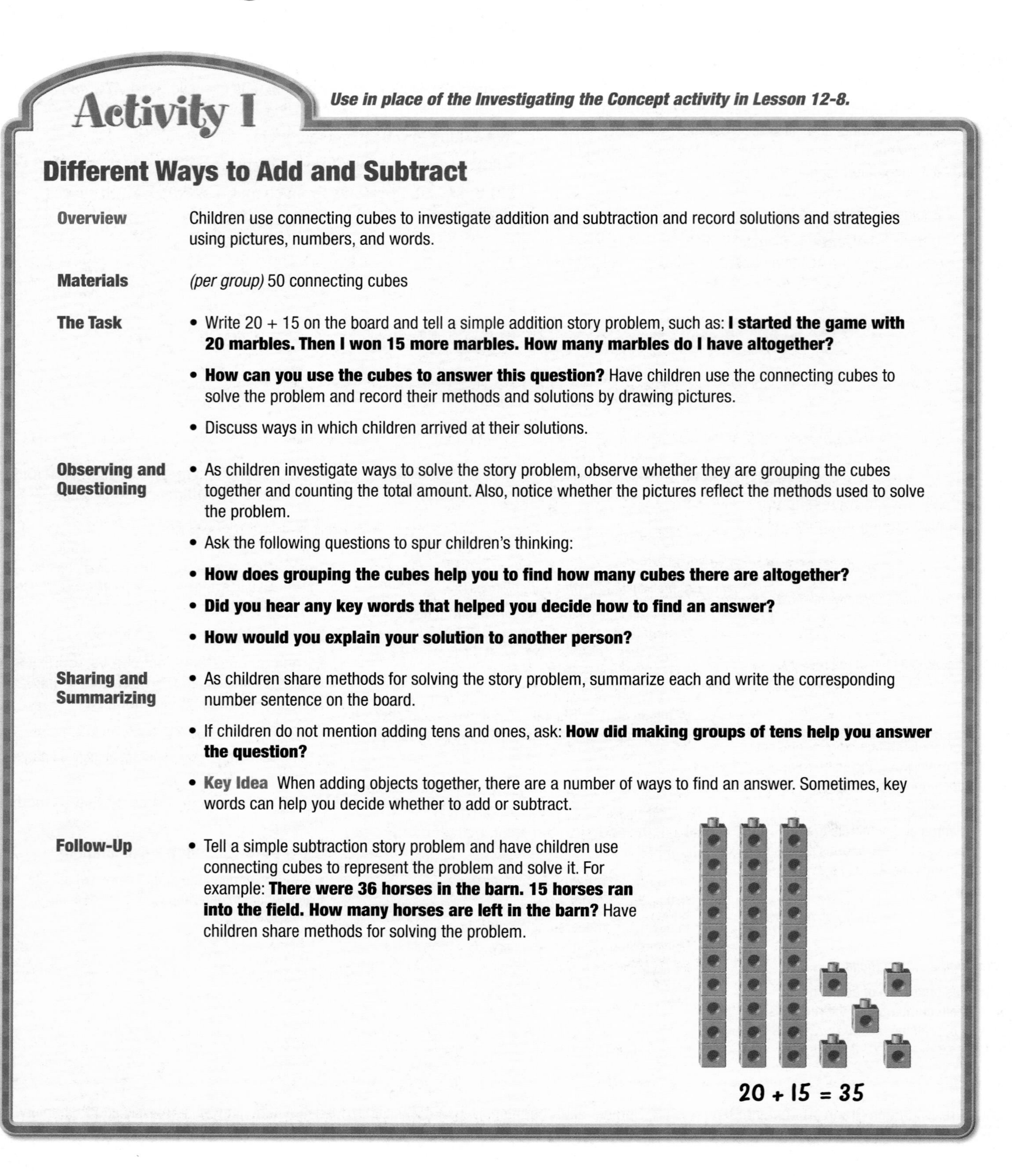

Activity 1

Use in place of the Investigating the Concept activity in Lesson 12-8.

Different Ways to Add and Subtract

Overview Children use connecting cubes to investigate addition and subtraction and record solutions and strategies using pictures, numbers, and words.

Materials *(per group)* 50 connecting cubes

The Task

- Write 20 + 15 on the board and tell a simple addition story problem, such as: **I started the game with 20 marbles. Then I won 15 more marbles. How many marbles do I have altogether?**
- **How can you use the cubes to answer this question?** Have children use the connecting cubes to solve the problem and record their methods and solutions by drawing pictures.
- Discuss ways in which children arrived at their solutions.

Observing and Questioning

- As children investigate ways to solve the story problem, observe whether they are grouping the cubes together and counting the total amount. Also, notice whether the pictures reflect the methods used to solve the problem.
- Ask the following questions to spur children's thinking:
- **How does grouping the cubes help you to find how many cubes there are altogether?**
- **Did you hear any key words that helped you decide how to find an answer?**
- **How would you explain your solution to another person?**

Sharing and Summarizing

- As children share methods for solving the story problem, summarize each and write the corresponding number sentence on the board.
- If children do not mention adding tens and ones, ask: **How did making groups of tens help you answer the question?**
- **Key Idea** When adding objects together, there are a number of ways to find an answer. Sometimes, key words can help you decide whether to add or subtract.

Follow-Up

- Tell a simple subtraction story problem and have children use connecting cubes to represent the problem and solve it. For example: **There were 36 horses in the barn. 15 horses ran into the field. How many horses are left in the barn?** Have children share methods for solving the problem.

Link to *Investigations in Number, Data, and Space®* See the **Joint-Usage Plan** available from Pearson Scott Foresman.

Activity 2

Use in place of the Investigating the Concept activity in Lesson 12-9.

Expanded Addition

Overview

Children use cubes to explore methods for solving addition problems with and without regrouping and record methods of solving by drawing pictures.

Materials

(per group) Connecting cubes

The Task

- Write 14 + 11 and 25 + 17 on the board.
- Have children use the cubes to represent each problem.
- Children then solve each problem and explain the methods they used for each using pictures, numbers, and words.
- As a class, discuss how the problems are the same and how they are different.

Observing and Questioning

- As you circulate around the room, observe whether children begin by adding the ones and remember to regroup 10 ones as 1 ten.
- If children have difficulty regrouping, ask: **How are the problems alike? How are they different?**
- **How does knowing your basic facts help you solve the problems?**
- **How can place value help you solve the problems?**

Sharing and Summarizing

- As children share the ways they solved each problem, summarize each.
- If children do not mention regrouping, ask: **How can regrouping the ones help you solve this addition problem?** In the work below, the child regrouped 10 ones into 1 ten and then solved the problem.
- **Key Idea** Some addition problems involve regrouping 10 ones as 1 ten. When the sum of the ones places is greater than 10, 10 ones can be regrouped as 1 ten. This type of addition problem can be solved by using knowledge of place value.

Follow-Up

- Write 37 + 27 on the board. Have children represent the addition problem using cubes, solve the problem, and show the methods used to solve it using pictures, numbers, and words. Discuss methods as a class.

When I combine 5 cubes and 7 cubes, I get 1 group of 10 and 2 left over.

Math Story

Paco and His Flying Saucer (Genre: Realistic fiction)

In this story, a 6-year-old boy wants to buy a red flying saucer. First, he must earn enough money to pay for it. Along the way, he learns how to add amounts of money.

Introducing the Story

Show children the cover and read the title. Tell children this story is about a boy who earns money to buy a red flying saucer.

Reading the Story

Have children read the story through once without stopping so that they can enjoy the story and the art.

Read the story again. Complete a horizontal bar graph titled, "Paco's Chores" on the chalkboard. Label the bars with the names of each chore, divide each bar into squares, and write "0¢, 5¢, 10¢, 15¢," and so on below the graph. Ask volunteers to color the bars. Tell children that they can use this reading strategy, understanding graphs, whenever they listen to a story or solve math problems. (For more on *Understand Graphic Sources: Graphs,* see Reading for Math Success, pp. 479–480.)

Page 12A

Page 12B

Page 12C

Page 12D **Page 12E**

Page 12F

Follow-up Activities

- **Show Money Amounts with Coins** Remind children that Paco earned money doing chores. Ask them how much money he made for watering the plants, feeding the hamster, and taking out the garbage. *(30¢ each)* Discuss with children which coins his mother could have given him for 30¢. Have children use money to represent the amount of money Paco earned for each chore and then count all of the coins to find out how much money Paco earned in all.
- **Main Idea** Challenge children to identify the main idea of this selection by telling what the story is all about. *(Earning money to buy a toy)* If children need help, give them three choices, making the correct answer obvious: going to the zoo, playing with a dog, earning money to buy a toy. Then ask children to provide details from the story that support the main idea by telling how Paco earned money to buy the toy. *(He watered the plants, fed the hamster, and took out the garbage.)*
- **Extend the Story** Ask leading questions about how Paco might earn money to buy the boomerang: **How much money does Paco need to earn?** *(75¢)* **What tasks do you think Paco might do to earn the money? What coins could his mom use to pay him 75¢?**

Home-School Connection

Purpose Provide families with a quick overview of the material that will be covered in Chapter 12. Included on this page: a family letter, a math activity, references to literature related to the chapter, and new math vocabulary words.

Using Student Page 457

You may wish to read and discuss the family letter with children prior to having them sign it and sending the page home.

The Home-School Connection booklet includes:

- Chapter 12 Family Letter in English and Spanish
- Study Buddies 23
- Study Buddies 24

Study Buddies pages provide reinforcement activities for children to work on with a partner. Each Study Buddy has a page for the child and a page of prompts to help the partner guide the child's learning.

Vocabulary

regroup *(pp. 465–466)*

Home-School Connection

Dear Family,

Today my class started Chapter 12, **Two-Digit Addition and Subtraction.** I will learn to add two-digit numbers and regroup when there are 10 or more ones. I will learn to subtract one two-digit number from another and regroup when there are not enough ones. Here are some of the math words I will be learning and some things we can do to help me with my math.

Love,

____

Math Activity to Do at Home

Set out 10 dimes. Count the dimes by 10s with your child. Then pose addition problems for your child to solve using the dimes. For example, "How much are 3 tens and 3 tens?" Do the same with subtraction problems.

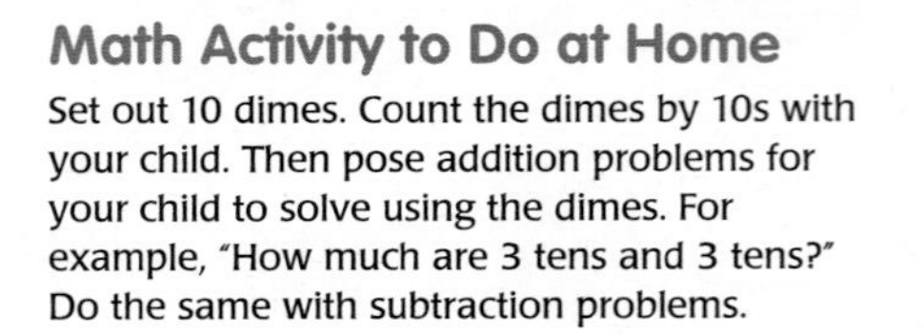

Books to Read Together

Reading math stories reinforces concepts. Look for these titles in your local library:

100 Days of School
By Trudy Harris
(Millbrook Press, 1999)

Shark Swimathon
By Stuart J. Murphy
(HarperCollins, 2001)

Take It to the NET
More Activities
www.scottforesman.com

My New Math Words

regrouping in addition You *make a ten* when the sum of the ones is 10 or more.

regrouping in subtraction You *break apart a ten* when there are not enough ones to subtract.

four hundred fifty-seven 457

Math Vocabulary Kit

Every vocabulary word is written on a laminated card with the definition of the word printed on the back. Vocabulary activities are provided in the *Math Vocabulary Kit Teacher's Guide.*

Add the word from the Vocabulary list at left to your Math Word Wall as it is introduced.

regroup

Name ____________________ Practice Game

Money in the Bank

What You Need

1 small game marker

How to Play

1. Toss your marker at the bank.
2. Add the amount the marker lands on to Paco's nickel.
3. Write a number sentence on a separate sheet of paper.
4. Keep playing until you have the 75¢ Paco needs to buy that boomerang!

Practice Game

for School or Home

Purpose Provide children with an opportunity to practice skills they have previously learned.

Using Student Page 458

You may wish to discuss these questions with your children before they play "Money in the Bank."

- **What are some ways to add amounts of money?**
- **What number sentence would you write if you start with 5¢ and your marker lands on 25¢? What is the sum?**

Give children the materials for the game.

Describe the game and explain the directions. Lead children through the process of tossing the marker, writing a number sentence, and finding the sum. Make sure children understand that in subsequent turns, they add the amount shown to the total they had from the previous turn. Allow children to complete the game.

Describe another way to play: Both children toss a marker on the gameboard. Then they find the difference between the two amounts. Children add that difference to the 5¢ that Paco has. Play continues in this manner until children reach the 75¢ that Paco needs.

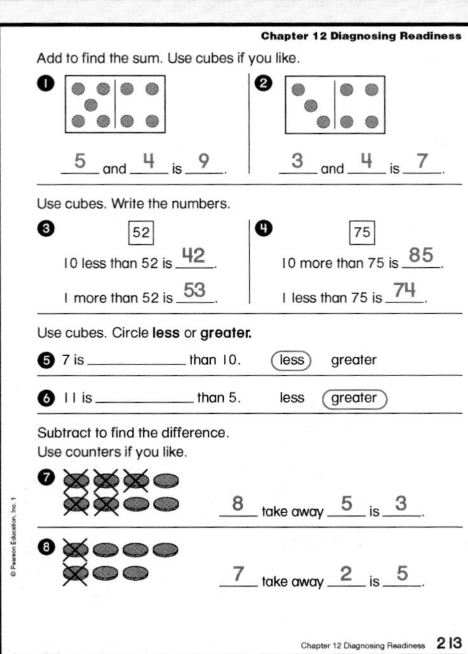
Chapter 12 Diagnosing Readiness

Add to find the sum. Use cubes if you like.

1. 5 and 4 is 9.
2. 3 and 4 is 7.

Use cubes. Write the numbers.

3. 52 — 10 less than 52 is 42. 1 more than 52 is 53.
4. 75 — 10 more than 75 is 85. 1 less than 75 is 74.

Use cubes. Circle **less** or **greater**.

5. 7 is ________ than 10. (less) greater
6. 11 is ________ than 5. less (greater)

Subtract to find the difference. Use counters if you like.

7. 8 take away 5 is 3.
8. 7 take away 2 is 5.

Chapter 12 Diagnosing Readiness 213

Item Analysis for Diagnosis and Intervention

Objective	Items	Student Book Pages*	Intervention System
Find the sum of two addends.	1–2	47–48	B5
Given a two-digit number, write the numbers that are 10 more/10 less and 1 more/1 less.	3–4	295–296	A25, A26
Compare a given number to both 5 and 10.	5–6	29–30 or 21–22	A8
Find the difference between two numbers.	7–8	63–64	B11

*For each lesson, there is a *Reteaching* activity in *Reaching All Learners* and a *Reteaching* master.

12-1

Adding Groups of 10

Lesson Organizer

Quick Lesson Overview

Objective Add two multiples of 10 for sums to 100.

Math Understanding Adding groups of 10 is similar to adding numbers less than 10.

Professional Development Note

Research Base

Mental arithmetic activities help children develop number sense (National Research Council, 2001). In this lesson, children mentally add groups of 10 after working with place-value models, which connect adding tens with adding ones.

NCTM Standards

- Number and Operations

(For a complete correlation to the NCTM Standards and Grades Pre-K through 2 Expectations, see Pages 457G and 457H.)

Getting Started

Spiral Review

Problem of the Day 12-1

Mari has a puppy. If it measured 1 kilogram more it would measure 4 kilograms. How many kilograms does Mari's puppy measure?

Topics Reviewed
- Kilograms
- Subtraction
- Problem-Solving Skill: One-Step Problem

Answer The puppy weighs 3 kilograms; $4 - 1 = 3$.

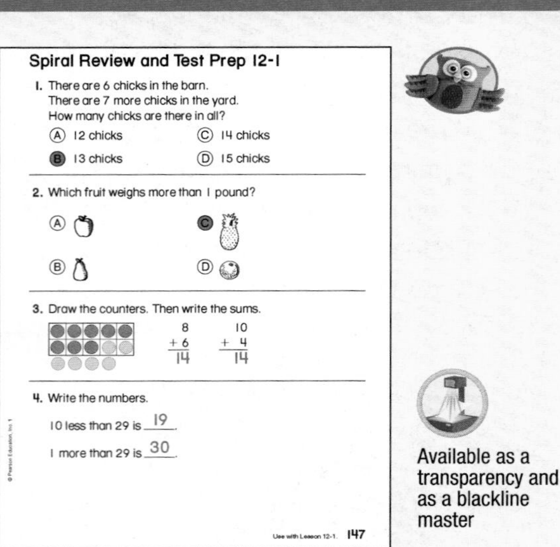

Spiral Review and Test Prep 12-1

1. There are 6 chicks in the barn. There are 7 more chicks in the yard. How many chicks are there in all?
   - (A) 12 chicks
   - (B) 13 chicks
   - (C) 14 chicks
   - (D) 15 chicks
2. Which fruit weighs more than 1 pound?
   - (A)
   - (B)
   - (C)
   - (D)
3. Draw the counters. Then write the sums.
   $8 + 6 = 14$ $10 + 4 = 14$
4. Write the numbers.
   10 less than 29 is 19
   1 more than 29 is 30

Use with Lesson 12-1. 147

Available as a transparency and as a blackline master

Topics Reviewed
1. Applying Addition Fact Strategies
2. Pounds
3. Making 10 to Add
4. 1 More, 1 Less; 10 More, 10 Less

Investigating the Concept

Groups of 10

15–20 MIN **Visual/Spatial/Kinesthetic** PAIRS

Materials Place-value models (9 ones); *(per pair)* place-value models (10 tens); Number Cards 0–11 (Teaching Tool 9)

What to Do

- On the board, write $3 + 6 =$ ___ and $30 + 60 =$ ___. Demonstrate how to use models to find the sums for both equations. Discuss the similarities and differences between the two problems.
- Provide pairs of children with models and number cards 1–5. Have each child choose a number card and model the number of tens shown on the card. Then have the pair add its two groups of 10 together and write the number sentence. Repeat the activity.

Ongoing Assessment

- **Reasoning** **How can 5 + 2 = 7 help you find the sum for 50 + 20?** *(Think of the numbers as tens instead of ones.)*
- **When adding tens, what is always in the ones place?** *(0)*

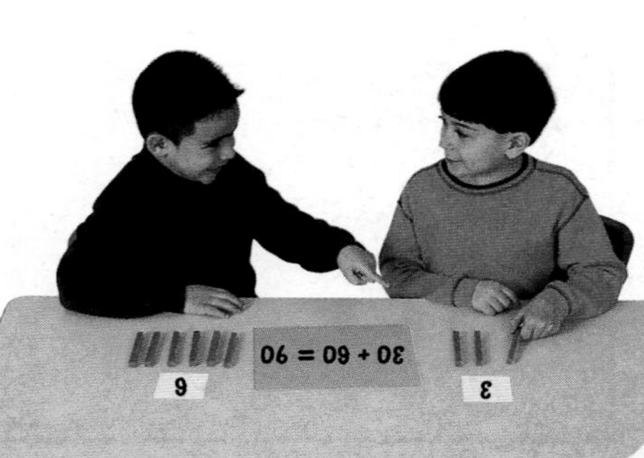

Reaching All Learners

Oral Language in Math

Hear and Solve

10–15 MIN **Auditory/Linguistic**

Materials *(per child)* Place-value models (10 tens)

- Model the activity for the class by saying a story problem involving the addition of two multiples of 10, such as: **I had 30 stickers, and my friend gave me 30 more stickers. How many stickers do I have altogether?** *(60)* Have children use tens if necessary to solve the problem.
- Invite children to make up their own problems and to say them aloud for the class to solve.

I had 20 baseball cards. My dad bought me 60 more. How many do I have now?

English Language Learners

Access Content

Add Groups of Tens

10–15 MIN **Linguistic/Kinesthetic**

Materials *(per pair)* Place-value models (10 tens); 2 index cards labeled with plus signs; 2 index cards labeled with equal signs; index cards labeled with decade numbers 10–100

- Demonstrate the activity by placing 4 tens on one side of the table and 3 tens on the other, with a plus sign between the groups and an equal sign at the end.
- Ask a child to find the corresponding index cards (40 and 30), say the numbers, and make a number sentence (40 + 30 = 70) with the five cards.
- Partners work together to make problems using the models and the cards.

Reteaching

Zero Cover-Up

5–10 MIN **Visual/Spatial/Kinesthetic**

SMALL GROUP

Materials *(per group)* Index cards labeled with addition problems in which addends are multiples of 10 and sums do not exceed 100; 2 small squares of paper

- Remind children that when adding groups of 10, you add the digits in the tens place and keep the zero at the end.
- Have children take turns picking a card, placing the small paper squares over the zeros, adding the digits in the tens place, and saying, for example, "If 2 + 5 = 7, then (removing the paper squares) 20 + 50 = 70."

20 + 50 = —

Math and Technology

Checking Tens

10–15 MIN **Logical/Mathematical**

PAIRS

Materials *(per pair)* Number Cards 0–11 (Teaching Tool 9); calculator

- Have children pick two number cards with numbers 1 to 5 and add the digits, such as 3 + 4 = 7. Ask children to say what the number sentence would be if the numbers were in the tens place and a zero was in the ones place. *(30 + 40 = 70)*
- Have children use calculators to check. **If 3 + 4 = 7, will 30 + 40 = 70?**

Objective Add two multiples of 10 for sums to 100.

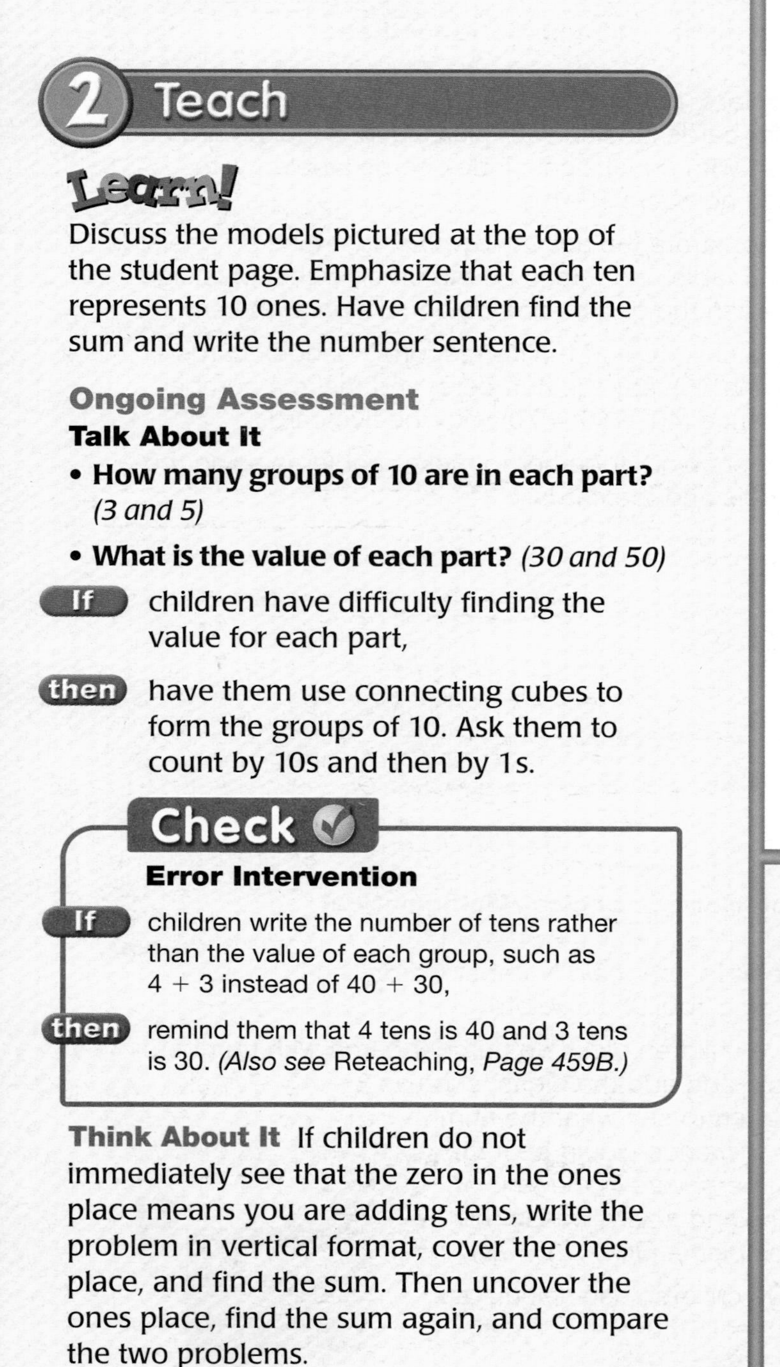

1 Warm Up

Activate Prior Knowledge Review skip counting by 10s. Start with 10 and go around the room, having children take turns saying each next multiple. When they reach 100, have them start over.

2 Teach

Learn!

Discuss the models pictured at the top of the student page. Emphasize that each ten represents 10 ones. Have children find the sum and write the number sentence.

Ongoing Assessment

Talk About It

- **How many groups of 10 are in each part?** *(3 and 5)*
- **What is the value of each part?** *(30 and 50)*

If children have difficulty finding the value for each part,

then have them use connecting cubes to form the groups of 10. Ask them to count by 10s and then by 1s.

Check

Error Intervention

If children write the number of tens rather than the value of each group, such as 4 + 3 instead of 40 + 30,

then remind them that 4 tens is 40 and 3 tens is 30. *(Also see* Reteaching, *Page 459B.)*

Think About It If children do not immediately see that the zero in the ones place means you are adding tens, write the problem in vertical format, cover the ones place, and find the sum. Then uncover the ones place, find the sum again, and compare the two problems.

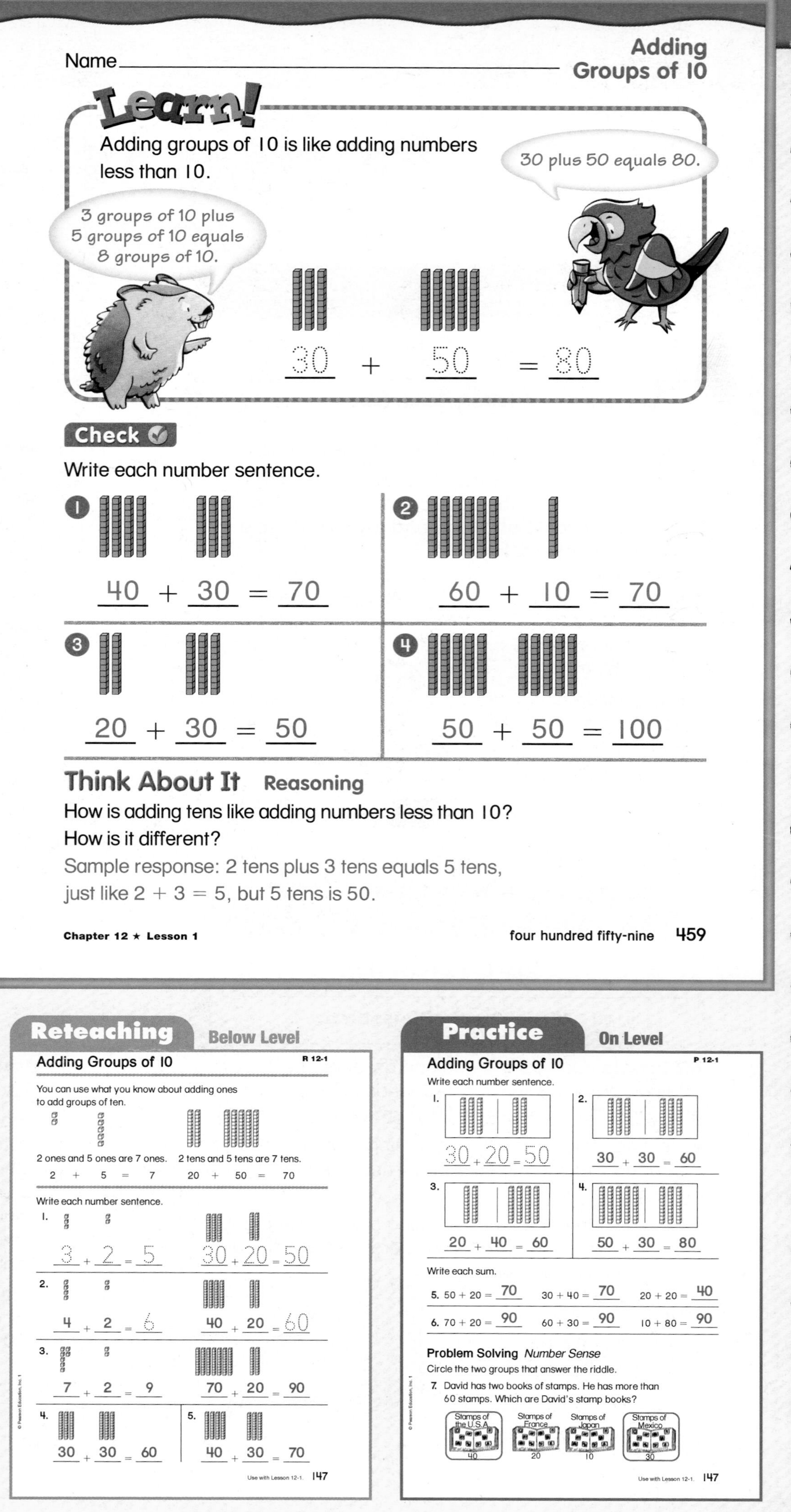

Name ____________

Adding Groups of 10

Learn!

Adding groups of 10 is like adding numbers less than 10.

30 + 50 = 80

Check

Write each number sentence.

1. 40 + 30 = 70
2. 60 + 10 = 70
3. 20 + 30 = 50
4. 50 + 50 = 100

Think About It Reasoning

How is adding tens like adding numbers less than 10? How is it different?

Sample response: 2 tens plus 3 tens equals 5 tens, just like 2 + 3 = 5, but 5 tens is 50.

Chapter 12 ★ Lesson 1 — four hundred fifty-nine 459

Reteaching Below Level

Adding Groups of 10 — R 12-1

You can use what you know about adding ones to add groups of ten.

2 ones and 5 ones are 7 ones. 2 + 5 = 7

2 tens and 5 tens are 7 tens. 20 + 50 = 70

Write each number sentence.

1. 3 + 2 = 5; 30 + 20 = 50
2. 4 + 2 = 6; 40 + 20 = 60
3. 7 + 2 = 9; 70 + 20 = 90
4. 30 + 30 = 60
5. 40 + 30 = 70

Use with Lesson 12-1. 147

Practice On Level

Adding Groups of 10 — P 12-1

Write each number sentence.

1. 30 + 20 = 50
2. 30 + 30 = 60
3. 20 + 40 = 60
4. 50 + 30 = 80

Write each sum.

5. 50 + 20 = 70; 30 + 40 = 70; 20 + 20 = 40
6. 70 + 20 = 90; 60 + 30 = 90; 10 + 80 = 90

Problem Solving *Number Sense*

Circle the two groups that answer the riddle.

7. David has two books of stamps. He has more than 60 stamps. Which are David's stamp books?

Stamps of the U.S.A. 40; Stamps of France 20; Stamps of Japan 10; Stamps of Mexico 30

Use with Lesson 12-1. 147

Practice

Write each sum.

5. $40 + 10 = $ 50

6. $20 + 60 = $ 80

7. $30 + 30 = $ 60 $70 + 20 = $ 90 $20 + 50 = $ 70

8. $60 + 40 = $ 100 $50 + 10 = $ 60 $40 + 40 = $ 80

9. $80 + 10 = $ 90 $40 + 30 = $ 70 $20 + 10 = $ 30

10. $30 + 60 = $ 90 $50 + 40 = $ 90 $10 + 30 = $ 40

Problem Solving Number Sense

Circle the two groups that answer the question.

11. Maria has two groups of stickers.
She has more than 70 stickers in all.
Which are Maria's stickers?

Butterflies 10 Snakes 30 Birds 20 Fish 50

Home Connection Your child added groups of 10 to make sums through 100. **Home Activity** Ask your child to draw a picture of models like those shown above to show 20 + 40 and then to tell the sum. *(60)*

3 Practice

Explain that in Exercises 7–10, children will find the sums without using pictures of models.

Reading Assist: Draw Conclusions Have children look at Exercise 11. Ask them to tell whether or not there is more than one correct answer. Have them explain their conclusions.

Leveled Practice

Below Level Use place-value models.

On Level Complete all exercises as written.

Above Level For Exercises 5–10, write the number sentences using number words such as "Forty plus ten equals fifty."

Early Finishers Ask children to make up a new problem like the one in Exercise 11. Have them trade with a partner to solve.

4 Assess

Journal Idea Ask children to draw two groups of 10 (with each group having fewer than 6 tens) and write a number sentence to find the sum.

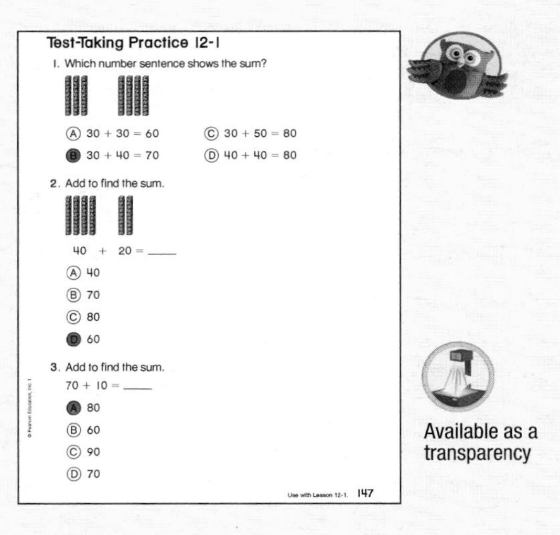
Test-Taking Practice 12-1

1. Which number sentence shows the sum?
Ⓐ 30 + 30 = 60 Ⓒ 30 + 50 = 80
Ⓑ 30 + 40 = 70 Ⓓ 40 + 40 = 80

2. Add to find the sum.
40 + 20 = ____
Ⓐ 40
Ⓑ 70
Ⓒ 80
Ⓓ 60

3. Add to find the sum.
70 + 10 = ____
Ⓐ 80
Ⓑ 60
Ⓒ 90
Ⓓ 70

Use with Lesson 12-1. 147

Available as a transparency

Enrichment Above Level

Dimes and More Dimes E 12-1 VISUAL THINKING

Draw the missing dimes.
Write each number sentence.

1. 20¢ + 30¢ = 50¢
2. 40¢ + 40¢ = 80¢
3. 10¢ + 50¢ = 60¢
4. 20¢ + 40¢ = 60¢

Circle the two groups that answer the question.

5. Kate has two purses.
She has more than 80¢ in all.
Circle Kate's two purses.

Use with Lesson 12-1. 147

Problem Solving

Adding Groups of 10 PS 12-1

Look at the sum. Find 3 ways to add tens to make the sum.

Answers may vary. Sample answers given.

1. (70) 60 + 10 = 70; 50 + 20 = 70; 40 + 30 = 70
2. (80) 70 + 10 = 80; 40 + 40 = 80; 60 + 20 = 80
3. (60) 50 + 10 = 60; 40 + 20 = 60; 30 + 30 = 60
4. (90) 80 + 10 = 90; 70 + 20 = 90; 60 + 30 = 90

Circle the two groups that answer the question.

5. Randy has 2 groups of coins.
He has more than 80 coins in all.
Which are Randy's coins?

Coins of South America 50; Coins of Europe 30; Coins of Asia 40; Coins of Africa 20

Use with Lesson 12-1. 147

Adding Tens to Two-Digit Numbers

Lesson Organizer

Quick Lesson Overview

Objective Add a multiple of 10 to a two-digit number.

Math Understanding When adding tens to a two-digit number, only the tens digit changes.

Professional Development Note

How Children Learn Math Before children learn the algorithms for adding two-digit numbers, it is important that they understand the place-value concepts on which the rules are based. Be sure that children use different manipulatives and a hundred chart to add, before introducing algorithms.

NCTM Standards

- Number and Operations

(For a complete correlation to the NCTM Standards and Grades Pre-K through 2 Expectations, see Pages 457G and 457H.)

Getting Started

Spiral Review

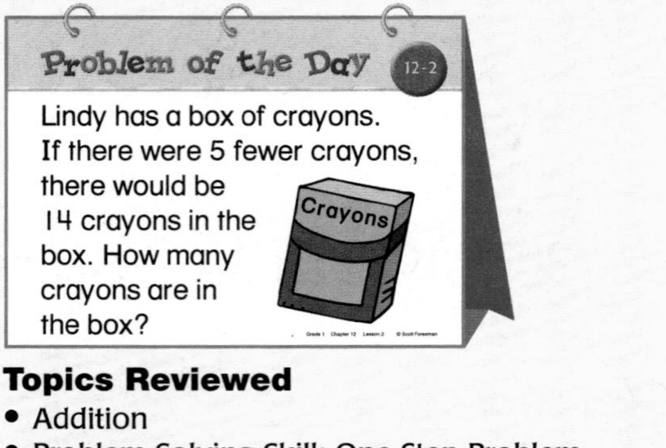

Problem of the Day 12-2

Lindy has a box of crayons. If there were 5 fewer crayons, there would be 14 crayons in the box. How many crayons are in the box?

Topics Reviewed
- Addition
- Problem-Solving Skill: One-Step Problem

Answer There are 14 + 5, or 19 crayons in the box.

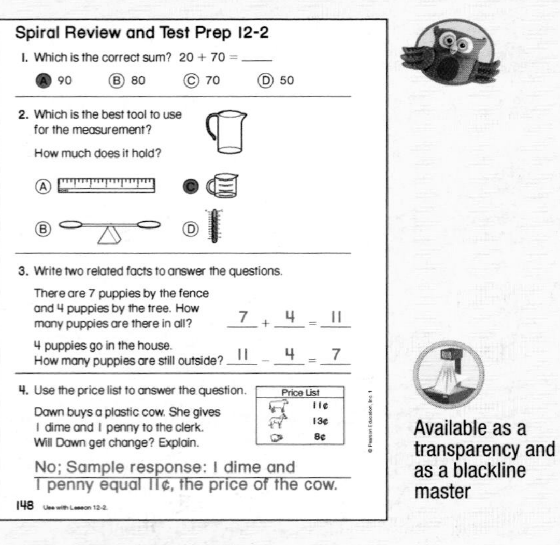

Spiral Review and Test Prep 12-2

1. Which is the correct sum? 20 + 70 = ____

(A) 90 (B) 80 (C) 70 (D) 50

2. Which is the best tool to use for the measurement?

How much does it hold?

(A) (B) (C) (D)

3. Write two related facts to answer the questions.

There are 7 puppies by the fence and 4 puppies by the tree. How many puppies are there in all? 7 + 4 = 11

4 puppies go in the house. How many puppies are still outside? 11 − 4 = 7

4. Use the price list to answer the question.

Dawn buys a plastic cow. She gives 1 dime and 1 penny to the clerk. Will Dawn get change? Explain.

Price List	
	11¢
	13¢
	8¢

No; Sample response: 1 dime and 1 penny equal 11¢, the price of the cow.

148 Use with Lesson 12-2.

© Pearson Education, Inc. 1

Available as a transparency and as a blackline master

Topics Reviewed
1. Adding Groups of 10
2. Choosing a Measurement Tool
3. Using Related Facts
4. Use Data from a Table

Investigating the Concept

Adding on a Hundred Chart

15–20 MIN **Visual/Spatial/Kinesthetic** WHOLE CLASS

Materials *(per child)* Hundred Chart (Workmat 6)

What to Do

- On the board, write 55 + 30 = ___. Using an overhead transparency of the hundred chart, demonstrate how to add. Have children follow along on their own workmats.
- **Place a finger on 55. How can we show that we add 10 to 55?** *(Move down 1 row.)* **How can we add 30?** *(Move down a total of 3 rows.)* **Where do we land?** *(85)*
- Repeat, having children solve similar problems using a hundred chart.

Ongoing Assessment

- **How can we use a hundred chart to solve 39 + 50?** *(Start on 39. Move down 5 rows.)*
- **Reasoning If we move down on a hundred chart to add, how do we move to subtract?** *(Move up.)*

Reaching All Learners

Math Vocabulary

Add Tens, Move Ones

10–15 MIN **Linguistic/Kinesthetic** PAIRS

Materials *(per pair)* Place-value models (9 tens and 9 ones)

- Have pairs make two groups of 10 and say a problem, such as "4 tens plus 3 tens equals 7 tens, or 40 + 30 = 70."
- Pairs place some ones with one group of 10 and then say the problem. For example, 43 + 30 = 73.
- Ask children to move the ones to the other group. **How does the problem change?** *(40 + 33 = 73)*

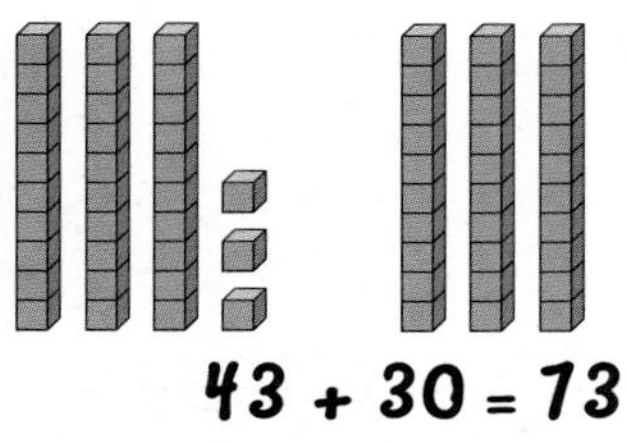

Activate Prior Knowledge/Build Background

English Language Learners

Ones Drop

5–10 MIN **Visual/Spatial/Kinesthetic**

Materials *(per pair)* Number Cards 0–11 (Teaching Tool 9); index cards labeled with decade addition problems and answers written vertically

- Have pairs choose a card, such as 50 + 30 = 80. One child picks a number card between 1 and 9 and places it over the zero in one of the addends.
- The partner reads the problem, such as 54 + 30 = ___, moves down the 4 card to cover the zero in the answer, and says 84.
- Repeat with other cards.

Reteaching

Count Up by 10s

10–15 MIN **Linguistic/Kinesthetic** PAIRS

Materials *(per pair)* Place-value models (tens); index cards labeled with two-digit numbers

- Have one child pick a number card and place it on the table.
- Have the other child think of a decade number and show it with tens next to the number card.
- Have partners work together to say and solve the problem by counting up by 10s from the number on the card. The total should not exceed 99.

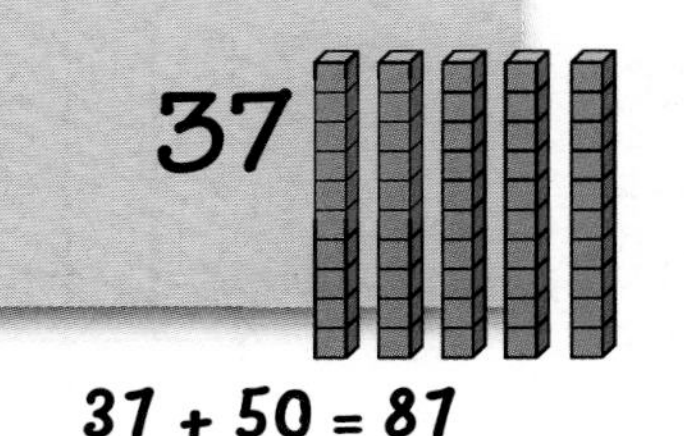

Students with Special Needs

Counting On by 10s

5–10 MIN **Visual/Spatial/Linguistic** SMALL GROUP

Materials *(per child)* Hundred Chart (Workmat 6)

- Have children point to 27 on their hundred charts.
- Ask children to point to the number that is 10 more. **What do you notice about this number?** *(It is in the box just below 27.)* Remind children that for every 10 you add, you move down one row.
- Have children point to 33. **How much is 33 + 20? Go down 2 rows because 20 is 2 tens.** *(53)*
- Repeat with other problems.

Objective Add a multiple of 10 to a two-digit number.

1 Warm Up

Activate Prior Knowledge Review how to add 10 to a one-digit number. Name a one-digit number. Ask children to tell how many 10 more would be. Repeat, inviting the child who tells the sum to say the next one-digit number.

2 Teach

Learn!

Direct attention to the puzzle box and place-value models on the top of the student page. Ask children to count on by 10s to solve the problem. Then have them write the number sentence.

Ongoing Assessment

Talk About It

- **How many did we begin with?** *(36)*
- **How many more were added?** *(40)*
- **What would the sum have been if we had added 50 to 36 instead of adding 40?** *(86)*

If children have difficulty counting on by 10s,

then have them use a hundred chart.

Check

Error Intervention

If children do not record the correct sum,

then check to be sure they are writing the values for the tens correctly. *(Also see* Reteaching, *Page 461B.)*

Think About It Have children look at the number 14 in Exercise 6. **Which number is in the ones place?** *(4)* **Which number is in the tens place?** *(1)* **When you add 40, what is the sum?** *(54)* **Which digit changes?** *(The tens)* **Which digit stays the same?** *(The ones)* **Explain.**

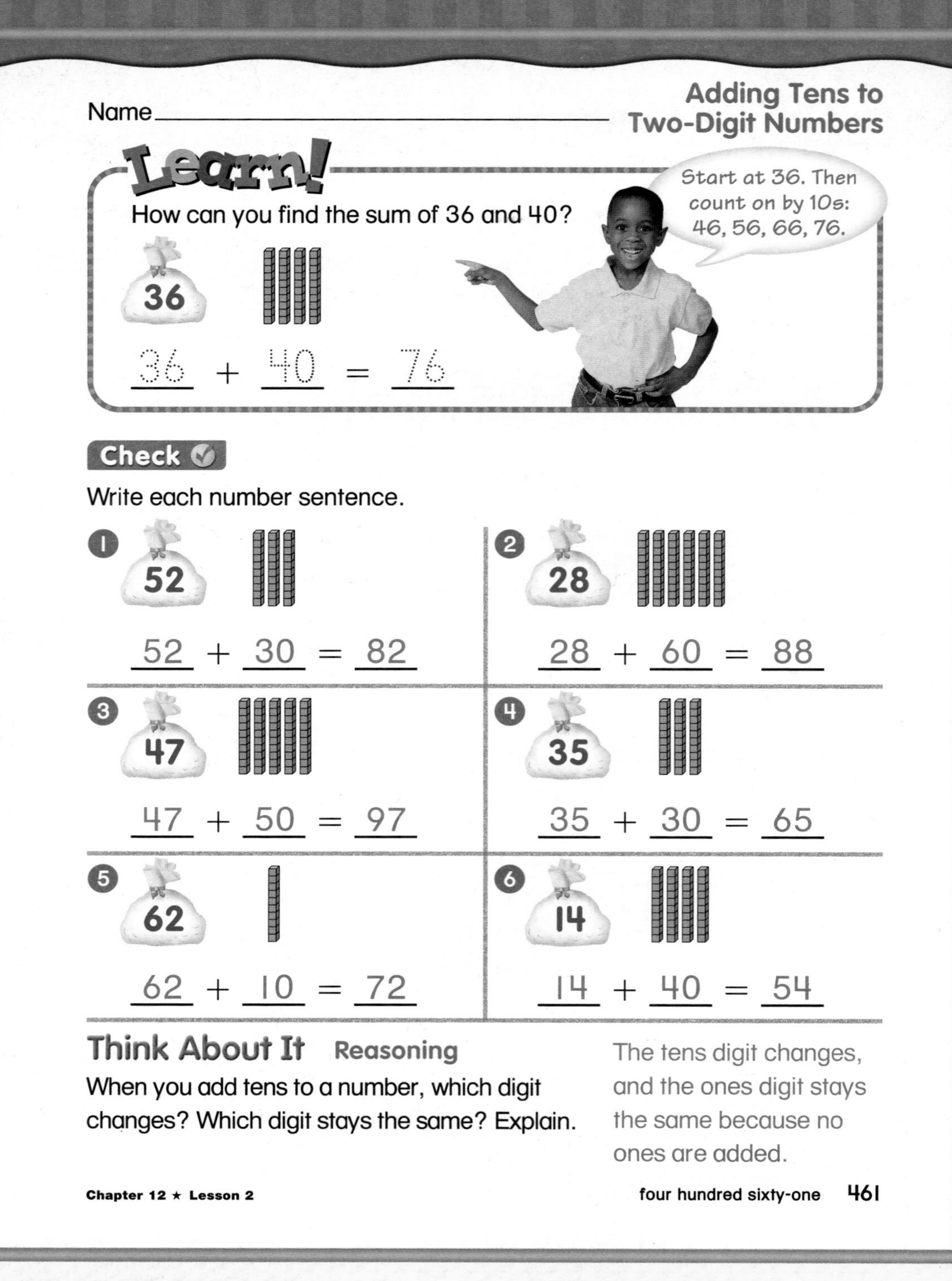

Name ____________

Adding Tens to Two-Digit Numbers

Learn!

How can you find the sum of 36 and 40?

36 + 40 = 76

Check

Write each number sentence.

1. 52 + 30 = 82
2. 28 + 60 = 88
3. 47 + 50 = 97
4. 35 + 30 = 65
5. 62 + 10 = 72
6. 14 + 40 = 54

Think About It Reasoning

When you add tens to a number, which digit changes? Which digit stays the same? Explain.

The tens digit changes, and the ones digit stays the same because no ones are added.

Chapter 12 ★ Lesson 2 four hundred sixty-one 461

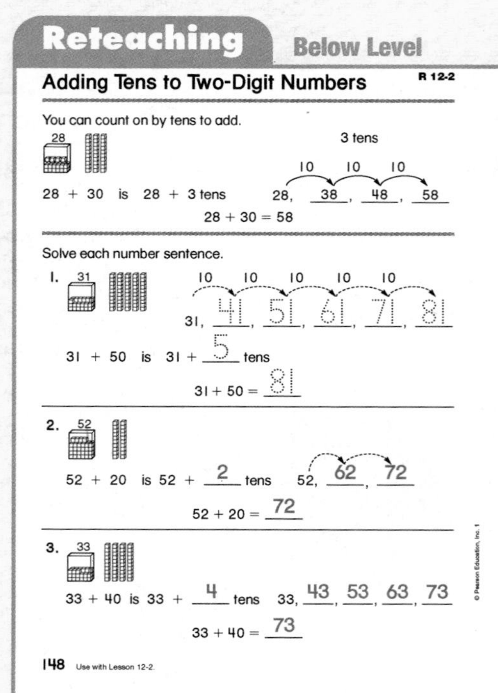

Reteaching Below Level

Adding Tens to Two-Digit Numbers R 12-2

You can count on by tens to add.

28 + 30 is 28 + 3 tens

3 tens: 28, 38, 48, 58

28 + 30 = 58

Solve each number sentence.

1. 31, 41, 51, 61, 71, 81
31 + 50 is 31 + 5 tens
31 + 50 = 81

2. 52 + 20 is 52 + 2 tens 52, 62, 72
52 + 20 = 72

3. 33 + 40 is 33 + 4 tens 33, 43, 53, 63, 73
33 + 40 = 73

148 Use with Lesson 12-2

Practice On Level

Adding Tens to Two-Digit Numbers P 12-2

Write each number sentence.

1. 36 + 20 = 56
2. 15 + 60 = 75
3. 27 + 50 = 77
4. 54 + 40 = 94
5. 63 + 30 = 93
6. 47 + 30 = 77

Problem Solving *Algebra*

7. Write the missing numbers. Then write the next addition problem in the pattern.

37	47	57	67	77
+ 10	+ 10	+ 10	+ 10	+ 10
47	57	67	77	87

148 Use with Lesson 12-2

 EC NTL 12 11 10 9 8 7 6 5

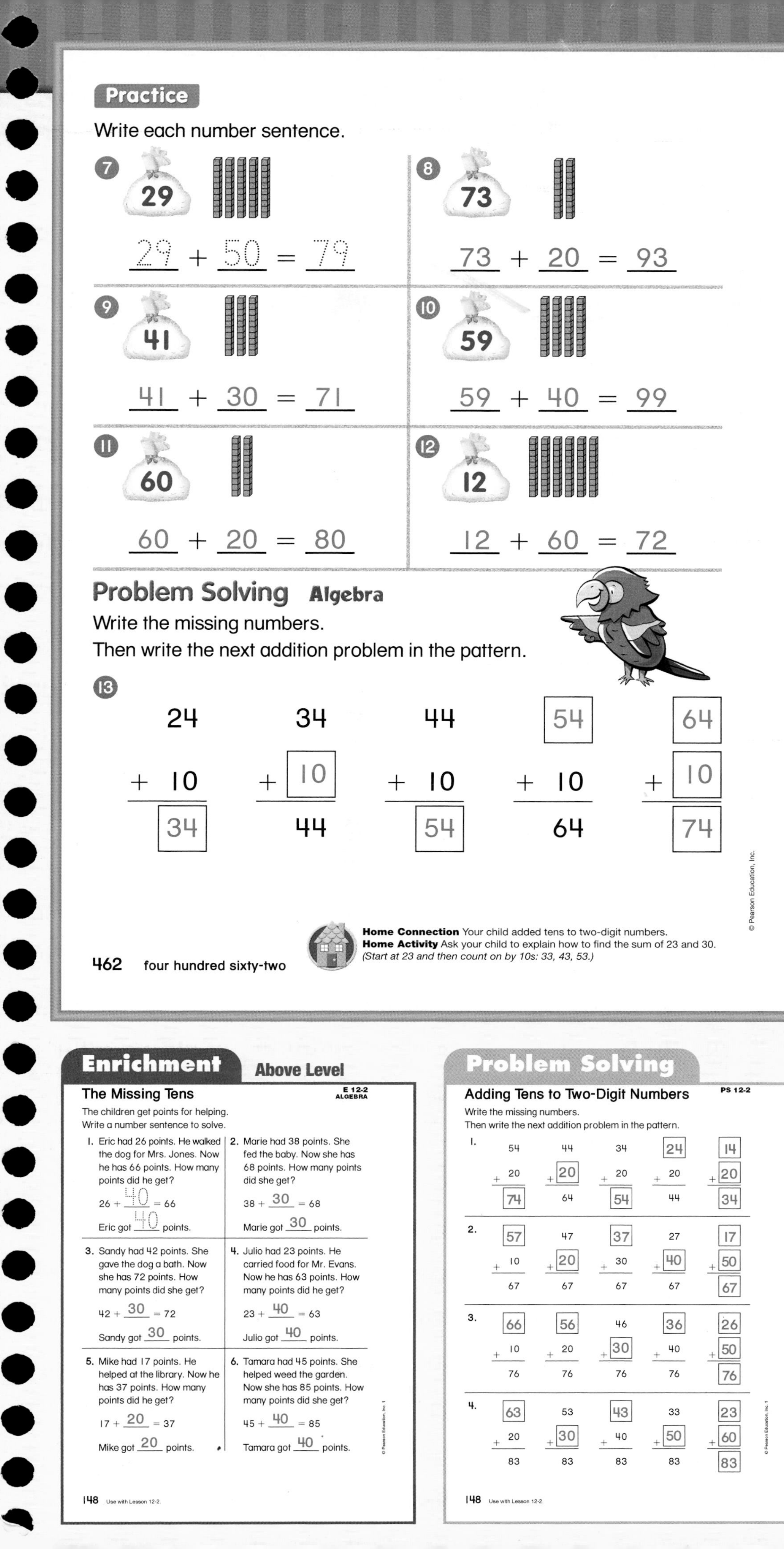
Practice

Write each number sentence.

7. 29 + 50 = 79
8. 73 + 20 = 93
9. 41 + 30 = 71
10. 59 + 40 = 99
11. 60 + 20 = 80
12. 12 + 60 = 72

Problem Solving **Algebra**

Write the missing numbers.
Then write the next addition problem in the pattern.

13.

24	34	44	54	64
+ 10	+ 10	+ 10	+ 10	+ 10
34	44	54	64	74

Home Connection Your child added tens to two-digit numbers.
Home Activity Ask your child to explain how to find the sum of 23 and 30. *(Start at 23 and then count on by 10s: 33, 43, 53.)*

Enrichment Above Level

The Missing Tens E 12-2 ALGEBRA

The children get points for helping.
Write a number sentence to solve.

1. Eric had 26 points. He walked the dog for Mrs. Jones. Now he has 66 points. How many points did he get?
26 + 40 = 66
Eric got 40 points.

2. Marie had 38 points. She fed the baby. Now she has 68 points. How many points did she get?
38 + 30 = 68
Marie got 30 points.

3. Sandy had 42 points. She gave the dog a bath. Now she has 72 points. How many points did she get?
42 + 30 = 72
Sandy got 30 points.

4. Julio had 23 points. He carried food for Mr. Evans. Now he has 63 points. How many points did he get?
23 + 40 = 63
Julio got 40 points.

5. Mike had 17 points. He helped at the library. Now he has 37 points. How many points did he get?
17 + 20 = 37
Mike got 20 points.

6. Tamara had 45 points. She helped weed the garden. Now she has 85 points. How many points did she get?
45 + 40 = 85
Tamara got 40 points.

148 Use with Lesson 12-2.

Problem Solving

Adding Tens to Two-Digit Numbers PS 12-2

Write the missing numbers.
Then write the next addition problem in the pattern.

1.

54	44	34	24	14
+ 20	+ 20	+ 20	+ 20	+ 20
74	64	54	44	34

2.

57	47	37	27	17
+ 10	+ 20	+ 30	+ 40	+ 50
67	67	67	67	67

3.

66	56	46	36	26
+ 10	+ 20	+ 30	+ 40	+ 50
76	76	76	76	76

4.

63	53	43	33	23
+ 20	+ 30	+ 40	+ 50	+ 60
83	83	83	83	83

148 Use with Lesson 12-2.

3 Practice

For Exercises 7–12, have children continue adding tens to two-digit numbers.

Leveled Practice

Below Level Complete Exercises 7–12 using place-value models.

On Level Complete all exercises as written.

Above Level Write each problem vertically as well as horizontally.

Early Finishers Have children toss two number cubes to make a two-digit number. Then ask them to toss one number cube and add that many tens. Have them write the number sentence. Repeat as time allows.

4 Assess

Journal Idea On the board, write several addition sentences without their sums. Use a two-digit number and a multiple of 10 for each sentence. Have children choose one of the addition sentences, draw models to show it, and find the sum.

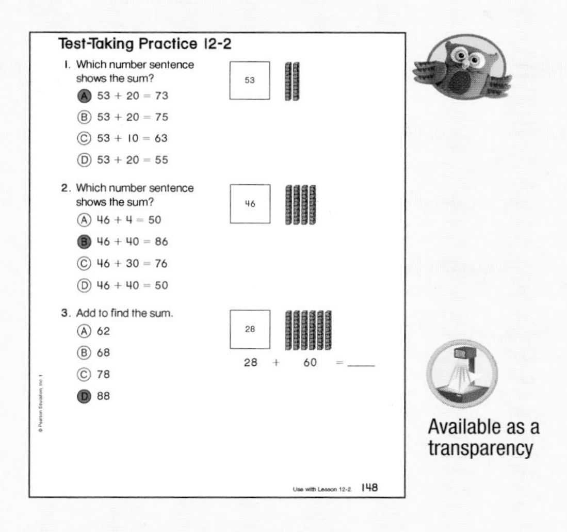
Test-Taking Practice 12-2

1. Which number sentence shows the sum?
Ⓐ 53 + 20 = 73
Ⓑ 53 + 20 = 75
Ⓒ 53 + 10 = 63
Ⓓ 53 + 20 = 55

2. Which number sentence shows the sum?
Ⓐ 46 + 4 = 50
Ⓑ 46 + 40 = 86
Ⓒ 46 + 30 = 76
Ⓓ 46 + 40 = 50

3. Add to find the sum.
Ⓐ 62
Ⓑ 68
Ⓒ 78
Ⓓ 88

28 + 60 = ___

Use with Lesson 12-2. 148

Available as a transparency

12-3 Adding Two-Digit Numbers

Lesson Organizer

Quick Lesson Overview

Objective Add two two-digit numbers without regrouping.

Math Understanding When adding two-digit numbers, the ones are combined with the ones, and the tens are combined with the tens.

Professional Development Note

Math Background In this lesson, children begin to learn the algorithms for two-digit addition. However, the same objectives will be revisited in the next two grades, so mastery is not expected now.

NCTM Standards

- Number and Operations

(For a complete correlation to the NCTM Standards and Grades Pre-K through 2 Expectations, see Pages 457G and 457H.)

Getting Started

Spiral Review

Problem of the Day 12-3

Tim is taller than Tam. Tom is shorter than Tam. Name the boys in order from shortest to tallest. (Hint: You can draw a picture.)

Topics Reviewed

- Length (Height)
- Problem-Solving Strategy: Draw a Picture

Answer From shortest to tallest: Tom, Tam, Tim

Spiral Review and Test Prep 12-3

1. Which number sentence shows the sum?
   - Ⓐ 74 + 2 = 76
   - Ⓑ 74 + 10 = 84
   - Ⓒ 74 + 11 = 85
   - Ⓓ 74 + 20 = 94
2. Marco builds a tower using 9 blue blocks and 8 green blocks. How many blocks does he use in all?
   - Ⓐ 17 blocks
   - Ⓑ 16 blocks
   - Ⓒ 18 blocks
   - Ⓓ 1 block

Use the spinner and tally chart for Exercises 3 and 4.

Gray	𝍸 𝍸 I
White	𝍸

3. Julia spun the spinner 16 times. She made a tally mark in the chart for each spin. How many times did the spinner land on gray? 11 times
4. Julia spins the spinner again. **Predict:** On which color is the spinner less likely to land? white

Use with Lesson 12-3. 149

Available as a transparency and as a blackline master

Topics Reviewed

1. Adding Tens to Two-Digit Numbers
2. Doubles Plus 1 and Doubles Minus 1
3. Using Tally Marks
4. More Likely or Less Likely

Investigating the Concept

Model Two-Digit Addition

Materials *(per child)* Place-Value Mat A (Workmat 4); place-value models (9 tens and 9 ones)

What to Do

- Have children use models to solve the following story: **23 bats were hanging upside-down in a cave. 14 bats were dangling from a ledge. How many bats were there in all?** *(37)* Have children combine the ones first and then the tens. Then have them write the number sentence in vertical format.
- Repeat the story, changing the numbers each time. Use two-digit numbers that will not need regrouping when added.

Ongoing Assessment

- **What is the sum of 63 and 11?** *(74)*
- **Reasoning How is adding two-digit numbers like adding one-digit numbers?** *(For both, you add the ones together, but in two-digit addition, you also add the tens.)*

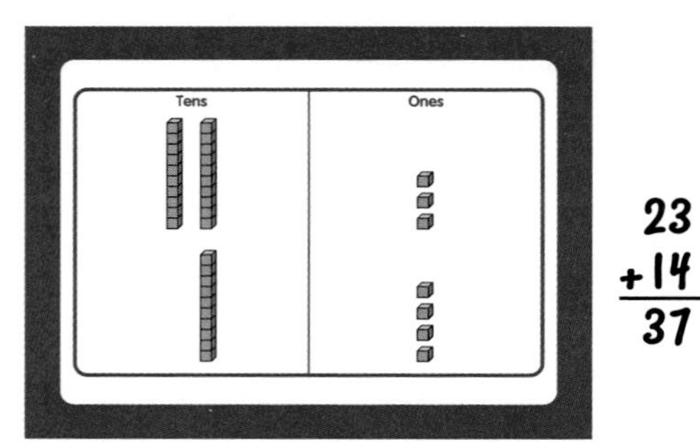

Reaching All Learners

Reading in Math

Trading Problems

10–15 MIN **Social/Cooperative**

Materials *(per pair)* Place-Value Mat A (Workmat 4); place-value models (9 tens and 9 ones)

- For each pair, name 2 two-digit numbers that can be added without regrouping. Have children work in pairs to write an addition story problem using the numbers.
- When children have finished writing the story problems, have pairs trade and solve each other's problems using tens and ones on a place-value mat.

We had 14 marbles and got 23 more. How many marbles do we have in all?

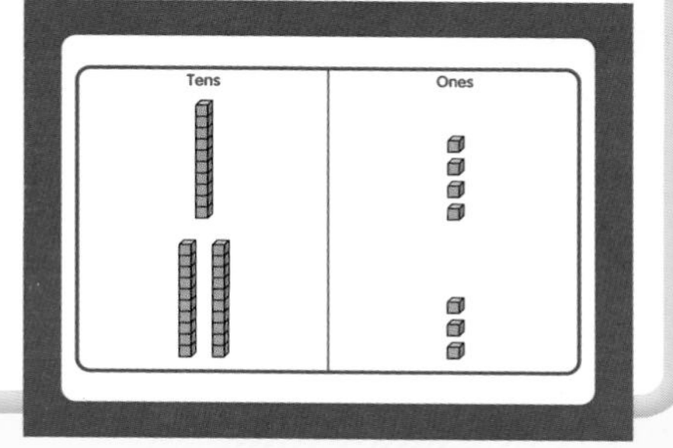

Access Content

English Language Learners

Add Ones and Add Tens

10–15 MIN **Visual/Spatial/Kinesthetic**

Materials *(per pair)* Index cards labeled with two-digit addition problems that do not require regrouping

- Review how to add two-digit numbers by first adding the ones and then adding the tens.
- Demonstrate with a problem card, such as 23 + 46. Cover the tens column. **Add ones: 3 + 6 = 9.** Write 9 under the ones column. Cover the ones column. **Add tens: 2 + 4 = 6.** Write 6 under the tens column. **23 + 46 = 69.**
- Give each child a problem card and have pairs repeat the activity.

Reteaching

Adding Tens and Ones

10–15 MIN **Visual/Spatial/Kinesthetic**

PAIRS

Materials *(per pair)* Place-Value Mat A (Workmat 4); 3 sets of Number Cards 0–11 (Teaching Tool 9); place-value models (9 tens and 9 ones)

- Using only the numbers 1 to 4, have one child pick four number cards and place two of them in the tens column and two of them in the ones column to make an addition problem on the place-value mat.
- Have the partner show the problem using tens and ones. Then have partners solve the problem.
- Repeat with other numbers.

75 in all.

Advanced Learners

Number Code Game

10–15 MIN **Logical/Mathematical**

Materials *(per group)* Place-Value Mat A (Workmat 4); 2 each of five different items, such as beans, checkers, counters, connecting cubes, pennies

- Have the group decide on and list a value from 1 to 5 for each different item.
- Have children take turns placing assorted items on the place-value mat to represent digits for a two-digit addition problem. Have other children use the value list to decode the problem and then solve it.

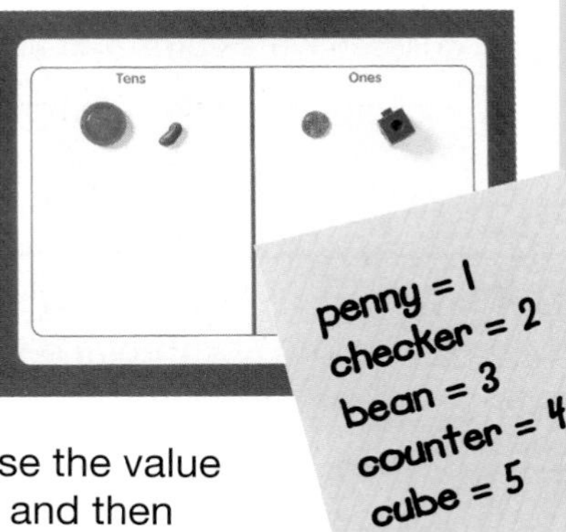

Objective Add two two-digit numbers without regrouping.

1 Warm Up

Activate Prior Knowledge Review addition of basic facts. From Number Cards 0–11 (Teaching Tool 9), choose two number cards and ask children to find the sum of the two numbers. Replace the cards and shuffle them. Have the child who gave the correct sum choose the next two cards.

2 Teach

Learn!

Direct children's attention to the place-value models at the top of the student page. Guide them through the process of first adding the ones and then adding the tens.

Ongoing Assessment

Talk About It

- **How many groups of 10 are there in the sum of 21 and 18?** *(3 groups of 10)*
- **Would you ever add a number in the ones place to a number in the tens place? Explain.** *(No; the numbers in the tens place represent groups of 10, not ones.)*

If children have difficulty understanding that they can add ones only to ones and tens only to tens,

then have them use connecting cubes to model the problems.

Check

Error Intervention

If children write sums that are incorrect,

then allow them to use a completed Addition Chart (Teaching Tool 39). *(Also see Reteaching, Page 463B.)*

Think About It You may wish to have children show 57 with place-value models. Then children can separate the models into two groups.

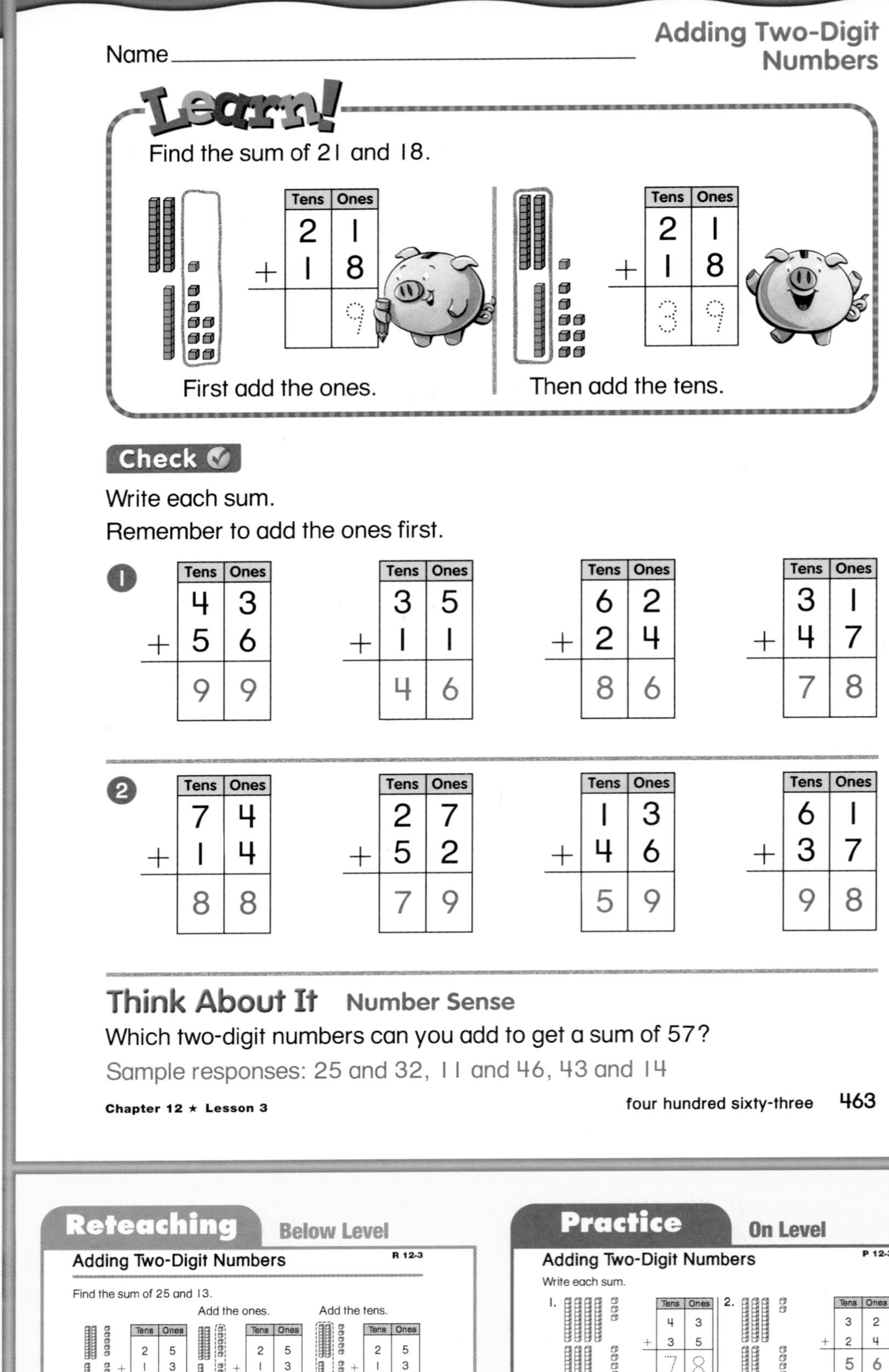

Name ____________________

Adding Two-Digit Numbers

Learn!

Find the sum of 21 and 18.

	Tens	Ones
	2	1
+	1	8
		9

First add the ones.

	Tens	Ones
	2	1
+	1	8
	3	9

Then add the tens.

Check

Write each sum.

Remember to add the ones first.

1.

	Tens	Ones			Tens	Ones			Tens	Ones			Tens	Ones
	4	3			3	5			6	2			3	1
+	5	6		+	1	1		+	2	4		+	4	7
	9	9			4	6			8	6			7	8

2.

	Tens	Ones			Tens	Ones			Tens	Ones			Tens	Ones
	7	4			2	7			1	3			6	1
+	1	4		+	5	2		+	4	6		+	3	7
	8	8			7	9			5	9			9	8

Think About It Number Sense

Which two-digit numbers can you add to get a sum of 57?

Sample responses: 25 and 32, 11 and 46, 43 and 14

Chapter 12 ★ Lesson 3 four hundred sixty-three 463

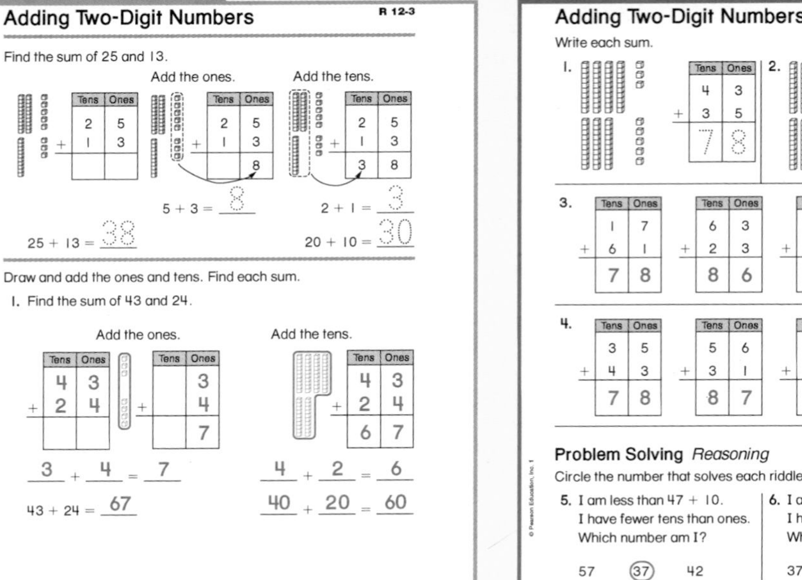

Reteaching Below Level

Adding Two-Digit Numbers R 12-3

Find the sum of 25 and 13.

Add the ones. Add the tens.

	Tens	Ones
	2	5
+	1	3
	3	8

5 + 3 = 8

2 + 1 = 3

25 + 13 = 38

20 + 10 = 30

Draw and add the ones and tens. Find each sum.

1. Find the sum of 43 and 24.

Add the ones. Add the tens.

	Tens	Ones
	4	3
+	2	4
	6	7

3 + 4 = 7

4 + 2 = 6

43 + 24 = 67

40 + 20 = 60

Use with Lesson 12-3 149

Practice On Level

Adding Two-Digit Numbers P 12-3

Write each sum.

1. 43 + 35 = 78
2. 32 + 24 = 56
3. 17 + 61 = 78; 63 + 23 = 86; 43 + 52 = 95; 53 + 25 = 78
4. 35 + 43 = 78; 56 + 31 = 87; 43 + 21 = 64; 26 + 22 = 48

Problem Solving *Reasoning*

Circle the number that solves each riddle.

5. I am less than 47 + 10. I have fewer tens than ones. Which number am I? 57 (37) 42
6. I am greater than 15 + 23. I have more ones than tens. Which number am I? 37 (45) 55

Use with Lesson 12-3 149

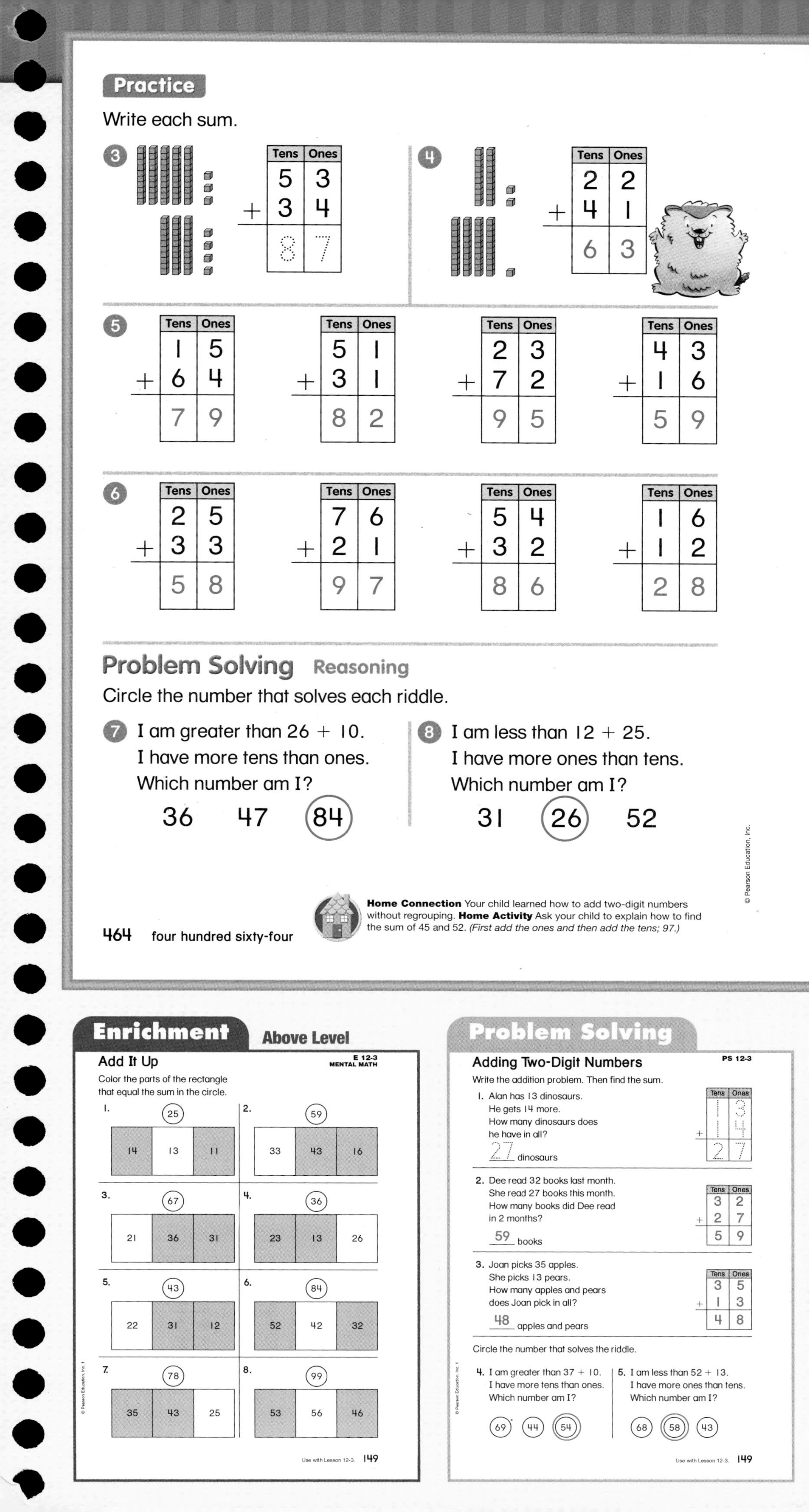

Practice

Write each sum.

3.

	Tens	Ones
	5	3
+	3	4
	8	7

4.

	Tens	Ones
	2	2
+	4	1
	6	3

5.

	Tens	Ones
	1	5
+	6	4
	7	9

	Tens	Ones
	5	1
+	3	1
	8	2

	Tens	Ones
	2	3
+	7	2
	9	5

	Tens	Ones
	4	3
+	1	6
	5	9

6.

	Tens	Ones
	2	5
+	3	3
	5	8

	Tens	Ones
	7	6
+	2	1
	9	7

	Tens	Ones
	5	4
+	3	2
	8	6

	Tens	Ones
	1	6
+	1	2
	2	8

Problem Solving Reasoning

Circle the number that solves each riddle.

7. I am greater than 26 + 10.
I have more tens than ones.
Which number am I?
36 47 (84)

8. I am less than 12 + 25.
I have more ones than tens.
Which number am I?
31 (26) 52

Home Connection Your child learned how to add two-digit numbers without regrouping. **Home Activity** Ask your child to explain how to find the sum of 45 and 52. *(First add the ones and then add the tens; 97.)*

Enrichment Above Level

Add It Up — E 12-3 MENTAL MATH

Color the parts of the rectangle that equal the sum in the circle.

1. (25) 14 13 11
2. (59) 33 43 16
3. (67) 21 36 31
4. (36) 23 13 26
5. (43) 22 31 12
6. (84) 52 42 32
7. (78) 35 43 25
8. (99) 53 56 46

Use with Lesson 12-3. 149

Problem Solving

Adding Two-Digit Numbers — PS 12-3

Write the addition problem. Then find the sum.

1. Alan has 13 dinosaurs. He gets 14 more. How many dinosaurs does he have in all? 27 dinosaurs

	Tens	Ones
	1	3
+	1	4
	2	7

2. Dee read 32 books last month. She read 27 books this month. How many books did Dee read in 2 months? 59 books

	Tens	Ones
	3	2
+	2	7
	5	9

3. Joan picks 35 apples. She picks 13 pears. How many apples and pears does Joan pick in all? 48 apples and pears

	Tens	Ones
	3	5
+	1	3
	4	8

Circle the number that solves the riddle.

4. I am greater than 37 + 10. I have more tens than ones. Which number am I? 69 44 (54)

5. I am less than 52 + 13. I have more ones than tens. Which number am I? 68 (58) 43

Use with Lesson 12-3. 149

3 Practice

For Exercises 7 and 8, have children cross out answers that do not match the clues.

Leveled Practice

Below Level Use place-value models to complete all exercises.

On Level Complete all exercises mentally.

Above Level Write the problems in Exercise 6 with the addends in reverse order. Then find the sums.

Early Finishers Ask children to write a story for one of the problems on the student page. Then have children trade story problems and solve.

4 Assess

Journal Idea On the board, write the following numbers: 43, 25, 14, 31, 12, and 23. Ask children to choose two of the numbers, write an addition problem, draw models, and then solve the problem.

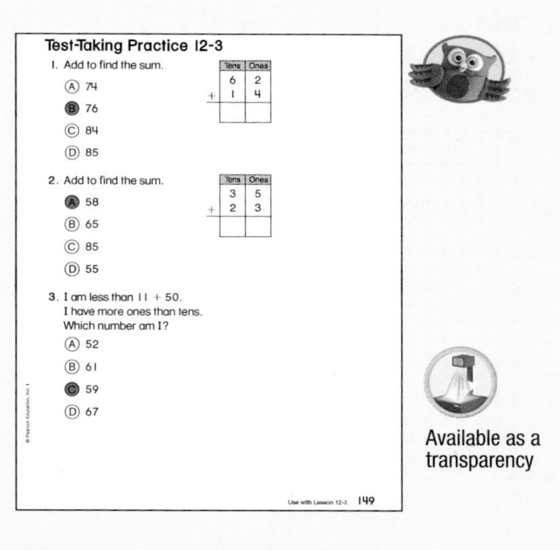

Test-Taking Practice 12-3

1. Add to find the sum. 62 + 14
Ⓐ 74 Ⓑ 76 Ⓒ 84 Ⓓ 85

2. Add to find the sum. 35 + 23
Ⓐ 58 Ⓑ 65 Ⓒ 85 Ⓓ 55

3. I am less than 11 + 50. I have more ones than tens. Which number am I?
Ⓐ 52 Ⓑ 61 Ⓒ 59 Ⓓ 67

Use with Lesson 12-3. 149

Available as a transparency

12-4 Regrouping in Addition

Lesson Organizer

Quick Lesson Overview

Objective Use models to add a one-digit quantity to a two-digit quantity with and without regrouping.

Math Understanding When there are 10 or more ones in a quantity, 10 of the ones can be regrouped to make a new ten without changing the quantity.

Vocabulary Regroup

Materials for Student Pages *(per pair)* Place-Value Mat A (Workmat 4); 85 connecting cubes

Professional Development Note

Managing Instruction When children are learning the concept of regrouping, they need to use a variety of groupable models. In addition to connecting cubes, consider using straws or craft sticks bundled in groups of 10 as well as groups of 10 beans or counters in small paper cups.

NCTM Standards

- Number and Operations

(For a complete correlation to the NCTM Standards and Grades Pre-K through 2 Expectations, see Pages 457G and 457H.)

Getting Started

Spiral Review

Problem of the Day 12-4

Sue has red, yellow, and pink roses. If she puts 3 roses in a vase, how many different ways can she arrange the colors? Make a table to help.

Red Roses										
Yellow Roses										
Pink Roses										

Topics Reviewed
- Problem-Solving Strategy: Make a Table

Answer Sue can fill the vase in 10 different ways.

Red Roses	3	2	2	1	1	1	0	0	0	0
Yellow Roses	0	1	0	2	0	1	3	2	1	0
Pink Roses	0	0	1	0	2	1	0	1	2	3

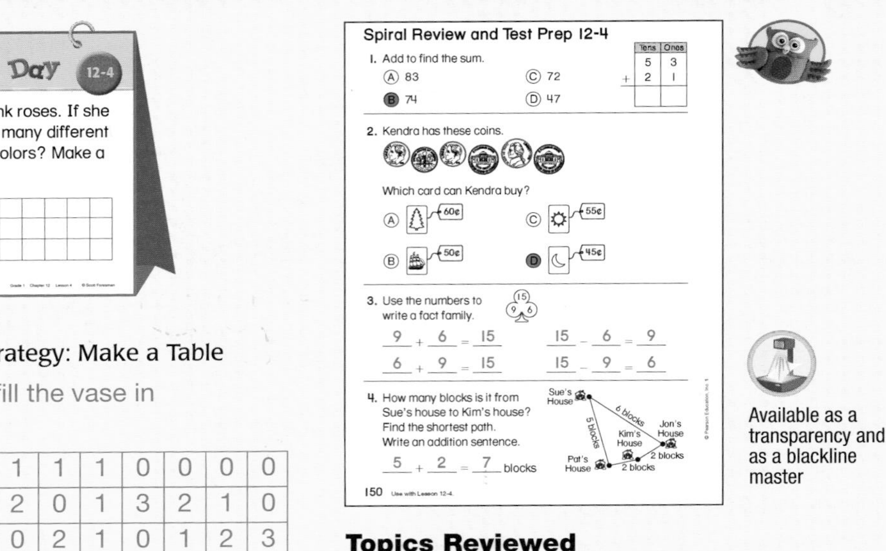

Spiral Review and Test Prep 12-4

1. Add to find the sum.

	Tens	Ones
	5	3
+	2	1

Ⓐ 83 Ⓑ 74 Ⓒ 72 Ⓓ 47

2. Kendra has these coins.

Which card can Kendra buy?

Ⓐ 60¢ Ⓑ 50¢ Ⓒ 55¢ Ⓓ 45¢

3. Use the numbers to write a fact family.

9 + 6 = 15 15 − 6 = 9

6 + 9 = 15 15 − 9 = 6

4. How many blocks is it from Sue's house to Kim's house? Find the shortest path. Write an addition sentence.

5 + 2 = 7 blocks

150 Use with Lesson 12-4.

Available as a transparency and as a blackline master

Topics Reviewed
1. Adding Two-Digit Numbers
2. Counting Dimes and Nickels
3. Fact Families
4. Use Data from a Map

Investigating the Concept

Deciding When to Regroup

PAIRS

Materials *(per pair)* Place-Value Mat A (Workmat 4); 85 connecting cubes

What to Do

- Write 35 + 7 = __ on the board. Ask children to use cubes to show 35 on their mats. Next, have them add 7. **How many are there in all?** *(42)* Explain that when there are 10 or more ones, 10 ones can be regrouped to make 1 ten.
- Starting with 42 cubes, have children add 4. **Are there enough ones to regroup?** *(No)* Write 42 + 4 = 46 on the board. Continue adding small amounts, each time asking if there are enough ones to regroup.

Ongoing Assessment

- **If you add 5 to 16, will you need to regroup?** *(Yes)*
- **Reasoning** **When should you regroup?** *(Regroup when there are 10 or more ones.)*

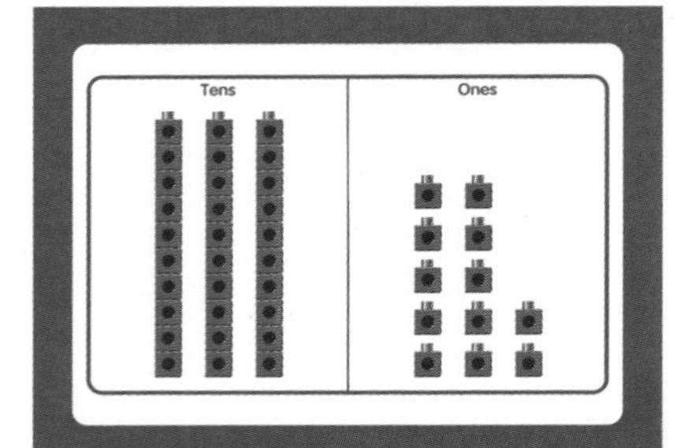

Reaching All Learners

Math Vocabulary

Everyone Regroup!

5–10 MIN **Linguistic/Kinesthetic**

- Draw a vertical line on the board and write "tens" on the left and "ones" on the right.
- Invite 3 children to stand near the ones. **How many ones are there?** *(3)* **Do we have enough to regroup?** *(No)* Invite 6 more children to join them. **Do we have enough now?** *(No)* Invite 5 more children. **How many do we have now?** *(14)* **Can we regroup?** *(Yes)*
- Have 10 children join hands and move to the tens section.
- Repeat with other numbers.

Extend Language

English Language Learners

Regroup and Move

10–15 MIN **Linguistic/Kinesthetic** PAIRS

Materials *(per pair)* Place-Value Mat A (Workmat 4); connecting cubes

- Have pairs use cubes to show 27 on the place-value mat. Ask children to add 4 cubes to the ones place. Have children count their ones. **Can you regroup to make a group of 10?** *(Yes)*
- Have children connect 10 cubes, say "regroup," and move them to the tens column.

Reteaching

Chains of Tens

10–15 MIN **Kinesthetic**

Materials *(per pair)* 99 paper clips; index cards labeled with addition problems that require regrouping

- Give pairs addition problems, such as 36 + 6.
- Have pairs show 36 by linking paper clips in 3 chains of ten and setting 6 single clips to the side. Have children add 6 paper clips to the ones and regroup when they have more than 10 single clips. Ask children to say how many clips they now have. *(42)*
- Give each pair a card with an addition problem to solve with paper clips.

Math and Social Studies

Transporting by Freight Train

10–15 MIN **Logical/Mathematical/Kinesthetic** PAIRS

Materials *(per pair)* 50 connecting cubes

- Explain that many companies send their products by train from one part of the country to another.
- Tell children that a railroad line will use only trains with exactly 10 boxcars. One company has 26 full boxcars. What can the company do? Ask children to use connecting cubes to show how many more boxcars the company needs to fill in order to transport its product.
- Repeat with other numbers.

Objective Use models to add a one-digit quantity to a two-digit quantity with and without regrouping.

1 Warm Up

Activate Prior Knowledge Review addition of two-digit numbers without regrouping. On the board, write 13 + 24 in vertical format. Invite a volunteer to explain how to find the sum. Repeat for other problems without regrouping.

2 Teach

Learn!

Have children use connecting cubes and Workmat 4 to model the problem at the top of the student page. Introduce the term regroup. Have children use their cubes to solve several other problems, some that require regrouping and some that do not.

Ongoing Assessment

Talk About It

- **Why should you regroup when you add 4 to 38?** *(Because there are more than 10 ones in all)*
- **Which number can you add to 38 without regrouping?** *(1)*

If children are confused about when to regroup,

then have them put all of the ones on a ten-frame. Explain that when the ten-frame is full, they need to regroup.

Check

Error Intervention

If children write an incorrect number of tens in any of the sums,

then watch as they use the models and have them recount the tens after they regroup. *(Also see* Reteaching, *Page 465B.)*

Think About It Have children show 6 ones and then add 1 more. **Do you need to regroup?** *(No)* Continue adding 1 until children can regroup and answer *yes* to the question.

Name ____________

Regrouping in Addition

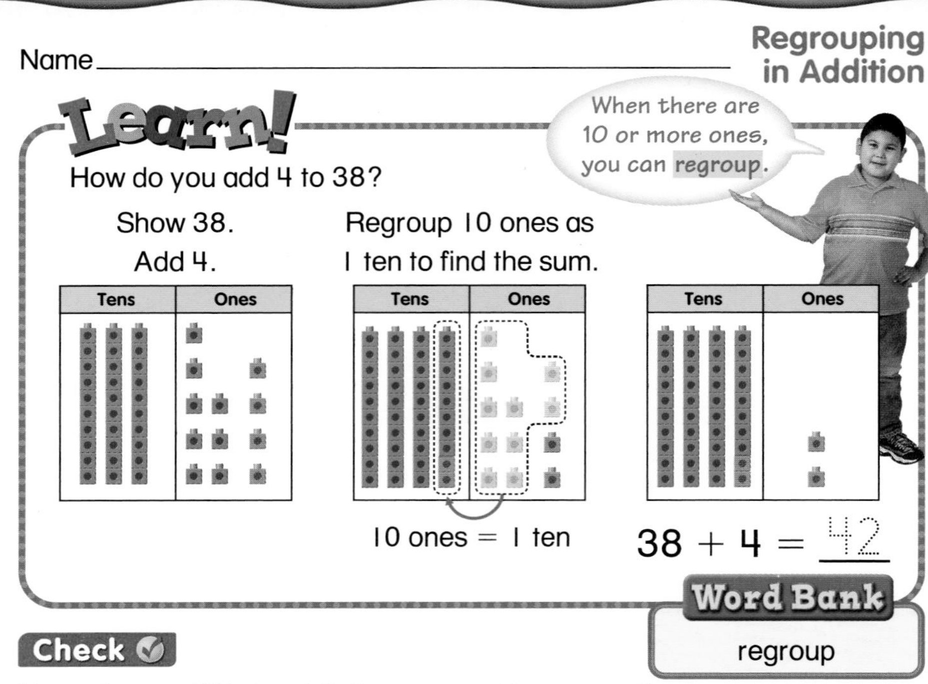

Word Bank

regroup

Check

Use cubes and Workmat 4. Do you need to regroup? Circle **yes** or **no**. Then write the sum.

	Show.	Add.	Do you need to regroup?	Find the sum.
1	15	8	(yes) no	15 + 8 = 23
2	34	3	yes (no)	34 + 3 = 37
3	65	5	(yes) no	65 + 5 = 70
4	77	6	(yes) no	77 + 6 = 83

Think About It Reasoning

How do you know when you need to regroup? You need to regroup when there are 10 or more ones.

Reteaching Below Level

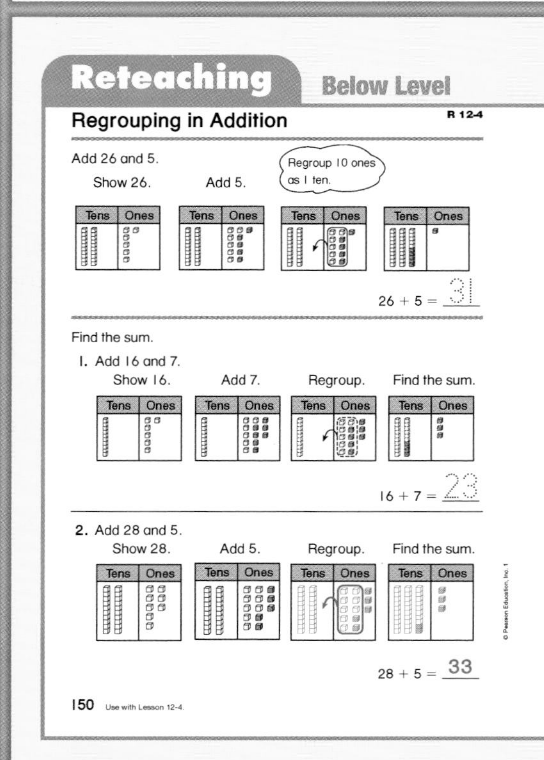

Regrouping in Addition R 12-4

Add 26 and 5.

Show 26. Add 5. Regroup 10 ones as 1 ten.

26 + 5 = 31

Find the sum.

1. Add 16 and 7.

Show 16. Add 7. Regroup. Find the sum.

16 + 7 = 23

2. Add 28 and 5.

Show 28. Add 5. Regroup. Find the sum.

28 + 5 = 33

150 Use with Lesson 12-4.

Practice On Level

Regrouping in Addition P 12-4

Use cubes and Workmat 4. Circle **yes** or **no**. Then write the sum.

	Show	Add	Do you need to regroup?	Find the sum.
1.	27	6	(yes) no	27 + 6 = 33
2.	43	5	yes (no)	43 + 5 = 48
3.	34	8	(yes) no	34 + 8 = 42
4.	17	4	(yes) no	17 + 4 = 21
5.	56	3	yes (no)	56 + 3 = 59
6.	93	2	yes (no)	93 + 2 = 95
7.	87	7	(yes) no	87 + 7 = 94
8.	68	5	(yes) no	68 + 5 = 73

Problem Solving *Number Sense*

Use the number line to add.

45 46 47 48 49 50 51 52 53 54 55

9. 47 + 6 = 53

10. 49 + 1 = 50

11. 46 + 3 = 49

12. 48 + 5 = 53

150 Use with Lesson 12-4.

Practice

Use cubes and Workmat 4. Do you need to regroup?
Circle **yes** or **no.** Then write the sum.

	Show.	Add.	Do you need to regroup?	Find the sum.
5	47	5	(yes) no	47 + 5 = 52
6	62	8	(yes) no	62 + 8 = 70
7	54	4	yes (no)	54 + 4 = 58
8	23	6	yes (no)	23 + 6 = 29
9	35	7	(yes) no	35 + 7 = 42
10	16	9	(yes) no	16 + 9 = 25
11	81	2	yes (no)	81 + 2 = 83
12	78	3	(yes) no	78 + 3 = 81

Problem Solving Number Sense

Use the number line to add.

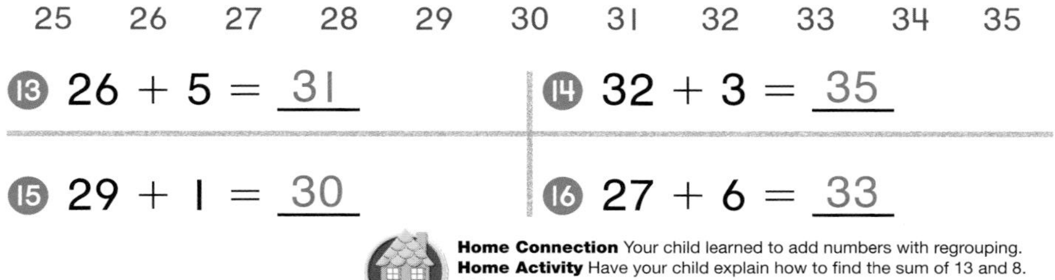

25 26 27 28 29 30 31 32 33 34 35

13. 26 + 5 = 31
14. 32 + 3 = 35
15. 29 + 1 = 30
16. 27 + 6 = 33

Home Connection Your child learned to add numbers with regrouping.
Home Activity Have your child explain how to find the sum of 13 and 8. *(21)*

3 Practice

For Exercises 5–12, have children model each problem, circle *yes* or *no* to tell if they regrouped, and write the sum.

Reading Assist: Make Predictions Before modeling problems with cubes, have children look at the numbers and predict whether or not they will need to regroup.

Leveled Practice

Below Level Work with a partner to complete all exercises.

On Level Complete all exercises individually.

Above Level Complete exercises without cubes.

Early Finishers Ask children to make up a story problem for one of the exercises. Then have them trade with a partner to solve.

4 Assess

Journal Idea Have children start with the number 25 and write and solve an addition problem that requires regrouping.

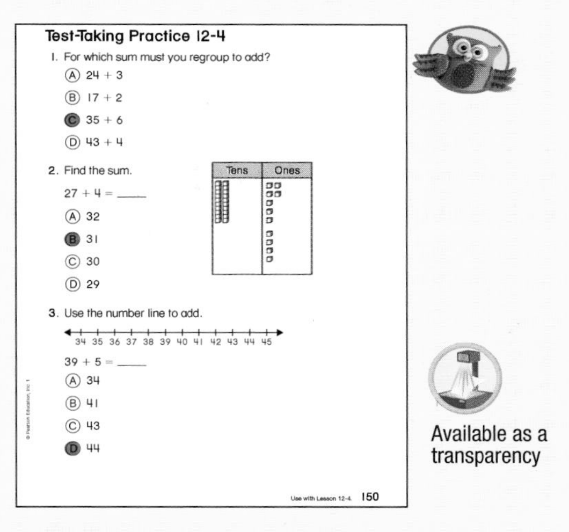

Test-Taking Practice 12-4

1. For which sum must you regroup to add?
   - Ⓐ 24 + 3
   - Ⓑ 17 + 2
   - Ⓒ 35 + 6 (filled)
   - Ⓓ 43 + 4
2. Find the sum.
   27 + 4 = ____
   - Ⓐ 32
   - Ⓑ 31 (filled)
   - Ⓒ 30
   - Ⓓ 29

Tens	Ones

3. Use the number line to add.
   34 35 36 37 38 39 40 41 42 43 44 45
   39 + 5 = ____
   - Ⓐ 34
   - Ⓑ 41
   - Ⓒ 43
   - Ⓓ 44 (filled)

© Pearson Education, Inc. 1

Use with Lesson 12-4. 150

Available as a transparency

Enrichment Above Level

Find the Rule! E 12-4 PATTERNS

Complete the number pattern. Write the rule.

1. Rule: Add 8

14	+	8	22
16	+	8	24
18	+	8	26
20	+	8	28
22	+	8	30
24	+	8	32

2. Rule: Add 9

25	+	9	34
28	+	9	37
31	+	9	40
34	+	9	43
37	+	9	46
40	+	9	49

3. Rule: Add 7

44	+	7	51
48	+	7	55
52	+	7	59
56	+	7	63
60	+	7	67
64	+	7	71

4. Rule: Add 6

57	+	6	63
59	+	6	65
61	+	6	67
63	+	6	69
65	+	6	71
67	+	6	73

© Pearson Education, Inc. 1

150 Use with Lesson 12-4.

Problem Solving

Regrouping in Addition PS 12-4

Write the addition problem. Then find the sum.

1. At the circus, Mark saw 14 clowns in a wagon. He saw 5 clowns riding bikes. How many clowns did Mark see in all?
   19 clowns

	Tens	Ones
	1	4
+		5
	1	9

2. Kim Lee saw 26 elephants march into the ring. 7 more elephants followed them. How many elephants were there in all?
   33 elephants

	Tens	Ones
	2	6
+		7
	3	3

3. Rob saw 15 lions and 8 tigers. How many lions and tigers did Rob see in all?
   23 lions and tigers

	Tens	Ones
	1	5
+		8
	2	3

Use the number line to add.

45 46 47 48 49 50 51 52 53 54 55

4. 48 + 3 = 51
5. 46 + 7 = 53

© Pearson Education, Inc. 1

150 Use with Lesson 12-4.

Exact Answer or Estimate?

Lesson Organizer

Quick Lesson Overview 

Objective Solve problems by deciding whether an estimate is enough or whether an exact answer is needed.

Math Understanding Sometimes a problem can be solved without finding the exact answer.

Math Monsters Videos Use Episode 14: *Estimation* with or anytime after Lesson 12-5.

Professional Development Note

Math Background Children need to use mental addition strategies to help them decide whether or not an estimate is all that is needed for solving a problem. Help children think of the tens that are closest to the original numbers in the problems.

NCTM Standards

- Number and Operations

(For a complete correlation to the NCTM Standards and Grades Pre-K through 2 Expectations, see Pages 457G and 457H.)

Getting Started

Spiral Review

Problem of the Day 12-5

Solve. Tell how you found your answer. Suki has 25 stamps. Her mother gives her 13 more stamps. Does Suki have enough stamps to mail 40 party invitations?

Topics Reviewed

- Addition
- Comparing numbers
- Problem-Solving Skill: Multiple-Step Problem

Answer Suki has 25 + 13 = 38 stamps. Since 38 < 40, she does not have enough stamps to mail 40 party invitations.

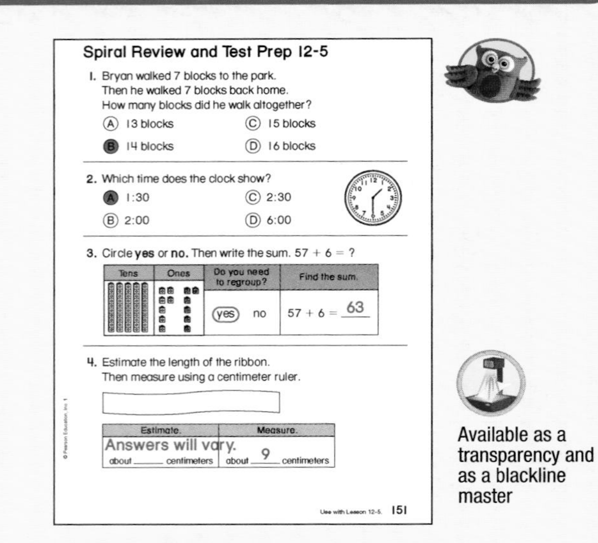
Spiral Review and Test Prep 12-5

1. Bryan walked 7 blocks to the park. Then he walked 7 blocks back home. How many blocks did he walk altogether?
   - (A) 13 blocks
   - (B) 14 blocks
   - (C) 15 blocks
   - (D) 16 blocks
2. Which time does the clock show?
   - (A) 1:30
   - (B) 2:00
   - (C) 2:30
   - (D) 6:00
3. Circle **yes** or **no**. Then write the sum. 57 + 6 = ?

Tens	Ones	Do you need to regroup?	Find the sum.
		(yes) no	57 + 6 = 63

4. Estimate the length of the ribbon. Then measure using a centimeter ruler.

Estimate.	Measure.
Answers will vary. about ___ centimeters	about 9 centimeters

Use with Lesson 12-5. 151

Available as a transparency and as a blackline master

Topics Reviewed

1. Doubles
2. Telling and Writing Time to the Half Hour
3. Regrouping in Addition
4. Estimating and Measuring with Centimeters

Investigating the Concept

Exact Answer or Estimate?

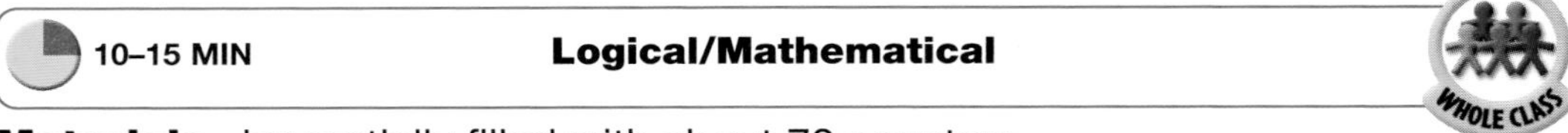

WHOLE CLASS

Materials Jar partially filled with about 70 counters

What to Do

- Show children a jar partially filled with counters. **Are there enough counters to give 1 to each child in the class?**
- Ask children to decide if they need an exact answer or an estimate to solve the problem.
- Ask children to estimate whether there are as many counters as there are children. Have them look at the counters along the sides and bottom of the jar to estimate. To check, have them count only until they have counted one for each child.

Ongoing Assessment

- **If we want to know exactly how many counters are in the jar, is an estimate sufficient?** *(No; an exact answer is needed.)*
- **Reasoning** **Why don't we need to find out exactly how many counters are in the jar?** *(All that is needed is 1 counter for each child, and there are more than that in the jar.)*

Reaching All Learners

Reading in Math

Solving Problems

5–10 MIN **Auditory/Logical/Mathematical**

Materials *(per child)* 2 index cards labeled "exact answer" and "estimate"

- Explain that clues can help you decide if you can *estimate* or if you must find an *exact answer* to solve a story problem.
- Use word clues as you state problems that can be solved with estimates and those that require exact answers.
- Have children raise the cards that indicate their choices.

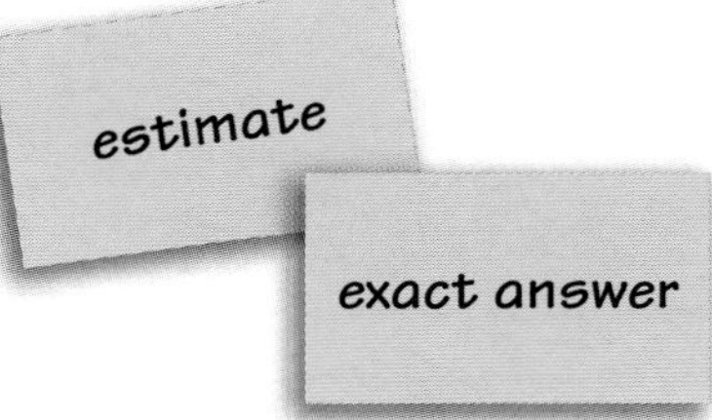

English Language Learners

Extend Language

Understanding *Estimate* and *Exact Answer*

10–15 MIN **Auditory/Linguistic**

Materials Plastic jar filled with beans

- Remind children of the meanings of *estimate* and *exact answer*. **About how many beans are in the jar? Can you give an exact answer or an estimate?** Invite children to estimate. **Let's count the beans.**
- After children have counted, ask: **Is this number an exact answer or an estimate?** *(Exact answer)*

Reteaching

Make a Good Estimate

5–10 MIN **Logical/Mathematical**

Materials *(per group)* 2 plastic bags; place-value models (20 ones); 20 paper plates

- Set out 10 paper plates. Pass around a bag with 6 cubes in it. **Do you think there are enough cubes in the bag to put 1 on every plate? Estimate.** *(No; there are not enough. The number of cubes is obviously less than 10.)*
- Set out 10 more plates and then pass around two bags, with 6 cubes in each bag. **Are there enough cubes to put 1 on every plate now? Estimate.** *(Children might estimate that there are not enough cubes because 6 + 6 is less than the 10 + 10 needed for 20 plates.)*
- Continue with other numbers of plates and cubes.

Math and Social Studies

Estimate or Exact Number?

5–10 MIN **Auditory/Linguistic**

- Make a chart with the headings "Estimate" and "Exact Number."
- Talk about situations for which an estimate is acceptable and for which an exact number is needed: **When you need to know if you have enough money to buy something, is an estimate sufficient? If you are bringing cherries to a picnic, can you estimate the number to bring?**
- List children's responses in the chart and discuss the reasons for the placement of each.

Estimate	Exact Number
Number of things to bring to a picnic	Money to buy things at a store

Objective Solve problems by deciding whether an estimate is enough or whether an exact answer is needed.

1 Warm Up

Activate Prior Knowledge Review estimation. Show a jar filled with large objects and another same-sized jar filled with small objects. **Which do you think contains more? Why?**

2 Teach

Learn!

Read the problem in Exercise 1. Explain that children need to decide whether an estimate is sufficient for solving the problem. Guide them to see that because 9 is less than 10, 9 + 9 is less than 20.

Ongoing Assessment

Talk About It

- **Why is an estimate sufficient for solving this problem?** *(We know that there are more children than muffins without finding the exact sum.)*
- **If the problem asked how many muffins Yukiko had in all, would we need an exact answer or an estimate?** *(Exact answer)*

If children cannot decide whether an exact answer or an estimate is needed,

then guide them to see that since there are 20 children (10 + 10) and only 9 + 9 muffins, there are fewer muffins than children.

Check ✓

Error Intervention

If children circle *exact answer,*

then use manipulatives to model the problem. *(Also see* Reteaching, *Page 467B.)*

Think About It Help children generalize from this specific example about how to decide whether an exact answer or an estimate is needed.

Name ____________________

PROBLEM-SOLVING SKILL
Exact Answer or Estimate?

Learn!

When can you estimate to solve a problem?

1. Yukiko has 2 packages of muffins.
   Each package contains 9 muffins.
   There are 20 children in her class.
   Are there enough muffins for all of the children?

Read and Understand

We need to know if 2 packages of muffins are enough for 20 children. Do we need an exact answer or an estimate?

Plan and Solve

9 is less than 10, so 9 + 9 is less than 10 + 10. We can estimate that 2 packages contain fewer than 20 muffins.

exact answer (estimate)

Look Back and Check

Does your answer make sense?

Think About It Reasoning

How did you decide whether you needed an exact answer or an estimate?

Sample response: If you can answer the question using easier numbers, such as tens, then you don't need an exact answer.

Reteaching Below Level

PROBLEM-SOLVING SKILL R 12-5

Exact Answer or Estimate?

Al has 2 bags of name tags.
Each bag has 12 name tags.
There are 18 children in his group.
Does he have enough name tags for all of the children?

Read and Understand

You need to know if 2 bags of name tags are enough for 18 children.
Do you need an exact answer or an estimate?

Plan and Solve

12 is more than 10, so 12 + 12 is greater than 10 + 10.
18 is less than 10 + 10. You can estimate that there are enough.

exact answer (estimate)

Look Back and Check

Does your answer make sense?

Is an exact answer or an estimate needed to solve each problem?

Circle **exact answer** or **estimate.**

1. Jody wants to buy 4 stickers. They cost 7¢ each. Jody has 45¢. Does she have enough money?
   exact answer (estimate)
2. Jody has 12 stickers. She has 3 pages left in her sticker book. Can she put 4 stickers on each page?
   (exact answer) estimate

Practice On Level

PROBLEM-SOLVING STRATEGY P 12-5

Exact Answer or Estimate?

Circle **exact answer** or **estimate.**

1. Lizzie is making curtains.
   Each window is 36 inches wide.
   There are 2 windows.
   How much cloth should Lizzie buy?
   Do we need an exact answer or an estimate?
   (exact answer) estimate
2. Don wants to buy peaches. They cost 50¢.
   Don has 2 quarters, a dime, and a nickel.
   Does he have enough money?
   Do we need an exact answer or an estimate?
   exact answer (estimate)
3. Eric has 6 packs of trading cards.
   Each pack has 8 trading cards.
   He wants to give one trading card to each child in his class.
   There are 20 children in his class.
   Does he have enough cards?
   Do we need an exact answer or an estimate?
   exact answer (estimate)

Problem Solving *Estimation*

Circle the better estimate.

4. About how many grapes can you eat?
   (about 10) about 100
5. How many quarters can you hold in your hand?
   (about 5) about 50

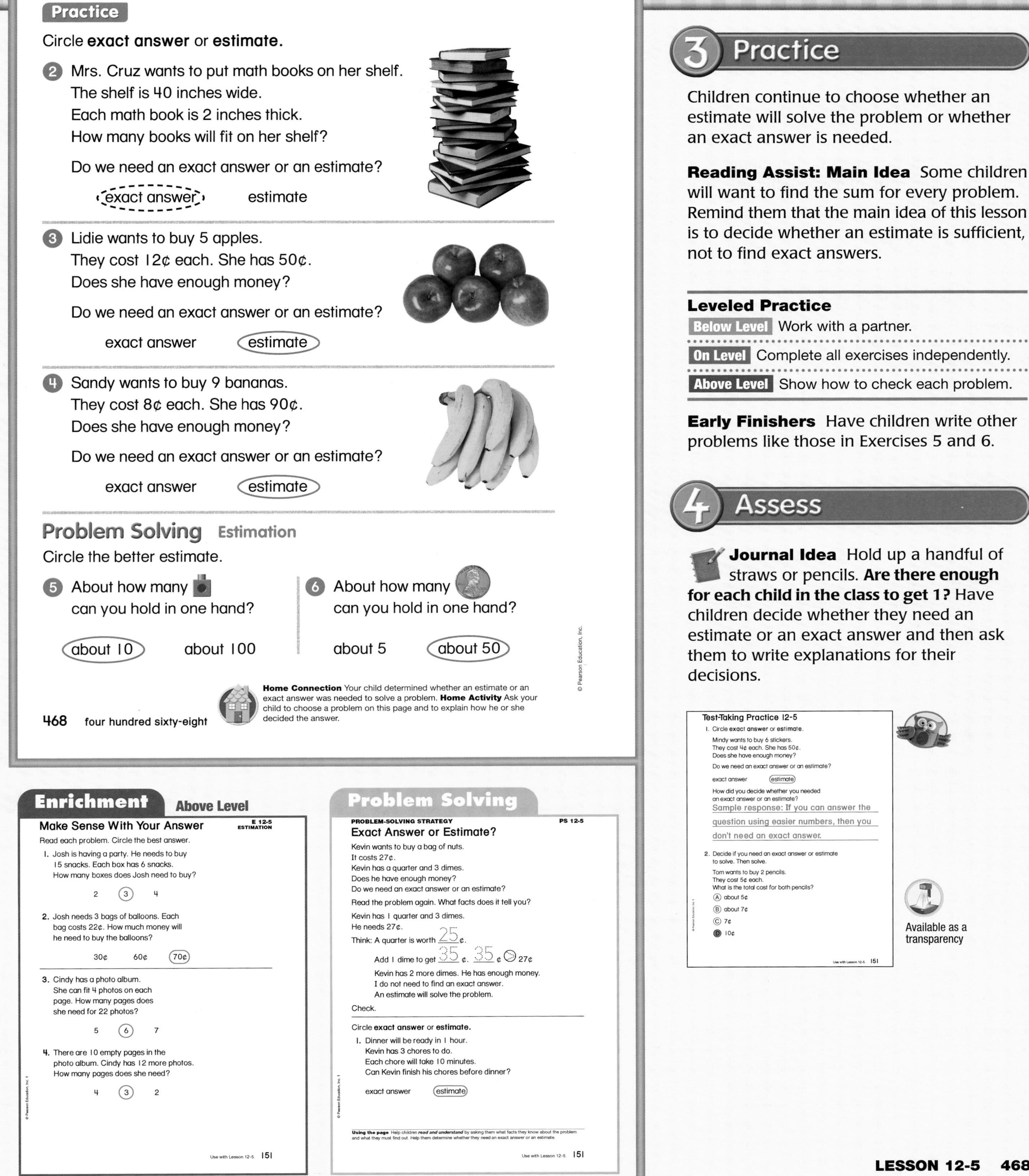

Practice

Circle **exact answer** or **estimate.**

2. Mrs. Cruz wants to put math books on her shelf.
The shelf is 40 inches wide.
Each math book is 2 inches thick.
How many books will fit on her shelf?

Do we need an exact answer or an estimate?

(exact answer) estimate

3. Lidie wants to buy 5 apples.
They cost 12¢ each. She has 50¢.
Does she have enough money?

Do we need an exact answer or an estimate?

exact answer (estimate)

4. Sandy wants to buy 9 bananas.
They cost 8¢ each. She has 90¢.
Does she have enough money?

Do we need an exact answer or an estimate?

exact answer (estimate)

Problem Solving Estimation

Circle the better estimate.

5. About how many [picture] can you hold in one hand?

(about 10) about 100

6. About how many [picture] can you hold in one hand?

about 5 (about 50)

Home Connection Your child determined whether an estimate or an exact answer was needed to solve a problem. **Home Activity** Ask your child to choose a problem on this page and to explain how he or she decided the answer.

3 Practice

Children continue to choose whether an estimate will solve the problem or whether an exact answer is needed.

Reading Assist: Main Idea Some children will want to find the sum for every problem. Remind them that the main idea of this lesson is to decide whether an estimate is sufficient, not to find exact answers.

Leveled Practice

Below Level Work with a partner.

On Level Complete all exercises independently.

Above Level Show how to check each problem.

Early Finishers Have children write other problems like those in Exercises 5 and 6.

4 Assess

Journal Idea Hold up a handful of straws or pencils. **Are there enough for each child in the class to get 1?** Have children decide whether they need an estimate or an exact answer and then ask them to write explanations for their decisions.

Test-Taking Practice 12-5

1. Circle **exact answer** or **estimate**.
Mindy wants to buy 6 stickers.
They cost 4¢ each. She has 50¢.
Does she have enough money?
Do we need an exact answer or an estimate?
exact answer (estimate)
How did you decide whether you needed an exact answer or an estimate?
Sample response: If you can answer the question using easier numbers, then you don't need an exact answer.

2. Decide if you need an exact answer or estimate to solve. Then solve.
Tom wants to buy 2 pencils.
They cost 5¢ each.
What is the total cost for both pencils?
Ⓐ about 5¢
Ⓑ about 7¢
Ⓒ 7¢
Ⓓ 10¢

Use with Lesson 12-5. 151

Available as a transparency

Enrichment Above Level

E 12-5 ESTIMATION

Make Sense With Your Answer

Read each problem. Circle the best answer.

1. Josh is having a party. He needs to buy 15 snacks. Each box has 6 snacks. How many boxes does Josh need to buy?
2 (3) 4

2. Josh needs 3 bags of balloons. Each bag costs 22¢. How much money will he need to buy the balloons?
30¢ 60¢ (70¢)

3. Cindy has a photo album. She can fit 4 photos on each page. How many pages does she need for 22 photos?
5 (6) 7

4. There are 10 empty pages in the photo album. Cindy has 12 more photos. How many pages does she need?
4 (3) 2

Use with Lesson 12-5. 151

Problem Solving

PROBLEM-SOLVING STRATEGY PS 12-5

Exact Answer or Estimate?

Kevin wants to buy a bag of nuts.
It costs 27¢.
Kevin has a quarter and 3 dimes.
Does he have enough money?
Do we need an exact answer or an estimate?

Read the problem again. What facts does it tell you?
Kevin has 1 quarter and 3 dimes.
He needs 27¢.

Think: A quarter is worth 25 ¢.
Add 1 dime to get 35 ¢. 35 ¢ (>) 27¢
Kevin has 2 more dimes. He has enough money.
I do not need to find an exact answer.
An estimate will solve the problem.

Check.

Circle **exact answer** or **estimate.**

1. Dinner will be ready in 1 hour.
Kevin has 3 chores to do.
Each chore will take 10 minutes.
Can Kevin finish his chores before dinner?
exact answer (estimate)

Using the page Help children *read and understand* by asking them what facts they know about the problem and what they must find out. Help them determine whether they need an exact answer or an estimate.

Use with Lesson 12-5. 151

Diagnostic Checkpoint

Purpose Provide assessment of children's progress to date by checking their understanding of key content covered in the previous section.

Vocabulary Review

You may wish to review this vocabulary term before assigning the page:

regroup To use 1 ten to form 10 ones; 1 hundred to form 10 tens; 12 ones to form 1 ten 2 ones; and so on *(pp. 465–466)*

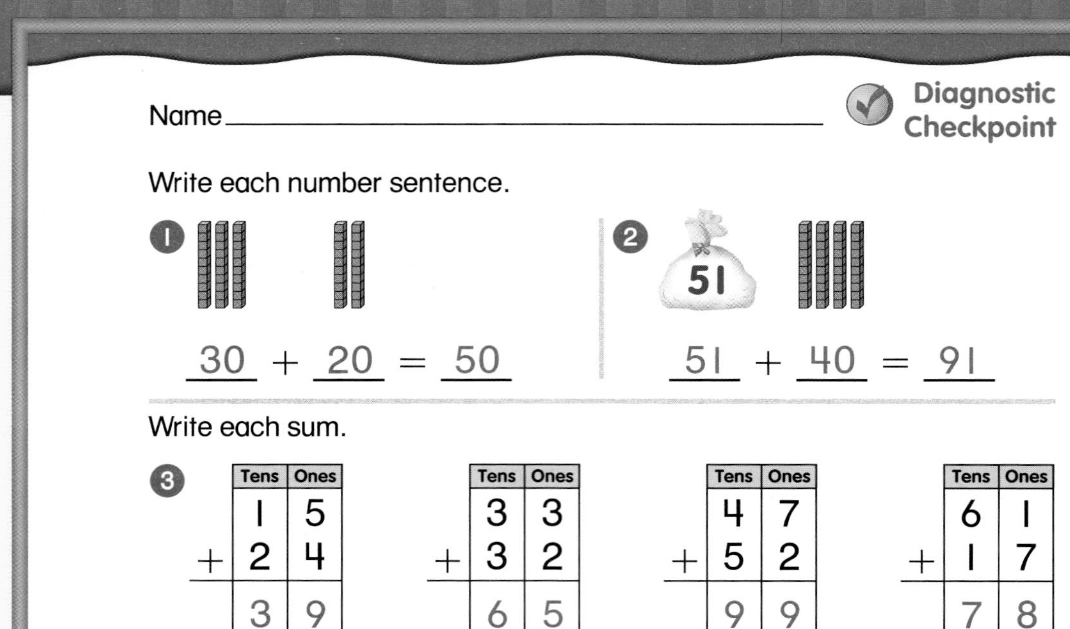

Name ______________________

Diagnostic Checkpoint

Write each number sentence.

1. 30 + 20 = 50

2. 51 + 40 = 91

Write each sum.

3.

Tens	Ones
1	5
+ 2	4
3	9

Tens	Ones
3	3
+ 3	2
6	5

Tens	Ones
4	7
+ 5	2
9	9

Tens	Ones
6	1
+ 1	7
7	8

Use cubes and Workmat 4. Do you need to regroup?
Circle **yes** or **no**. Then write the sum.

Show.	Add.	Do you need to regroup?	Find the sum.
4. 35	5	(yes) no	35 + 5 = 40
5. 43	6	yes (no)	43 + 6 = 49

Circle **exact answer** or **estimate.**

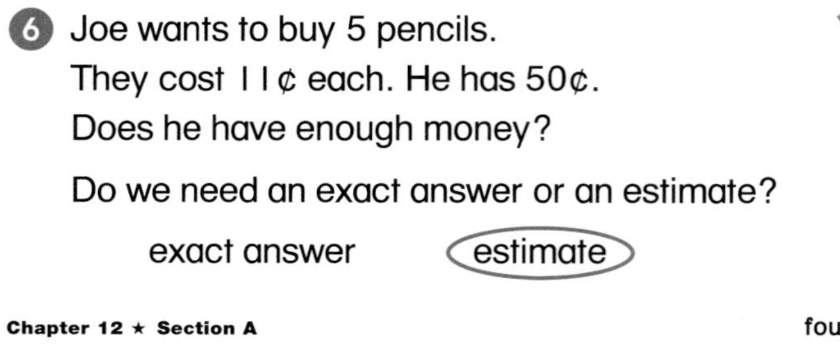

6. Joe wants to buy 5 pencils.
They cost 11¢ each. He has 50¢.
Does he have enough money?

Do we need an exact answer or an estimate?

exact answer (estimate)

Chapter 12 ★ Section A — four hundred sixty-nine 469

Item Analysis for Diagnosis and Intervention

Objective	Items	Student Book Pages*	Intervention System
Add two multiples of 10 for sums to 100.	1	459–460	C1
Add tens to a two-digit number.	2	461–462	C2
Add two two-digit numbers without regrouping.	3	463–464	C4
Use models to add a one-digit quantity to a two-digit quantity with and without regrouping.	4–5	465–466	C3
Solve problems by deciding whether an estimate is enough or whether an exact answer is needed.	6	467–468	E10

*For each lesson, there is a *Reteaching* activity in *Reaching All Learners* and a *Reteaching* master.

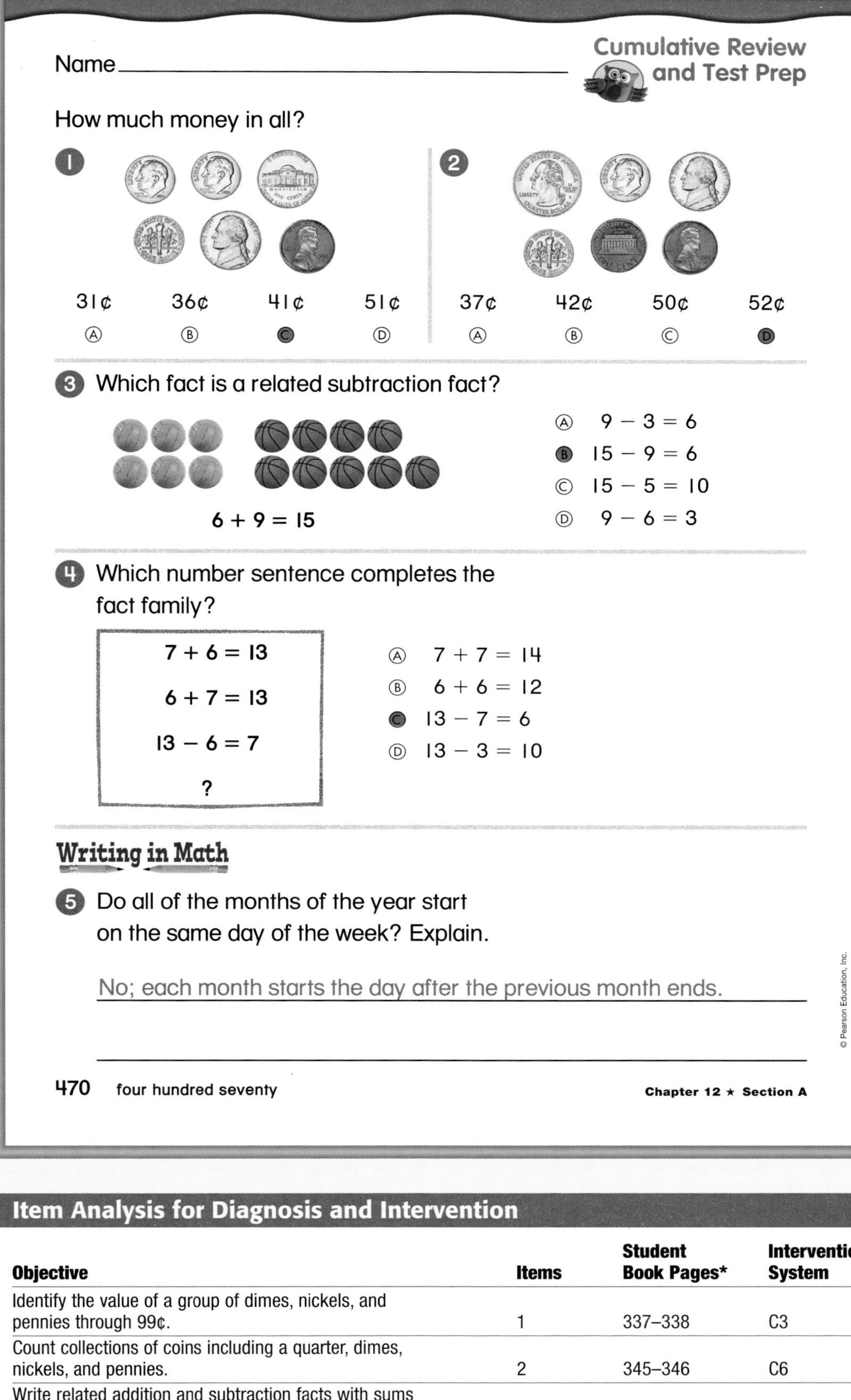

Name ____________________

Cumulative Review and Test Prep

How much money in all?

1

31¢ Ⓐ 36¢ Ⓑ 41¢ Ⓒ 51¢ Ⓓ

2

37¢ Ⓐ 42¢ Ⓑ 50¢ Ⓒ 52¢ Ⓓ

3 Which fact is a related subtraction fact?

$6 + 9 = 15$

Ⓐ $9 - 3 = 6$
Ⓑ $15 - 9 = 6$
Ⓒ $15 - 5 = 10$
Ⓓ $9 - 6 = 3$

4 Which number sentence completes the fact family?

$7 + 6 = 13$
$6 + 7 = 13$
$13 - 6 = 7$
?

Ⓐ $7 + 7 = 14$
Ⓑ $6 + 6 = 12$
Ⓒ $13 - 7 = 6$
Ⓓ $13 - 3 = 10$

Writing in Math

5 Do all of the months of the year start on the same day of the week? Explain.

No; each month starts the day after the previous month ends.

Cumulative Review and Test Prep

Purpose Provide children with a review of math concepts. Items appear as they would on a standardized test so children become familiar with that format.

Item Analysis for Diagnosis and Intervention

Objective	Items	Student Book Pages*	Intervention System
Identify the value of a group of dimes, nickels, and pennies through 99¢.	1	337–338	C3
Count collections of coins including a quarter, dimes, nickels, and pennies.	2	345–346	C6
Write related addition and subtraction facts with sums through 18.	3	435–436	B36
Write the addition and subtraction sentences that make up a fact family.	4	437–438	B37
Identify and order the months of the year.	5	227–228	D8

*For each lesson, there is a *Reteaching* activity in *Reaching All Learners* and a *Reteaching* master.

12-6 Subtracting Groups of 10

Lesson Organizer

Quick Lesson Overview

Objective Subtract a multiple of 10 from a multiple of 10, 100, or less.

Math Understanding Subtracting groups of ten is similar to subtracting numbers less than 10.

Professional Development Note

Research Base

Helping children become proficient with mental arithmetic can help them learn methods for performing more complex calculations (National Research Council, 2001). In this lesson, children mentally subtract groups of 10, using place-value models to help them relate subtracting tens to subtracting ones.

NCTM Standards

- Number and Operations

(For a complete correlation to the NCTM Standards and Grades Pre-K through 2 Expectations, see Pages 457G and 457H.)

Getting Started

Spiral Review

Topics Reviewed

- Subtraction
- Problem-Solving Skill: One-Step Problem

Answer Six clowns are crying; $10 - 4 = 6$.

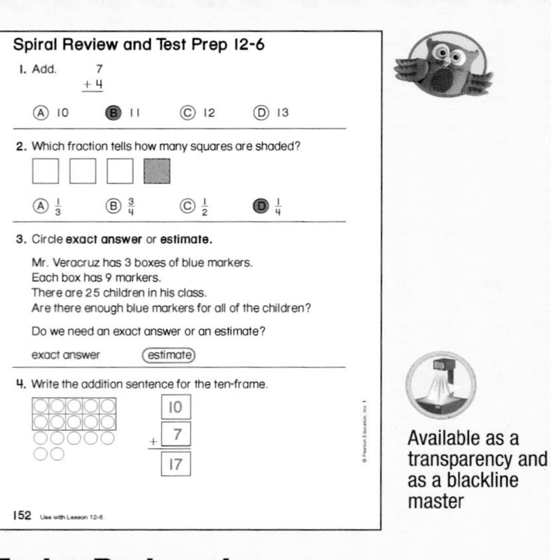

Spiral Review and Test Prep 12-6

1. Add. 7 + 4

Ⓐ 10 Ⓑ 11 Ⓒ 12 Ⓓ 13

2. Which fraction tells how many squares are shaded?

Ⓐ $\frac{1}{3}$ Ⓑ $\frac{3}{4}$ Ⓒ $\frac{1}{2}$ Ⓓ $\frac{1}{4}$

3. Circle **exact answer** or **estimate.**

Mr. Veracruz has 3 boxes of blue markers.
Each box has 9 markers.
There are 25 children in his class.
Are there enough blue markers for all of the children?

Do we need an exact answer or an estimate?

exact answer (estimate)

4. Write the addition sentence for the ten-frame.

10 + 7 = 17

152 Use with Lesson 12-6

Available as a transparency and as a blackline master

Topics Reviewed

1. Applying Addition Fact Strategies
2. Fractions of a Set
3. Exact Answer or Estimate?
4. Adding 10

Investigating the Concept

Subtracting Tens from Tens

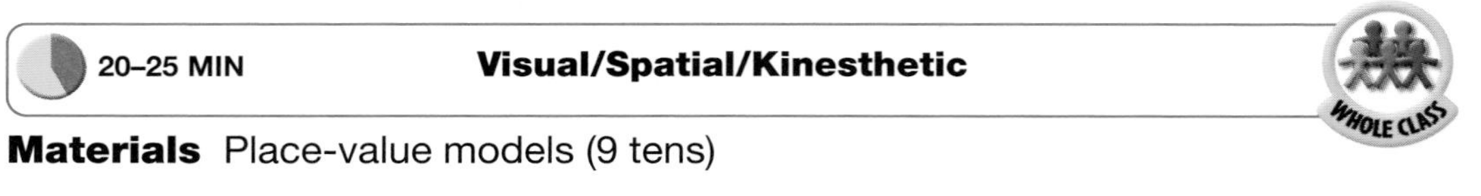

Materials Place-value models (9 tens)

What to Do

- Have 8 children come to the front of the class, each holding a ten. **How many tens are there?** *(8)* **How many ones are there in all?** *(80)*
- Ask 3 children to sit down. **Now how many tens are there?** *(5)* **How many ones are there in all?** *(50)* On the board, write $80 - 30 = 50$. Repeat the activity for other subtraction problems involving multiples of 10.

Ongoing Assessment

- **Which subtraction fact can help you find the difference in 90 – 20?** *(9 – 2 = 7)*
- **Reasoning How is subtracting tens from tens like subtracting one-digit numbers? How is it different?** *(The numbers in the tens place are subtracted just like one-digit numbers, but there is always a zero in the ones place.)*

Reaching All Learners

Oral Language in Math

Tens in Counting Rhymes

10–15 MIN **Auditory/Linguistic** WHOLE CLASS

- To demonstrate that subtracting tens is similar to subtracting ones, revisit number rhymes using tens instead of ones.
- For example, instead of the ones in this rhyme:

  Ten potatoes in a pot,

  Take two out and eight stay hot …
- Use tens:

  One hundred potatoes in a pot,

  Take twenty out and ___ stay hot.

  Eighty potatoes in the pan,

  Take twenty out, there's ___ to plan …
- Write the numbers on the board as they are subtracted.

100 – 20 = 80

80 – 20 = 60

Access Content

English Language Learners

Add a Zero

5–10 MIN **Auditory/Linguistic**

- Write the problem 9 − 6 = ___ on the board. Have a volunteer read aloud and solve the problem.
- Point to the 9 and 6 as you add a zero to each. **90 minus 60 equals 30.** Have volunteers add zeros to additional one-digit subtraction problems and pronounce the names of the numbers following the oral pattern you established.
- For each problem, invite different volunteers to solve the problems and say the answers.

Reteaching

Subtract Tens

15–20 MIN **Auditory/Logical/Mathematical**

Materials Place-value models (9 tens and 9 ones)

- Write 5 − 3 = 2 on the board. Demonstrate the problem using ones: **5 ones minus 3 ones equals 2 ones.**
- Review how to subtract tens. **I write 5 in the tens place and zero in the ones place to show 5 tens, or 50.** Write 50 − 30 = 20 on the board.
- Show 5 tens. Remove 3 tens. **5 tens minus 3 tens equals 2 tens. Subtract tens the same way you subtract ones.**
- Have children do other subtraction problems using multiples of 10.

Advanced Learners

Subtracting Groups of 100

5–10 MIN **Logical/Mathematical** PAIRS

Materials *(per pair)* Place-value models (9 hundreds)

- Discuss the answer to this question: **In what way is subtracting groups of 100 like subtracting groups of 10?** *(8 hundreds minus 2 hundreds equals 6 hundreds like 8 tens minus 2 tens equals 6 tens. A hundred contains two zeros instead of one.)*
- Have partners use hundreds to practice subtracting by hundreds.
- Help children write number sentences that show subtraction with groups of 100.

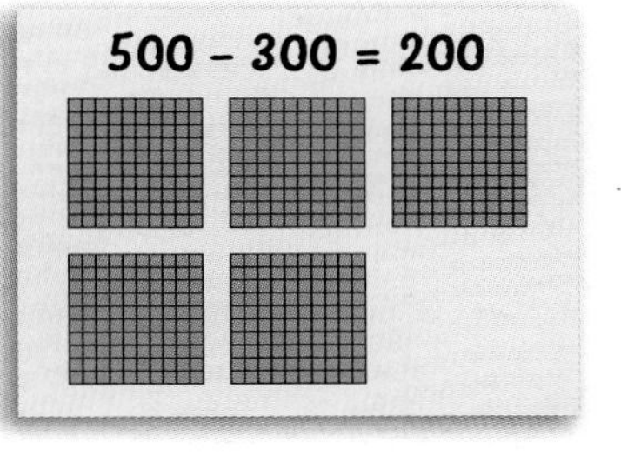

Objective Subtract a multiple of 10 from a multiple of 10, 100 or less.

1 Warm Up

Activate Prior Knowledge Review skip counting backward by 10s. Write multiples of 10 on separate index cards, shuffle, and place facedown. Have children choose cards and count backward by 10s from their numbers.

2 Teach

Learn!

Direct children's attention to the models at the top of the student page. Remind them that each group of 10 is the same as 10 ones. Have them find the difference and write the number sentence.

Ongoing Assessment

Talk About It

- **How can 7 − 3 = 4 help you find the difference for 70 − 30?** *(Think of the 7, 3, and 4 as tens instead of ones.)*
- **When subtracting tens, which number is always in the ones place?** *(0)*

If children have difficulty using basic facts to help them subtract tens,

then show both problems with models. Use ones to subtract 7 − 3 and tens to subtract 70 − 30.

Check

Error Intervention

If children write the number of tens rather than the value of the groups, such as 6 − 5 instead of 60 − 50,

then remind them that 6 tens is 60 and 5 tens is 50. *(Also see* Reteaching, *Page 471B.)*

Think About It You may wish to have children look at Exercise 4 as they formulate their answers.

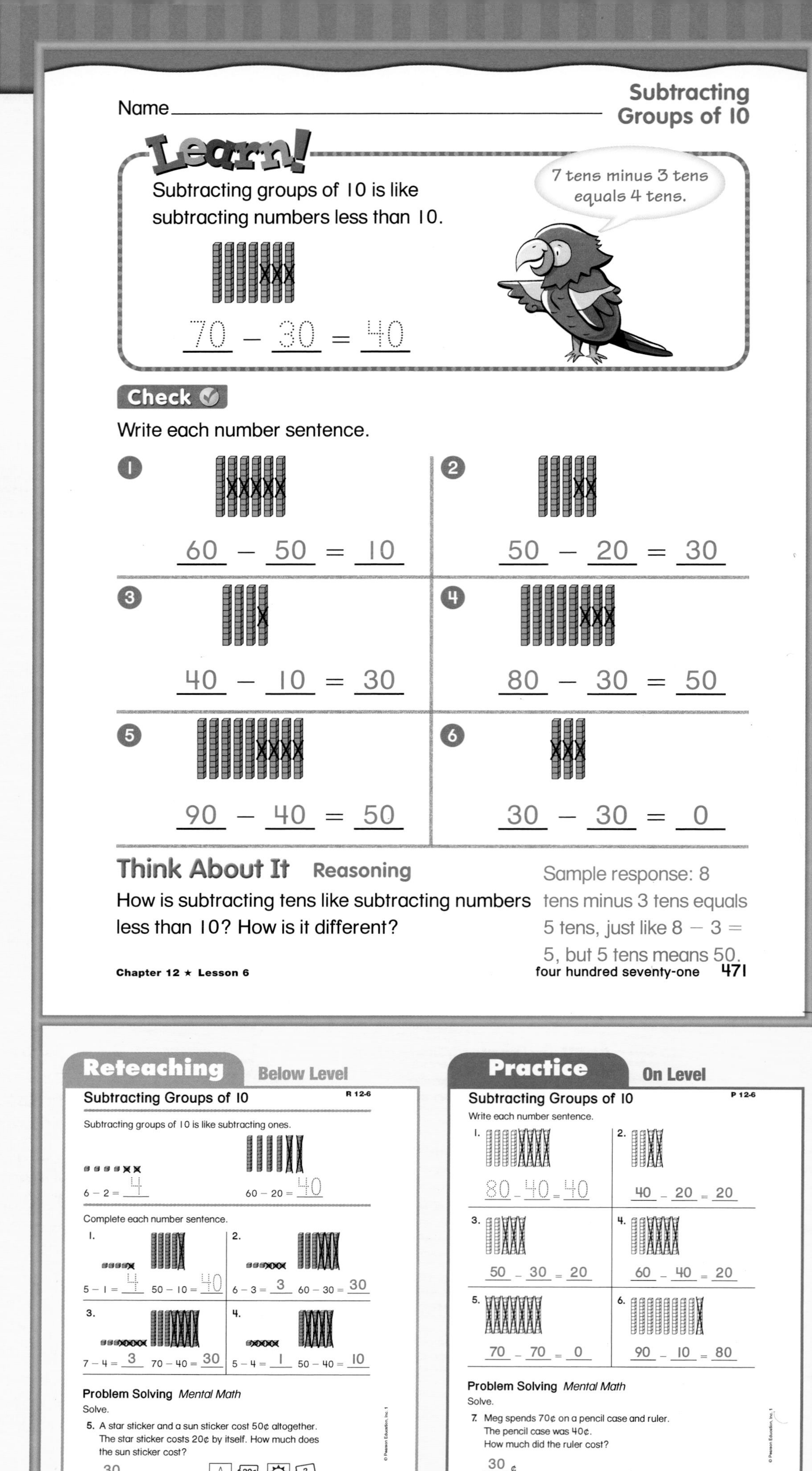

Name ____________________ Subtracting Groups of 10

Learn!

Subtracting groups of 10 is like subtracting numbers less than 10.

70 − 30 = 40

Check

Write each number sentence.

1. 60 − 50 = 10
2. 50 − 20 = 30
3. 40 − 10 = 30
4. 80 − 30 = 50
5. 90 − 40 = 50
6. 30 − 30 = 0

Think About It Reasoning

How is subtracting tens like subtracting numbers less than 10? How is it different?

Sample response: 8 tens minus 3 tens equals 5 tens, just like 8 − 3 = 5, but 5 tens means 50.

Chapter 12 ★ Lesson 6 four hundred seventy-one 471

Reteaching Below Level

Subtracting Groups of 10 R 12-6

Subtracting groups of 10 is like subtracting ones.

6 − 2 = 4 60 − 20 = 40

Complete each number sentence.

1. 5 − 1 = 4 50 − 10 = 40
2. 6 − 3 = 3 60 − 30 = 30
3. 7 − 4 = 3 70 − 40 = 30
4. 5 − 4 = 1 50 − 40 = 10

Problem Solving *Mental Math*

Solve.

5. A star sticker and a sun sticker cost 50¢ altogether. The star sticker costs 20¢ by itself. How much does the sun sticker cost?

30 ¢

152 Use with Lesson 12-6

Practice On Level

Subtracting Groups of 10 P 12-6

Write each number sentence.

1. 80 − 40 = 40
2. 40 − 20 = 20
3. 50 − 30 = 20
4. 60 − 40 = 20
5. 70 − 70 = 0
6. 90 − 10 = 80

Problem Solving *Mental Math*

Solve.

7. Meg spends 70¢ on a pencil case and ruler. The pencil case was 40¢. How much did the ruler cost?

30 ¢

152 Use with Lesson 12-6

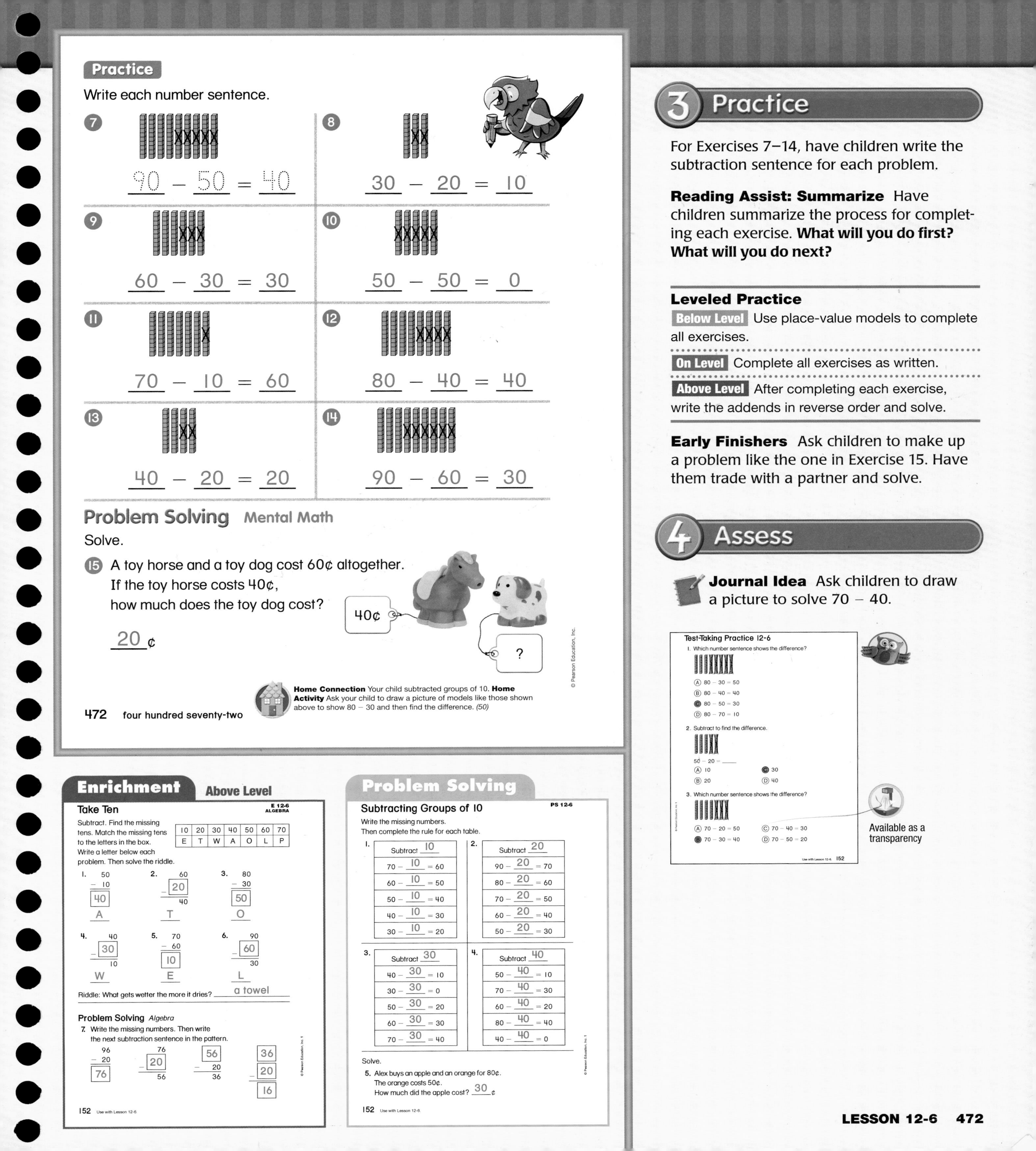

Practice

Write each number sentence.

7. 90 − 50 = 40

8. 30 − 20 = 10

9. 60 − 30 = 30

10. 50 − 50 = 0

11. 70 − 10 = 60

12. 80 − 40 = 40

13. 40 − 20 = 20

14. 90 − 60 = 30

Problem Solving Mental Math

Solve.

15. A toy horse and a toy dog cost 60¢ altogether. If the toy horse costs 40¢, how much does the toy dog cost?

20 ¢

Home Connection Your child subtracted groups of 10. **Home Activity** Ask your child to draw a picture of models like those shown above to show 80 − 30 and then find the difference. *(50)*

3 Practice

For Exercises 7–14, have children write the subtraction sentence for each problem.

Reading Assist: Summarize Have children summarize the process for completing each exercise. **What will you do first? What will you do next?**

Leveled Practice

Below Level Use place-value models to complete all exercises.

On Level Complete all exercises as written.

Above Level After completing each exercise, write the addends in reverse order and solve.

Early Finishers Ask children to make up a problem like the one in Exercise 15. Have them trade with a partner and solve.

4 Assess

Journal Idea Ask children to draw a picture to solve 70 − 40.

Test-Taking Practice 12-6

1. Which number sentence shows the difference?
   - Ⓐ 80 − 30 = 50
   - Ⓑ 80 − 40 = 40
   - ● 80 − 50 = 30
   - Ⓓ 80 − 70 = 10
2. Subtract to find the difference.
   50 − 20 = ____
   - Ⓐ 10
   - ● 30
   - Ⓑ 20
   - Ⓓ 40
3. Which number sentence shows the difference?
   - Ⓐ 70 − 20 = 50
   - Ⓒ 70 − 40 = 30
   - ● 70 − 30 = 40
   - Ⓓ 70 − 50 = 20

Use with Lesson 12-6. 152

Available as a transparency

Enrichment Above Level

Take Ten E 12-6 ALGEBRA

Subtract. Find the missing tens. Match the missing tens to the letters in the box. Write a letter below each problem. Then solve the riddle.

10	20	30	40	50	60	70
E	T	W	A	O	L	P

1. 50 − 10 = 40 — A
2. 60 − 20 = 40 — T
3. 80 − 30 = 50 — O
4. 40 − 30 = 10 — W
5. 70 − 60 = 10 — E
6. 90 − 60 = 30 — L

Riddle: What gets wetter the more it dries? a towel

Problem Solving *Algebra*

7. Write the missing numbers. Then write the next subtraction sentence in the pattern.

96 − 20 = 76; 76 − 20 = 56; 56 − 20 = 36; 36 − 20 = 16

152 Use with Lesson 12-6.

Problem Solving

Subtracting Groups of 10 PS 12-6

Write the missing numbers. Then complete the rule for each table.

1. Subtract 10

70 − 10 = 60
60 − 10 = 50
50 − 10 = 40
40 − 10 = 30
30 − 10 = 20

2. Subtract 20

90 − 20 = 70
80 − 20 = 60
70 − 20 = 50
60 − 20 = 40
50 − 20 = 30

3. Subtract 30

40 − 30 = 10
30 − 30 = 0
50 − 30 = 20
60 − 30 = 30
70 − 30 = 40

4. Subtract 40

50 − 40 = 10
70 − 40 = 30
60 − 40 = 20
80 − 40 = 40
40 − 40 = 0

Solve.

5. Alex buys an apple and an orange for 80¢. The orange costs 50¢. How much did the apple cost? 30 ¢

152 Use with Lesson 12-6.

12-7 Subtracting Tens from Two-Digit Numbers

Lesson Organizer

Quick Lesson Overview

Objective Subtract a multiple of 10 from a two-digit number.

Math Understanding When subtracting tens from a two-digit number, only the tens digit changes.

Professional Development Note

Effective Questioning Techniques
Ask questions about subtraction that help children think about the place-value ideas involved. **If we take away all of the tens from 64, how many ones are left? What problems could we write which would require us to subtract some tens from 58?**

NCTM Standards

- Number and Operations

(For a complete correlation to the NCTM Standards and Grades Pre-K through 2 Expectations, see Pages 457G and 457H.)

Getting Started

Spiral Review

Problem of the Day 12-7

Clare used some pints of milk to make pudding. If she used 1 less pint, she would have used 3 pints. How many pints of milk did Clare use?

Topics Reviewed

- Addition
- Problem-Solving Skill: One-Step Problem

Answer Clare used 4 pints of milk; 3 + 1 = 4.

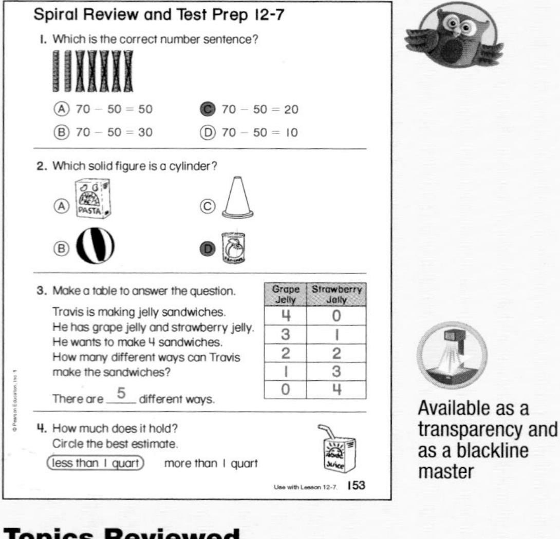

Spiral Review and Test Prep 12-7

1. Which is the correct number sentence?

Ⓐ 70 − 50 = 50 Ⓒ 70 − 50 = 20
Ⓑ 70 − 50 = 30 Ⓓ 70 − 50 = 10

2. Which solid figure is a cylinder?

Ⓐ Ⓒ
Ⓑ Ⓓ

3. Make a table to answer the question.

Travis is making jelly sandwiches. He has grape jelly and strawberry jelly. He wants to make 4 sandwiches. How many different ways can Travis make the sandwiches?

Grape Jelly	Strawberry Jelly
4	0
3	1
2	2
1	3
0	4

There are 5 different ways.

4. How much does it hold? Circle the best estimate.

less than 1 quart more than 1 quart

Use with Lesson 12-7. 153

Available as a transparency and as a blackline master

Topics Reviewed

1. Subtracting Groups of 10
2. Identifying Solid Figures
3. Make a Table
4. Cups, Pints, and Quarts

Investigating the Concept

Subtracting on a Hundred Chart

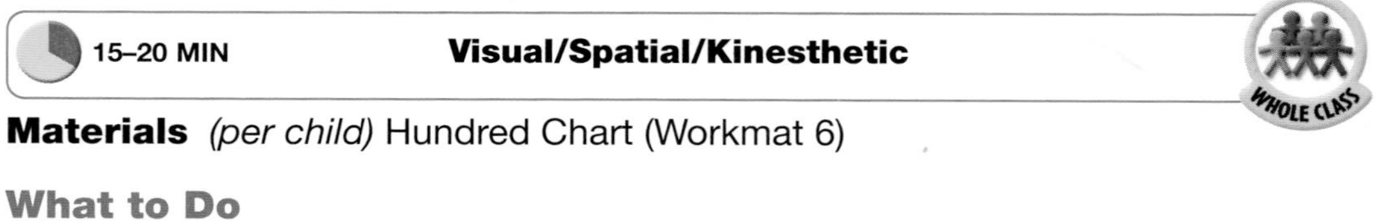

15–20 MIN **Visual/Spatial/Kinesthetic** WHOLE CLASS

Materials *(per child)* Hundred Chart (Workmat 6)

What to Do

- On the board, write 73 − 50 = ___. Using an overhead transparency of the hundred chart, demonstrate how to subtract. Have children follow along on their workmats.
- **Place a finger on 73. How can we show that we subtract 10 from 73?** *(Move up 1 row.)* **How can we subtract 50?** *(Move up 5 rows.)* **Where do we land?** *(23)*
- Repeat, having children solve similar problems using a hundred chart.

To subtract 50, I move up 5 rows.

Ongoing Assessment

- **How can we use a hundred chart to solve 88 − 30?** *(Start on 88 and move up 3 rows to 58.)*
- **Reasoning** **What is the difference between adding and subtracting on a hundred chart?** *(Move up to subtract and move down to add.)*

Reaching All Learners

Oral Language in Math

Help Peter Piper Pack

10–15 MIN **Auditory/Linguistic**

- Teach the class this tongue twister:

  Peter Piper picked a peck of pickled peppers.
- Write numbers that show totals of vegetables that Peter picks, such as 24 pecks of peppers.
- **Peter packs 10 pecks of peppers. How many pecks of vegetables are left?** *(24 − 10 = 14)*
- Have children join you in saying: **Peter packs 10 pecks of peppers. That leaves 14 pecks of vegetables.**
- Have children make up subtraction problems involving subtracting tens.

Access Content

English Language Learners

Countdown

5–10 MIN **Auditory/Linguistic**

Materials *(per group)* Hundred Chart (Workmat 6)

- As you point to each number on the hundred chart, count backward by 10s from 90 to 10. Have children count aloud with you.
- Point to 96 on the chart and count backward to 16 by 10s. Repeat as children help.
- Point to 72 and ask a volunteer to count backward by 10s. The other children might want to help.
- Point to other non-decade numbers, again asking children to count backward by 10s.

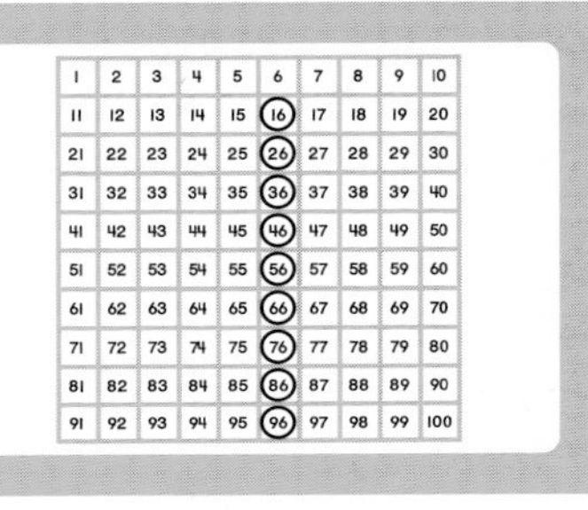

1	2	3	4	5	6	7	8	9	10
11	12	13	14	15	16	17	18	19	20
21	22	23	24	25	26	27	28	29	30
31	32	33	34	35	36	37	38	39	40
41	42	43	44	45	46	47	48	49	50
51	52	53	54	55	56	57	58	59	60
61	62	63	64	65	66	67	68	69	70
71	72	73	74	75	76	77	78	79	80
81	82	83	84	85	86	87	88	89	90
91	92	93	94	95	96	97	98	99	100

Reteaching

Acting Out Subtraction Problems

10–15 MIN **Kinesthetic**

SMALL GROUP

Materials *(per child)* 9 bundles of 10 crayons; single crayons

- Distribute the bundles and single crayons to children.
- Use children's names to present problems, such as: **Frannie has 34 crayons. She gives 20 of them to Jack. How many crayons does Frannie have now?** Have the children mentioned act out the problem. Show them the accompanying number sentence: 34 − 20 = 14.
- Give all of the children in the group a chance to act out and solve similar problems.

Math and Physical Education

Say and Hop

15–20 MIN **Logical/Mathematical/Kinesthetic**

SMALL GROUP

Materials Chalk

- On a paved area, draw 5 large squares for each child.
- Have children stand in front of their squares. Say a two-digit number less than 100, such as 87. Have the first child say the number that is 10 less than that number. For each correct response, children hop into the next square. For each wrong answer, children step back into the previous square.
- The first child to hop off the last square states a two-digit number for the next child.

Objective Subtract a multiple of 10 from a two-digit number.

1 Warm Up

Activate Prior Knowledge Review counting back by 10s from a number that is not a multiple of 10. Use an overhead projector to display a hundred chart. Point to a non-decade number, such as 93, and have children count back by 10s. Repeat for other numbers.

2 Teach

Learn!

Read aloud the question at the top of the student page. Have children count back by 10s to solve the problem. Then have them write the number sentence.

Ongoing Assessment

Talk About It

- **How many groups of 10 are left?** *(2 groups of 10)*
- **How did you find out how many were left?** *(Cross out to subtract 3 tens. Count the tens and ones that are left.)*

If children have difficulty counting back by 10s,

then have them use a hundred chart.

Check

Error Intervention

If children do not record the correct difference,

then check that they are starting with the correct number and subtracting the correct value for the group of tens. *(Also see Reteaching, Page 473B.)*

Think About It Have children look at the minuends and differences in each exercise. **Which number is in the tens place? Which number is in the ones place? Which digit changes? Which digit stays the same? Why?**

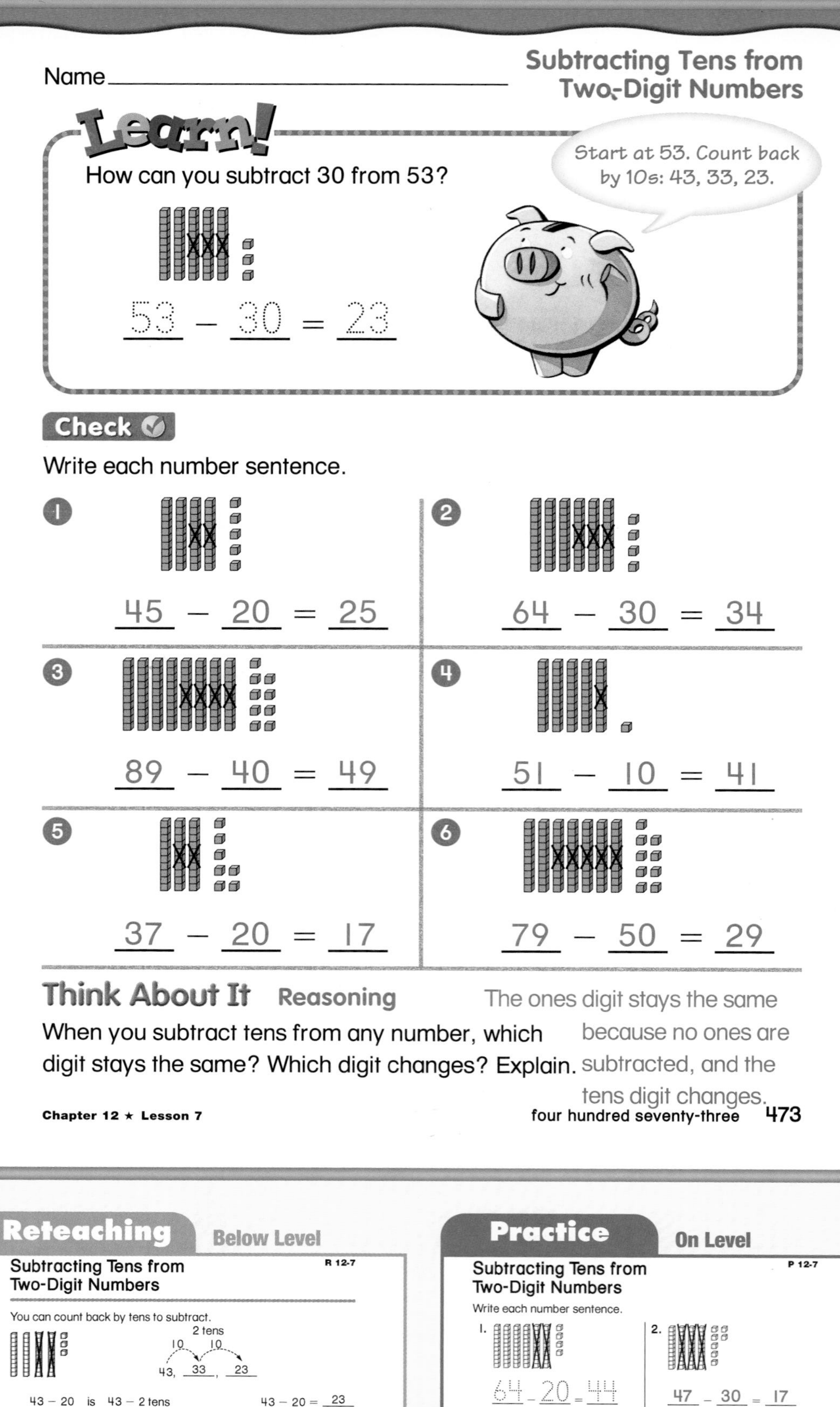

Name ______________________

Subtracting Tens from Two-Digit Numbers

Learn!

How can you subtract 30 from 53?

53 – 30 = 23

Check

Write each number sentence.

1. 45 – 20 = 25
2. 64 – 30 = 34
3. 89 – 40 = 49
4. 51 – 10 = 41
5. 37 – 20 = 17
6. 79 – 50 = 29

Think About It Reasoning

When you subtract tens from any number, which digit stays the same? Which digit changes? Explain. The ones digit stays the same because no ones are subtracted, and the tens digit changes.

Chapter 12 ★ Lesson 7 — four hundred seventy-three 473

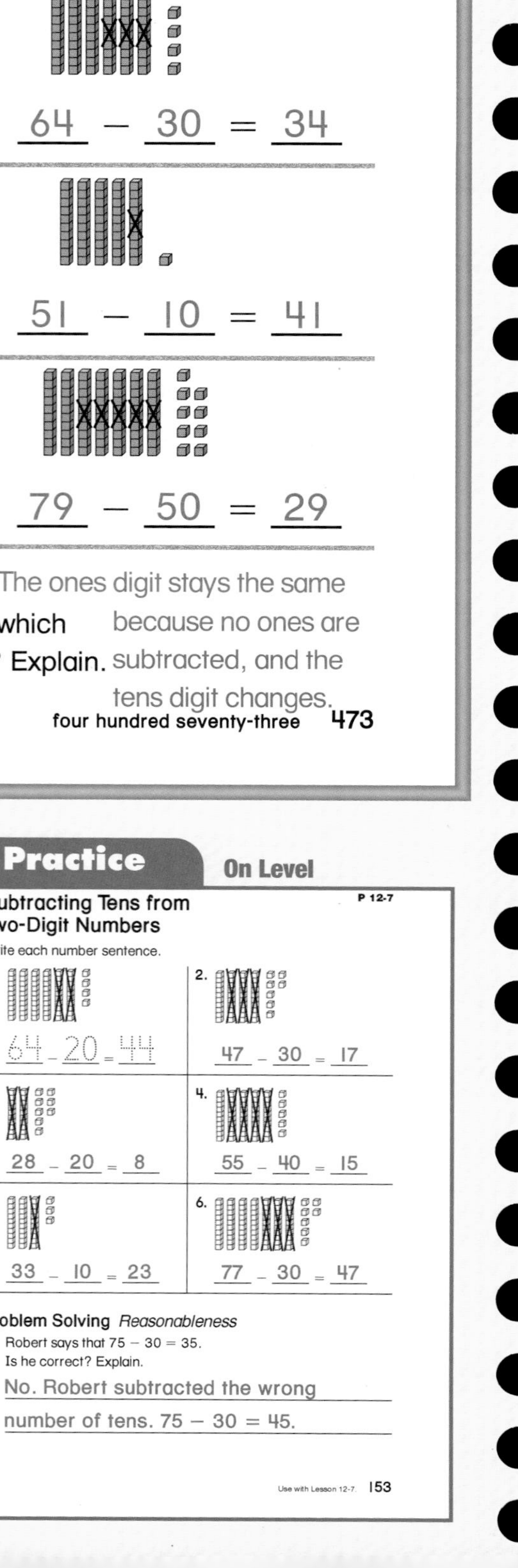

Reteaching Below Level

Subtracting Tens from Two-Digit Numbers — R 12-7

You can count back by tens to subtract.

2 tens: 43, 33, 23

43 – 20 is 43 – 2 tens   43 – 20 = 23

Solve each number sentence.

1. 34, 24 — 34 – 10 is 34 – 1 ten   34 – 10 = 24
2. 52, 42, 32, 22 — 52 – 30 is 52 – 3 tens   52 – 30 = 22
3. 64, 54, 44, 34, 24 — 64 – 40 is 64 – 4 tens   64 – 40 = 24

Use with Lesson 12-7. 153

Practice On Level

Subtracting Tens from Two-Digit Numbers — P 12-7

Write each number sentence.

1. 64 – 20 = 44
2. 47 – 30 = 17
3. 28 – 20 = 8
4. 55 – 40 = 15
5. 33 – 10 = 23
6. 77 – 30 = 47

Problem Solving *Reasonableness*

7. Robert says that 75 – 30 = 35. Is he correct? Explain.
No. Robert subtracted the wrong number of tens. 75 – 30 = 45.

Use with Lesson 12-7. 153

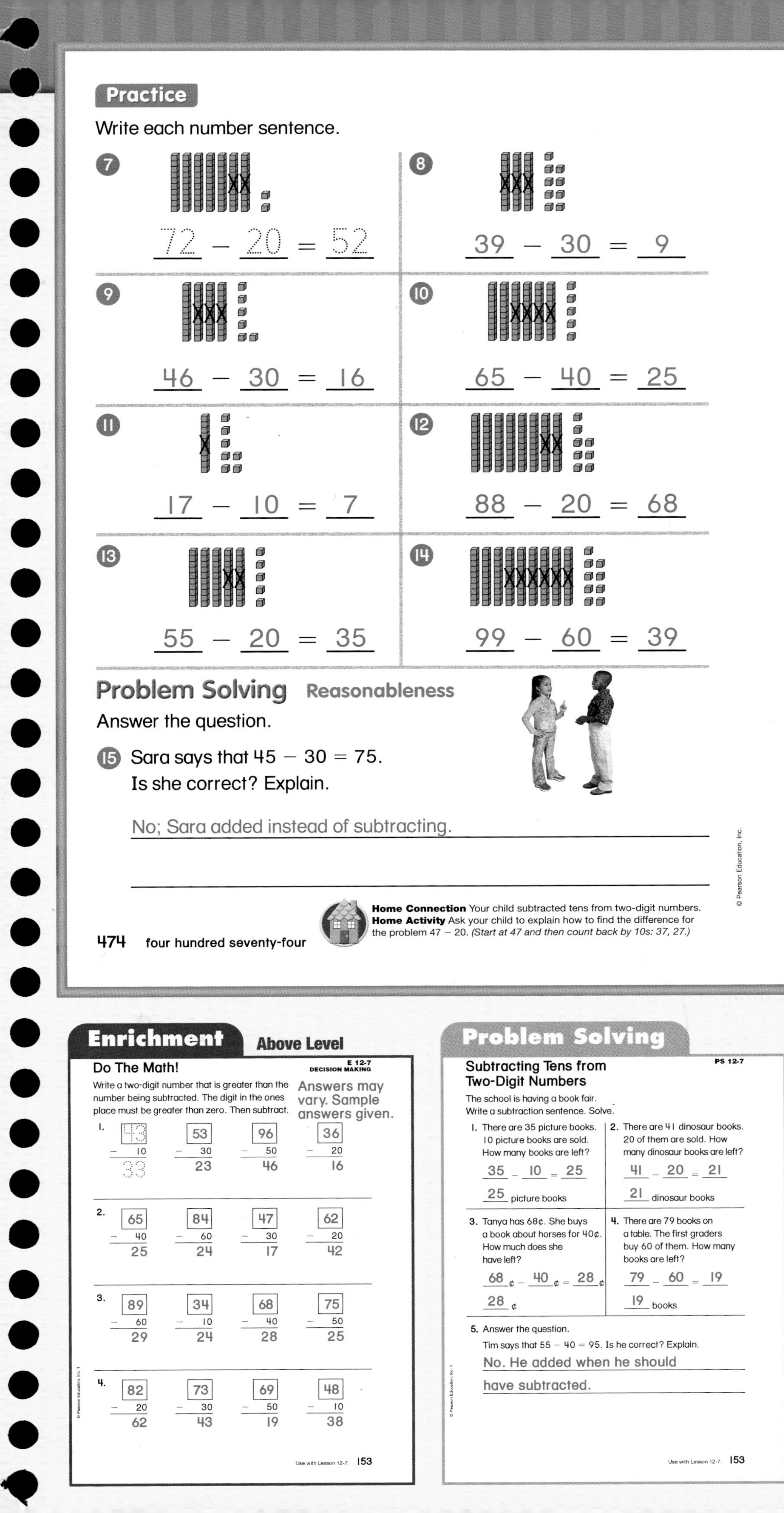

Practice

Write each number sentence.

7. 72 − 20 = 52
8. 39 − 30 = 9
9. 46 − 30 = 16
10. 65 − 40 = 25
11. 17 − 10 = 7
12. 88 − 20 = 68
13. 55 − 20 = 35
14. 99 − 60 = 39

Problem Solving Reasonableness

Answer the question.

15. Sara says that 45 − 30 = 75. Is she correct? Explain.

No; Sara added instead of subtracting.

Home Connection Your child subtracted tens from two-digit numbers. **Home Activity** Ask your child to explain how to find the difference for the problem 47 − 20. *(Start at 47 and then count back by 10s: 37, 27.)*

Enrichment Above Level

Do The Math! E 12-7 DECISION MAKING

Write a two-digit number that is greater than the number being subtracted. The digit in the ones place must be greater than zero. Then subtract.

Answers may vary. Sample answers given.

1. 43 − 10 = 33; 53 − 30 = 23; 96 − 50 = 46; 36 − 20 = 16
2. 65 − 40 = 25; 84 − 60 = 24; 47 − 30 = 17; 62 − 20 = 42
3. 89 − 60 = 29; 34 − 10 = 24; 68 − 40 = 28; 75 − 50 = 25
4. 82 − 20 = 62; 73 − 30 = 43; 69 − 50 = 19; 48 − 10 = 38

Use with Lesson 12-7 153

Problem Solving

Subtracting Tens from Two-Digit Numbers PS 12-7

The school is having a book fair. Write a subtraction sentence. Solve.

1. There are 35 picture books. 10 picture books are sold. How many books are left? 35 − 10 = 25; 25 picture books
2. There are 41 dinosaur books. 20 of them are sold. How many dinosaur books are left? 41 − 20 = 21; 21 dinosaur books
3. Tanya has 68¢. She buys a book about horses for 40¢. How much does she have left? 68¢ − 40¢ = 28¢; 28¢
4. There are 79 books on a table. The first graders buy 60 of them. How many books are left? 79 − 60 = 19; 19 books
5. Answer the question. Tim says that 55 − 40 = 95. Is he correct? Explain. No. He added when he should have subtracted.

Use with Lesson 12-7 153

3 Practice

For Exercises 7–14, have children write the number sentence for each pictured model.

Leveled Practice

Below Level Complete Exercises 7–14 using place-value models.

On Level Complete all exercises as written.

Above Level Write each problem vertically as well as horizontally.

Early Finishers On the board, write the following problems: 99 − 10 = __; 99 − 20 = __; and 99 − 30 = __. Ask children to find each difference and write problems to continue the pattern until there are no more tens.

4 Assess

Journal Idea On the board, write several subtraction problems showing how to subtract tens from a two-digit number. Have children choose one of the problems, draw models to show it, and find the difference.

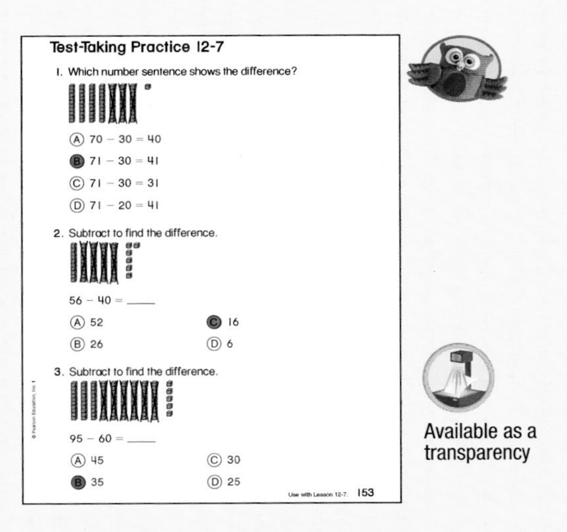

Test-Taking Practice 12-7

1. Which number sentence shows the difference?
   - (A) 70 − 30 = 40
   - (B) 71 − 30 = 41
   - (C) 71 − 30 = 31
   - (D) 71 − 20 = 41
2. Subtract to find the difference. 56 − 40 = ___
   - (A) 52
   - (B) 26
   - (C) 16
   - (D) 6
3. Subtract to find the difference. 95 − 60 = ___
   - (A) 45
   - (B) 35
   - (C) 30
   - (D) 25

Use with Lesson 12-7 153

Available as a transparency

12-8 Subtracting Two-Digit Numbers

Lesson Organizer

Quick Lesson Overview 

Objective Subtract a two-digit number from a two-digit number without regrouping.

Math Understanding When subtracting two-digit numbers, the ones are subtracted from the ones, and the tens are subtracted from the tens.

Professional Development Note

How Children Learn Math When writing two-digit problems in vertical format, remind children to align the numbers according to place value. It may help them to use lined paper turned sideways. The vertical lines will provide columns for the tens and ones.

NCTM Standards

- Number and Operations

(For a complete correlation to the NCTM Standards and Grades Pre-K through 2 Expectations, see Pages 457G and 457H.)

Getting Started

Spiral Review

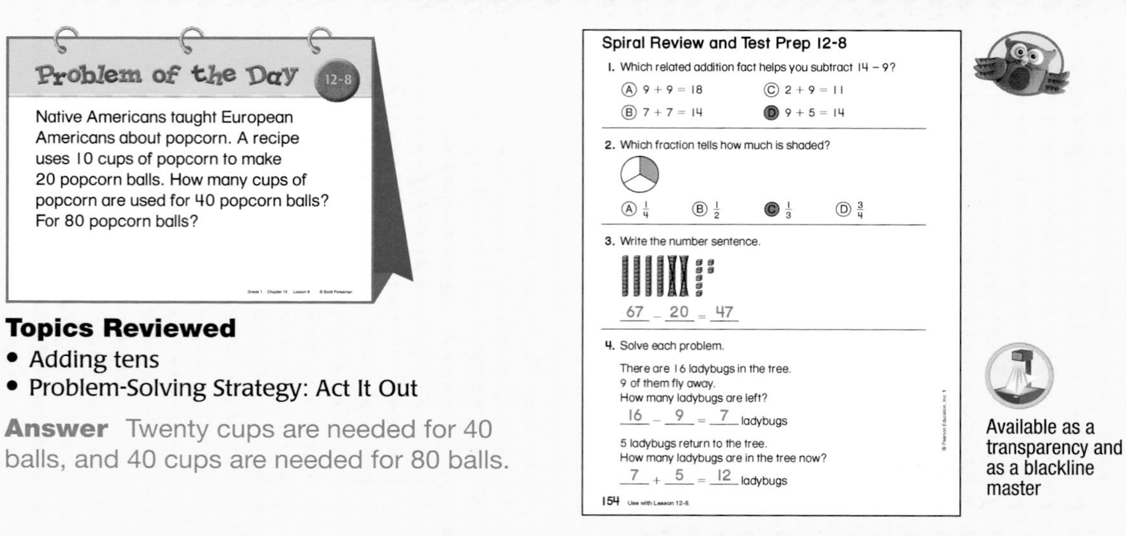

Problem of the Day 12-8

Native Americans taught European Americans about popcorn. A recipe uses 10 cups of popcorn to make 20 popcorn balls. How many cups of popcorn are used for 40 popcorn balls? For 80 popcorn balls?

Topics Reviewed
- Adding tens
- Problem-Solving Strategy: Act It Out

Answer Twenty cups are needed for 40 balls, and 40 cups are needed for 80 balls.

Spiral Review and Test Prep 12-8

1. Which related addition fact helps you subtract 14 − 9?
   Ⓐ 9 + 9 = 18 Ⓒ 2 + 9 = 11
   Ⓑ 7 + 7 = 14 Ⓓ 9 + 5 = 14
2. Which fraction tells how much is shaded?
   Ⓐ $\frac{1}{4}$ Ⓑ $\frac{1}{2}$ Ⓒ $\frac{1}{3}$ Ⓓ $\frac{3}{4}$
3. Write the number sentence.
   67 − 20 = 47
4. Solve each problem.
   There are 16 ladybugs in the tree. 9 of them fly away. How many ladybugs are left?
   16 − 9 = 7 ladybugs
   5 ladybugs return to the tree. How many ladybugs are in the tree now?
   7 + 5 = 12 ladybugs

154 Use with Lesson 12-8.

Available as a transparency and as a blackline master

Topics Reviewed
1. Using Addition to Subtract
2. Thirds and Fourths
3. Subtracting Tens from Two-Digit Numbers
4. Multiple-Step Problems

Investigating the Concept

Modeling Two-Digit Subtraction

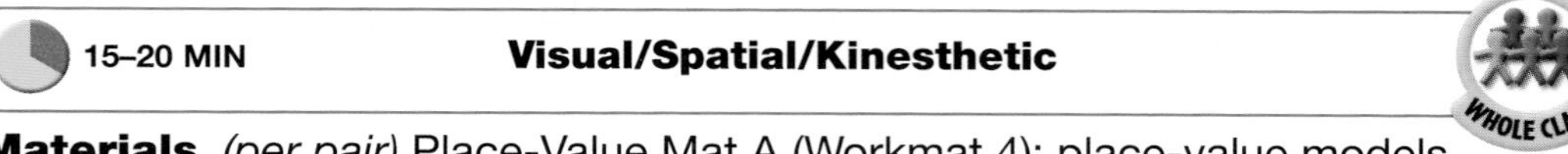

Materials *(per pair)* Place-Value Mat A (Workmat 4); place-value models (9 tens and 9 ones)

What to Do

- Tell the following story: **Rico collects stamps. He has 78 stamps. 42 of them show flags. How many stamps do not show flags?** Have children use models to solve the problem. Have them first take away 2 ones and then take away 4 tens. **How many are left?** *(36)* On the board, write 78 − 42 = 36 in vertical format.
- Repeat the story, changing the numbers each time. Use two-digit numbers that will not need regrouping when subtracted.

Ongoing Assessment

- **How many are left when you subtract 85 − 14?** *(71)*
- **Reasoning How do you find the difference for 65 − 23 without using blocks?** *(Subtract the ones and then subtract the tens.)*

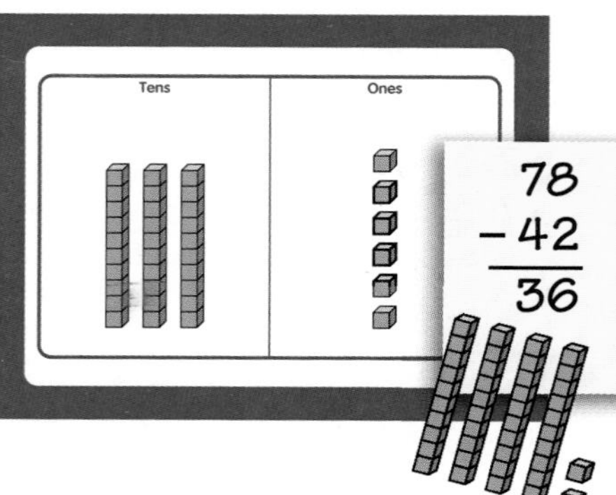

Reaching All Learners

Reading in Math

Make Up a Problem

15–20 MIN **Linguistic/Logical/Mathematical**

Materials *(per child)* Place-Value Mat A (Workmat 4); place-value models (5 tens and 9 ones)

- Write the following subtraction problems in vertical format: 36 − 26 = 10; 53 − 32 = 21; 25 − 14 = 11; 49 − 14 = 35.
- Tell a number story for one problem: **36 monkeys live on Monkey Island. 26 monkeys ate bananas for breakfast. How many monkeys did not eat bananas?** Demonstrate how to solve the problem using a place-value mat and models.
- Ask children to tell number stories for the other problems. Write their stories on the board.
- Have children use workmats and models to solve the problems.

Access Content

English Language Learners

Tens and Ones

10–15 MIN **Logical/Mathematical**

Materials *(per group)* Place-Value Mat A (Workmat 4); Number Cards 0–11 (Teaching Tool 9); index cards labeled "Tens" and "Ones"

- Divide the group into two teams. One member of each team picks a number card and an index card.
- The child writes the number in the tens or ones column. He or she then picks another number card to make a two-digit number.
- The team with the larger number chooses first in the next round.

Reteaching

Show and Solve

10–15 MIN **Visual/Spatial/Kinesthetic**

Materials *(per group)* Place-Value Mat A (Workmat 4); place-value models (9 tens and 9 ones)

- On the board, write 48 − 23 = __. Have a volunteer show 48 on the place-value mat using tens and ones. Have another volunteer remove 23. As a group, count the rods and cubes to arrive at the difference, 25.
- Write a few more subtraction problems on the board. Have groups of children use place-value models to solve them.

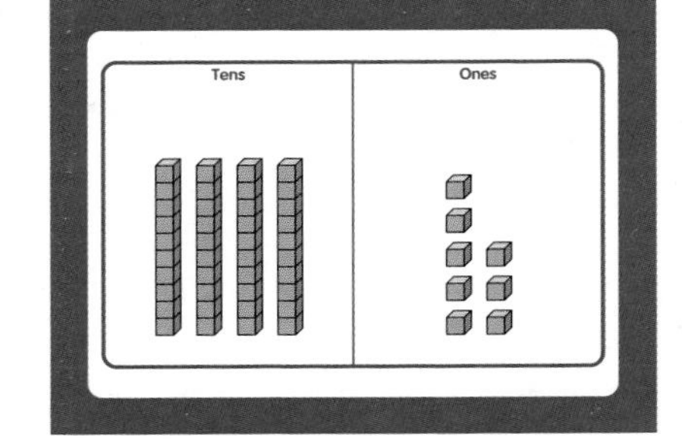

Advanced Learners

Check Subtraction Problems

10–15 MIN **Logical/Mathematical**

SMALL GROUP

- Describe how to check subtraction problems by adding the difference to the number being subtracted.
- Write 87 − 56 = 31. Add 31 and 56 to get 87.
- Then show an example with an incorrect difference, such as 87 − 56 = 33. Explain that adding the difference (33) to 56 results in 89. Since 89 is different from 87, 33 cannot be the correct difference.
- Have children use this method to check subtraction problems.

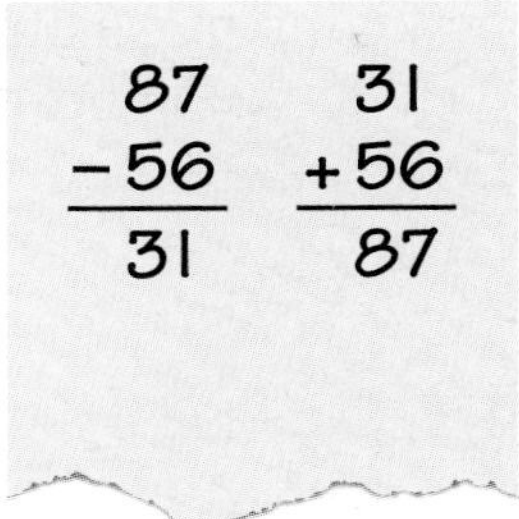

Objective Subtract a two-digit number from a two-digit number without regrouping.

1 Warm Up

Activate Prior Knowledge Review basic subtraction facts. Prepare two sets of Number Cards 0–11 (Teaching Tool 9). Have children pick one card from each set and use the numbers to name a subtraction fact. Repeat until all cards have been used.

2 Teach

Learn!

Read aloud the problem at the top of the student page. Guide children through the process of first subtracting the ones and then subtracting the tens.

Ongoing Assessment

Talk About It

- **How many groups of 10 did we start with?** *(2 groups of 10)*
- **How many would be left if we took away 24 instead of 14?** *(3)*

If children do not understand that they should subtract ones only from ones and tens only from tens,

then have them use place-value models to model the problem.

Check

Error Intervention

If children subtract incorrectly,

then have them review the basic facts and allow them to use a completed Subtraction Chart (Teaching Tool 40). *(Also see* Reteaching, *Page 475B.)*

Think About It Using a specific example can make the question more concrete for some children. One example is as follows: **Start with 32. Take away all of the ones. How many are left?**

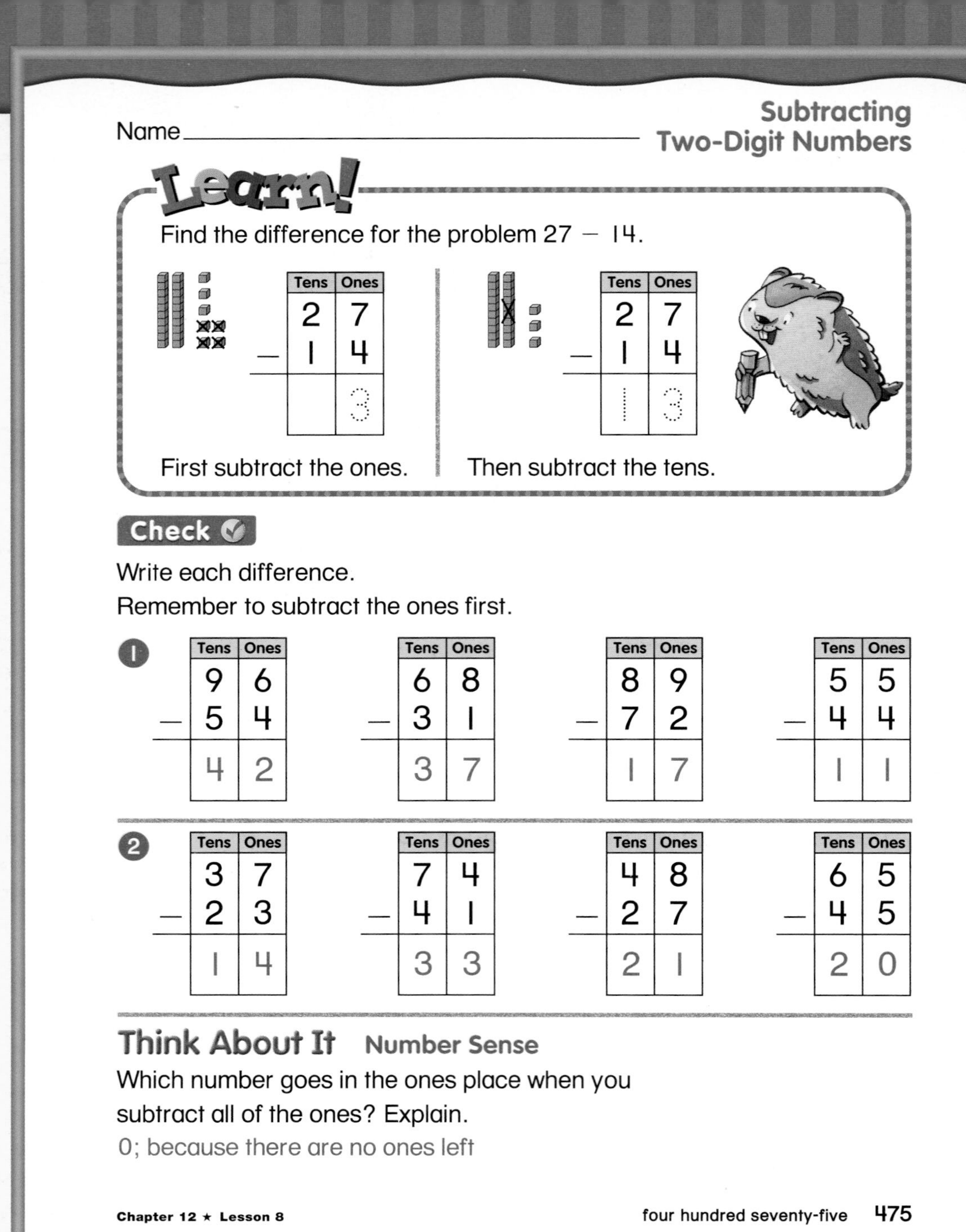

Name ______________________

Subtracting Two-Digit Numbers

Learn!

Find the difference for the problem 27 − 14.

	Tens	Ones
	2	7
−	1	4
		3

First subtract the ones.

	Tens	Ones
	2	7
−	1	4
	1	3

Then subtract the tens.

Check

Write each difference.
Remember to subtract the ones first.

1

	Tens	Ones
	9	6
−	5	4
	4	2

	Tens	Ones
	6	8
−	3	1
	3	7

	Tens	Ones
	8	9
−	7	2
	1	7

	Tens	Ones
	5	5
−	4	4
	1	1

2

	Tens	Ones
	3	7
−	2	3
	1	4

	Tens	Ones
	7	4
−	4	1
	3	3

	Tens	Ones
	4	8
−	2	7
	2	1

	Tens	Ones
	6	5
−	4	5
	2	0

Think About It Number Sense

Which number goes in the ones place when you subtract all of the ones? Explain.

0; because there are no ones left

Chapter 12 ★ Lesson 8 four hundred seventy-five 475

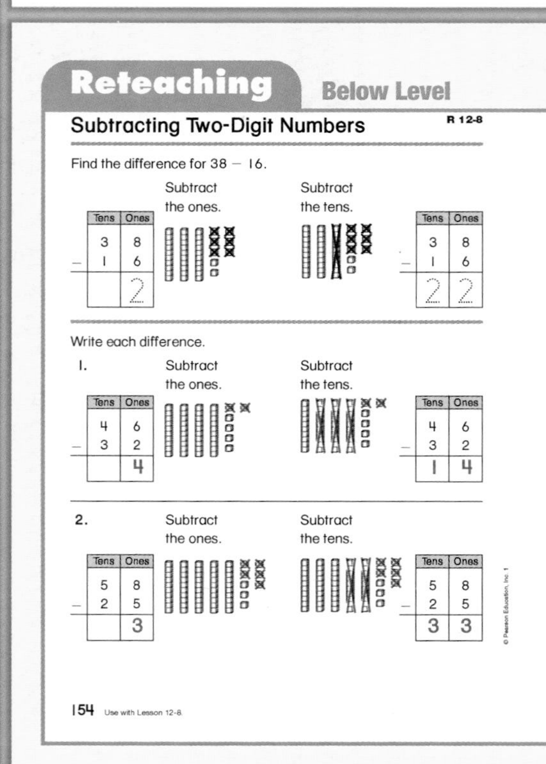

Reteaching Below Level

Subtracting Two-Digit Numbers R 12-8

Find the difference for 38 − 16.

Subtract the ones. Subtract the tens.

	Tens	Ones
	3	8
−	1	6
		2

	Tens	Ones
	3	8
−	1	6
	2	2

Write each difference.

1. Subtract the ones. Subtract the tens.

	Tens	Ones
	4	6
−	3	2
		4

	Tens	Ones
	4	6
−	3	2
	1	4

2. Subtract the ones. Subtract the tens.

	Tens	Ones
	5	8
−	2	5
		3

	Tens	Ones
	5	8
−	2	5
	3	3

154 Use with Lesson 12-8

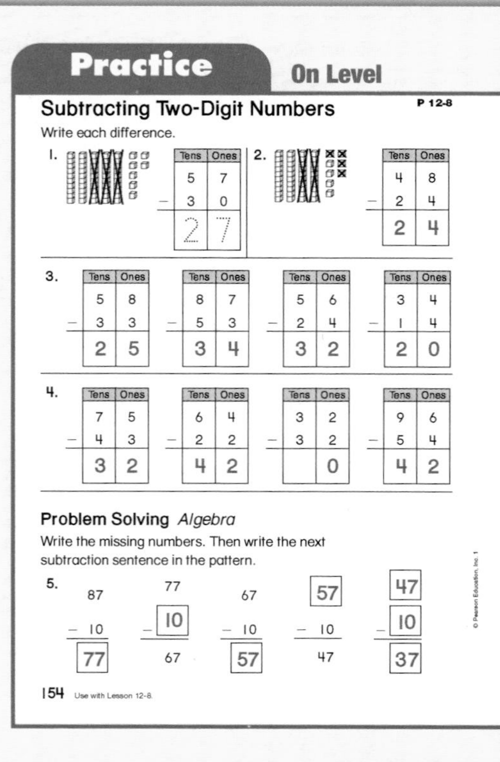

Practice On Level

Subtracting Two-Digit Numbers P 12-8

Write each difference.

1.

	Tens	Ones
	5	7
−	3	0
	2	7

2.

	Tens	Ones
	4	8
−	2	4
	2	4

3.

	Tens	Ones
	5	8
−	3	3
	2	5

	Tens	Ones
	8	7
−	5	3
	3	4

	Tens	Ones
	5	6
−	2	4
	3	2

	Tens	Ones
	3	4
−	1	4
	2	0

4.

	Tens	Ones
	7	5
−	4	3
	3	2

	Tens	Ones
	6	4
−	2	2
	4	2

	Tens	Ones
	3	2
−	3	2
		0

	Tens	Ones
	9	6
−	5	4
	4	2

Problem Solving *Algebra*

Write the missing numbers. Then write the next subtraction sentence in the pattern.

5. 87 − 10 = 77; 77 − 10 = 67; 67 − 10 = 57; 57 − 10 = 47; 47 − 10 = 37

154 Use with Lesson 12-8

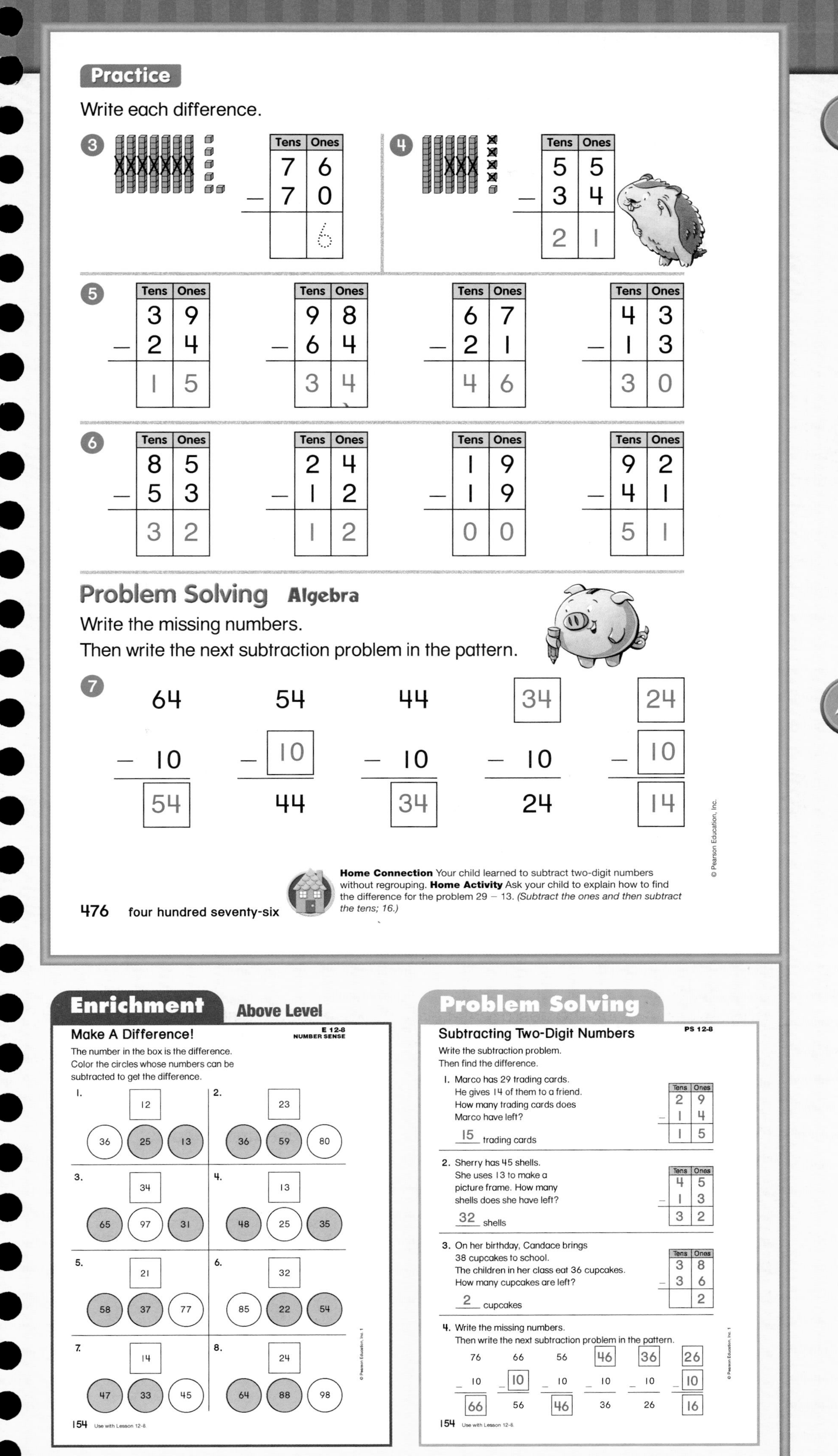

Practice

Write each difference.

3. 76 − 70 = 6 (Tens: 7 − 7; Ones: 6 − 0 = 6)

4. 55 − 34 = 21 (Tens: 5 − 3 = 2; Ones: 5 − 4 = 1)

5. 39 − 24 = 15 | 98 − 64 = 34 | 67 − 21 = 46 | 43 − 13 = 30

6. 85 − 53 = 32 | 24 − 12 = 12 | 19 − 19 = 00 | 92 − 41 = 51

Problem Solving **Algebra**

Write the missing numbers.
Then write the next subtraction problem in the pattern.

7. 64 − 10 = 54 | 54 − 10 = 44 | 44 − 10 = 34 | 34 − 10 = 24 | 24 − 10 = 14

Home Connection Your child learned to subtract two-digit numbers without regrouping. **Home Activity** Ask your child to explain how to find the difference for the problem 29 − 13. *(Subtract the ones and then subtract the tens; 16.)*

476 four hundred seventy-six

© Pearson Education, Inc.

Enrichment Above Level

Make A Difference! E 12-8 NUMBER SENSE

The number in the box is the difference. Color the circles whose numbers can be subtracted to get the difference.

1. 12: 36, 25, 13
2. 23: 36, 59, 80
3. 34: 65, 97, 31
4. 13: 48, 25, 35
5. 21: 58, 37, 77
6. 32: 85, 22, 54
7. 14: 47, 33, 45
8. 24: 64, 88, 98

154 Use with Lesson 12-8.

Problem Solving

Subtracting Two-Digit Numbers PS 12-8

Write the subtraction problem.
Then find the difference.

1. Marco has 29 trading cards. He gives 14 of them to a friend. How many trading cards does Marco have left? 15 trading cards (29 − 14 = 15)
2. Sherry has 45 shells. She uses 13 to make a picture frame. How many shells does she have left? 32 shells (45 − 13 = 32)
3. On her birthday, Candace brings 38 cupcakes to school. The children in her class eat 36 cupcakes. How many cupcakes are left? 2 cupcakes (38 − 36 = 2)
4. Write the missing numbers. Then write the next subtraction problem in the pattern.
76 − 10 = 66 | 66 − 10 = 56 | 56 − 10 = 46 | 46 − 10 = 36 | 36 − 10 = 26 | 26 − 10 = 16

154 Use with Lesson 12-6.

3 Practice

For Exercises 3–6, have children continue to subtract two-digit numbers, first subtracting the ones and then subtracting the tens.

After children have completed Exercise 7, discuss the patterns in the subtraction sentences.

Leveled Practice

Below Level Use place-value models to complete all exercises.

On Level Complete all exercises mentally.

Above Level For each problem in Exercise 6, write a new problem that has the same answer.

Early Finishers Have children practice subtracting from 99. Ask them to toss two number cubes (1–6) and make a two-digit number. Then have them mentally subtract that number from 99. Repeat as time allows.

4 Assess

Journal Idea Ask children to draw a picture to show 79 − 53. Have them write the problem vertically and find the difference.

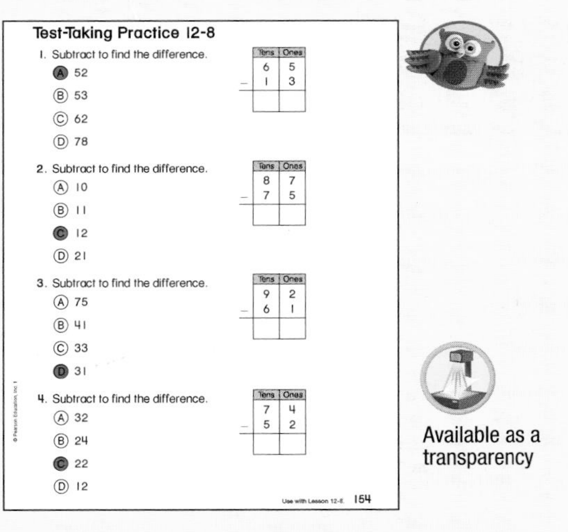

Test-Taking Practice 12-8

1. Subtract to find the difference. 65 − 13
   (A) 52 (B) 53 (C) 62 (D) 78
2. Subtract to find the difference. 87 − 75
   (A) 10 (B) 11 (C) 12 (D) 21
3. Subtract to find the difference. 92 − 61
   (A) 75 (B) 41 (C) 33 (D) 31
4. Subtract to find the difference. 74 − 52
   (A) 32 (B) 24 (C) 22 (D) 12

Use with Lesson 12-8. 154

Available as a transparency

Regrouping in Subtraction

Lesson Organizer

Quick Lesson Overview

Objective Use models to subtract a one-digit quantity from a two-digit quantity with and without regrouping.

Math Understanding When there are fewer ones to begin with than are being subtracted, a ten can be regrouped into 10 ones without changing the original quantity.

Materials for Student Pages
(per pair) Place-Value Mat A (Workmat 4); 90 connecting cubes

Professional Development Note

Math Background Regrouping in subtraction means breaking apart a ten to make more ones. Be sure that children have had previous experiences exploring numbers as different quantities of tens and ones. For example, 56 can be thought of as 5 tens and 6 ones, 4 tens and 16 ones, 3 tens and 26 ones, and so on.

NCTM Standards

- Number and Operations

(For a complete correlation to the NCTM Standards and Grades Pre-K through 2 Expectations, see Pages 457G and 457H.)

Getting Started

Spiral Review

Problem of the Day 12-9

Carly drew a red shape. She did not draw a triangle. Which shape did Carly draw?

Shape A Shape B Shape C

Topics Reviewed
- Plane shapes
- Problem-Solving Strategy: Use Logical Reasoning

Answer Shape B, the red square, is the only shape that is both red and not a triangle.

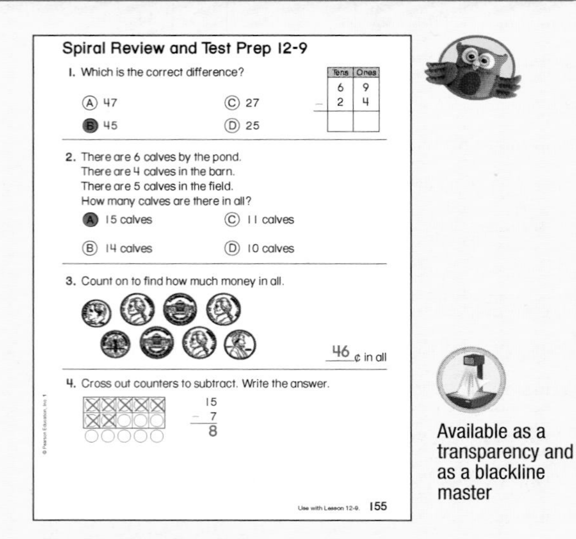

Spiral Review and Test Prep 12-9

1. Which is the correct difference?

	Tens	Ones
	6	9
−	2	4

Ⓐ 47 Ⓑ 45 Ⓒ 27 Ⓓ 25

2. There are 6 calves by the pond.
There are 4 calves in the barn.
There are 5 calves in the field.
How many calves are there in all?

Ⓐ 15 calves Ⓑ 14 calves Ⓒ 11 calves Ⓓ 10 calves

3. Count on to find how much money in all.

46 ¢ in all

4. Cross out counters to subtract. Write the answer.

15
− 7
8

© Pearson Education, Inc. 1

Use with Lesson 12-9. 155

Available as a transparency and as a blackline master

Topics Reviewed
1. Subtracting Two-Digit Numbers
2. Adding Three Numbers
3. Counting Dimes, Nickels, and Pennies
4. Using 10 to Subtract

Investigating the Concept

Break Apart a Ten

Materials *(per pair)* Place-Value Mat A (Workmat 4); 95 connecting cubes

What to Do

- Write 45 − 6 = __ on the board. Ask children to use cubes to show 45 on their workmats. **How can we subtract 6 ones from 5 ones?** Explain that when there are fewer ones than are being subtracted, 1 ten can be regrouped into 10 ones. Have children break apart 1 ten into 10 ones. **How many ones do you have now?** *(15)* **How many tens?** *(3)* Have children complete the problem.
- Repeat for other problems. Include some that require regrouping and some that do not.

Ongoing Assessment

- **Reasoning When should you regroup?** *(Regroup when you begin with fewer ones than are being subtracted.)*
- **If you subtract 7 from 93, do you need to regroup?** *(Yes)*

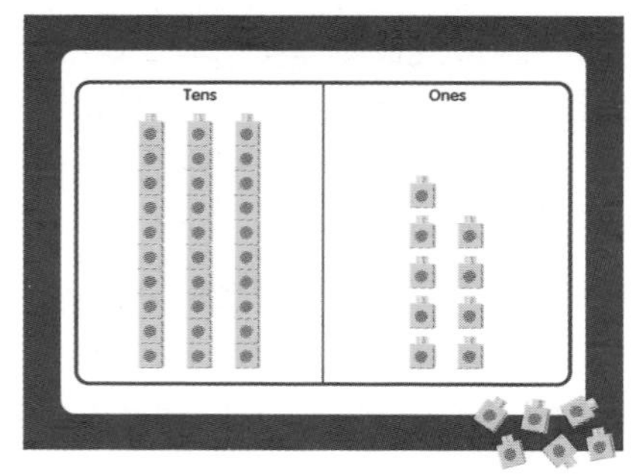

Reaching All Learners

Math and Literature

Subtracting with Sharks

15–20 MIN **Auditory/Visual/Spatial**

Materials *Shark Swimathon: Subtracting Two-Digit Numbers* by Stuart J. Murphy (HarperCollins Children's Books, 2001)

- Introduce *Shark Swimathon* by telling children that the book is about a shark swim team that needs to swim 75 laps to make money to go to swim camp. **Do you think the team will reach its goal?** Then read aloud the book and let children respond freely to it.
- Revisit the subtraction problems in the story and discuss how they can be solved. Include problems that involve regrouping.

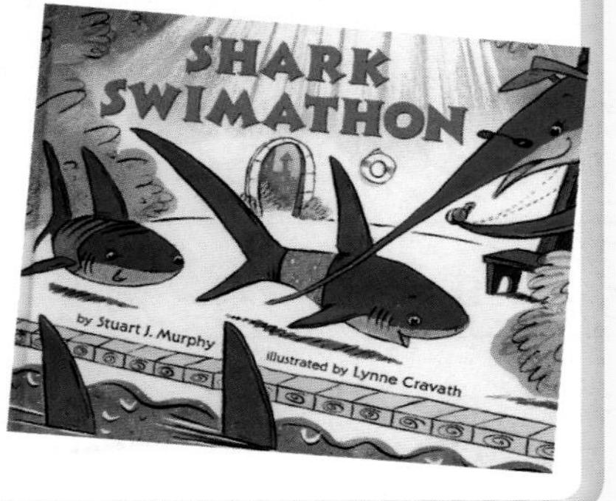

Access Content

English Language Learners

Different Ways to Make a Number

5–10 MIN **Auditory/Kinesthetic**

Materials *(per child)* 99 connecting cubes

- Have children connect cubes into 5 groups of 10 and 4 single cubes. **I can make 54 with 5 tens and 4 ones.**
- **Let's break apart 1 ten.** Break apart 1 group of ten into 10 single cubes. **I can make 54 with 4 tens and 14 ones.**
- Give children a different two-digit number and have them show two ways to make the number, using your example as a model.

Reteaching

Craft Stick Subtraction

5–10 MIN **Linguistic/Kinesthetic**

Materials Craft sticks; rubber bands

- Write 73 on the board. **How many tens?** *(7)* **ones?** *(3)* Show the number with craft sticks fastened in 7 groups of ten and 3 single sticks.
- **Let's subtract 25 craft sticks. Can we take 5 single sticks from these 3 single sticks? What can we do?** If children do not suggest it, break apart a bundle of 10 and add 10 to the single sticks. Subtract 5 from the 13 sticks, and subtract 2 tens. Write 73 − 25 = 48.
- Repeat with other problems.

Math and Science

Temperature Difference

15–20 MIN **Logical/Mathematical**

- For a week have children note the daily temperature by reading a thermometer or finding the listing in the newspaper. Write the day, date, and temperature on a bulletin board.
- At the end of the week, ask children to subtract the differences in temperature for any two days. For more dramatic differences in temperature, compare temperatures during the month.
- Keep a log to record how the daily temperatures rise and fall.

Objective Use models to subtract a one-digit quantity from a two-digit quantity with and without regrouping.

1 Warm Up

Activate Prior Knowledge Review different ways to name two-digit numbers. **How many tens and ones are in 38?** *(3 tens and 8 ones)* **How can we show 38 with just 2 tens?** *(2 tens and 18 ones)* Repeat for other numbers.

2 Teach

Learn!

Have children use connecting cubes to model the problem at the top of the student page. **Do you have enough ones to subtract 8?** *(No)* Ask children to regroup, or break apart, a ten. **Now do you have enough ones?** *(Yes)* Have children finish solving the problem and write the difference.

Ongoing Assessment

Talk About It

- **After regrouping, how many ones did you have?** *(13 ones)* **How many tens?** *(3 tens)*
- **Do you need to regroup to solve 48 − 7? Explain.** *(No; you can subtract 7 from 8.)*

If children have difficulty deciding whether or not regrouping is necessary,

then ask: **Can you take 5 ones from 3 ones? If you regroup, will there be enough ones?**

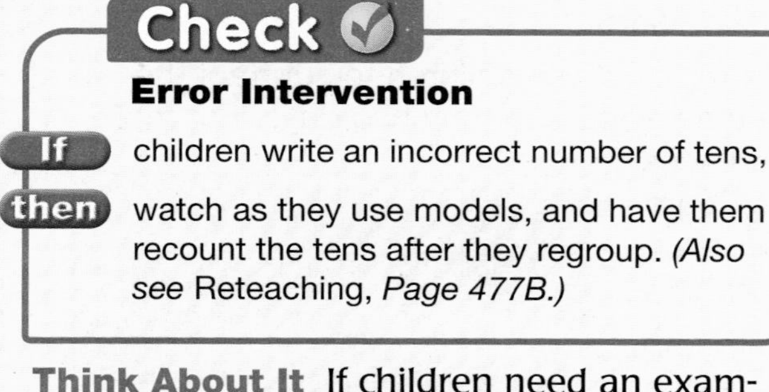

Check

Error Intervention

If children write an incorrect number of tens,

then watch as they use models, and have them recount the tens after they regroup. *(Also see* Reteaching, *Page 477B.)*

Think About It If children need an example, have them show 1 ten and 4 ones and then have them subtract 1. **Do you need to regroup?** *(No)* Continue subtracting 1 until children have to regroup.

Name ________________

Regrouping in Subtraction

Learn!

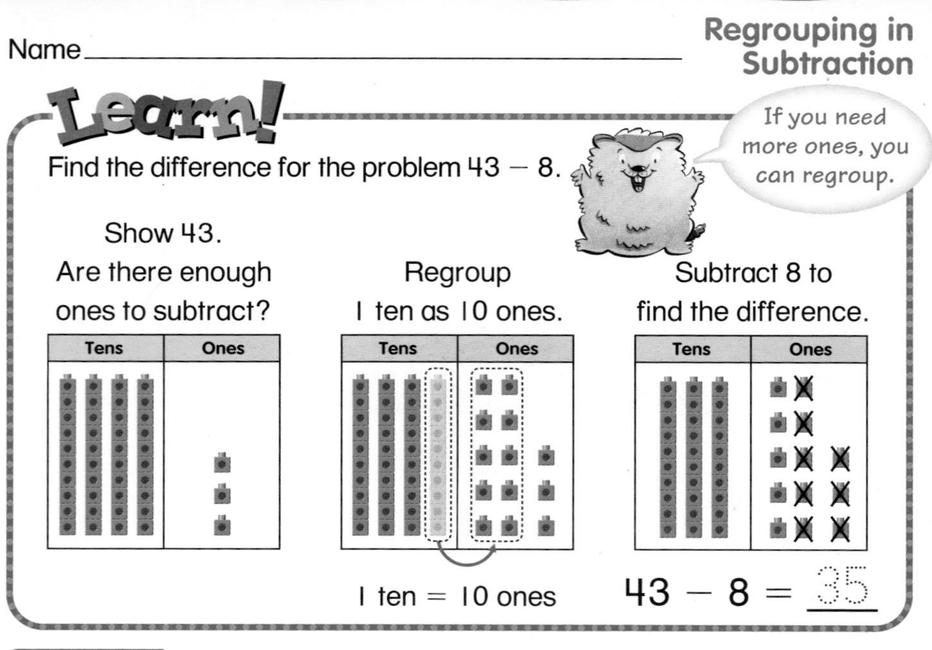

Check

Use cubes and Workmat 4. Do you need to regroup?
Circle **yes** or **no**. Then write the difference.

Show.	Subtract.	Do you need to regroup?	Find the difference.
1 32	5	(yes) no	32 − 5 = 27
2 56	4	yes (no)	56 − 4 = 52
3 75	9	(yes) no	75 − 9 = 66

Think About It Reasoning
How do you know when you need to regroup? *When there are more ones being subtracted than you have, you need to regroup a ten into 10 ones.*

Reteaching Below Level

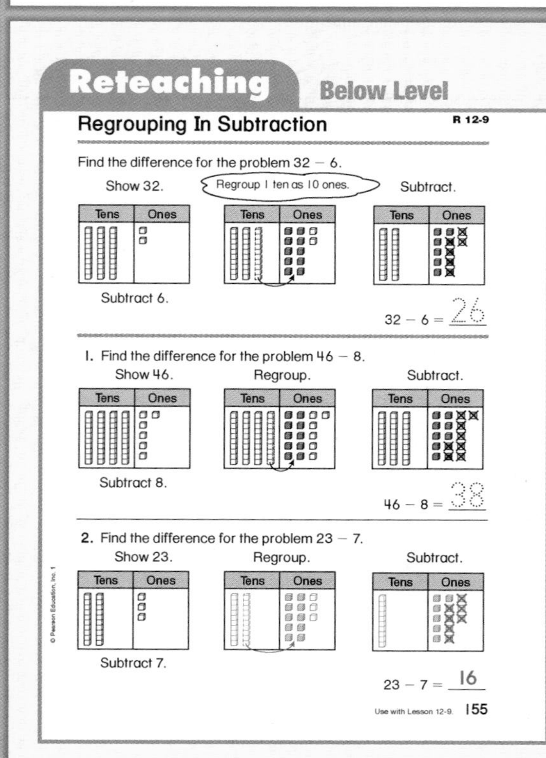

Regrouping In Subtraction R 12-9

Find the difference for the problem 32 − 6.
Show 32. Regroup 1 ten as 10 ones. Subtract.
Tens Ones
Subtract 6.
32 − 6 = 26

1. Find the difference for the problem 46 − 8.
Show 46. Regroup. Subtract.
Subtract 8.
46 − 8 = 38

2. Find the difference for the problem 23 − 7.
Show 23. Regroup. Subtract.
Subtract 7.
23 − 7 = 16

Use with Lesson 12-9. 155

Practice On Level

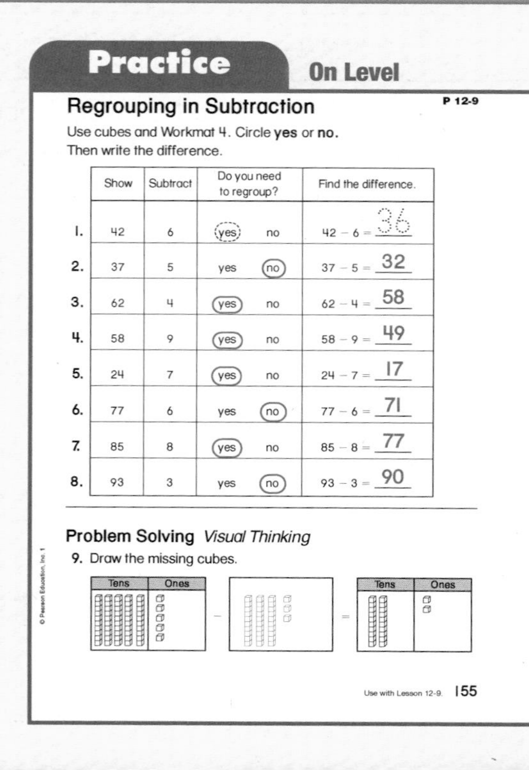

Regrouping in Subtraction P 12-9

Use cubes and Workmat 4. Circle **yes** or **no**.
Then write the difference.

	Show	Subtract	Do you need to regroup?	Find the difference.
1.	42	6	(yes) no	42 − 6 = 36
2.	37	5	yes (no)	37 − 5 = 32
3.	62	4	(yes) no	62 − 4 = 58
4.	58	9	(yes) no	58 − 9 = 49
5.	24	7	(yes) no	24 − 7 = 17
6.	77	6	yes (no)	77 − 6 = 71
7.	85	8	(yes) no	85 − 8 = 77
8.	93	3	yes (no)	93 − 3 = 90

Problem Solving *Visual Thinking*
9. Draw the missing cubes.
Tens Ones − = Tens Ones

Use with Lesson 12-9. 155

Practice

Use cubes and Workmat 4. Do you need to regroup? Circle **yes** or **no.** Then write the difference.

Show.	Subtract.	Do you need to regroup?	Find the difference.
4 47	8	(yes) no	47 − 8 = 39
5 28	6	yes (no)	28 − 6 = 22
6 86	9	(yes) no	86 − 9 = 77
7 12	5	(yes) no	12 − 5 = 7
8 34	3	yes (no)	34 − 3 = 31
9 95	8	(yes) no	95 − 8 = 87
10 53	7	(yes) no	53 − 7 = 46

Problem Solving Visual Thinking

Use the number line to subtract.

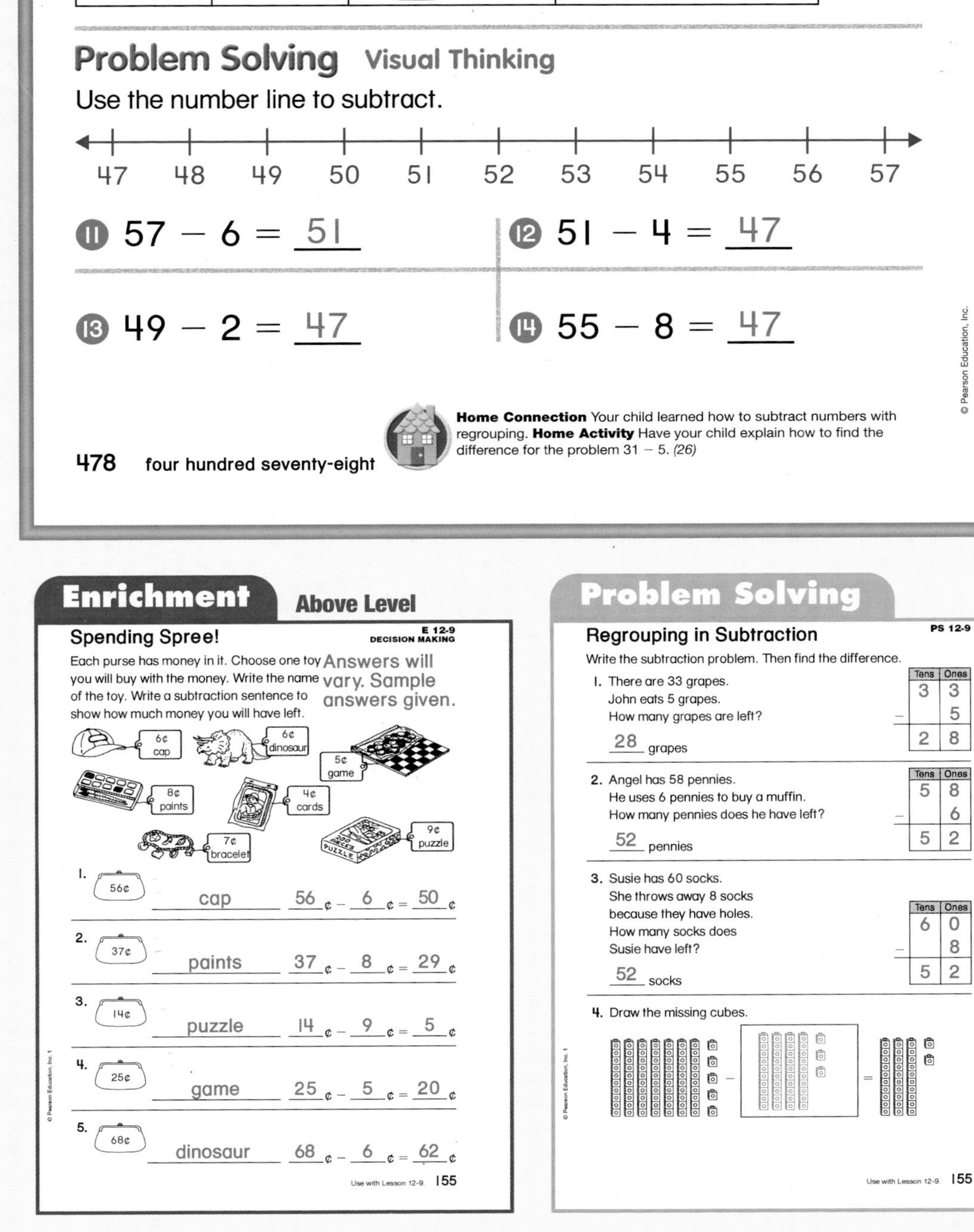

11 57 − 6 = 51

12 51 − 4 = 47

13 49 − 2 = 47

14 55 − 8 = 47

Home Connection Your child learned how to subtract numbers with regrouping. **Home Activity** Have your child explain how to find the difference for the problem 31 − 5. *(26)*

Enrichment Above Level

Spending Spree! E 12-9 DECISION MAKING

Each purse has money in it. Choose one toy you will buy with the money. Write the name of the toy. Write a subtraction sentence to show how much money you will have left. Answers will vary. Sample answers given.

6¢ cap, 6¢ dinosaur, 5¢ game, 8¢ paints, 4¢ cards, 7¢ bracelet, 9¢ puzzle

1. 56¢ cap 56¢ − 6¢ = 50¢
2. 37¢ paints 37¢ − 8¢ = 29¢
3. 14¢ puzzle 14¢ − 9¢ = 5¢
4. 25¢ game 25¢ − 5¢ = 20¢
5. 68¢ dinosaur 68¢ − 6¢ = 62¢

Use with Lesson 12-9 155

Problem Solving

Regrouping in Subtraction PS 12-9

Write the subtraction problem. Then find the difference.

1. There are 33 grapes. John eats 5 grapes. How many grapes are left? 28 grapes

	Tens	Ones
	3	3
−		5
	2	8

2. Angel has 58 pennies. He uses 6 pennies to buy a muffin. How many pennies does he have left? 52 pennies

	Tens	Ones
	5	8
−		6
	5	2

3. Susie has 60 socks. She throws away 8 socks because they have holes. How many socks does Susie have left? 52 socks

	Tens	Ones
	6	0
−		8
	5	2

4. Draw the missing cubes.

Use with Lesson 12-9 155

3 Practice

For Exercises 4–10, have children model the problem, circle *yes* or *no* to tell if they need to regroup, and write the difference.

Reading Assist: Make Predictions Have children look at the number of ones in the starting number (the minuend) and the number of ones being subtracted (the subtrahend) and predict whether or not they will need to regroup.

Leveled Practice

Below Level Work with a partner to complete all exercises.

On Level Complete all exercises individually.

Above Level Complete exercises without cubes.

Early Finishers Ask children to make up a problem like the ones in Exercises 11–14. Have them trade with a partner and solve.

4 Assess

Journal Idea Ask children to write a subtraction problem that requires regrouping and to draw a picture to solve it.

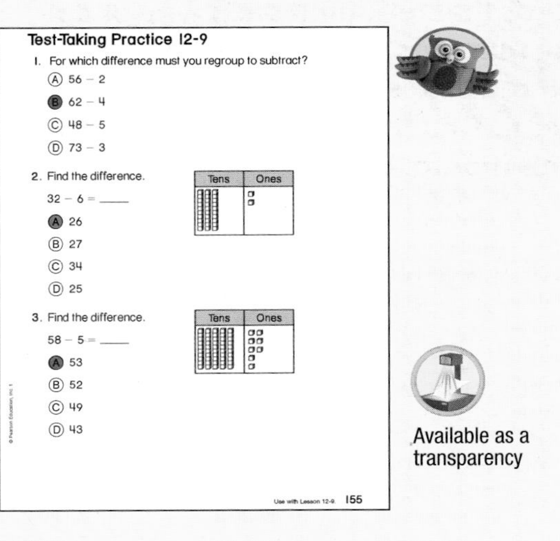

Test-Taking Practice 12-9

1. For which difference must you regroup to subtract?
   - Ⓐ 56 − 2
   - Ⓑ 62 − 4 (filled)
   - Ⓒ 48 − 5
   - Ⓓ 73 − 3
2. Find the difference. 32 − 6 = ___
   - Ⓐ 26 (filled)
   - Ⓑ 27
   - Ⓒ 34
   - Ⓓ 25
3. Find the difference. 58 − 5 = ___
   - Ⓐ 53 (filled)
   - Ⓑ 52
   - Ⓒ 49
   - Ⓓ 43

Use with Lesson 12-9 155

Available as a transparency

Reading for Math Success

Purpose Show children how to apply the reading skill, *Understand Graphic Sources: Graphs,* to their math work. Help prepare children for the problem-solving strategy lesson, *Make a Graph,* which follows.

Using Student Page 479

Reading Skills and Math Understanding Children learn that graphics such as graphs, lists, charts, and tables are sources of information. In math, children learn to read and interpret information in charts and graphs in order to solve problems.

Model the Process Tell children that making a graph is one way to display information. Draw a simple bar graph like the following on the board.

Weather This Month

Sunny
Rainy
Cloudy

0 1 2 3 4 5 6 7

When I read a graph, I read the title first. It tells me what the graph is about. I look at the words that tell about each type of day and the numbers at the bottom. I see that the colored boxes for "Sunny" end at the number 6. That means there were 6 sunny days this month. Model other entries in the graph.

Guide the Activity Have children read Exercise 1 and ask questions to see if they understand the data in the chart. Discuss with children how they could transfer the three numbers for each class to the bar graph. For example, for Room A, they can color in from 0 to 15. Then they can count on to add the next 10 and count on again to add the final 20. Repeat the process for Room B.

Think About It Let children share how they got their answers. Children may have used the numbers at the bottom of the graph or looked to see which class had the longer bar.

Name ____________________

Understand Graphic Sources: Graphs

1 Read this math problem.

Two first-grade classes collected soup labels to raise money for their school. The chart shows how many soup labels each class collected. Which class collected more?

Soup Labels Collected			
	Month 1	Month 2	Month 3
Room A	15	10	20
Room B	20	5	15

Then the classes made a graph to find out.

Soup Labels Collected

Room A
Room B

0 5 10 15 20 25 30 35 40 45 50

2 How many soup labels did Room A collect? 45 soup labels

3 How many soup labels did Room B collect? 40 soup labels

Think About It **Reasoning**
Which class collected more?
How can you use the graph to tell?

Room A collected more; the longer bar shows which class collected more.

4. Read another math problem.

The first-grade classes also collected box tops to raise money for their school. The chart shows how many box tops each class collected. Which class collected more box tops?

Box Tops Collected			
	Month 1	Month 2	Month 3
Room A	20	10	50
Room B	30	40	20

5. Complete the graph below to show how many box tops each class collected.

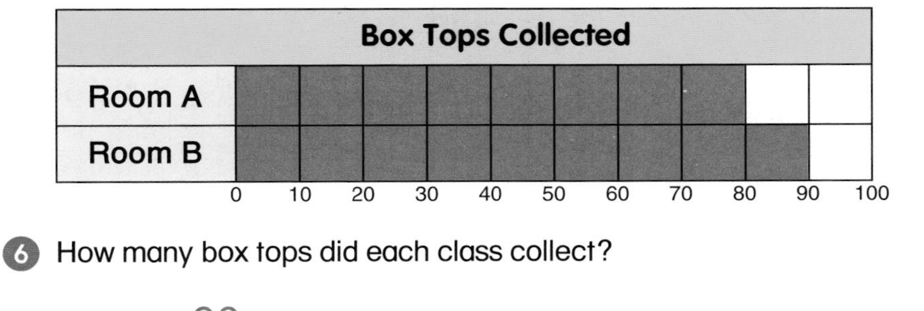

6. How many box tops did each class collect?

Room A: 80 box tops

Room B: 90 box tops

7. Which class collected more box tops?

Room B

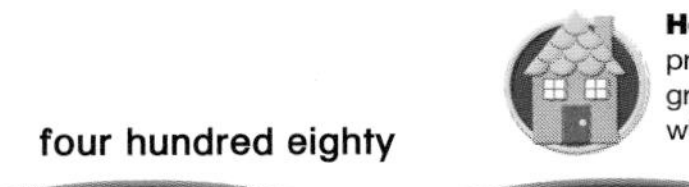

Home Connection Your child completed a graph to help solve a word problem. **Home Activity** Ask your child to explain how he or she used the graph on this page to determine how many box tops each class collected and which class collected more.

Using Student Page 480

Have children independently read the story problem in Exercise 4. You may want to discuss the information in the chart before children begin to transfer that information to the bar graph in Exercise 5. Have children complete Exercises 6 and 7 independently.

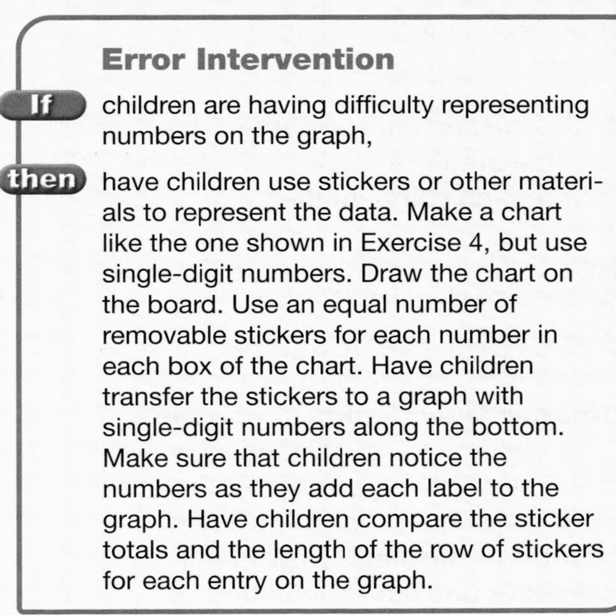

Error Intervention

If children are having difficulty representing numbers on the graph,

then have children use stickers or other materials to represent the data. Make a chart like the one shown in Exercise 4, but use single-digit numbers. Draw the chart on the board. Use an equal number of removable stickers for each number in each box of the chart. Have children transfer the stickers to a graph with single-digit numbers along the bottom. Make sure that children notice the numbers as they add each label to the graph. Have children compare the sticker totals and the length of the row of stickers for each entry on the graph.

Journal Idea Children can make bar graphs to tally points earned by classes in school contests or to keep track of the weather for a given month.

Make a Graph

Lesson Organizer

Quick Lesson Overview

Objective Solve problems by making and interpreting bar graphs.

Math Understanding Organizing data in a graph can make it easier to interpret and compare the data.

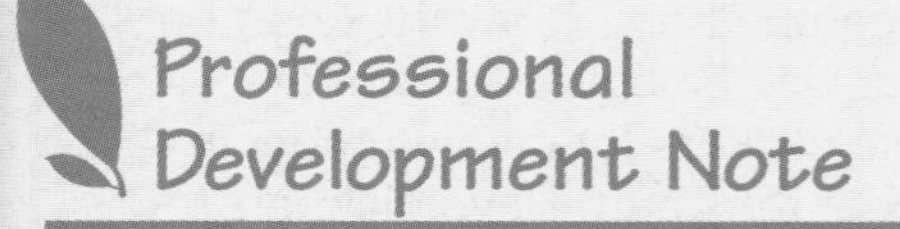

Professional Development Note

Effective Questioning Techniques Guide children to see relationships among data on a graph by asking comparative questions. **Which has the most or the least? How many more does one have than another? How many more does one need in order to have as many as another?**

NCTM Standards

- Number and Operations
- Data Analysis and Probability

(For a complete correlation to the NCTM Standards and Grades Pre-K through 2 Expectations, see Pages 457G and 457H.)

Getting Started

Spiral Review

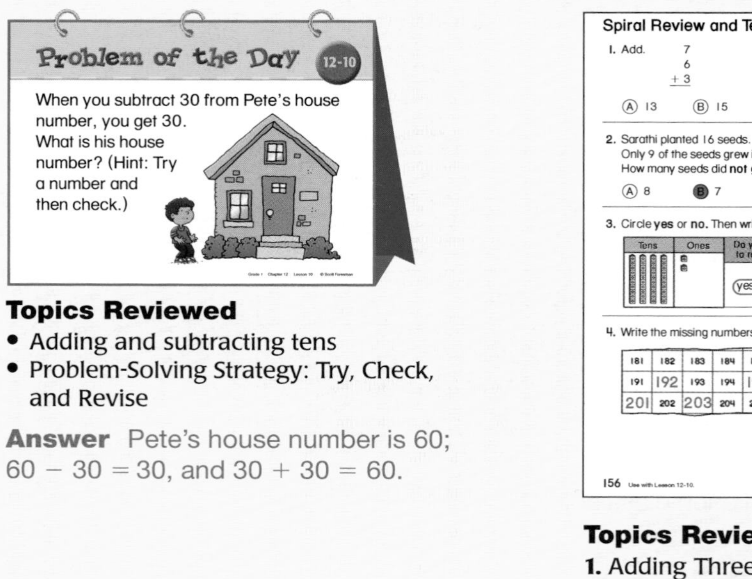

Topics Reviewed

- Adding and subtracting tens
- Problem-Solving Strategy: Try, Check, and Revise

Answer Pete's house number is 60; $60 - 30 = 30$, and $30 + 30 = 60$.

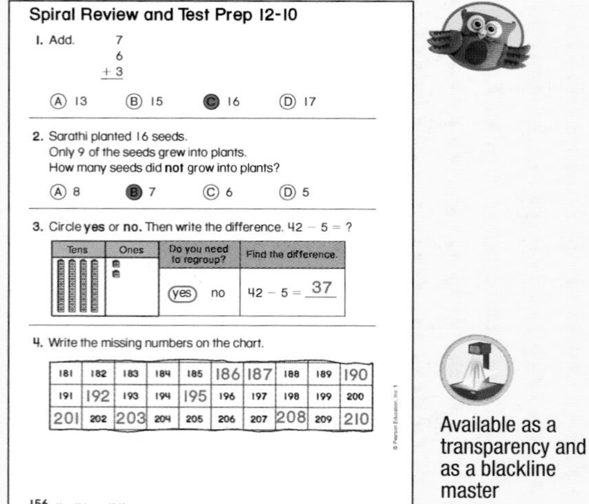

Spiral Review and Test Prep 12-10

1. Add. 7 + 6 + 3

Ⓐ 13 Ⓑ 15 Ⓒ 16 Ⓓ 17

2. Sarathi planted 16 seeds.
Only 9 of the seeds grew into plants.
How many seeds did **not** grow into plants?

Ⓐ 8 Ⓑ 7 Ⓒ 6 Ⓓ 5

3. Circle **yes** or **no.** Then write the difference. $42 - 5 = ?$

Tens	Ones	Do you need to regroup?	Find the difference.
		yes no	$42 - 5 =$ 37

4. Write the missing numbers on the chart.

181	182	183	184	185	186	187	188	189	190
191	192	193	194	195	196	197	198	199	200
201	202	203	204	205	206	207	208	209	210

156 Use with Lesson 12-10.

Available as a transparency and as a blackline master

Topics Reviewed

1. Adding Three Numbers
2. Applying Subtraction Fact Strategies
3. Regrouping in Subtraction
4. Hundreds

Investigating the Concept

Make a Graph to Solve a Problem

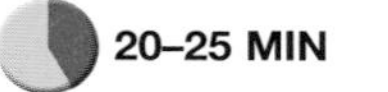

20–25 MIN **Logical/Mathematical**

What to Do

- On the board, draw the following chart:

Pennies Collected				
	Week 1	Week 2	Week 3	Week 4
John	5	10	5	5
Kim	15	5	5	10

- Explain that the chart shows how many pennies that each child collected in each of 4 weeks. **Who collected the most?** *(Kim)* Have volunteers make a bar graph with increments of 5 to show the data.

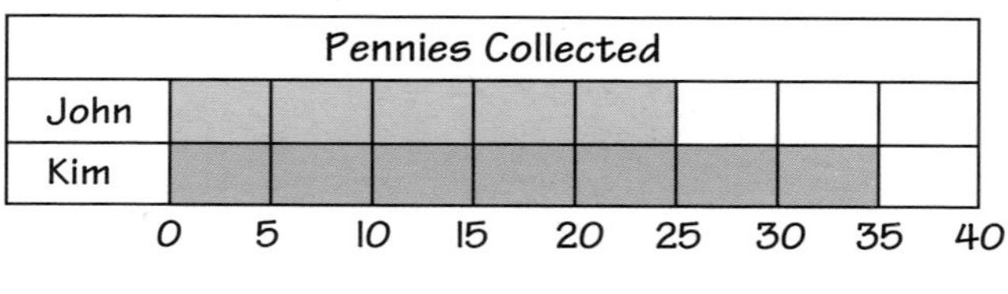

Ongoing Assessment

- **Who collected more pennies?** *(Kim)*
- **Reasoning How does the graph help you answer the question?** *(The graph makes the data easy to see. The longer bar shows the person with more.)*

Reaching All Learners

Reading in Math

Summarize the Results

10–15 MIN **Visual/Spatial** WHOLE CLASS

- Explain that Mr. Mottley's students are trying to see if they read more books last week than Ms. Fender's students.
- Make a chart titled "Books Read." Have days of the week as headings and a row for each class. Include this information: Monday: Mr. Mottley 15, Ms. Fender 5; Tuesday: Mr. Mottley 5, Ms. Fender 5; Wednesday: Mr. Mottley 0, Ms. Fender 5; Thursday: Mr. Mottley 5, Ms. Fender 10; Friday: Mr. Mottley 0, Ms. Fender 5.
- Have children explain how making a graph can help them see which class read more.

Activate Prior Knowledge/Build Background

English Language Learners

Everyday Charts and Graphs

10–15 MIN **Linguistic/Kinesthetic**

Materials Classroom charts and graphs

- Review charts by using a classroom chart of favorite lunches.
- Display or sketch a simple bar graph related to the chart. Describe the differences between a chart and a graph. Make sure children understand that each bar on the graph represents the number at the base or side of the graph.
- Help children transfer data from a classroom chart to a graph.

Favorite Lunches

Pizza

Hamburger

Macaroni

0 5 10 15 20 25 30 35 40

Reteaching

Making a Bar Graph

10–15 MIN **Visual/Spatial** SMALL GROUP

Materials *(per group)* Posterboard; markers; crayons

- Explain that three classes collected food for a food pantry. Copy this information on the board: "Grade 1—35; Grade 2—25; Grade 3—30."
- Help children make a bar graph to show the totals.
- Have children color in one box for every 5 items collected. **Which grade collected the most?** *(Grade 1)*

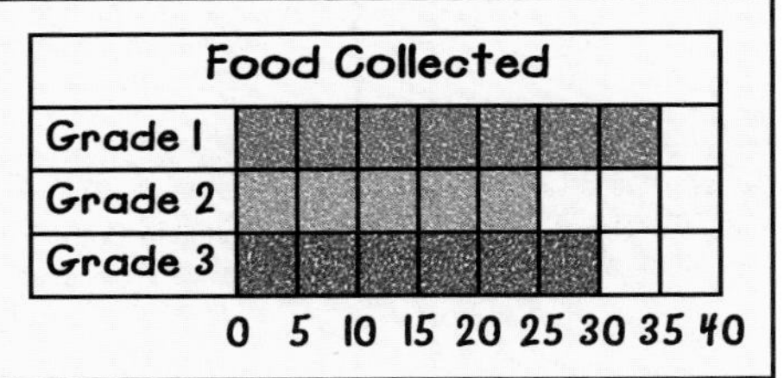

Math and Social Studies

Work I Want to Do

15–20 MIN **Linguistic/Kinesthetic**

- Discuss some types of workers in your community, such as teachers, builders, doctors, police officers, and mail carriers. Discuss how these workers help the community.
- Have students suggest jobs that they would like to do. List their suggestions in a chart. Make a bar graph to display the information about the jobs. After you finish the graph, have children tell which kinds of work most of them would like to do.

Work We Want to Do

Teacher

Police Officer

Doctor

Mail Carrier

Builder

0 5 10 15 20 25 30

Objective Solve problems by making and interpreting bar graphs.

1 Warm Up

Activate Prior Knowledge Review bar graphs. Display a bar graph titled "Favorite Lunches." Shade 3 boxes for *hot dog,* 2 boxes for *soup,* and 5 boxes for *pizza.* Ask questions to help children interpret the data. **Which lunch is the favorite?** *(Pizza)* **How many children chose hot dogs?** *(3)* **How many more children chose pizza than soup?** (3 more)

2 Teach

Learn!

Read the problem aloud to children. Point out that each box on the bar graph stands for 5 cans. Discuss how to shade the graph to show the data in the chart.

Ongoing Assessment

Talk About It

- **Which team collected the fewest cans?** *(The Blue Team)*
- **How many more cans did the Green Team collect than the Blue Team?** *(15 more)*

If children have difficulty transferring data from the chart to the graph,

then have them cross out each number of cans on the chart as they color the graph.

Check

Error Intervention

If children have difficulty reading the graph,

then help them count by 5s as they point to each number at the bottom of the graph. *(Also see* Reteaching, *Page 481B.)*

Think About It Have volunteers draw a tally chart and a picture graph on the board to show the same data.

Name ______________________

PROBLEM-SOLVING STRATEGY
Make a Graph

Learn!

You can make a graph to solve this problem.

1. Amy's class collected cans for recycling. Which team collected more cans?

Cans Collected				
	Week 1	Week 2	Week 3	Week 4
Blue Team	5	15	10	5
Green Team	20	10	5	15

Read and Understand

The chart shows how many cans each team collected. We want to find which team collected the greater number of cans.

Plan and Solve

Use the information in the chart to make a graph.
Color one box for every 5 cans.

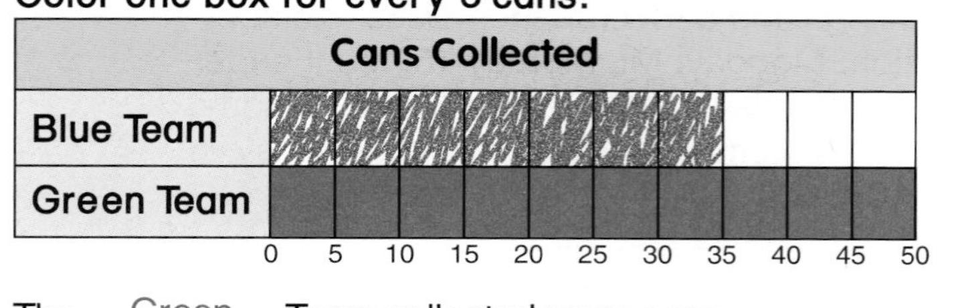

The ___Green___ Team collected more cans.

Look Back and Check

How can you be sure your answer is correct?

Think About It Reasoning
How could you show the same information using a tally chart or a picture graph?

Make a set of 5 tally marks for each box shaded, or draw a picture to stand for every group of 5 cans.

Reteaching Below Level

PROBLEM-SOLVING STRATEGY R 12-10
Make a Graph

The bead store sells red, white, and blue beads. Which color bead did they sell the most?

Count by tens. Then count on by fives.

Beads Sold				
	Week 1	Week 2	Week 3	Week 4
Red Beads	10	5	10	10
Blue Beads	10	5	5	10
White Beads	10	10	10	10

Read and Understand

The chart shows how many of each color beads were sold. We want to find which color sold the most.

Plan and Solve

Use the information in the chart to make a graph.
Color one box for every 5 beads sold.

Count the boxes by fives.

Beads Sold

Red Beads
Blue Beads
White Beads
0 5 10 15 20 25 30 35 40 45 50
Number of Beads Sold

The ___white___ beads sold the most.

Look Back and Check

How can you be sure your answer is correct?

Practice On Level

PROBLEM-SOLVING STRATEGY P 12-10
Make a Graph

Make a graph to solve the problem.
Color one box for every 10 books.

1. The first grade classes made a chart showing how many books they read each day. Which class read the most books?

Number of Books Read

Class	Day 1	Day 2	Day 3	Day 4	Day 5
Mrs. Miller's Class	30	20	10	10	30
Mr. Lee's Class	10	30	20	10	10
Miss Plum's Class	20	20	10	20	10

Mrs. Miller's Class
Mr. Lee's Class
Miss Plum's Class
0 10 20 30 40 50 60 70 80 90 100

___Mrs. Miller's___ class read the most books.

Writing in Math

2. Write another question that could be answered using the graph.
Answers will vary.

Practice

Make a graph to solve the problem.

2. Miguel's class collected paper for recycling. The chart shows how many pounds of paper each team collected. Which team collected the most paper? **Color one box for every 10 pounds of paper.**

Paper Collected (in Pounds)				
	Week 1	Week 2	Week 3	Week 4
Yellow Team	10	20	20	30
Orange Team	20	30	30	20
Purple Team	20	20	10	30

Paper Collected

Yellow Team										
Orange Team										
Purple Team										
	0	10	20	30	40	50	60	70	80	90	100

The Orange Team collected the most paper.

Writing in Math

3. Write another question that could be answered using the bar graph above.

Answers will vary.

Home Connection Your child made graphs to solve problems. **Home Activity** Ask your child to explain how he or she made and used the graph on this page to solve the problem above.

Enrichment Above Level

Graph It! E 12-10 DATA

What color bike do children like the most? Ask 15 children if they like red, blue, or silver bikes the best. Make a tally. Use the tally chart to make a graph. Color 1 square for each tally. Answers may vary.

		Total
Red		
Blue		
Silver		

Color Bike Liked Best

Red										
Blue										
Silver										
	0	1	2	3	4	5	6	7	8	9	10

1. What color did children like the most? Check children's graphs.
2. How many children liked silver bikes? Check children's graphs.
3. Did more children like blue or red bikes? Check children's graphs.
4. What was the least favorite color for a bike? Check children's graphs.
5. Write a question that can be answered using the graph.

Check children's graphs.

156 Use with Lesson 12-10.

Problem Solving

PROBLEM-SOLVING STRATEGY PS 12-10

Make a Graph

The first grade has 3 soccer teams. Which team scored the most goals?

Goals Scored				
	Game 1	Game 2	Game 3	Game 4
Orange Team	10	10	10	10
Yellow Team	20	10	20	10
Red Team	10	10	10	20

The chart shows how many goals each team scored. We want to find which team scored the most goals. Use the information in the chart to make a graph. Color one box for every ten goals.

Goals Scored

Orange Team										
Yellow Team										
Red Team										
	0	10	20	30	40	50	60	70	80	90	100

The yellow team scored the most goals.

Check your answer. Make sure you colored the correct number of boxes.

Writing in Math

1. Write another question that could be answered using the graph.

Questions will vary.

Using the page To help children *plan and solve*, ask them what they must find and how making the graph would help them solve the problem. Have children complete the graph to solve.

156 Use with Lesson 12-10

3 Practice

Read the problem in Exercise 2. Explain that each box on the bar graph stands for 10 pounds of paper.

Leveled Practice

Below Level Work with a partner.

On Level Complete the exercises as written.

Above Level For Exercise 3, write several questions that could be answered using the graph.

Early Finishers Have children make a new graph to show the same data, but ask them to make each box stand for 5 pounds of paper.

4 Assess

Journal Idea Display the following chart and have children make a bar graph to show the data:

Jars Collected			
	Week 1	Week 2	Week 3
Red Team	5	5	10
Blue Team	10	10	10
Green Team	15	5	5

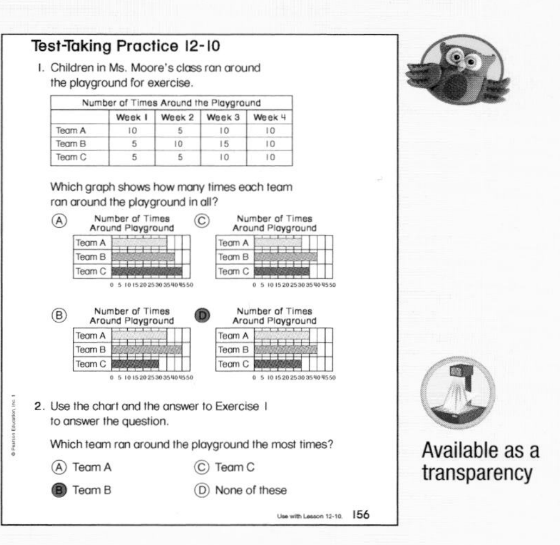

Test-Taking Practice 12-10

1. Children in Ms. Moore's class ran around the playground for exercise.

Number of Times Around the Playground				
	Week 1	Week 2	Week 3	Week 4
Team A	10	5	10	10
Team B	5	10	15	10
Team C	5	5	10	10

Which graph shows how many times each team ran around the playground in all?

Ⓐ Number of Times Around Playground (Team A, Team B, Team C; 0 5 10 15 20 25 30 35 40 45 50)

Ⓒ Number of Times Around Playground (Team A, Team B, Team C; 0 5 10 15 20 25 30 35 40 45 50)

Ⓑ Number of Times Around Playground (Team A, Team B, Team C; 0 5 10 15 20 25 30 35 40 45 50)

Ⓓ Number of Times Around Playground (Team A, Team B, Team C; 0 5 10 15 20 25 30 35 40 45 50)

2. Use the chart and the answer to Exercise 1 to answer the question.

Which team ran around the playground the most times?

Ⓐ Team A Ⓒ Team C

Ⓑ Team B Ⓓ None of these

Use with Lesson 12-10. 156

Available as a transparency

Caring for Kittens

Lesson Organizer

Quick Lesson Overview

Objective Review and apply concepts, skills, and strategies learned in this and previous chapters.

Math Understanding Some real-world problems can be solved using known concepts, skills, and strategies.

Professional Development Note

Math Background Children have had experience adding and subtracting two-digit numbers. They have also had experience regrouping to add and to subtract. Children can apply what they know to solve new problems.

NCTM Standards

- Number and Operations

(For a complete correlation to the NCTM Standards and Grades Pre-K through 2 Expectations, see Pages 457G and 457H.)

Getting Started

Spiral Review

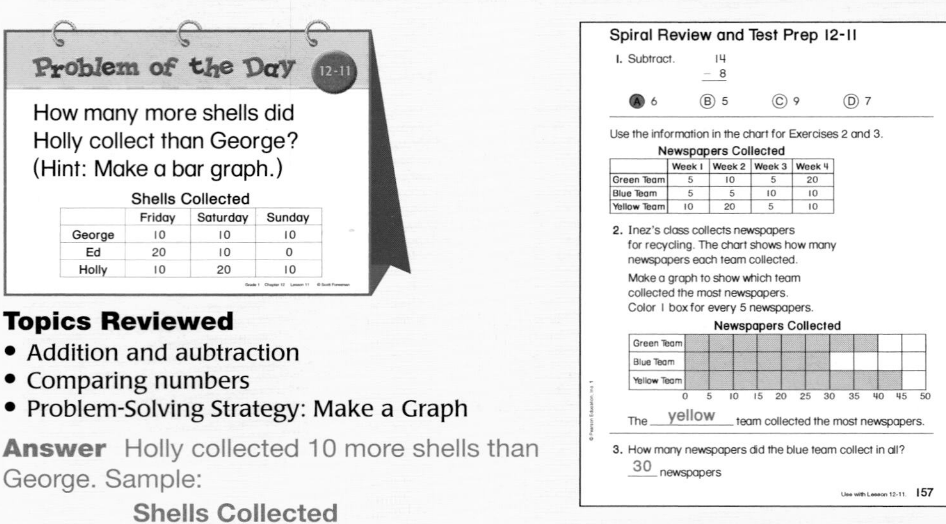

Problem of the Day 12-11

How many more shells did Holly collect than George? (Hint: Make a bar graph.)

Shells Collected

	Friday	Saturday	Sunday
George	10	10	10
Ed	20	10	0
Holly	10	20	10

Spiral Review and Test Prep 12-11

1. Subtract. 14 − 8

Ⓐ 6 Ⓑ 5 Ⓒ 9 Ⓓ 7

Use the information in the chart for Exercises 2 and 3.

Newspapers Collected

	Week 1	Week 2	Week 3	Week 4
Green Team	5	10	5	20
Blue Team	5	5	10	10
Yellow Team	10	20	5	10

2. Inez's class collects newspapers for recycling. The chart shows how many newspapers each team collected.

Make a graph to show which team collected the most newspapers.
Color 1 box for every 5 newspapers.

Newspapers Collected

Green Team
Blue Team
Yellow Team
0 5 10 15 20 25 30 35 40 45 50

The yellow team collected the most newspapers.

3. How many newspapers did the blue team collect in all?
30 newspapers

Use with Lesson 12-11. 157

Topics Reviewed

- Addition and aubtraction
- Comparing numbers
- Problem-Solving Strategy: Make a Graph

Answer Holly collected 10 more shells than George. Sample:

Shells Collected

George
Ed
Holly
0 10 20 30 40 50

Available as a transparency and as a blackline master

Topics Reviewed

1. Applying Subtraction Fact Strategies
2. Act It Out
3. Make a Graph
4. Use Data from a Graph

Investigating the Concept

Reviewing Addition and Subtraction

10–15 MIN **Logical/Mathematical** WHOLE CLASS

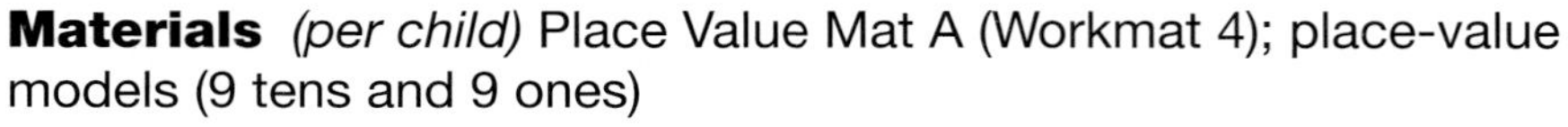

Materials *(per child)* Place Value Mat A (Workmat 4); place-value models (9 tens and 9 ones)

What to Do

- Write 31 + 13 vertically in tens and ones columns on the board. Have children use models to find the sum. *(44)* Write 39 + 13 vertically in tens and ones columns. Discuss whether it is necessary to regroup. Have children use models to find the sum. *(52)*
- Write 52 − 15 vertically in tens and ones columns. Discuss whether it is necessary to break apart a ten before subtracting. Have children use their mats to find the difference. *(37)*

Ongoing Assessment

- **Reasoning When is it necessary to regroup for addition?** *(When there are 10 or more ones)*
- **When is it necessary to break apart a ten for subtraction?** *(When there are not enough ones to subtract)*

Reaching All Learners

Math and Literature

17 Kings and 42 Elephants

10–15 MIN **Auditory/Linguistic**

Materials *17 Kings and 42 Elephants* by Margaret Mahy (Dial Books, 1993)

- After children have enjoyed the rhythm and rhyme of the story and have discussed the various animals that the kings meet on their adventure, suggest that children use the book's format to create their own books.
- Talk about the combinations of animals that children would like to include. **How many kings and elephants would that be altogether?**
- Write the text as children dictate. Have them illustrate the books.

Access Content

English Language Learners

Pet Supply Store

10–15 MIN **Kinesthetic**

Materials *(per group)* Pet food bits; containers; paper bags; markers; dimes; pennies

- Help children set up a pet supply store. Place pet food bits in small containers. Have children label the prices.
- Customers take handfuls of different bits and place them in bags. Cashiers count the number of bits in each bag and find the total.
- Customers count out dimes and pennies to pay for the total amount they owe.

Reteaching

Add and Subtract Aiming Game

15–20 MIN **Kinesthetic**

Materials *(per group)* Chart paper; beanbags; markers

- Draw a large target board on chart paper and mark each ring with decade numbers.
- Have children toss two beanbags onto the target and add the numbers on which the beanbags land. Explain that if beanbags go outside the target, that number must be subtracted. Record totals of points for each round.

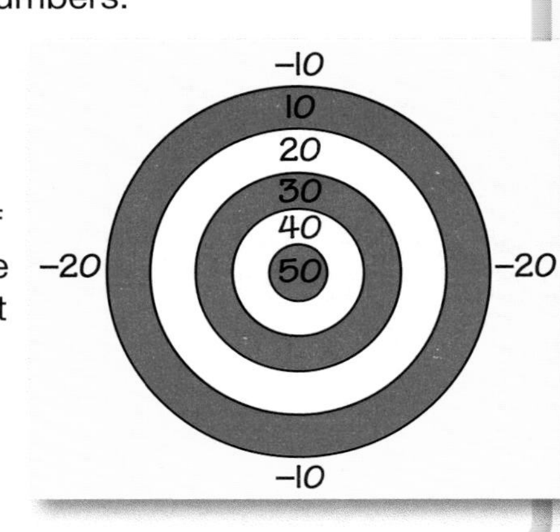

Advanced Learners

Play Twenty-Nine

15–20 MIN **Social/Cooperative**

Materials *(per group)* Index cards labeled with colored dots and numbers to match a standard deck of 52 cards, including 4 sets of face cards with animal stickers

- For this game, two pairs play against each other to reach 29 points.
- Divide cards among the four players. Players take turns putting down cards. Picture cards have a value of 0.
- The first child puts down a number card, such as a 10. The next child puts down a card, such as a 9, and adds it to the first one, making a sum of 19.
- The next player can add 10 to the 19 and win the cards by making 29. The total cannot go over 29.
- Play until no more combinations are possible.

Objective Review and apply concepts, skills, and strategies learned in this and previous chapters.

1 Warm Up

Activate Prior Knowledge Review adding and subtracting without regrouping. Say an addition problem. Have children show it on Place-Value Mat A (Workmat 4) and add to find the sum. Repeat with a subtraction problem.

2 Teach

Explain to children that they will use what they already know to solve the problems on the student page. Read the first problem aloud.

Ongoing Assessment

Talk About It

- **What do we need to find out?** *(How many fish bits Haruo gave his kitten)*
- **What do we know?** *(Haruo fed the kitten 33 bits in the morning and 20 bits in the evening.)*
- **How can we solve this problem?** *(Sample responses: Act it out; use counters; draw a picture; use numbers.)*
- **Which addition sentence solves this problem?** *(33 + 20 = 53)*

If children cannot complete the addition sentence,

then have them circle the numbers in the story and rewrite them vertically.

Error Intervention

If children have difficulty determining the operations to use for Exercises 1–3,

then have them circle the numbers from the problems and together discuss what question each problem is asking and whether addition or subtraction should be used to solve the problem. *(Also see Reteaching, Page 483B.)*

Name ____________________

PROBLEM-SOLVING APPLICATIONS
Caring for Kittens

Dorling Kindersley

Do You Know... that kittens should have regular checkups at the vet to help them stay healthy?

1. Haruo fed his kitten 33 fish bits in the morning and 20 fish bits in the evening. How many fish bits did Haruo feed his kitten altogether?

33 (+) 20 = 53 fish bits

2. The next day Haruo gave his kitten 44 fish bits. His kitten ate only 20 of them. How many fish bits were left?

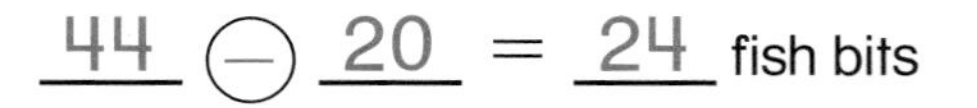

44 (−) 20 = 24 fish bits

Fun Fact! House cats belong to the same family as lions, tigers, and jaguars. They are all felines.

3. The animal shelter had 8 tabby kittens and 5 ragdoll kittens. How many kittens did the shelter have in all?

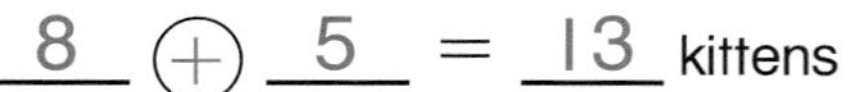

8 (+) 5 = 13 kittens

6 kittens were adopted. How many kittens were left?

13 (−) 6 = 7 kittens

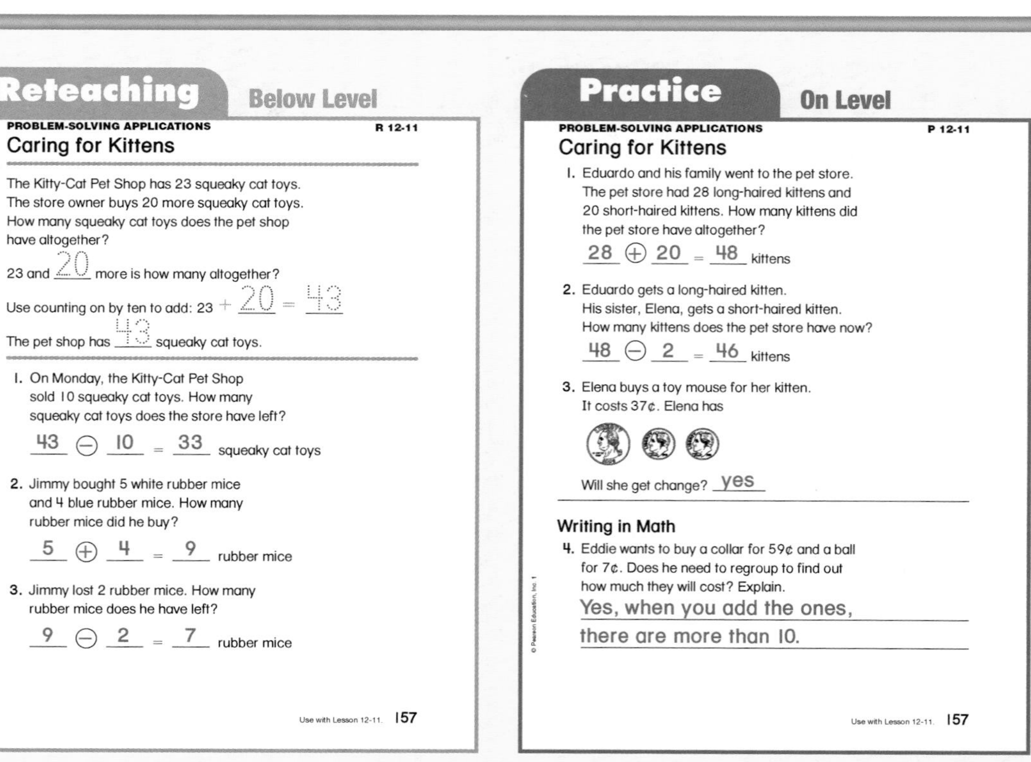

Reteaching Below Level

PROBLEM-SOLVING APPLICATIONS R 12-11
Caring for Kittens

The Kitty-Cat Pet Shop has 23 squeaky cat toys. The store owner buys 20 more squeaky cat toys. How many squeaky cat toys does the pet shop have altogether?

23 and 20 more is how many altogether?

Use counting on by ten to add: 23 + 20 = 43

The pet shop has 43 squeaky cat toys.

1. On Monday, the Kitty-Cat Pet Shop sold 10 squeaky cat toys. How many squeaky cat toys does the store have left?
43 (−) 10 = 33 squeaky cat toys

2. Jimmy bought 5 white rubber mice and 4 blue rubber mice. How many rubber mice did he buy?
5 (+) 4 = 9 rubber mice

3. Jimmy lost 2 rubber mice. How many rubber mice does he have left?
9 (−) 2 = 7 rubber mice

Use with Lesson 12-11. 157

Practice On Level

PROBLEM-SOLVING APPLICATIONS P 12-11
Caring for Kittens

1. Eduardo and his family went to the pet store. The pet store had 28 long-haired kittens and 20 short-haired kittens. How many kittens did the pet store have altogether?
28 (+) 20 = 48 kittens

2. Eduardo gets a long-haired kitten. His sister, Elena, gets a short-haired kitten. How many kittens does the pet store have now?
48 (−) 2 = 46 kittens

3. Elena buys a toy mouse for her kitten. It costs 37¢. Elena has
Will she get change? yes

Writing in Math

4. Eddie wants to buy a collar for 59¢ and a ball for 7¢. Does he need to regroup to find out how much they will cost? Explain.
Yes, when you add the ones, there are more than 10.

Use with Lesson 12-11. 157

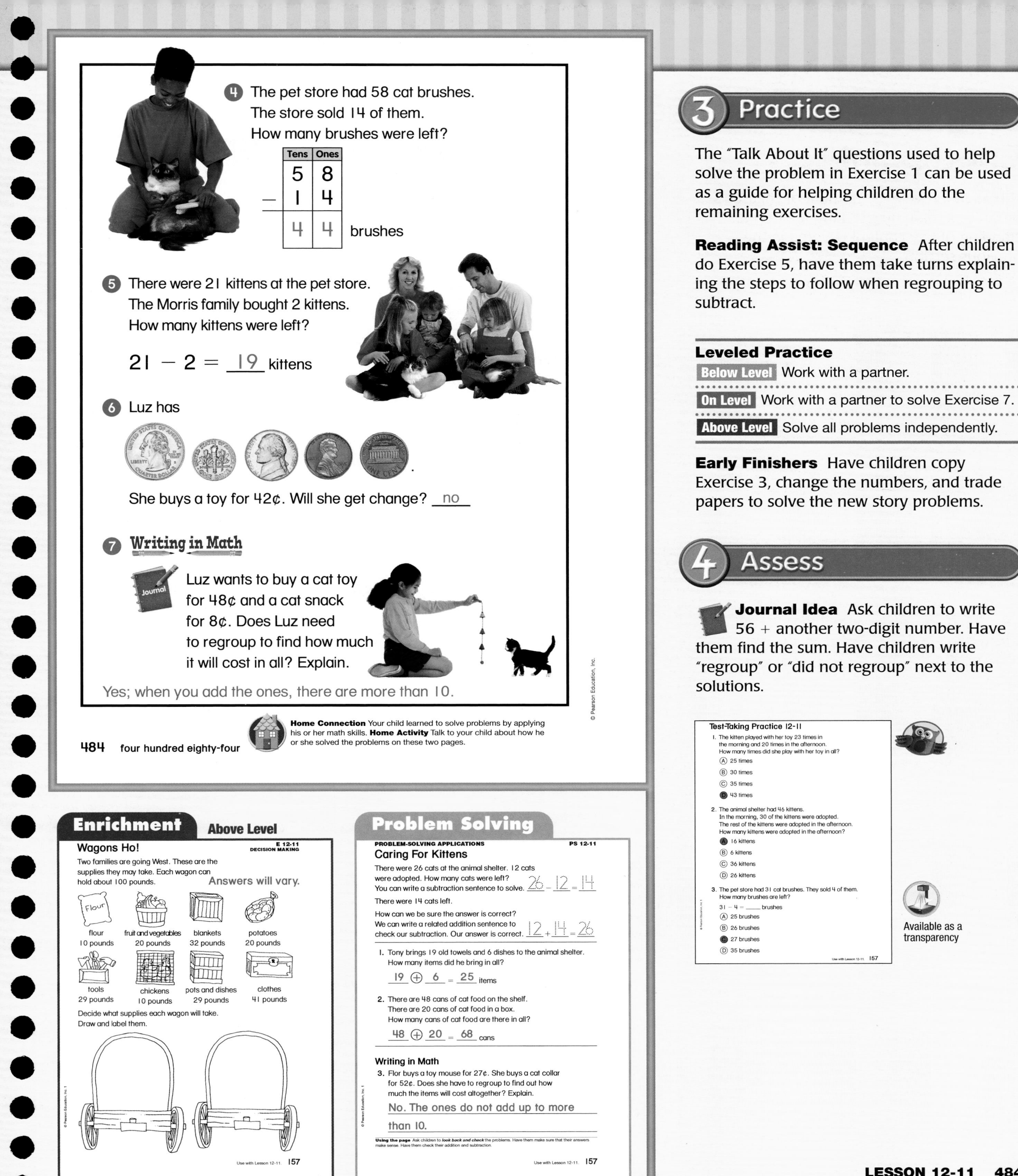

4. The pet store had 58 cat brushes.
The store sold 14 of them.
How many brushes were left?

	Tens	Ones
	5	8
−	1	4
	4	4

brushes

5. There were 21 kittens at the pet store.
The Morris family bought 2 kittens.
How many kittens were left?

21 − 2 = 19 kittens

6. Luz has [coins].

She buys a toy for 42¢. Will she get change? no

7. **Writing in Math**

Luz wants to buy a cat toy for 48¢ and a cat snack for 8¢. Does Luz need to regroup to find how much it will cost in all? Explain.

Yes; when you add the ones, there are more than 10.

Home Connection Your child learned to solve problems by applying his or her math skills. **Home Activity** Talk to your child about how he or she solved the problems on these two pages.

Enrichment — Above Level

Wagons Ho! E 12-11 DECISION MAKING

Two families are going West. These are the supplies they may take. Each wagon can hold about 100 pounds.

Answers will vary.

Item	Weight
flour	10 pounds
fruit and vegetables	20 pounds
blankets	32 pounds
potatoes	20 pounds
tools	29 pounds
chickens	10 pounds
pots and dishes	29 pounds
clothes	41 pounds

Decide what supplies each wagon will take. Draw and label them.

Use with Lesson 12-11. 157

Problem Solving

PROBLEM-SOLVING APPLICATIONS PS 12-11

Caring For Kittens

There were 26 cats at the animal shelter. 12 cats were adopted. How many cats were left?
You can write a subtraction sentence to solve. 26 − 12 = 14

There were 14 cats left.

How can we be sure the answer is correct?
We can write a related addition sentence to check our subtraction. Our answer is correct. 12 + 14 = 26

1. Tony brings 19 old towels and 6 dishes to the animal shelter. How many items did he bring in all?
19 + 6 = 25 items

2. There are 48 cans of cat food on the shelf. There are 20 cans of cat food in a box. How many cans of cat food are there in all?
48 + 20 = 68 cans

Writing in Math

3. Flor buys a toy mouse for 27¢. She buys a cat collar for 52¢. Does she have to regroup to find out how much the items will cost altogether? Explain.
No. The ones do not add up to more than 10.

Using the page Ask children to ***look back and check*** the problems. Have them make sure that their answers make sense. Have them check their addition and subtraction.

Use with Lesson 12-11. 157

3 Practice

The "Talk About It" questions used to help solve the problem in Exercise 1 can be used as a guide for helping children do the remaining exercises.

Reading Assist: Sequence After children do Exercise 5, have them take turns explaining the steps to follow when regrouping to subtract.

Leveled Practice

Below Level Work with a partner.

On Level Work with a partner to solve Exercise 7.

Above Level Solve all problems independently.

Early Finishers Have children copy Exercise 3, change the numbers, and trade papers to solve the new story problems.

4 Assess

Journal Idea Ask children to write 56 + another two-digit number. Have them find the sum. Have children write "regroup" or "did not regroup" next to the solutions.

Test-Taking Practice 12-11

1. The kitten played with her toy 23 times in the morning and 20 times in the afternoon. How many times did she play with her toy in all?
   - Ⓐ 25 times
   - Ⓑ 30 times
   - Ⓒ 35 times
   - Ⓓ 43 times (marked)

2. The animal shelter had 46 kittens. In the morning, 30 of the kittens were adopted. The rest of the kittens were adopted in the afternoon. How many kittens were adopted in the afternoon?
   - Ⓐ 16 kittens (marked)
   - Ⓑ 6 kittens
   - Ⓒ 36 kittens
   - Ⓓ 26 kittens

3. The pet store had 31 cat brushes. They sold 4 of them. How many brushes are left?
   31 − 4 = ____ brushes
   - Ⓐ 25 brushes
   - Ⓑ 26 brushes
   - Ⓒ 27 brushes (marked)
   - Ⓓ 35 brushes

Use with Lesson 12-11. 157

Available as a transparency

Diagnostic Checkpoint

Purpose Provide assessment of children's progress to date by checking their understanding of key content covered in the previous section.

Name ______________________ Diagnostic Checkpoint

Write each number sentence.

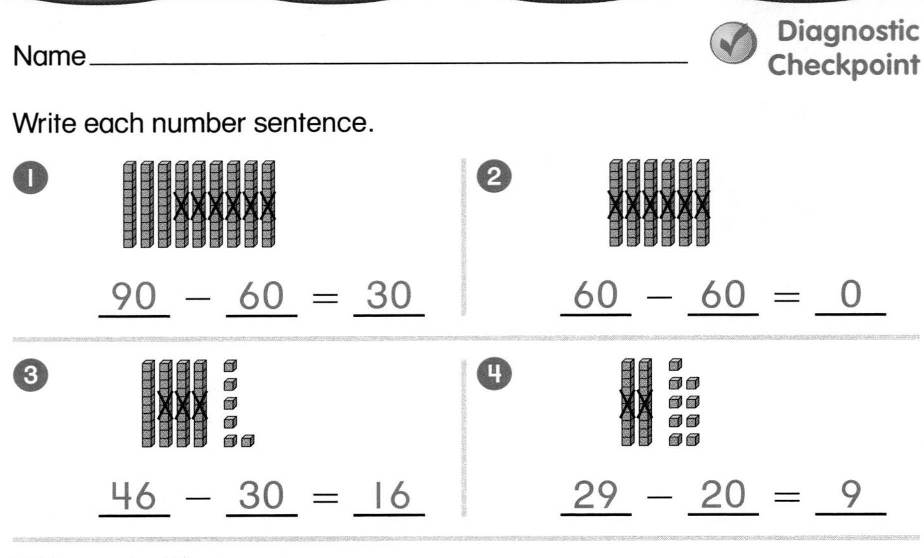

1. 90 − 60 = 30
2. 60 − 60 = 0
3. 46 − 30 = 16
4. 29 − 20 = 9

Write each difference.

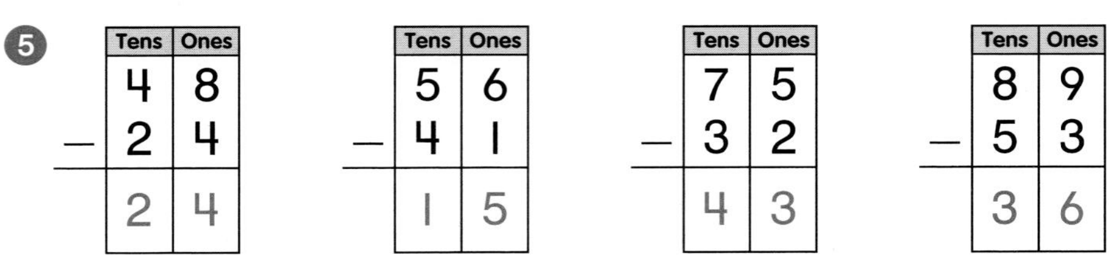

5.

	Tens	Ones
	4	8
−	2	4
	2	4

	Tens	Ones
	5	6
−	4	1
	1	5

	Tens	Ones
	7	5
−	3	2
	4	3

	Tens	Ones
	8	9
−	5	3
	3	6

Use cubes and Workmat 4. Do you need to regroup?
Circle **yes** or **no.** Then write the difference.

Show.	Subtract.	Do you need to regroup?	Find the difference.
6 61	5	(yes) no	61 − 5 = 56
7 47	6	yes (no)	47 − 6 = 41

Item Analysis for Diagnosis and Intervention

Objective	Items	Student Book Pages*	Intervention System
Subtract a multiple of 10 from a multiple of 10, 100 or less.	1–2	471–472	C5
Subtract a multiple of 10 from a two-digit number.	3–4	473–474	C6
Subtract a two-digit number from a two-digit number without regrouping.	5	475–476	C8
Use models to subtract a one-digit quantity from a two-digit quantity with and without regrouping.	6–7	477–478	C7

*For each lesson, there is a *Reteaching* activity in *Reaching All Learners* and a *Reteaching* master.

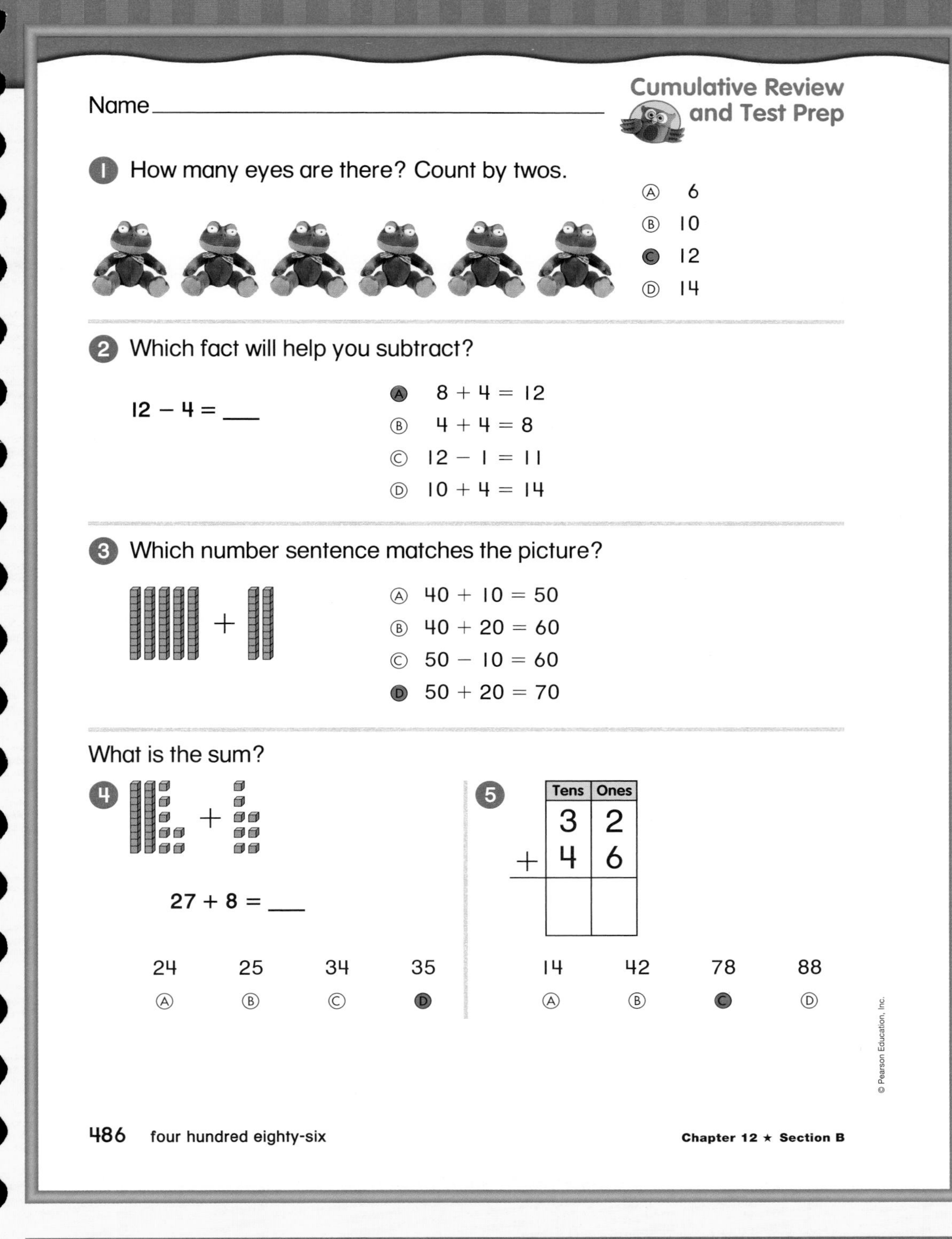

Name ______________________

Cumulative Review and Test Prep

1 How many eyes are there? Count by twos.

Ⓐ 6
Ⓑ 10
● 12
Ⓓ 14

2 Which fact will help you subtract?

12 − 4 = ___

● 8 + 4 = 12
Ⓑ 4 + 4 = 8
Ⓒ 12 − 1 = 11
Ⓓ 10 + 4 = 14

3 Which number sentence matches the picture?

Ⓐ 40 + 10 = 50
Ⓑ 40 + 20 = 60
Ⓒ 50 − 10 = 60
● 50 + 20 = 70

What is the sum?

4 27 + 8 = ___

24 Ⓐ 25 Ⓑ 34 Ⓒ 35 ●

5

Tens	Ones
3	2
+ 4	6

14 Ⓐ 42 Ⓑ 78 ● 88 Ⓓ

Cumulative Review and Test Prep

Purpose Provide children with a review of math concepts. Items appear as they would on a standardized test so children become familiar with that format.

Item Analysis for Diagnosis and Intervention

Objective	Items	Student Book Pages*	Intervention System
Skip count to find the total number of items arranged in sets of 10s, 5s, and 2s.	1	257–258	A15
Select and apply subtraction fact strategies.	2	443–444	B40
Add two multiples of 10 for sums to 100.	3	459–460	C1
Use models to add a one-digit quantity to a two-digit quantity with and without regrouping.	4	465–466	C3
Add two two-digit numbers without regrouping.	5	463–464	C4

*For each lesson, there is a *Reteaching* activity in *Reaching All Learners* and a *Reteaching* master.

Enrichment

Purpose Provide children with related mathematical topics and applications beyond the basic chapter content.

Using Student Page 487

Remind children that they have already learned how to add and subtract two-digit numbers. Tell them that this page will show them that they can add and subtract three-digit numbers using similar strategies.

Before having children work through the page, you may want to use Place-Value Mat B (Workmat 5) and place-value models to model how to add and subtract hundreds, tens, and ones. Have children work in pairs. Write 256 on the board and have one child use models to make this number on the mat. Write 413 on the board and have the child's partner make this number on the same mat. Ask children to combine the ones, the tens, and the hundreds and then tell the sum. Repeat, using number pairs that do not require regrouping, such as 123 + 456 and 315 + 401. To model subtraction, have one child model a number such as 653, and then have the child's partner remove, or subtract, 412. Repeat for other number pairs, such as 543 − 241 and 364 − 120.

When children are comfortable with the process, read the directions on the page and make sure they understand how to complete the exercises.

When adding or subtracting three-digit numbers, emphasize that children must begin with the ones place and move left to each greater place value. Stress that this order will be essential later, when regrouping becomes part of the process.

Name ______________________

Learning with Technology

Add and Subtract Using a Calculator

You can use a calculator to add and subtract.

Draw a path from **Start** to **Target.**
Use your calculator to help you.

1 Add.
Find the **Target Sum.**

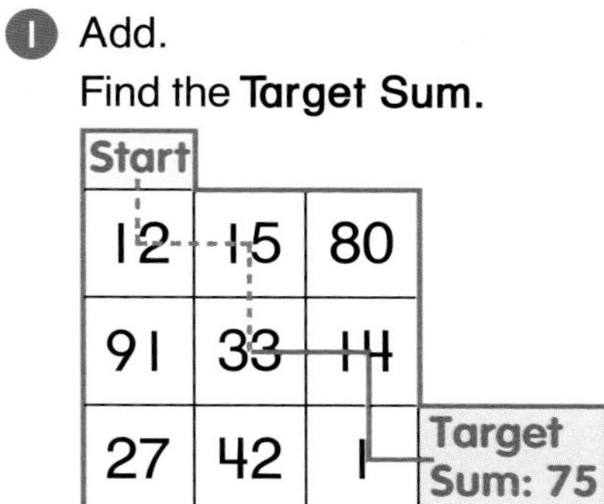

Start		
12	15	80
91	33	14
27	42	1

Target Sum: 75

2 Subtract.
Find the **Target Difference.**

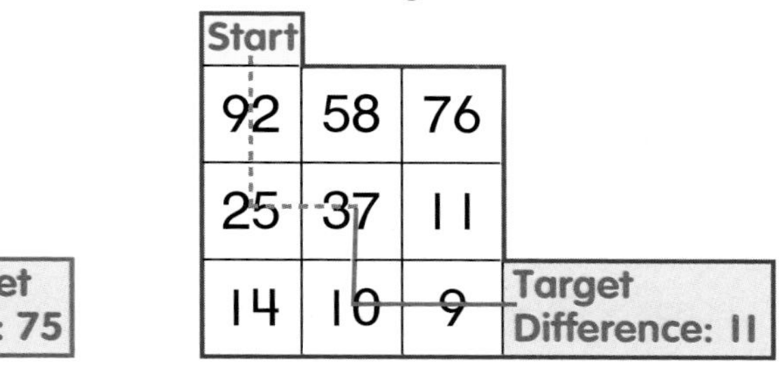

Start		
92	58	76
25	37	11
14	10	9

Target Difference: 11

Add and subtract in Exercises 3 and 4.
Find the **Target** number.

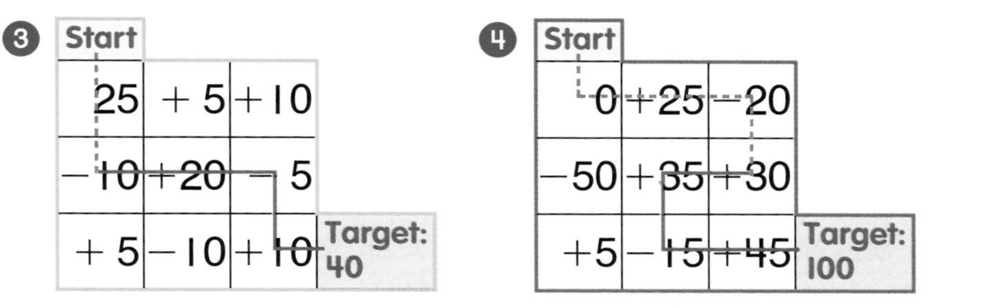

3

Start		
25	+ 5	+ 10
− 10	+ 20	− 5
+ 5	− 10	+ 10

Target: 40

4

Start		
0	+ 25	− 20
− 50	+ 35	+ 30
+ 5	− 15	+ 45

Target: 100

Think About It Number Sense

In Exercise 2, how did you use a calculator to figure out that you were close to the Target Difference? Answers will vary.

Home Connection Your child used a calculator to add and subtract two-digit numbers. **Home Activity** Ask your child to explain how to find the sum of 23 and 48 on a calculator.

Learning with Technology

Purpose Add and subtract one- and two-digit numbers using a calculator.

Using Student Page 488

Distribute calculators to children. Briefly review the keys on the calculator that they will be using: the ON/C key, the + and − symbol key, and the digits 0–9.

Explain to children that they will use their calculators in each exercise to find a path from Start to the Target number. Tell children that they can move down or to the left or right as they move from square to square on each grid. Guide children through Exercise 1. Help them reason that 12 + 91 is greater than the target sum of 75, so they must move to the right and find 12 + 15. Help students conclude that they must next move down and add 33, since adding 80 would create a sum greater than 75. If necessary, continue to work through Exercise 1.

Have children complete Exercise 2 independently. After reminding children that they can add and subtract as they work their way through the paths for Exercises 3 and 4, have them complete the exercises on their own. Remind children to press the ON/C key before they begin a new exercise.

Think About It Point out that every time children enter a number into the calculator, they should be comparing the partial sum to the Target number. This process should help children choose the next number to add or subtract.

Test Talk

Purpose Teach children a particular test-taking strategy and help them become more comfortable with the language and format used on standardized tests.

Using Student Page 489

This page is designed to give children practice in using writing in math.

Children often have difficulty on standardized tests not because they haven't been introduced to the concept or skill being tested, but because they fail to understand what they are being asked to do or how they are being asked to do it. This page can help with both the what and the how.

Discuss the question in Exercise 1. Point out to children that this question does not have answer choices and that they will need to write their own answers to the question. Ask children to explain why they would use addition to solve the problem and have a volunteer add the numbers of cans together. Then have a volunteer read the question in the problem and the written answer. Emphasize how the answer is short but completely answers the question. Help children compose several similar problems in a whole-group setting. Write the problems on the board and discuss them.

Have children complete Exercise 2 independently. When they have finished, ask children to explain how they found their answers. Then ask a volunteer to read the question in the problem and the answer he or she wrote. Discuss whether the answer is short but complete.

Name ____________________

CHAPTER 12 Test Talk

Read Together

Use Writing in Math

When you write an answer to a math question, your answer should be **short** but **complete.**

Test-Taking Strategies
Understand the Question
Get Information for the Answer
Plan How to Find the Answer
Make Smart Choices
Use Writing in Math

1. There were 43 cans in the recycling bin. Sharon put 20 more cans in the bin. How many cans are in the bin now?

   Now there are 63 cans in the recycling bin.

Here is how a boy named Tony solved this problem. He added the number of cans: 43 cans + 20 cans = 63 cans in all. Then he used words from the question to help him write his answer.

Which words did Tony use?
Raise your hand if you can find some of them.

Your Turn

Read the problem. Then write a **short** but **complete** answer to the question.

2. In May, Mr. Murphy's class collected 59 cans. Ms. Nelson's class collected 38 cans. How many more cans did Mr. Murphy's class collect?

   Mr. Murphy's class collected 21 more cans.

   ____

Home Connection Your child prepared for standardized tests by writing a complete answer to a math question. **Home Activity** Have your child explain how he or she solved the problem in Exercise 2. Then ask your child which words from the question he or she used in the answer.

Test-Taking Strategies

Understand the Question
- Look for important words.
- Turn the question into a statement: "I need to find out …"

Get Information for the Answer
- Get information from text.
- Get information from pictures, maps, diagrams, tables, graphs.

Plan How to Find the Answer
- Think about problem-solving skills and strategies.
- Choose computation methods.

Make Smart Choices
- Eliminate wrong answers.
- Try working backward from an answer.
- Check answers for reasonableness; estimate.

Use Writing in Math
- Make your answer brief but complete.
- Use words from the problem and use math terms accurately.
- Describe steps in order.
- Draw pictures to explain your thinking.

Name ________________________

Discover Math in Your World

All Aboard!

Read Together

Have you ever been on a train? It is fun to travel by train. The first trains in the United States were built many years ago. Today's trains can go much faster than the first ones could. Use subtraction to find out how much faster.

Tracking Train Speeds

1. The first trains could travel 20 miles in one hour. Stagecoaches could travel only 7 miles in one hour. How many more miles could the first trains travel in one hour?

   __13__ miles

2. Today, most passenger trains in the United States travel 79 miles in one hour. How many more miles can they travel in one hour than the first trains?

   __59__ miles

3. The fastest trains in Japan and France can travel 186 miles in one hour. The fastest train in the United States can travel 150 miles in one hour. How many more miles can the trains in Japan and France travel in one hour?

   __36__ miles

Take It to the NET
Video and Activities
www.scottforesman.com

Home Connection Your child solved problems that compared the speeds of different trains and a stagecoach. **Home Activity** Discuss the distance 20 miles in relation to your home and another location. Then ask your child to tell you how many more miles a passenger train in the United States can travel in one hour than a stagecoach could travel decades ago. *(143 miles)*

Take It to the NET
Video and Activities
www.scottforesman.com

The video includes pre-viewing and post-viewing questions.
A Discovery Channel Blackline Master is also provided.

Discover Math in Your World

Purpose Help children connect math content to everyday applications.

Using Student Page 490

In this activity, children will use their subtraction skills with two-digit numbers to compare the speeds of different trains.

Discuss trains with children. Ask if they have ever seen a train or gone for a ride on one. Discuss with them the uses of trains *(Transportation of both people and goods*) and the different cars on a train. *(Engine, caboose, passenger car, freight car, coal car)*

Read the paragraph at the top of the page and discuss the photo. Read each question with children, making sure they understand. Ask children what operation they will use to solve each problem and to explain how they chose their answer.

Note: In Exercise 3, children need to subtract three-digit numbers. Help them write the problem in vertical form and subtract from right to left. Children should be able to subtract the ones and the tens. If they need help, simply direct them to subtract the hundreds in the same way.

Children will not be formally introduced to subtracting three-digit numbers until Grade 2, but this page may be used to lay the groundwork for future instruction.

Chapter Test

Purpose Assess children's progress by checking their understanding of the concepts and skills covered in Chapter 12. Use as a review, practice test, or chapter test.

MindPoint Quiz Show CD-ROM Use *MindPoint Quiz Show* for additional practice on Chapter 12.

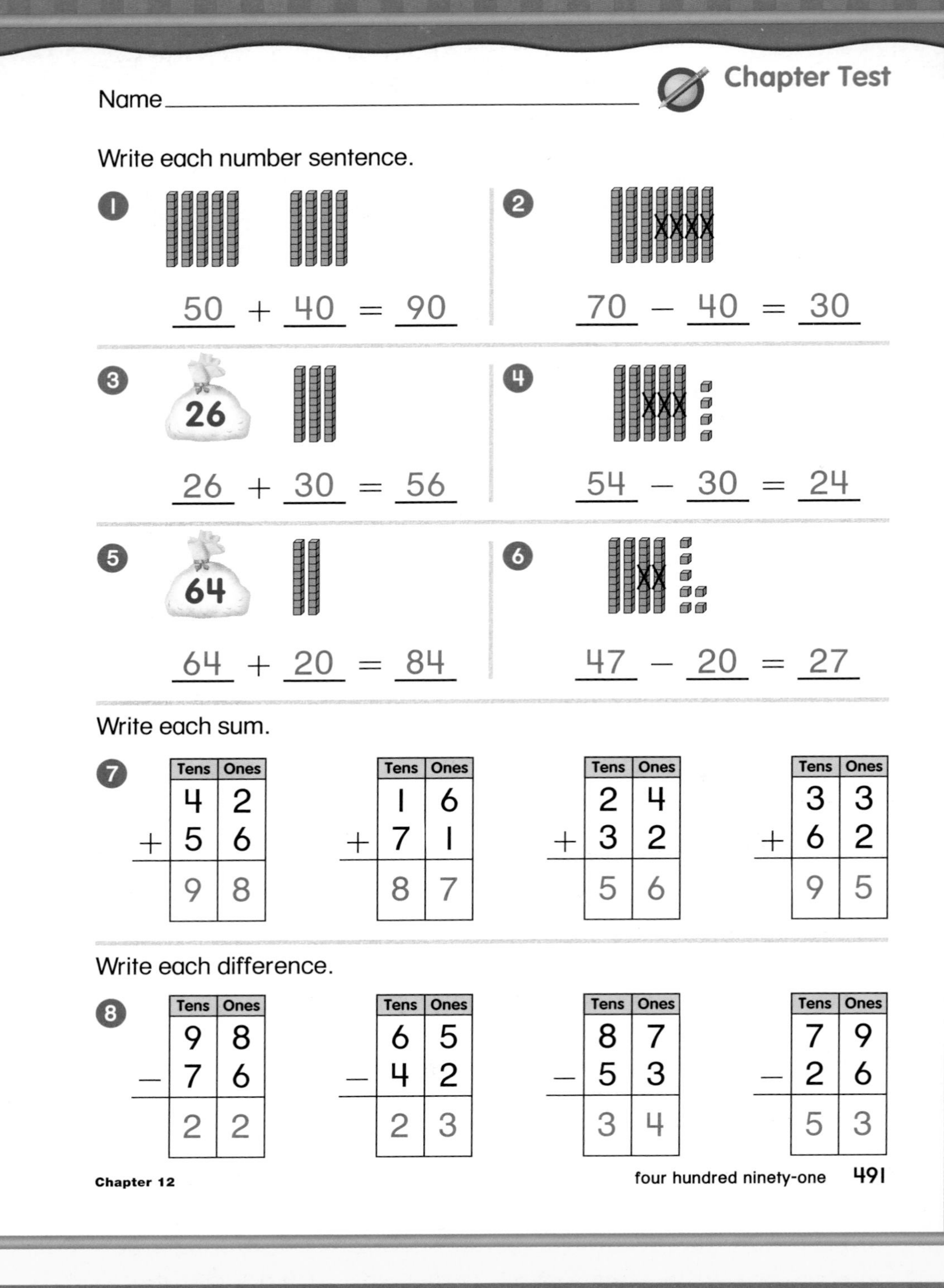

Name ____________________

Chapter Test

Write each number sentence.

1. 50 + 40 = 90
2. 70 − 40 = 30
3. 26 + 30 = 56
4. 54 − 30 = 24
5. 64 + 20 = 84
6. 47 − 20 = 27

Write each sum.

7.

	Tens	Ones
	4	2
+	5	6
	9	8

	Tens	Ones
	1	6
+	7	1
	8	7

	Tens	Ones
	2	4
+	3	2
	5	6

	Tens	Ones
	3	3
+	6	2
	9	5

Write each difference.

8.

	Tens	Ones
	9	8
−	7	6
	2	2

	Tens	Ones
	6	5
−	4	2
	2	3

	Tens	Ones
	8	7
−	5	3
	3	4

	Tens	Ones
	7	9
−	2	6
	5	3

Item Analysis for Diagnosis and Intervention

Objective	Items	Student Book Pages*	Intervention System
Add two multiples of 10 for sums to 100.	1	459–460	C1
Subtract a multiple of 10 from a multiple of 10, 100 or less.	2	471–472	C5
Add tens to a two-digit number.	3, 5	461–462	C2
Subtract a multiple of 10 from a two-digit number.	4, 6	473–474	C6
Add two two-digit numbers without regrouping.	7	463–464	C4
Subtract a two-digit number from a two-digit number without regrouping.	8	475–476	C8

*For each lesson, there is a *Reteaching* activity in *Reaching All Learners* and a *Reteaching* master.

Use cubes and Workmat 4. Do you need to regroup?
Circle **yes** or **no.** Then write the sum.

Show.	Add.	Do you need to regroup?	Find the sum.
9 55	8	(yes) no	55 + 8 = 63
10 34	5	yes (no)	34 + 5 = 39
11 47	6	(yes) no	47 + 6 = 53

Use cubes and Workmat 4. Do you need to regroup?
Circle **yes** or **no.** Then write the difference.

Show.	Subtract.	Do you need to regroup?	Find the difference.
12 52	8	(yes) no	52 − 8 = 44
13 29	7	yes (no)	29 − 7 = 22
14 35	9	(yes) no	35 − 9 = 26

Circle **exact answer** or **estimate.**

15 Julio has 2 baskets of apples.
Each basket has 12 apples.
There are 20 children in his class.
Are there enough apples for all of the children?

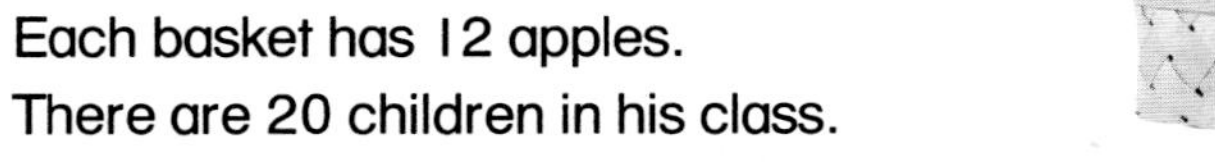

Do we need an exact answer or an estimate?

exact answer (estimate)

Item Analysis for Diagnosis and Intervention

Objective	Items	Student Book Pages*	Intervention System
Use models to add a one-digit quantity to a two-digit quantity with and without regrouping.	9–11	465–466	C3
Use models to subtract a one-digit quantity from a two-digit quantity with and without regrouping.	12–14	477–478	C7
Solve problems by deciding whether an estimate is enough or whether an exact answer is needed.	15	467–468	E10

*For each lesson, there is a *Reteaching* activity in *Reaching All Learners* and a *Reteaching* master.

Assessment Sourcebook

These additional assessment options may be found in the *Assessment Sourcebook:*

- Chapter 12 Free-Response Test (Forms A and B)
- Chapter 12 Multiple-Choice Test (Forms C and D)
- Chapter 12 Performance Assessment (Forms E and F)
- Chapters 1–12 Cumulative Test

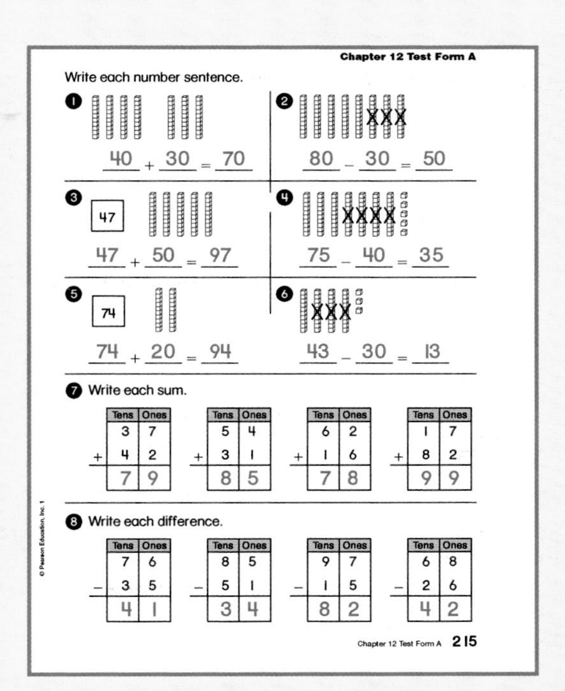

Chapter 12 Test Form A

Write each number sentence.

1 40 + 30 = 70
2 80 − 30 = 50
3 47 + 50 = 97
4 75 − 40 = 35
5 74 + 20 = 94
6 43 − 30 = 13

7 Write each sum.

Tens	Ones
3	7
+ 4	2
7	9

Tens	Ones
5	4
+ 3	1
8	5

Tens	Ones
6	2
+ 1	6
7	8

Tens	Ones
1	7
+ 8	2
9	9

8 Write each difference.

Tens	Ones
7	6
− 3	5
4	1

Tens	Ones
8	5
− 5	1
3	4

Tens	Ones
9	7
− 1	5
8	2

Tens	Ones
6	8
− 2	6
4	2

Chapter 12 Test Form A 215

Use cubes and Workmat 4. Do you need to regroup?
Circle **yes** or **no.** Then write the sum.

Show.	Add.	Do you need to regroup?	Find the sum.
7 86	9	(yes) no	86 + 9 = 95
8 53	6	yes (no)	53 + 6 = 59
9 67	8	(yes) no	67 + 8 = 75

Use cubes and Workmat 4. Do you need to regroup?
Circle **yes** or **no.** Then write the difference.

Show.	Subtract.	Do you need to regroup?	Find the difference.
10 78	6	yes (no)	78 − 6 = 72
11 81	8	(yes) no	81 − 8 = 73
12 94	5	(yes) no	94 − 5 = 89

13 Circle **exact answer** or **estimate.**
Juanita has 2 sheets of stickers.
Each sheet has 15 stickers.
There are 27 children in her class.
Are there enough stickers for all of the children in her class?
Do we need an exact answer or an estimate?

exact answer (estimate)

216 Chapter 12 Test Form A

Cumulative Review and Test Prep

Purpose Provide children with a review of math concepts. Items on page 492A appear as they would on a standardized test so children become familiar with that format.

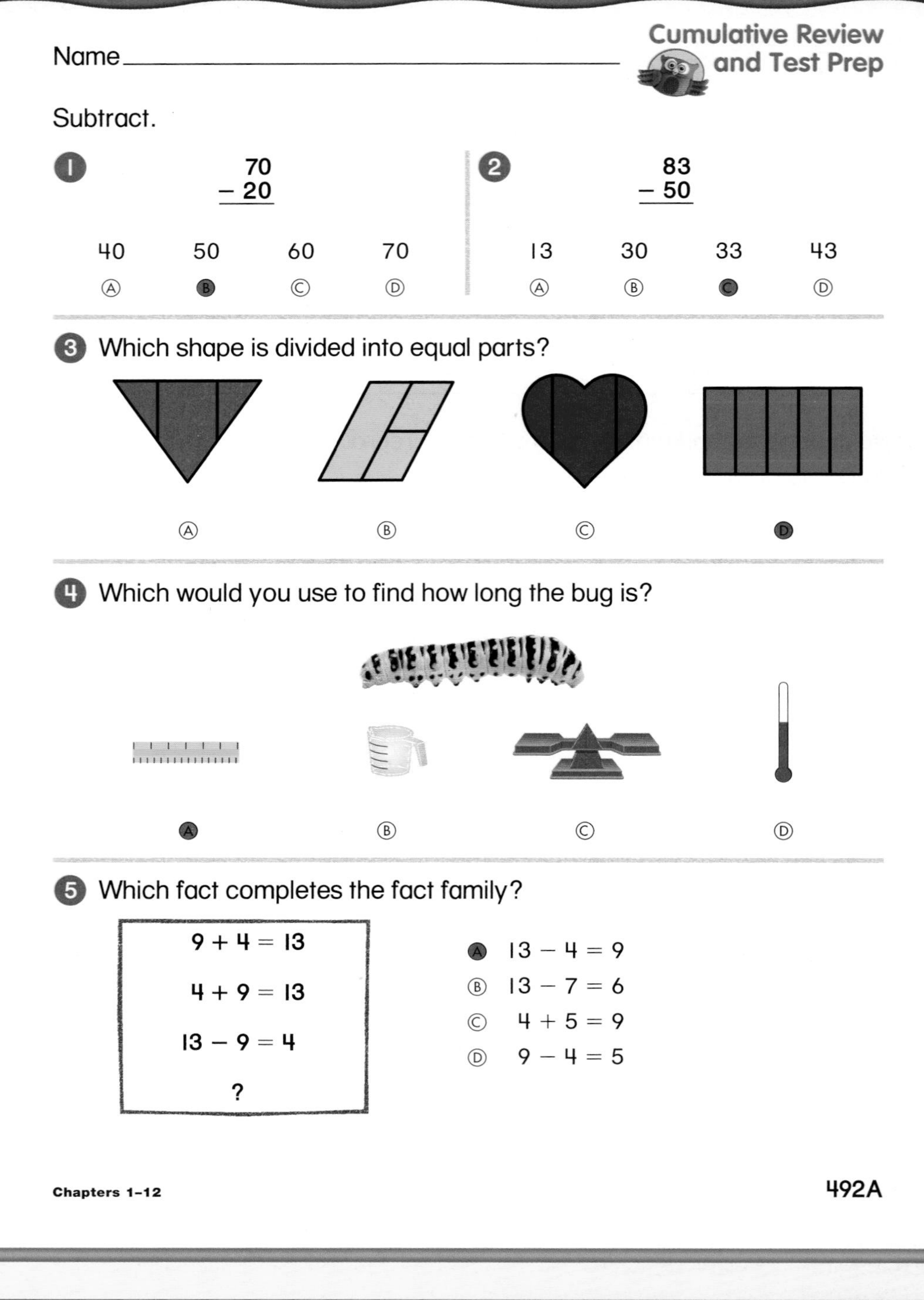

Name ______________________

Cumulative Review and Test Prep

Subtract.

1. 70 − 20

Ⓐ 40 Ⓑ 50 Ⓒ 60 Ⓓ 70

2. 83 − 50

Ⓐ 13 Ⓑ 30 Ⓒ 33 Ⓓ 43

3. Which shape is divided into equal parts?

Ⓐ Ⓑ Ⓒ Ⓓ

4. Which would you use to find how long the bug is?

Ⓐ Ⓑ Ⓒ Ⓓ

5. Which fact completes the fact family?

$9 + 4 = 13$

$4 + 9 = 13$

$13 - 9 = 4$

?

Ⓐ $13 - 4 = 9$

Ⓑ $13 - 7 = 6$

Ⓒ $4 + 5 = 9$

Ⓓ $9 - 4 = 5$

Chapters 1–12

492A

Item Analysis for Diagnosis and Intervention

Objective	Review Items	Student Book Pages*	Intervention System
Subtract a multiple of 10 from a multiple of 10, 100 or less.	1	471–472	C5
Subtract a multiple of 10 from a two-digit number.	2	473–474	C6
Determine whether a shape has been divided into equal or unequal parts and, if applicable, count the number of equal parts into which it has been divided.	3	181–182	A59
Identify appropriate tools for measuring length, weight, capacity, and temperature.	4	397–398	D10
Write the addition and subtraction sentences that make up a fact family.	5	437–438	B37

*For each lesson, there is a *Reteaching* activity in *Reaching All Learners* and a *Reteaching* master.

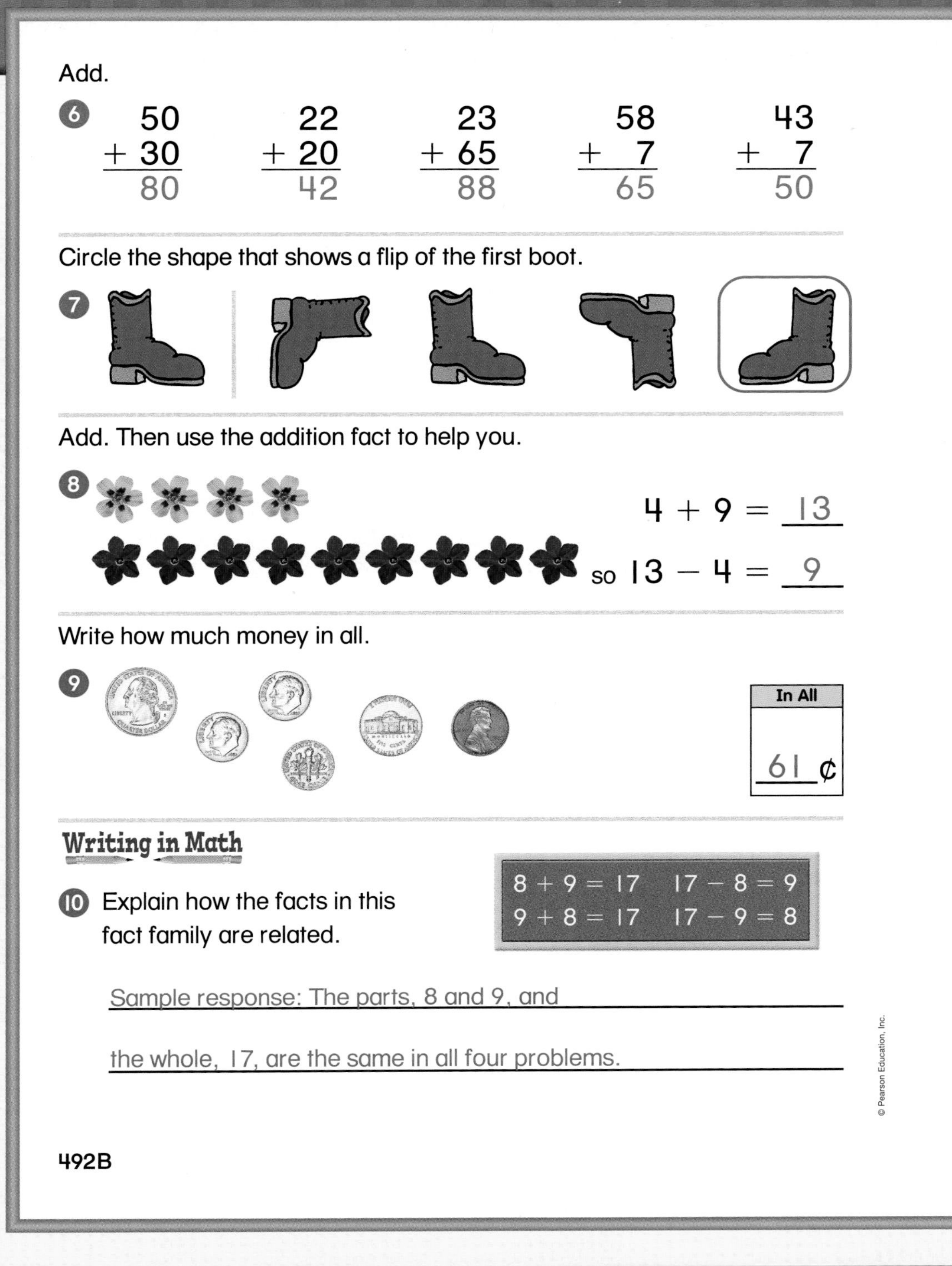

Add.

6.

50	22	23	58	43
+ 30	+ 20	+ 65	+ 7	+ 7
80	42	88	65	50

Circle the shape that shows a flip of the first boot.

7.

Add. Then use the addition fact to help you.

8. $4 + 9 = $ 13

so $13 - 4 = $ 9

Write how much money in all.

9. In All: 61 ¢

Writing in Math

10. Explain how the facts in this fact family are related.

$8 + 9 = 17$	$17 - 8 = 9$
$9 + 8 = 17$	$17 - 9 = 8$

Sample response: The parts, 8 and 9, and the whole, 17, are the same in all four problems.

492B

Item Analysis for Diagnosis and Intervention

Objective	Review Items	Student Book Pages*	Intervention System
Add two multiples of 10 for sums to 100.	6	459–460	C1
Add tens to a two-digit number.	6	461–462	C2
Add two two-digit numbers without regrouping.	6	463–464	C4
Use models to add a one-digit quantity to a two-digit quantity with and without regrouping.	6	465–466	C3
Perform a slide, flip, or turn on an object and identify the resulting position.	7	173–174	D53
Find differences by using known addition facts.	8	439–440	B38
Count collections of coins including a quarter, dimes, nickels, and pennies.	9	345–346	A37
Write the addition and subtraction sentences that make up a fact family.	10	437–438	B37

*For each lesson, there is a *Reteaching* activity in *Reaching All Learners* and a *Reteaching* master.

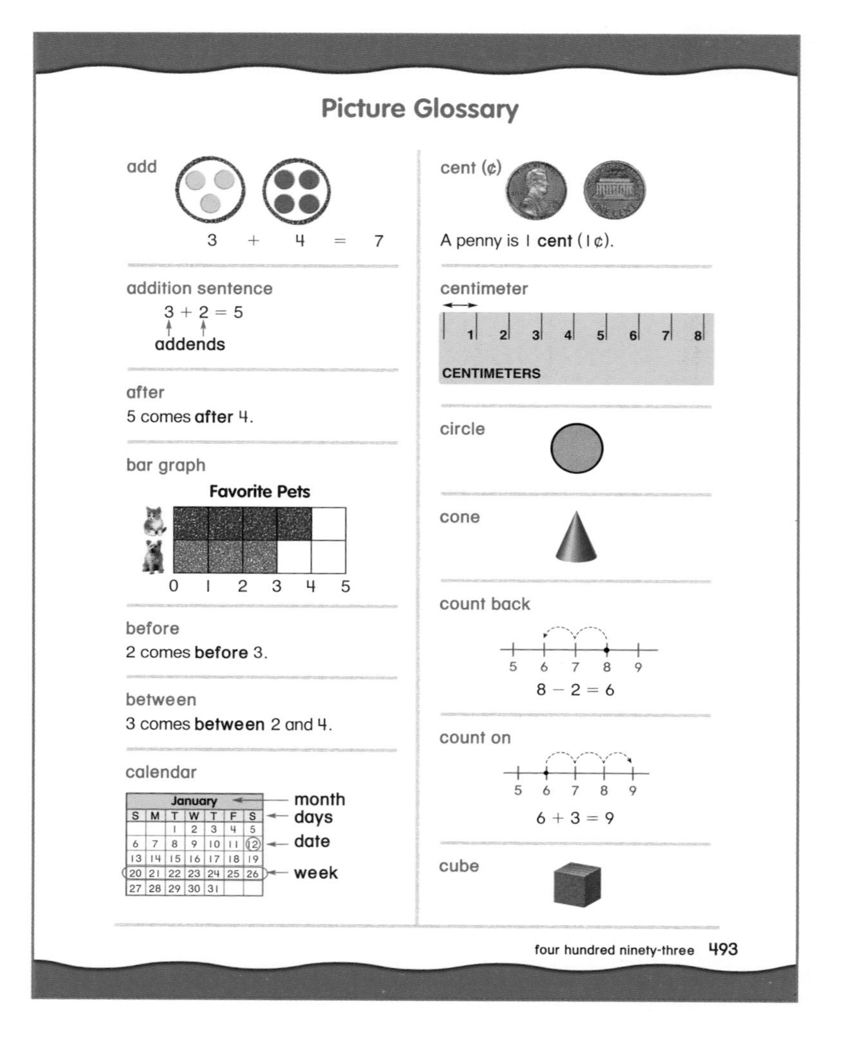

Picture Glossary

add

3 + 4 = 7

addition sentence

3 + 2 = 5

addends

after

5 comes **after** 4.

bar graph

Favorite Pets

0 1 2 3 4 5

before

2 comes **before** 3.

between

3 comes **between** 2 and 4.

calendar

January — month

S M T W T F S — days

12 — date

20 21 22 23 24 25 26 — week

cent (¢)

A penny is 1 **cent** (1¢).

centimeter

1 2 3 4 5 6 7 8

CENTIMETERS

circle

cone

count back

5 6 7 8 9

8 − 2 = 6

count on

5 6 7 8 9

6 + 3 = 9

cube

four hundred ninety-three 493

cup

cylinder

difference

8 − 3 = 5

8
− 3
5

difference

dime

10¢ or 10 cents

dollar

$1.00 or 100¢

doubles fact

3 + 3 = 6

equal parts

$\frac{1}{4}$	$\frac{1}{4}$	$\frac{1}{4}$	$\frac{1}{4}$

4 equal parts

equals (=)

2 + 3 = 5   5 = 3 + 2

equals

estimate

about 10 strawberries

even numbers

2, 4, 6, 8, 10, ...

fact family

7 + 2 = 9   9 − 7 = 2

2 + 7 = 9   9 − 2 = 7

foot

A **foot** is 12 inches.

fraction

$\frac{1}{2}$ $\frac{1}{3}$ $\frac{1}{4}$

greater than (>)

4 is **greater than** 2.

4 > 2

494 four hundred ninety-four

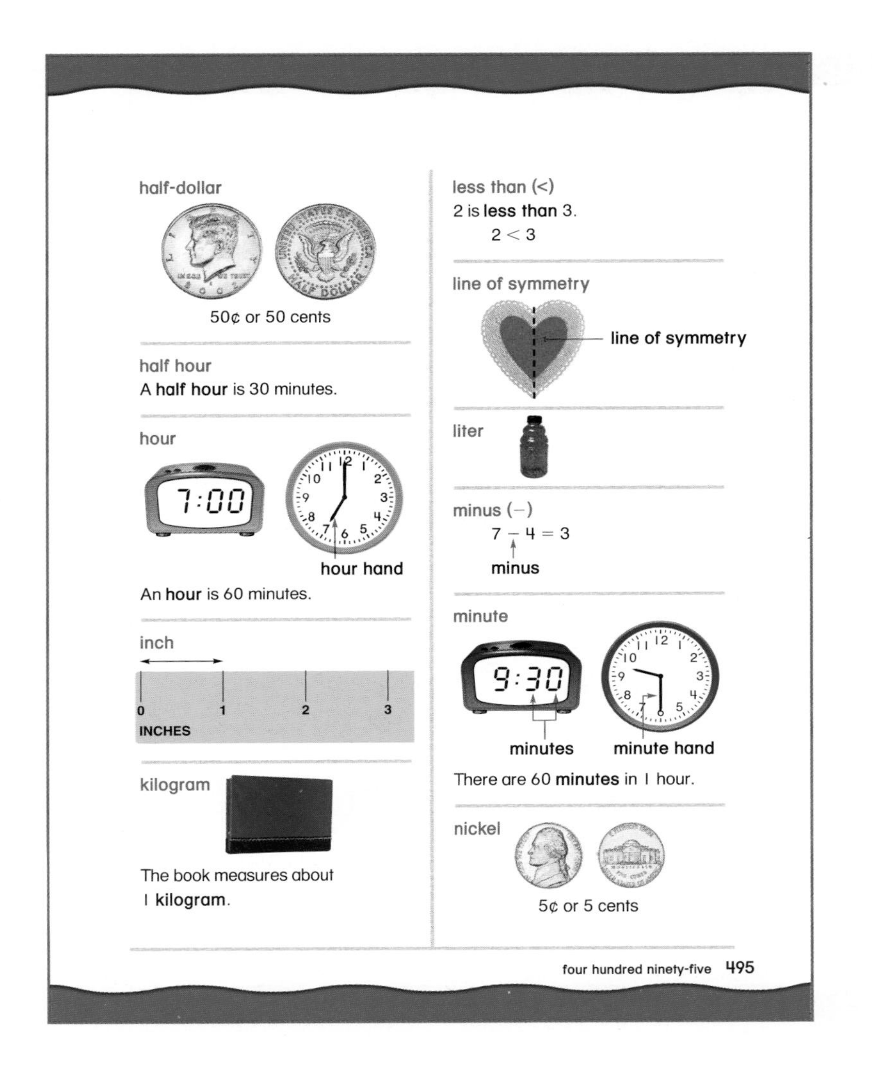

half-dollar

50¢ or 50 cents

half hour

A **half hour** is 30 minutes.

hour

7:00

hour hand

An **hour** is 60 minutes.

inch

0 1 2 3
INCHES

kilogram

The book measures about 1 **kilogram**.

less than (<)

2 is **less than** 3.

$2 < 3$

line of symmetry

line of symmetry

liter

minus (−)

$7 - 4 = 3$

minus

minute

9:30

minutes

minute hand

There are 60 **minutes** in 1 hour.

nickel

5¢ or 5 cents

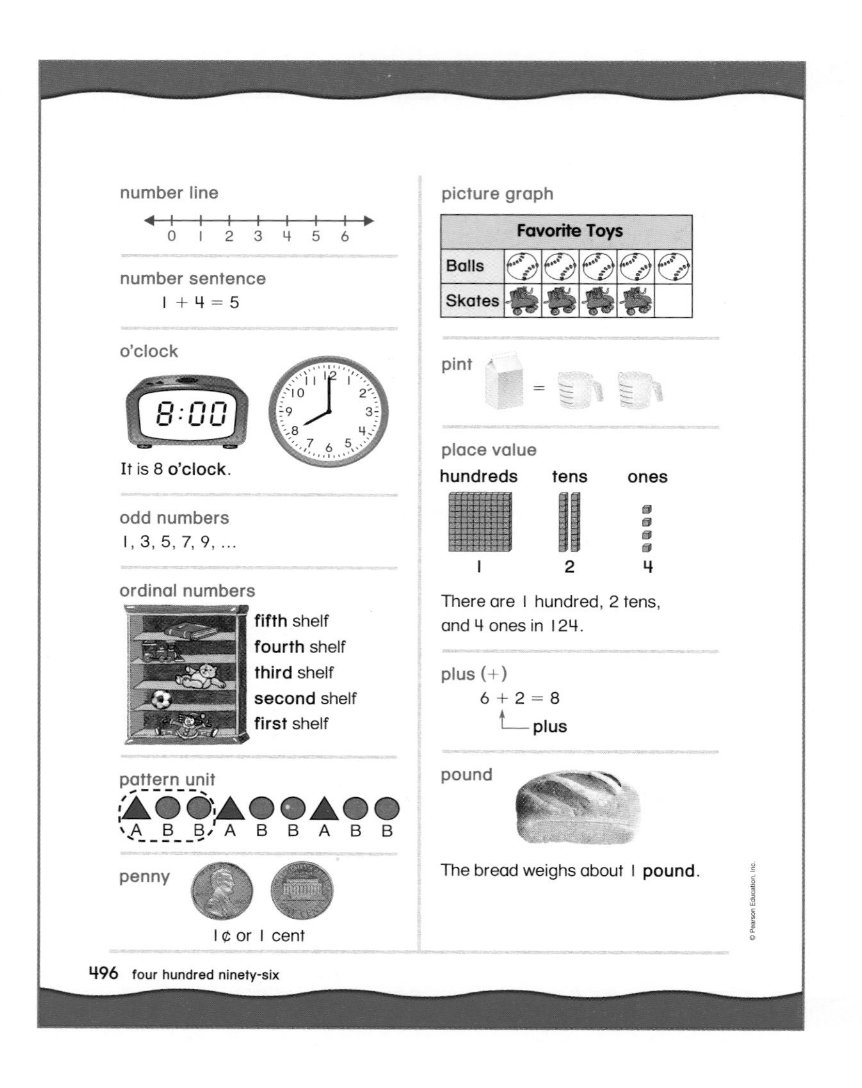

number line

0 1 2 3 4 5 6

number sentence

1 + 4 = 5

o'clock

8:00

It is 8 **o'clock**.

odd numbers

1, 3, 5, 7, 9, ...

ordinal numbers

fifth shelf
fourth shelf
third shelf
second shelf
first shelf

pattern unit

A B B A B B A B B

penny

1¢ or 1 cent

picture graph

Favorite Toys
Balls
Skates

pint

place value

hundreds	tens	ones
1	2	4

There are 1 hundred, 2 tens, and 4 ones in 124.

plus (+)

6 + 2 = 8

plus

pound

The bread weighs about 1 **pound**.

© Pearson Education, Inc.

496 four hundred ninety-six

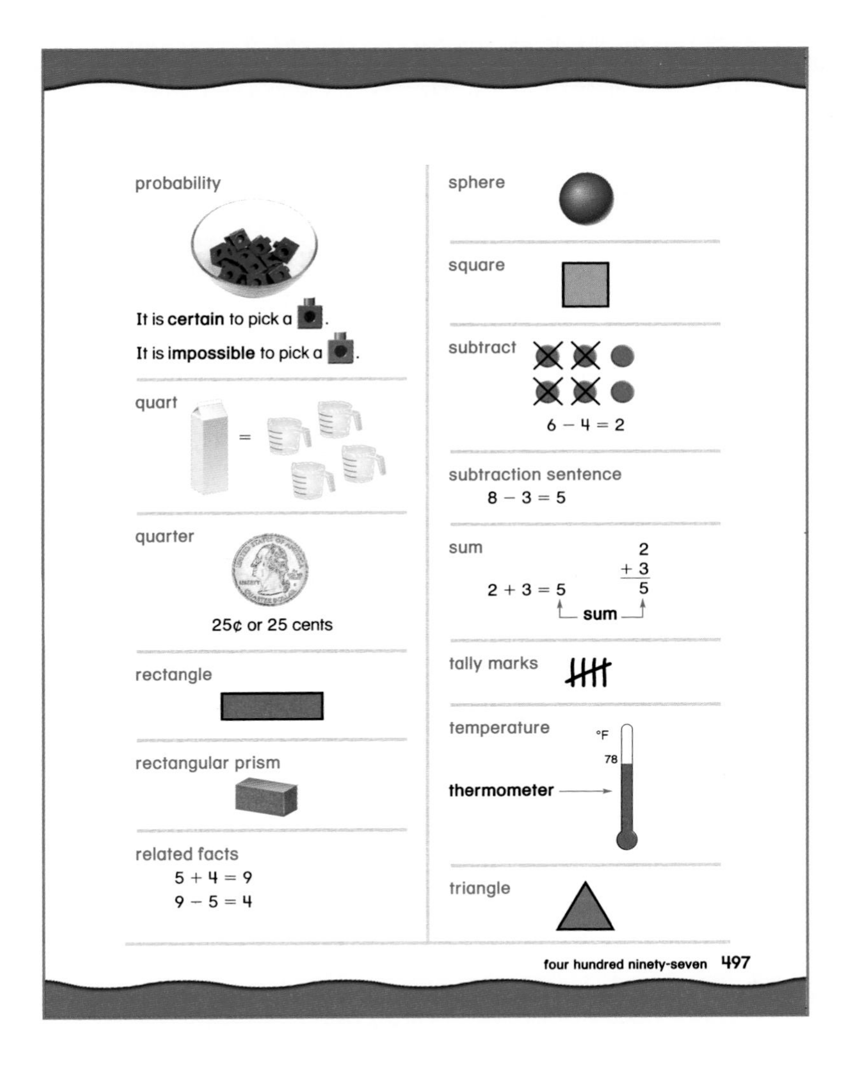
probability

It is **certain** to pick a ■.

It is **impossible** to pick a ■.

quart

quarter

25¢ or 25 cents

rectangle

rectangular prism

related facts

$5 + 4 = 9$

$9 - 5 = 4$

sphere

square

subtract

$6 - 4 = 2$

subtraction sentence

$8 - 3 = 5$

sum

$2 + 3 = 5$

$$\begin{array}{r} 2 \\ +\ 3 \\ \hline 5 \end{array}$$

sum

tally marks

temperature

°F

78

thermometer

triangle

four hundred ninety-seven 497

Credits

Cover: Jose Pardo

Text

Dorling Kindersley (DK) is an international publishing company specializing in the creation of high-quality reference content for books, CD-ROMs, online materials, and video. The hallmark of DK content is its unique combination of educational value and strong visual style. This combination allows DK to deliver appealing, accessible, and engaging educational content that delights children, parents, and teachers around the world. Scott Foresman is delighted to have been able to use selected extracts of DK content within this Scott Foresman Math program.

33–34: *Flip-Flap* by Sandra Jenkins. Copyright ©1995 by Dorling Kindersley Limited; 79–80: *Bugs! Bugs!* Bugs! by Jennifer Dussling. Copyright ©1998 by Dorling Kindersley Limited; 113–114: *Rabbit* by Mark Evans. Text copyright ©1992 by Mark Evans. Foreword copyright ©1992 by Roger Caras. Copyright ©1992 by Dorling Kindersley Limited; 145–146: *Puppies* by Carey Scott. Copyright ©1997 by Dorling Kindersley Limited; 193–194: *My Very First Colors, Shapes, Sizes, and Opposites Book* by Angela Wilkes. Copyright ©1993 by Dorling Kindersley Limited; 229–230: *Egg* by Robert Burton, photographed by Jane Burton and Kim Taylor. Copyright ©1994 by Dorling Kindersley Limited; 269–270: *My First Math Book* by David and Wendy Clemson. Copyright ©1994 by Dorling Kindersley Limited; 319–320: *My First Number Book* by Marie Heinst. Copyright ©1992, 1999 by Dorling Kindersley Limited; 353–354: *Counting Book* photographed by Dave King. Copyright ©1998 by Dorling Kindersley Limited; 405–406: *Children's Quick & Easy Cookbook* by Angela Wilkes. Text copyright ©1997 by Angela Wilkes. Copyright ©1997 by Dorling Kindersley Limited; 447–448: *A Day at Greenhill Farm* by Sue Nicholson. Copyright ©1998 by Dorling Kindersley Limited; 483–484: *Kitten* by Mark Evans. Text copyright ©1992 by Mark Evans. Foreword copyright ©1992 by Roger Caras. Copyright ©1992 by Dorling Kindersley Limited

Illustrations:

R2 **Carly Castillon** R3, R4 **Marisol Sarrazin** 1A, 1B, 1C, 1D, 1E, 1F, 2, 6, 11, 14, 16, 18, 21, 22, 25, 26, 28, 30, 35, 37 **Carly Castillon** 2A, 2B, 2C, 2D, 2E, 2F, 43, 44, 47, 48, 52, 63, 69, 70, 75, 76, 77, 342, 382 **Kathi Ember** 3A, 3B, 3C, 3D, 3E, 3F, 89, 90, 92, 93, 95, 97, 98, 101, 105, 106, 107, 108, 109, 111, 117 **John Patience** 4A, 4B, 4C, 4D, 4E, 4F, 80, 123, 124, 125, 126, 139, 140, 141, 142, 429, 430 **Karen Stormer Brooks** 4, 10, 12, 393, 394 **Janet Skiles** 5A, 5B, 5C, 5D, 5E, 5F, 155, 156, 157, 158, 166, 167, 168, 170, 171, 172, 173, 183, 184, 185, 189, 190 **Will Terry** 6A, 6B, 6C, 6D, 6E, 6F, 203, 204, 207, 208, 211, 212, 213, 217, 224, 226, 227, 228 **Jason Wolff** 7A, 7B, 7C, 7D, 7E, 7F, 240, 242, 251, 265, 266, 273 **Amy Vangsgard** 7, 8, 9, 32 **Remy Simard** 8A, 8B, 8C, 8D, 8E, 8F, 279, 280, 283, 284, 287, 288, 297, 300, 313, 323, 324 **Cameron Eagle** 9A, 9B, 9C, 9D, 9F, 329, 330, 333, 335, 336, 337, 338, 345, 357 **Laura Ovresat** 10A, 10B, 10C, 10D, 10E, 10F, 363, 364, 369, 370, 372, 377, 378, 395, 398, 403 **Bridget Starr Taylor** 11A, 11B, 11C, 11D, 11E, 11F, 415, 416, 417, 419, 420, 421, 425, 426, 427, 431, 432, 437, 440, 443, 444, 452 **Diane Greenseid** 12A, 12B, 12C, 12D, 12E, 12F, 459, 462, 463, 464, 471, 472, 473, 475, 476, 477, **Jackie Snider** 19, 20, 102, 109, 110, 116, 180, 197, 418 **Rose Mary Berlin** 45, 46, 61, 62, 65, 66, 88, 215, 216, 217, 219, 220, 231, 232, 238, 238B, 328A **Suwin Chan** 50, 57, 58, 59, 60, 82 **Jane Maday** 71, 72, 73, 218 **Paul Sharp** 94 **Terry Taylor** 103, 104 **Claudine Gevry** 108, 223, 224, 285, 286, 293, 309, 310, 311, 312, 321, 327, 328, 414A, 492B **Mike Dammer** 117, 349, 350, 456 **Rusty Fletcher** 122, 367, 368, 413 **Chi Chung** 127, 128, 130, 135, 153, 295, 296, 305 **Maryn Roos** 188, 191 **Ginna Magee** 213, 214 **George Ulrich** 244, 272, 278, 437, 438, 449 **Reggie Holladay** 257, 258, 395, 396, 399 **Margeaux Lucas** 257, 258, 408 **Eldon Doty** 259, 260 **Thomas Taylor** 261, 262 **John Sandford** 267, 268 **Linda Howard Bittner** 289, 290 **Nan Brooks** 301, 302, 305, 327 **Joe Stites** 315, 316, 317, 318, 321, 328, 400 **Donna Catanese** 326 **Carolyn Croll** 479, 480 **Jane Miles Smith ©2005 edition** R 15, R16 **Mike Dammer** 3, 8, 14, 22, 30 **Carly Castillon** 6 **Janet Skiles** 31 **Eldon Doty**

Photographs:

Every effort has been made to secure permission and provide appropriate credit for photographic material. The publisher deeply regrets any omission and pledges to correct errors called to its attention in subsequent editions. Unless otherwise acknowledged, all photographs are the property of Scott Foresman, a division of Pearson Education.

Photo locators denoted as follows: Top (T), Center (C), Bottom (B), Left (L), Right (R), Background (Bkgd)

1, 4 (BCL), 36 (TL, BR), 49 (T), 60, 67 (BR), 88A, 88B, 89, 102 (T), 116, 136, 143 (B), 144 (TC, BC, B), 154A, 154B, 157, 162 (All Other), 164, 176 (L), 187 (TL, TR, CR, BL), 202, 236 (CL), 238A, 271, 291 (T), 322, 328B, 339, 340 (BL, TR), 341, 366, 373, 374 (C), 376 (T, B), 384, 386, 387, 388 (TR), 391 (CR), 392 (CL, TR), 397, 398 (T, CC, CL, BL), 399 (TL, CL, CR), 408, 412 (TR), 414B (TL, TR), 431, 439 (TT, TB, CLT, CLB, BLT, BLB), 440, 450, 456 (T, C), 470, 472, 486, 492A, 492, 493 (TL), 496 (BR) Hemera Technologies 4 (TL, TR, BL, BC, BR), 10, 18, 36 (BC), 49 (CL), 51, 59 (R), 67 (TL, TR, CL, CR, BL), 68, 81, 87, 99, 100 (T, C), 101 (B), 102 (B), 111, 112 (BC), 115, 121, 133, 136, 144 (T), 154, 175, 187 (CL, BR), 276, 372, 374 (BL, BR), 375 (BL), 376 (C, BL, BR), 390, 391 (CL, BL), 392 (BL, CR, BR), 399 (BL, BCL, BCR, BR), 414B (BR), 434, 439 (CRT, BRT, BRB), 446 (B, T), 456 (BL, BR), 468 (T), 492B, 493 (BL) Getty Images 4 (TC, BCR), 33 (TL, CL), 34, 56, 79, 80 (TL, TR), 86, 100 (B), 113, 114, 142, 143 (T), 145, 146, 152, 193, 194, 221, 229, 230, 236 (TL), 269, 270, 319, 320, 353, 354, 388 (CRT), 405, 406, 439 (CRB), 445 (B), 446 (C), 447, 448, 483, 484 ©Dorling Kindersley 33 (BR) Philip Dowell/©Dorling Kindersley Artville 36 (TR), 49 (CR, BL, BR), 59 (L), 375 (CL) ©Comstock Inc. 73 (L, R), 101 (T), 112 (TC), 162 (CTR), 254, 340 (TC), 398 (TC), 80 (CR) Brian Kenney 222 ©John Lamb/Getty Images 375 (TL, B), 381, 385 Corbis 412 (TC) Digital Stock 445 (T) Tracy Morgan/©Dorling Kindersley WM1, WM3 Getty Images 347 (TR), 357 (TL, CL, BL, BC) Golden Dollar Obverse. 1999 United States Mint. All rights reserved. Used with permission/United States Mint. ©2005 edition R1 Getty Images, Brand X Pictures R2 Getty Images, Brand X Pictures R5 Getty Images R7 Getty Images R8 Getty Images 1 Hemera Technologies 14 Getty Images, Rubberball Productions 27 Rubberball Productions 33,34 ©Dorling Kindersley 36 Getty Images

Teacher's Edition Credits

Acknowledgements:

11B: "Ten potatoes in a pot" from TEN POTATOES IN A POT AND OTHER COUNTING RHYMES, Selected by Michael Jay Katz, p. 10. Copyright © 1990 by Michael Jay Katz. Reprinted by permission of HarperCollins Publishers.

Illustrations:

27B (©2005, 19B), 287B **Donna Catanese;** 33B, 97B, 113B, 191A, 193B, 205B, 229B, 243B, 261B, 267A **Bari Weissman;** 47B, 57B, 63B, 67B, 127B, 139B, 249A, 263A, 263B **Roberta Polfus;** 61B, 91B **Wendy Edelson;** 71B, 207B, 245B **Steve Henry;** 224 **Jason Wolff;** 291B, 309A **Reggie Holladay;** 303A **Lynda Calvert Weyant;** 313B, 315A, 317B **Linda Howard Bittner;** 369B, 397B, 401B **Jane Maday;** 377B **Deborah Borgo;** 421B, 471A, 473B **Janet Skiles**

Photographs:

209B (BR) Hemera Technologies, 395A (BR) Getty Images

Index

*Teacher's Edition references are in italics.

Index

D

E

M

Index

U

V

Notes

Notes

Notes

Notes

Notes

Notes

Notes

Notes